SYSTEMS ANALYSIS:

A DIAGNOSTIC APPROACH

SYSTEMS

ANALYSIS:

A DIAGNOSTIC

APPROACH

Van Court Hare, Jr.
Columbia University

Under the General Editorship of
Martin K. Starr, Columbia University

Harcourt, Brace & World, Inc.

New York / Chicago / San Francisco / Atlanta

FOREWORD

The increasing complexity of civilization, with the increasing complexities of its societies, economics, and industries, has made urgent the need for equal advances in our resources for control, understanding, and coordination. In the last twenty years great advances have been made, but they have sometimes been technically difficult and not widely understood. With the arrival of such technical methods there is always the danger that mere technical virtuosity may lose contact with good sense and understanding.

Van Court Hare's *Systems Analysis* admirably achieves its aim of introducing the reader to these methods, while basing the teaching on explanation and understanding rather than on any specialized technique. Formal mathematics are almost entirely avoided (although the reader is invited to think in ways that he will later discover to be essentially mathematical). The abundance of carefully graded exercises, which start at the most basic level, make the book suitable for self-tuition; the projects, for more prolonged work, will be useful in class.

Though starting from first principles, Professor Hare uses a treatment that is essentially modern, for it is based on the general thesis that the dominating factor in the complex system is the large quantity of information involved. The clear treatment of this aspect in the early chapters leads naturally to the full treatment of simplification methods in the later. I therefore welcome Van Court Hare's *Systems Analysis* as being clear, sound, and modern.

W. Ross Ashby

University of Illinois

EDITOR'S FOREWORD

In *The Grapes of Wrath*, John Steinbeck wrote, "Man, unlike any other thing organic or inorganic in the universe, grows beyond his work, walks up the stairs of his concepts, emerges ahead of his accomplishments." The *total systems concept* is such a stairway. Where it will lead, how it will change the world as we know it—we shall find this out in less time than many think.

Systems Analysis is one of the finest examples of the "new systems literature" for management. This literature tries to cope with the dynamics of structure. It emphasizes point and counterpoint, the balance of asymmetrical forces, flow and change.

The universal flux of systems is information. Information can take many forms: money, materials, satisfaction, and time. And all these forms can be related to one another according to the purpose of a particular system.

A text in this field must, therefore, employ the operationalist's philosophy, satisfy the empiricist's standards, and meet the rationalist's requirements. It must foster understanding about the nature of insight. It must stress both diagnosis and invention. It must deal abstractly with the form and meaning of details. This book achieves these goals.

In systems analysis we are searching for significant elements and regular patterns that have diagnostic validity. Only recently have we recognized that to manage complex systems we must understand how knowledge is obtained and how knowledge can be transferred. That, in essence, is what the systems concept requires. Not just some systematic, analytical procedure; not some cookbook approach, no matter how fine the recipes. This text presents a framework for the "new systems approach" which includes the context and environment that underlie our understanding of complex organizations.

What are the attributes of such a framework? It must catalyze valid insights and support consistent conclusions. It must relate the choice of the level of complexity of a system to the problem and the purpose of the system. It must suggest procedures and generate approaches that can *cope* (not overcope or undercope) with the chosen level of complexity. It must highlight connections and interactions so that diagnosis at one point in the system can be quickly related to all relevant connectives at other points in the system. It must provide measurable belief and confidence in the approach that is being used. It must enable interested parties—especially those who supply the data and those who use the results—to describe the system and to communicate with one another. It must make it possible to translate the different languages of subsystems into a unified expression of the total system.

These are the attributes that *Systems Analysis* displays.

Martin K. Starr

Columbia University

PREFACE

Systems analysis is the selection of elements, relationships, and procedures to achieve a specific purpose; some examples include the use of road maps to reach a specific city, office procedures to communicate information, and equipment combinations to handle a given set of jobs. This text surveys the field of systems analysis for the business student. The materials used are also applicable to most industrial, military, and administrative systems, and thus will be of interest to administrative, engineering, operations research, management science, and computer personnel.

This book attempts to show the reader that systems have several general properties and to give him a feeling for systems patterns. It develops skills in formalizing systems problems and provides a bridge between functional training and the systems requirements of problem formulation, analysis, and solution encountered in practice.

In the past, systems analysis has been treated from specialized viewpoints—such as paperwork, accounting, computer programing, aircraft design, and communication circuits—or from highly generalized viewpoints—such as philosophy systems, value systems, and pure mathematics. This book strikes a middle ground by stressing pattern formulation and diagnosis of system operations in a wide range of fields. As such, it will appeal more to "problem solvers" than to pure generalists or "how-to-do-it" readers.

The organization of this book makes it unique in the field of systems analysis. Although both specific and general materials are used, the main purpose of this textbook is to build basic skills in system definition, analysis, and solution of systems problems. Thus, we have the major divisions of System Definition, Systems Analysis and Diagnosis, and Systems Treatment.

Class testing of the many examples, illustrations, and problems at Columbia University over a period of three years has shown them to stimulate student imagination and curiosity in handling independent work, such as term projects.

In Chapters 1 through 5 special attention has been given to system definition so that the reader may be adequately prepared for this most critical step in systems analysis. The necessity for adjusting the system definition to the analyst's resources for analysis and control, together with appropriate simplification procedures, follows in Chapters 6 through 8. Chapters 9 through 12 contain selected procedures for systems analysis, including external and internal systems tests, search methods, logical and probabilistic diagnostic procedures, and systems simulation, and thus provide a range of tools for the reader. Problems of systems improvement and the implementation of system change conclude the treatment in Chapters 13 and 14.

Topics from the social sciences are introduced, for example, in Chapters 8 and 13, to complement quantitative system definitions and forms of analysis. This approach is a departure from that taken in traditional systems analysis textbooks and provides the reader with strategies for higher-level system definition and the diagnosis of implementation problems. Chapter 10, "Selected Search Problems and Techniques," contains topics not previously brought together in one text.

The reader will derive maximum benefit if he exploits the full range of examples, problems, and projects provided. However, should he become interested in a special topic, he can easily devote his energies to that subject through the references provided by the numerous footnotes and extensive bibliography.

The mathematical background assumed includes a first course in probability and statistics as well as a familiarity with undergraduate algebra. No knowledge of calculus is assumed. Appendices covering basic matrix calculations, an introduction to mathematical transformations, and an introduction to commercial codes, information measures, and field data collection are provided for reference. It would be helpful, although not necessary, for the reader to have had an introduction to data processing and operations research. The usual business school reader will also be familiar with one or more functional specialties (accounting, production, marketing, finance, etc.), and this knowledge will also be of use to him here.

I wish to acknowledge the moral and financial support provided by Dean Courtney C. Brown of the Graduate School of Business, Columbia University, in the completion of this work. I am indebted to my colleagues and students for innumerable suggestions. Acknowledgments for the use of previously published material are made where citations appear. Susan Alexion typed much of the manuscript with dispatch. I am particularly indebted to my parents for their initial stimulation and continued support of my interest in science and its wider applications, and to my wife, Auwe, for her care and patience over an extended writing schedule. Errors may remain in even the most diligently checked manuscript, and for these I must assume the final responsibility. Comments and suggestions for improvement of this text will be appreciated.

Van Court Hare, Jr.

Irvington, New York

CONTENTS

7

8

SYSTEMS ANALYSIS AND DIAGNOSIS

9

10

INTRODUCTION

The study of "systems" is by no means a new pursuit of the human mind. The Egyptian architects of Cheops' tomb relied on a system of measurement for its construction. Phoenician astronomers studied a system of the stars, and made rough predictions from their observations. Plato and other Greeks contemplated a system of society in which philosophers would be kings.

The development of a set of standards and procedures, or the development of a concept of society, or even a theory of the universe is as old as history itself. Man has always sought to find relationships: Satisfactory explanations for what he sees, hears, or dreams of.

Indeed, the history of both the physical and the social sciences has been a continuing enlargement upon this theme: Relevant and dependable relationships *must* be found if we are to advance knowledge and successfully conduct our affairs. The scientific method of inquiry, which demands such relevant and dependable relationships for its results, *is* systems analysis in its broadest sense.

THE NEW SYSTEMS ANALYSTS

Today, however, systems analysis and systems analysts are institutionalized in many specialized areas of activity, most frequently related to the diag-

1

nosis, design, evaluation, and treatment of complex hardware, information flow, and organizational systems that exist, or are conceived, to accomplish one or more *specific* objectives. The approach, methods, and tools used, as well as the results obtained, are of a kind unfamiliar in the past.

In such purposeful systems, from radar control devices to the operation of a business or a government agency, the investigator finds he must cross historical boundaries of knowledge and functions, if he is to achieve major improvements in the system's operation.

Hardware systems consisting of electrical, mechanical, hydraulic, optical, and chemical components are used by human operators, who have their own biological, medical, and social properties. To understand, to design, or to improve the operation of such a "total system," investigators must have available not only knowledge of, say, electrical engineering, but also knowledge of the other disciplines.

Moreover, to understand and to improve such systems by utilizing the relationships that result when diverse components are combined, investigators must be able to follow and exploit the chain of work flow, information flow, or material flow—the connecting links that tie the system together. And, these connecting links almost always lead across the boundaries of educational discipline and organizational function.

For example, we now have electronic radar detectors based on the analysis of a frog's eye. Electronic systems telemeter and record, on the ground, an astronaut's heart beat as he orbits 300 miles above the earth. Mechanical milling machines automatically produce parts from numerical directions given by a human, or a computer, and can store these skills for future use. Maser and laser devices, combinations of optics and electronics, set time standards to one part in ten billion, make optical stitching of detached human retinas possible, provide highly directive, wide-band communication possibilities, have been used in industrial welding and cutting equipment, and form the power source for "death ray" rifles, reportedly capable of stopping the enemy silently, without firing a shot. These mixed-discipline systems depend upon the *conscious exploitation* of the gaps between historical categories of knowledge.

Similarly, the operations of a business enterprise require the combination of numerous functions—purchasing, production, distribution, research and product design, sales, finance, legal and tax departments, and the like. But, the *flow* of information and material, required to fulfill the purpose of the business, by necessity cuts across these historical functions and departmental boundaries.

Changes in credit policy or credit timing do affect production scheduling decisions by generating more, or fewer, small orders. The formulation of sales bonus schemes does affect the patterns of distribution, wholesale and retail operations, and product profit margins by changing the product mix sold and by changing the sales methods used. The fact that a single machine tool can produce short runs of product at virtually no setup cost—and that minor modifications of product design can be made by patching together sections of paper tape, or feeding a modified formula to a computer—profoundly affects inventory levels, the labor complement to be hired, and the type of products we can offer for sale. Automatic assembly, packing, and order-picking equipment affects the physical layout of the factory, warehouse, and office, as well as the capital requirements of the firm. These developments also present mixed-discipline, systems analysis problems.

Thus, improvement in the business system *for the enterprise as a whole* requires the investigator to disregard formal boundaries, or to cross them at will.

The same argument holds in the development of the professional fields. The patent lawyer must know both engineering and law. The physicist finds a thin line exists between his specialty and chemistry. The designer of medical instruments turns into a combination physician and electronics expert. The modern corporate controller must have a general knowledge of all the basic sciences that affect his company's business, an ability to handle complex mathematics, and a talent for creating new systems.

In short, in the last ten years, it has become necessary to formalize a type of training and educational approach to systems that can generate large numbers of individuals and work groups whose purpose is specifically to cross forbidden boundaries and to relate diverse operations and specialties toward a definite systems purpose.

These are the new *systems analysts.*

SYSTEMS ANALYSIS AS AN INSTITUTION

Educators have always attempted to give their students the ability to relate and transfer knowledge from one problem to another, so that the student could multiply his successes and eliminate his mistakes. However, this has usually been done within a functional, or departmental framework at the university. Today, to satisfy the clear need for boundary-crossing people, most universities offer interdisciplinary degrees and hybrid courses (such as bioelectronics, electronic auditing, and mathematical planning), as well as courses pointed specifically at systems analysis in business systems and hardware systems.

Such courses in systems analysis are geared both to broaden the student's interest in related fields (such as electrical, mechanical, optical, and chemical engineering; or production planning, accounting, and electronic data processing) and to provide him with a number of tools, methods, and strategic approaches and with a *philosophy* for the analysis of a system as a total operation.

Today, systems analysts are institutionalized in *academia*. Some 120–150 English-language journals (and another 30–50 foreign-language journals) regularly carry articles of direct or related interest to systems analysts. A survey of the engineering, science, and business school catalogues of major United States institutions of higher learning shows that 20–30% of the university courses offered have a similar content—even if the classic courses in mathematics and statistics are excluded!

This educational trend, *which has not yet reached full momentum,* is backed by the employment of systems analysts in government, business, and industry.

In most organizations of any size, one may find a *systems analysis group, operations research group,* or *long-range-planning group* that is working on system diagnosis, design, and improvement. Some organizations, such as the Bell Telephone System, have made organized efforts of this type for 20 years or more, and most government and military agencies have been heavily engaged in systems analysis since World War II. Industry—from mining and refining, to brewing, clothing, appliances and amusement—has its "in house" groups, plus numerous outside consulting agencies.

From 1966 membership lists of professional societies, such as *The Operations Research Society of America, The Institute of Electrical and Electronics Engineers, The Association, for Computing Machinery, The Systems and Procedures Association, The General Systems Society, The Institute of Management Science* and similar organizations, plus various special groups in industry and government, we see that professionals engaged in systems analysis and related activities number no less than 300,000.

Moreover, technical developments in electronic data processing and the development of new theories of systems analysis have made available a substantial body of experience that treats systems problems in general. So, the efforts of systems analysts are also institutionalized in *theory* and *equipment.*

For example, Norbert Wiener's (1948) landmark work: *Cybernetics, or Communication and Control in the Animal and the Machine,* and Claude Shannon's work on *Information Theory* set the stage for a consolidation of system properties in a wide range of disciplines by viewing "systems problems" as problems of information transfer and control—the essential processes in the functioning of any organization.

Other investigators have isolated "patterns" of operation (such as the theory of queues), methods of analysis (such as dynamic programing), and strategies of test and evaluation (such as measures for system noise and variety) that have wide application.

The advent of electronic computation (10 million times faster than the mechanical calculator at this writing), the techniques of using stored logic program steps in the computer memory to automate problem solution and data processing, the computer's ability to control other equipment (and other computers and communication devices) on a microsecond, or "real-time" basis; and the programer's ability to make his machine duplicate, or simulate other operations (by means of appropriate logical design) have transformed the old methods of "pattern-seeking" and testing into revolutionized potentials for systems analysis.[1]

Using these theories, or models, we can predict and test system properties by computer simulation or mathematical computation *before* we construct actual systems. A newly proposed inventory control or accounting system, for example, can be specified, designed, tested, and evaluated before it is placed into operation—the effects of the new plan can be checked for possible side-effects in other operations of the system, say, production scheduling.

In addition, installing computers to handle an organization's data processing chores has furthered the view of an operation as a "total system," because this approach is necessary to gain the maximum efficiency and benefit from the expensive hardware.

This trend toward the "total system approach" in business was noted in a *Business Week* article (February 29, 1964, p. 85) as follows:

> "Progress has been so great and so fast [in the installation of computers] that only those totally involved with computers are capable of keeping track of it. Yet future progress will be even greater.
>
> "The most important evidence of that future progress will almost certainly be in the development of the 'total system.'
>
> "Most companies seriously concerned with putting computers to work already have a 'total system' plan in their files. Generally, its primary goal is to shorten the interval between receipt of an order and delivery of a product.
>
> "But a total system, also, is expected to pay large dividends by reducing inventory, eliminating rush orders and duplication of effort, improving customer service, improving purchasing through better vendor records, ending double-record keeping, and scheduling production—up to and including the actual running of the plant.
>
> "Often, too, a total system involves plans to standardize nomenclature, reduce employment fluctuations, keep personnel records, provide engineering information services, and give management a simple, but frequent, statement or chart on what actually is going on in the company, compared to schedules and forecasts."

The trend toward the "total systems viewpoint," as it is called in the popular literature, has had major effects on the design and the integration of operations in many fields, so that the effects of systems analysts are also institutionalized in *present applications*.

[1] In early 1966, a conservative estimate of the computer installations in operation was a number reaching 35,200 with an annual growth rate of 10–25%.

To take one representative illustration, a DC8-F can depart from New York as late as 1:00 A.M. and arrive on the West Coast before dawn, providing delivery of merchandise at the beginning of the business day. The ability to achieve this feat requires an integrated flow of material from dock to air to dock, the use of the principles of automation, and the highly organized sorting and handling of packages. One of the foremost examples of such a system can be found in United Airline's present installation at O'Hare Airport in Chicago:

"Freight moves automatically on tracks in a system of smooth-flowing distribution, sorting and loading. Operators in a control room push buttons to move freight on a maze of tracks that looks like a giant electric train set. The cargo is loaded on large pallets to fit the DC-8F's 7,508 cubic feet of cabin cargo space. Motorized transporters quickly carry each pallet from the freight terminal to the plane, and special loaders lift it aboard. No manual lifting is involved. The equipment permits loading 92,000 pounds of palletized freight aboard a single jet freighter in 22 minutes, a speed the industry has never seen before. (It takes two to four hours to load a piston cargo plane under the ordinary method.)" [2]

Similarly, some production operations are today entirely controlled by a computer control system, devised and implemented by systems analysts.

At Seadrift, Texas, Union Carbide Olefin's Company's ethylene plant is a production operation in which a computer controls valves and measures performance from the first to the last step. The major accomplishment due to the speed of response of the integrated control system is less product waste, which previously cost about 5% of plant capacity.

"Faster reaction and ability of a computer to take into consideration several interactions at once make it possible to design a plant that will operate at better than 99% of theoretical capacity. The 2% to 5% increase in efficiency that this represents could mean an increase of as much as 20% in the profit potential of the plant, since the extra production would come virtually free . . .

"In addition to the several hundred devices and gauges that sense, measure, and correct temperature, pressures, and flow rates, which are all tied into the computer, there are on-stream chemical analyzers that deliver a total of 289 different chemical analyses of the product stream from different parts of the plant.

"These analyses come in automatically at different intervals—from once every two minutes to once every half hour. It's no trouble for the computer to evaluate them, but it would drive human beings to distraction, probably to the point they would ignore most of the data . . .

"The computer will always read the information and act immediately. And that is one big reason why the plant operates at high efficiency." [3]

---

[2] *United Mainliner Magazine,* Vol. 8, No. 3, March, 1964, p. 9.
[3] "How Computers Did the Job at Seadrift," *Business Week,* November 9, 1963, pp. 146–8. Copyrighted © 1963 by McGraw-Hill, Inc.

Westinghouse's Tele-Computing Center in Braddock Hills, just east of Pittsburgh is an example of the system analyst's approach to improving paperwork flow and management control. Two Univac 409 Computers tie into a national teletype network that connects 300 sales offices, warehouses, and plants in 178 United States and Canadian cities. The system handles 17,000 messages daily, of which about 2000 are orders. Order-processing time is 2–3 *seconds*. The computer and teletype system check availability, calculate prices, discounts, and maintain inventory. The system prints by remote teletype at the proper warehouse all bills of lading and shipping labels. At the end of each day the system provides a record of what has been done, produces operating reports on 100 profit centers, and prints Westinghouse salary, pension, and dividend checks when they are needed. Here the improvement in efficiency has also been striking: one motor plant alone cut warehouse inventory from $5-million to $1.8-million, yet carries a wider range of items than before.[4]

Other current applications can be cited: Orbiting missiles, controlled by a complex of man-computer systems; analyses and designs for traffic flow; urban redevelopment plans; military logistics developments; automated diagnosis of medical symptoms; computer translation of scientific documents; the ever-increasing choice of instrumentation and control devices. But, the previous illustrations are sufficient to make our point.

The new systems analysts are not only here, they are institutionalized in the university, in government, in business, in industry, in the development of new theory and equipment, and in their efforts to change the scope and complexion of current, on-going operations. They are backed by millions of hours of educational effort, by billions of dollars in research, development and production funds, by myriad instrumentation, computation, and automation devices, and by the full-time thinking of some of the finest minds in the world. The scene is different: There has been a revolution in the concept, and in the use of systems since the days of Cheops' Tomb.

SYSTEMS ANALYSIS AND MANAGEMENT THEORY

The social and technical changes surveyed in the past few pages have had a profound effect upon management. The problems faced by the executive and the administrator have changed in *kind* as well as in content. Today, the question raised for the manager or supervisor is not so much, "Can the job be done?" The technical means to achieve a wide range of objectives with various degrees of effectiveness (and efficiency) are at hand. Rather, the reverse situation often confronts the manager: There are too many alternatives to be pursued, too many combinations from which to

[4] "Sperry Rand: Clearing Skies?" *Forbes Magazine,* April 1, 1964, pp. 20-24.

select, too many distractions to confound and confuse the decision-maker, too many things that can go wrong with the complex operations that must be administered. Today, the questions turn more to "Should the job be done?", "What choice shall be selected?", and "How can our programs be balanced?"

For example, in considering the management problems to be handled in the Department of Defense, Secretary McNamara has asked just such questions.[5] The problems of relevancy to stated objectives, the development and choice of clear alternatives, the balance and integration of plans and operating subsystems—all are part of what might be called a "systems philosophy of management."

"Our problems of choice among alternatives in strategy and in weapons systems have been complicated enormously by the bewildering array of entirely workable alternative courses which our technology can support. We believe the nation can afford whatever investment in national security is necessary. The difficult question is, 'What is required?' It is far more difficult to build a defense program on this kind of foundation than it is to set a budget ceiling and then squeeze into it whatever programs you can. However difficult, this is exactly what we set out to do.

". . . In each case competing programs and systems are judged on the basis of their contribution to the mission to be accomplished and to the defense effort as a whole. Balance within a given program and within the entire effort is sought, always with a single overriding objective—the defense of the nation." [6]

The Secretary then continues, explaining the need for quantitative methods to aid the judgment of the decision-maker:

"The judgment inherent in this balancing of programs and systems can no longer be intuitive nor rely on past experience alone. The range of choice is too broad, the number of alternatives too great. In the selection of weapons systems, in the design of forces and in determination of the level of the national defense effort, therefore, we are making greater use of a technique called 'systems analysis.' Perhaps it is best described as 'quantitative common sense.'

"Systems analysis takes a complex problem and sorts out the tangle of factors It aims to assist the decision-maker by furnishing him with quantitative estimates of the effectiveness and costs of each of the alternative courses which he could choose. Confronting a multiplicity of options we have turned to analytical techniques to assist us in our choice.

[5] Robert S. McNamara, "McNamara Defines His Job," *New York Times Magazine*, April 26, 1964 (© 1964 by the New York Times Company. Reprinted by permission.), adapted from the April–June, 1964, *Civil Service Journal*. The Department of Defense in 1964 involved 3,700,000 people scattered throughout the world, an inventory of real property of $150-billion, an annual budget of $50-billion, and the operation of multiple forces, airlines, shipping lines, communications, supply-distribution and maintenance systems, and 600 major installations.
[6] *Ibid.*

"I would not, if I could, attempt to substitute analytical techniques for judgment based upon experience. The very development and use of those techniques have placed an even greater premium on that experience and judgment, as issues have been clarified and basic problems exposed to dispassionate examination. The better the factual basis for reflective judgment, the better the judgment is likely to be. The need to provide that factual basis is the reason for emphasizing the analytical technique." [7]

Although the Department of Defense is an extreme case in the complexity of modern management, its problems mirror in exaggerated form those of the manager, operator, or designer of the smaller complex system.

For this reason, the modern manager needs to have available to him a theory, structured framework, or organized philosophy of how he will go about his job; specifically, how he will formulate his questions and problems, and how he will go about answering and solving them in a manner that can handle the growing *variety* of conditions, actions, and choices he must counter.

The key here is *variety*. And, the purpose of systems analysis, and systems analysts, from a management viewpoint, is the management and control *of* variety before variety controls and manages the manager.

From the management viewpoint, then, systems analysis takes on what one may consider a more philosophical tone. It treats problems of the complex system at a level of abstraction once removed from immediate detail, although requiring *selected* detail for its execution. It deals with the formulation and evaluation of precise alternatives, with the selection of activities and their level, with the integration of short- and long-range plans, with the specification of values and objectives, and with the implementation of strategies of diagnosis, trouble-shooting, repair and control.

These are the overriding decisions that commit organizations to courses of action, that control and hold them to a goal until a better one can be found. These are questions that bring into play considerations of goal changing, value changing, and innovations in policy as changes in technology and the environment take place.

We shall later refer to this "higher level of control" more extensively. However, we should note that the development of ability and power to control in the face of a variety of possible conditions requires the development of extensive *memory facilities* in the organization or system, in particular the development of efficient memory functions for the selection, storage, retrieval, recombination, and use of operating data, symbols, analytic procedures, and reserve plans of action.

By analogy, the development of systems control ability from a management viewpoint is similar to the development of a supervisory control program for a computer—as opposed to the development of a single efficient

[7] *Ibid.*

production program. The supervisory control program, like the human supervisor, is concerned with priorities and values, the allocation of space and time, with the selected use of *different* production programs, sources of data, plans, and procedures in response to changes in input conditions. The success of the supervisory program is judged by its effectiveness in long-range strategic decision making, or selection, rather than in terms of speed, day-to-day operating efficiency, or short-range tactics, as might be the case in the production program.

Thus, in making a study of systems analysis, we must cover, for the student of business, not only a number of specific systems properties, techniques, and methods, but also cover what eventually will become his major concern, the broader considerations of control at higher levels. We must cover a scope of discourse that runs the gamut from simple governors, quality control systems and simple multidiscipline devices to the problems faced by the "total system designer."

SYSTEMS DEFINITION

1 | DEFINING THE SYSTEM: A SURVEY

We define a system when we draw a map. For example, Figure 1-1 is a small road map that shows the interstate highways connecting cities A and B with those cities outside our map's border. The system *elements* are the cities (circles), and the *relationships* illustrated are the interstate highways (arrows).

Both the elements and the relationships shown in Figure 1-1, however, have been carefully selected to achieve a *specific purpose*—illustration of the interstate highway system in the area—and the choice of elements and relationships in our simple example is *relevant* to that end.

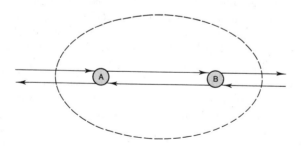

1-1 A simplified road map showing the interstate highway system between two cities and other cities outside the border.

THE OBJECTIVE OF A SYSTEM DEFINITION

In defining a system, the matter of relevance is all important. What happens within the boundary of our map could be described in many different ways—by a drawing, by equations, by a physical model, or by a verbal description. However, unless the elements and relationships to be considered within the map's borders are selected for a specific purpose, an infinite number of connections and combinations would be possible.

Let us elaborate for emphasis. The observer of this landscape could paint it, draw a topological map, write equations of the traffic flow passing through it, classify the flora and fauna there, develop a history of the area, examine and relate the chemical content of its soil and streams, or make a study of how religious belief affects local law, to mention a few of the projects that could illustrate *some* kind of relationship in the scene. But the investigator would hardly care to undertake all of these projects at one time. Indeed, it would be physically impossible for him to do so. The number of combinations of relationships and elements that could be chosen rapidly grows to greater than astronomical proportions *even when substantial restrictions are applied.*

Consider the choice of *elements* to be related. In our map in Figure 1-1, suppose we had 400 political subdivisions instead of two cities and that we made no restriction on those we would, or would not, consider. Three of the possible element arrangements are shown schematically in Figure 1-2. However, the total number of possible element combinations that could be drawn from this block of 400, if we consider all possibilities, is 2^{400} or approximately 10^{120}. This number of pictures can be contemplated, but not drawn, because 10^{120} exceeds the number of atoms in the known universe.[1] Our artist could never complete his job.

Such *combinatorial* numbers of impossible size occur in all selection processes that do not specify stringent restrictions on what may be considered relevant or useful to our purpose.

Similarly, if the number of *relationships* that could be considered between only a few elements were not restricted severely, the same result would obtain. For example, in Figure 1-1, suppose we did not illustrate *only* interstate highways, but attempted to consider *all* transportation relationships that could exist between the two cities, by whatever route or mode. Here, from the infinite lines in a plane specified by simply geometry, we have the result shown in Figure 1-3, which is useless as a road map. Without proper specification, our map of relationships turns into a black morass that serves no purpose.

[1] An estimate of the number of atoms in the known universe is 10^{76}. An even more impressive number of combinations can be generated by DNA molecules, which transmit genetic characteristics from one generation to another. These molecules can theoretically unite in $10^{2,400,000,000}$ ways.

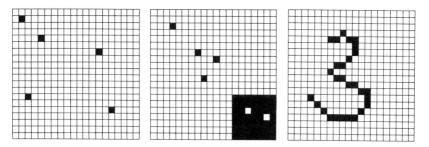

1-2 Three of the possible 10^{120} patterns that can be drawn by placing spots in a 20 × 20 grid.

1-3 A map of all the possible connections between the two cities shown in Figure 1-1.

An additional important property of system description also leads· to complexities for which we presently have no solution. It is often desirable to know if two systems have exactly the same structure, that is, if they are *isomorphic*. This is an important property, because if two systems *are* isomorphic, what we have learned about the properties of one such system will often allow us to make reasonable statements about the properties of the other. Yet, proving that two systems are isomorphic can involve us in combinatorial problems such as those mentioned above.

For example, each graph illustrated in Figure 1-4 has five elements and

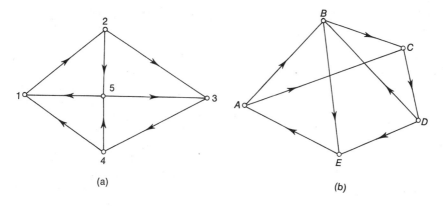

1-4 Two five-node, eight-arc graphs that are *isomorphic*. Stephen H. Unger "GIT—A Heuristic Program for Testing Parts of Directed Line Graphs for Isomorphism," in *Comm. Assoc. of Computing Machinery* **7**, 1, Jan. 1964, p. 27.

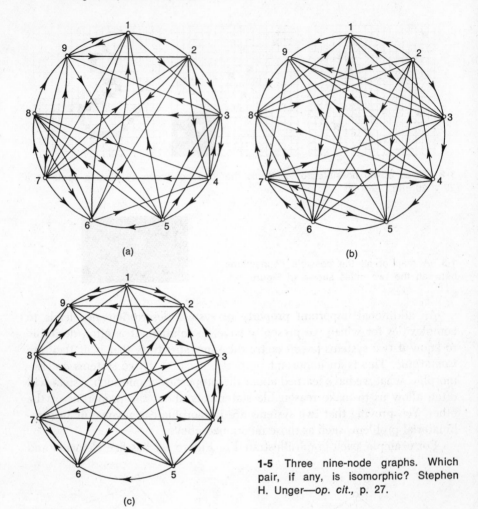

(a)

(b)

(c)

1-5 Three nine-node graphs. Which pair, if any, is isomorphic? Stephen H. Unger—*op. cit.,* p. 27.

eight relationships or *nodes* and *arcs,* to use the terminology of graph theory. Are the two systems isomorphic?

It is difficult to tell even in this simple case, because there are 5! possible node pairings that could be considered, and, in general, n! for the n-node graph. By enumeration or inspection, we can show that Figures 1-4a and 1-4b are isomorphic by relabeling Figure 1-4b as follows: $1 \rightarrow C$, $2 \rightarrow D, 3 \rightarrow E, 4 \rightarrow A,$ and $5 \rightarrow B.$ But this seeming ease in visualizing similar patterns disappears rapidly as the number of nodes increases. (Try to determine which pair of the nine-node graphs in Figure 1-5, if any, is isomorphic.)

To be even more explicit, suppose we had a computer available to enumerate and test our trials at the n-node graph problem, at one millisecond per trial. It would take about an hour to solve the ten-node problem, and about *40 years* to solve a 15-node problem by the obvious enumeration procedure.

This short discourse on the complexity and size of combinatorial numbers encountered in practice should convince us that the first step in defining a system is to specify the *purpose* and *restrictions* under which we will create our abstraction or formal picture of a given case. Moreover, our specification must take into account our ability to handle the types of analysis desired (as illustrated in later chapters) and should be as simple—in the sense of analytical efficiency—as our stated purpose will allow.

Unfortunately, although the principle of specification and simplification is clear, its method of application is not. At the present state of the art no theory of system simplification can guarantee that we have abstracted our system from the real world correctly, nor that we have simplified our choice of elements and relationships in an optimum way for a given purpose. In this all-important area of system definition, which commits us to a course of investigation and expenditure of effort, we must rely on art, experience, intuition, hunch, and hypothesis. To make matters worse, no method can guarantee (in all cases) that one system description is equivalent to another; no general way of proving isomorphism is available today.

Yet, our procedure for defining a system (or a problem to be solved) need not be a random process. We can organize our experience, classify our examples, and show which intuitions and hypotheses of selection have a greater chance of success for each class. We can provide a generalized framework for formulating systems descriptions. We can present a range of formats for systems definition that have wide application. And, we can cite a number of principles of systems simplification and a number of techniques for the investigator to use in combating system complexity and variety. We can also illustrate a number of general systems properties that can guide the definition in the specific case.

Such *heuristics*[2] form the basis for system definition (and later analysis) by turning our approach from a search for "the optimum" or "an optimum" system definition to one that, with high probability, will be suitable for our purposes. So, accepting this approach, we turn first to an over-all view of the system and its components as defined by a series of classical methods.

THE SYSTEM AS A NETWORK OR FLOW DIAGRAM

Consider a set of points that represent *elements*. (These points may be called *nodes, components, operations, vertices,* etc., depending on the

---

[2] The word heuristic comes from the Greek *heuriskein,* to discover, and pertains to methods serving to stimulate investigation, particularly those methods of demonstration which tend to lead a person to investigate further by himself. In mathematics and computer technology, heuristics take the form of rules of experience which aid in problem simplification and solution.

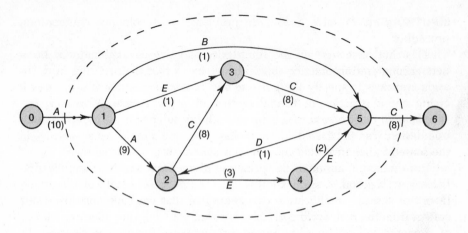

1-6 A system flow diagram used for definition.

reader's preference.) Our original collection of elements contains those that *may* be of interest for a given purpose. For example, our elements in an industrial system may be work centers, machines, departments, or divisions, depending upon the amount of detail needed in later analyses. The elements in a mechanical or electrical system may be physical components that perform a task and can be isolated. Clearly, some systems easily allow us to list their possible elements from physical, logical, organizational, or similar considerations. In other systems, the choice must be tentative.

However, whatever our initial choice, we should assume that we have a finite set of elements around which we can draw a clear boundary, as in Figure 1-6.

Next we investigate the *relationships* among the elements initially chosen and indicate these relationships by lines or arrows connecting the elements in question. (The relationships shown may be called *transactions, interactions, transmissions, connections, links, arcs, edges*, etc., again depending on the reader's preference.)

Our choice of the relationships to be shown will be set by our purposes in defining the system. For example, if we intend to study the operation of an order-processing system, the transactions shown will be the flow of orders and the subsequent documents produced. In an electrical system, the connections may represent the wires in a circuit. In a logical system, the links will show the sequence of operations to be performed. Relationships not important to our purpose will be omitted within our system boundary, and only relationships that affect our system (or will affect other systems) will be shown entering or leaving the boundary, as in Figure 1-6.

INPUTS AND OUTPUTS

Thus far, we have said nothing about *measuring* the relationships or about determining the element properties. For the moment, let us set this job aside and dwell upon the *structure* of the system as it now stands. Looking at Figure 1-6 in more detail, we see that we have done several things: (1) We defined a boundary that separated the elements we positively wanted from others we might have considered; (2) we selected the elements within the boundary that we would consider further; and (3) we selected the relationships within the boundary that we would consider further, showing these few important relationships within the boundary, as well as to and from the "outside world" across the boundary. We have thus far illustrated only undirected connections or relationships.

If we wished, however, we could indicate with arrowheads the direction of the relationships included or the direction of the effects produced by one element on another. Such a directed flow diagram is often necessary to describe adequately the operation of the system.

For example, let us adopt the convention that an arrow *emerging* from element A and entering element B will signify that A affects B, A precedes B, A initiates a transaction to B, or A's output is an input to B, etc. Conversely, an arrowhead *entering* an element, say B, will show that B is affected by A, B follows A, or B's input is A's output, etc. Such a convention is followed in Figure 1-6.

This convention indicates that some arrows enter the system boundary, and others leave the system boundary. Those arrows that cross the boundary represent the inputs and outputs to and from the whole system. And, to study the over-all operation of the system further, our problem is to relate the system's output to the input entering the system. In the order-processing system, we will wish to determine what production orders, documents, or products leave the boundary when given types of orders enter. In the electrical system, we will want to know what action, motion, or signal is transmitted from the system in response to various input signals. In the logical system, we will wish to know what results to expect when certain types of data or conditions are given as input conditions.

In short, our later analysis of the system may be concerned with *predicting* the outputs from the system, given certain input conditions. To do this, we must isolate the inputs and outputs and determine the structure within the boundary that may affect our prediction. In other problems, we may be given specified input and output conditions for the system, and be asked to restructure the internal operations of the system to meet these specifications most efficiently. In either problem, the simple flow diagram described thus far provides a starting definition.

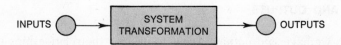

1-7 The system transformation, when summarized by combining internal system detail. This is the "black box" transformation of the system input to the system output, as described in Chapter 2.

MEASURING RELATIONSHIPS AND ELEMENT PROPERTIES

At this point, we may ask for more information about the system elements and relationships. Generally, the *relationships* of the flow diagram can be described by an *attribute* or a *variable*.[3] For example, in the order-processing system, we may want to know the type of document represented by the transaction (order, confirmation, release, file copy, etc.), or we may want to know some measure of the volume of transactions per week, the time required for the transaction to be completed, the dollar value of the transaction, etc. In the electrical circuit, the relationship may be a current flow, a magnetic coupling, or a similar physical measure. Indeed, a combination of variables may be used to describe the relationships involved in as much detail as may be necessary for analysis.

Similarly, the operation of the elements, often called their *transformation* properties, must be specified in sufficient detail to relate the internal inputs to the outputs. In particular, the transformation performed by an element is usually described by the mathematical function, logical operation, or process operation that relates predictively an element's output to its input. For example, an order-processing element may convert an order into a credit inquiry, an electrical operation may amplify an input signal into a larger output signal, or a logical operation may compare one input signal with another and produce an output (or not), depending upon the results. If we know each element input and transformation, we can predict the element output. By extension, if the element transformation properties are known, it is possible to compute a prediction of the *system* output.

In summary, our notion of the system element can be expanded into the quantitative or logical relation of an input set of variables (or attributes) to an output set of variables (or attributes) by a transformation, as noted in Figure 1-7.

Even where we do not wish to measure relationships but only to indicate their presence or absence, a quantitative notation (1 or 0) is useful to indicate structure. Similarly, where an element may not represent a process but simply a decision point or similar reference point in time or space, a structural notation using the (1, 0) convention is often useful for matrix and similar presentations.

[3] The dual of this description is discussed in Chapter 3.

	0	1	2	3	4	5	6
0		1					
1			1	1		1	
2				1	1		
3						1	
4						1	
5			1				1
6							

1-8 A system matrix, showing the same structure as the flow diagram in Figure 1-6. The conventions used are described in the text.

MATRIX DESCRIPTIONS OF THE SYSTEM

Each *element* in Figure 1-6 has been numbered. If we adopt the convention that the presence of an arrow will be indicated by a "1," and its absence by a blank, or "0," we can draw the table, or matrix, of Figure 1-8, which summarizes the *structure* of the system in compact form.

Standard conventions are used in Figure 1-8. If the element in our system emitting an arrow is designated as i and the element receiving an arrow is designated j, we number our matrix *rows* $i = 1, 2, 3, \ldots, n$, where n is the total number of elements within the system boundary *plus* those few outside elements affected by the system outputs and those elements offering inputs to the system. Similarly, we number our matrix *columns* $j = 1, 2, 3, \ldots, n$ obtaining a square table. We understand a "1" in cell (i, j) means an arrow goes *from* element i *to* element j; a blank means no connection.

The system matrix representation has some obvious advantages in providing rapid information for the investigator. The total number of arrows leaving a given element can be obtained by noting the number of entries in the given element's row. The total number of arrows entering an element is the total number of entries in that element's column. The element having the largest number of both entering and leaving arrows can be found by locating that element with the maximum number of entries in its row plus its column. The number of two-way transactions between elements can be found by isolating all cases for which there is an entry in both cell (i, j) and cell (j, i) that uses the same values for i and j in each case. Similarly, elements that receive but do not transmit can be isolated by a simple row-column inspection. Other system properties (such as loops) can be obtained also by inspection of the matrix. So, for ease of display, as well as

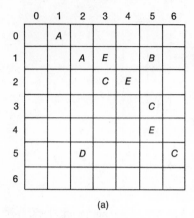
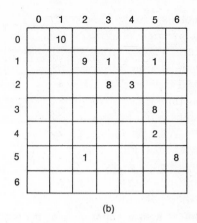

1-9 Variations of the system matrix of Figure 1-8 to include additional detail on the relationships between elements in the system, as described in text.

for theoretical considerations, we will frequently refer to the system matrix and its variants.

Notice also that the matrix display can be used to show measures of relationships in either attribute or variable form. Figure 1-9a shows an attribute display that uses the same type of transaction as that used in Figure 1-6 in place of the $(1, 0)$ convention. For example, the type of transaction is shown in Figure 1-6 by the letter code attached to each arrow, where A = order, B = inquiry, C = release, D = confirmation, and E = advice. The matrix in Figure 1-9a now carries both structural and transaction information. Figure 1-9b shows a similar display in which numbers indicate the frequency with which transactions occur in a given time period; e.g., ten orders enter the system per day on the average. In general, the matrix entry may be a complex code, or vector, that carries as much detail as necessary on each transaction.

A SHORT HISTORY OF SYSTEM DESCRIPTIONS

The general description of the system definition just presented has an interesting historical base. Because of the selection problem (and its resulting combinatorial numbers), descriptions of systems (or models of operations) have often conformed to the view of science in vogue at the particular time.[4]

In ancient Egypt, the picture of organizational structure used most often referred to the physical structures found in nature or made by man. It is

[4] K. W. Deutsch, "Communication Models in the Social Sciences," *Public Opinion Quarterly*, 16, 1952, pp. 356–380.

not surprising that organization charts of that time (and since) have shown a pyramid of power, with the control centered at the apex of the structure. Family "trees" are a similar "iconic" representation of relationships, gained from observations of nature. These were static pictures, however, and indicated change only through the revision of the parts of the picture as time passed. No short-range variations or day-to-day change in relationships could be shown.

With the industrial revolution and its emphasis on machinery and clockwork, the picture of a system changed from static to ordered and stable motion. The organization, or system, was conceived of as a group of gears and pinions. Different theories were set in this framework. The term "a big wheel" is still used to imply an organizational element who has many forceful relationships with others in his system. The new concept was stable movement; that is, movement which is totally predictable and subject to calculation. This was the time not only of wonderful machines but also of great interest in accurate prediction and a feeling that the world was deterministic.

The gear-theory view of the world, however, had serious limitations, too. No explanations could show how the unpredictable events (which everyone observed) came to pass. There were also no suitable systems descriptions explaining the strange delays in the scheduled train of events predicted by the deterministic theory.

Harvey's discovery of the correct circulation system of blood in the body had its profound effect on the history of system formulation. He focused attention on what might be called a "hydraulic concept of explanation." Harvey showed that many phenomena could be viewed in terms of "flows"—something roughly related to a plumbing system. This view not only fit a number of medical explanations, but also was general enough to handle explanations of the emerging sciences of electronics and hydraulics. Indeed, we still are indebted to this era for many of our concepts of flow diagrams and charts.

By an extension of the flow-view of operations to include storage and delay, thinkers such as Freud presented a picture of the world that included even more possibilities. Here the system had the ability to store responses and reflect earlier stimuli in reasonably unpredictable responses at a later date. The ability of the system to exhibit variety was enhanced. Freud, however, retained some of Harvey's strict hydraulic principles: He reasoned that inputs could be stored, but, if they were "repressed" beyond the ability of the human system, they would exhibit themselves in another, often perverse, form at a later date. This view was still relatively rigid, and for prediction left much to be desired.

Our present socio-psychology of systems definition—the conditioned way we select elements and relations we wish to consider—borrows much from this historical background. However, today we usually tend toward a world-view largely flavored by recent technical developments in science and computation.

We have come to see that nature holds an inherent element of uncertainty and chance in most cases of any interest. The act of measurement itself (or an attempt at it) often alters the situation, as Heisenberg's famous principle of uncertainty in physics has shown. Moreover, our knowledge of exotic devices, electronic computers, and control systems tells us that much of our present technology is geared to the construction and operation of *purposeful* or goal-seeking (*teleological*) systems.

In this "cybernetic" [5] view of the world, systems can have still greater variety of response to input, although many of the old views of organizations and systems remain. If the purposeful system, however, is described in a flow diagram, or even a more deterministic form, and yet is imbued with the ability to remember, store, and recombine facts—and to any extent to control its own future—a new range of description and system definitions is opened to us that was not possible before.

The current example of our world-view of systems definition then is based on what we can do with computers and sophisticated control systems, and we should be aware of the sociological and psychological power of this impetus when we formulate our system descriptions.

Therefore, in what follows, we will aim our discussion toward even more powerful descriptions of the systems we will encounter. But for simplicity, we have begun our historical sequence with the classical form of the flow diagram.

PROBLEMS

1.1   A Chinese laundryman issues tickets for each bundle of clothes received. The ticket contains one of 26 alphabetic characters and three numbers. In addition, the laundry changes the color of its tickets every two months, with six distinct colors per year. How many distinct bundles can the laundry identify with this ticket system per year?

1.2   A lithographer's plate has a series of 100 dots per inch. Each dot can be black or white, so there are 100×100 positions per square inch.

A. How many different, i.e., mathematically distinct, pictures could be displayed on a 10 by 10-inch cut, or black-and-white printed picture?

B. Suppose we allow each dot to be one of six colors, including white. What can you say about the variety of distinct pictures that can be displayed?

[5] *Cybernetics* is a word coined by the late Norbert Wiener from the Greek for "steersman," or one who controls. This word became the title of Wiener's now classic work, *Cybernetics, or Control and Communication in the Animal and the Machine*, 2nd ed., MIT Press, Cambridge, Mass., 1961.

C. Comment on the observer's ability to handle this variety of possibilities.

1.3   A system is composed of five nodes and four relationships, or arcs. Assuming no node is left unconnected, how many different graphs could be drawn if

A. The nodes are numbered 1, 2, 3, 4, and 5, and the arc directions must always progress from a smaller to a larger number.

B. As in A, but now let the directed relationships proceed in either direction.

C. In A, how many possibilities are there if the numbered nodes can be interchanged at will?

1.4   A frog sits on a lily pad in a lake. He faces two rows of five lily pads each. When the spirit moves him, he jumps to one of the five pads in the first row, and then again from where he is to the next row ahead.

A. How many paths could the frog take in moving forward?

B. How many paths would be possible if the frog faced N rows of r pads each, and if he progressed one row at each jump?

C. After the second jump in A, suppose the frog could jump both backward and forward from row to row. How many paths could he generate in five moves?

D. In C, how many paths could the frog generate if he could never jump to the same pad more than once?

1.5   We can describe a system by the transactions between operations, or elements, as shown in the table below. The value of each transaction is also shown.

A. Draw a flow diagram of this system.

B. Complete the equivalent system matrix to show all the information in A.

FROM	TO	VALUE
1	2	6
2	4	2
2	3	3
3	6	4
4	5	10
4	6	7
5	7	3
6	7	5

1.6   Subassembly A is composed of one part 1's, one part 2's, and three part 3's. Subassembly B is composed of two part 1's, no part 2's, and six part 3's.

A. Draw a diagram showing this relationship of parts to subassemblies.

B. If we need ten subassemblies A and 20 subassemblies B, how many parts of each type will we need?

C. Suppose two A's and three B's go into final product I, and one A and four B's go into final product II. How many parts of each kind will be required in total to make 100 I's and 200 II's?

1.7 Diagram the sequence of events you follow after arising in the morning until the time you reach work (or school). Do you see any repetitive, circular, or conditional loops in your diagram? Indicate what you do by using a box for an element and showing the sequence of events by arrows.

1.8 According to Louis Nizer in *My Life in Court*, a useful technique. he employs is to draw connecting lines with different colored pencils between related statements in testimony to check inconsistencies, omissions, and plausibility of a group of statements. [See *My Life in Court*, Doubleday, New York, 1961; Pyramid, New York, 1963, pp. 114–115.] Could you suggest a method of organizing this marked typescript into a table or chart?

1.9 Make a further study of the history of models and methods of system definition by reference to the articles by K. W. Deutsch, listed in the bibliography. Also see the articles by N. Wiener and A. Rosenblueth and N. Wiener. These references provide a good background for the material that follows.

PROJECT 1

Read Appendix E, the memorandum describing how to study your hometown. Perform such a study of your hometown, or, using similar methods, perform a study to define the important relationships in your school or company. The purpose of this project is to illustrate the usefulness of a wide range of materials in defining an organization or system.

2 | DETAILED METHODS OF SYSTEM DEFINITION: THE BLOCK DIAGRAM

Figure 2-1 shows three building blocks that define a system in more detail.

The blocks shown indicate the three major system operation types. Figure 2-1a represents a single transformation, or *conversion operation*. Figure 2-1b represents the application of a decision rule, or a *logical operation*. Figure 2-1c represents an observation phase, or *correction operation,* in which an operation's output is fed back for comparison with an operating standard. Several transformations and logical operations can be combined to produce (or to describe) a more complex system; the feedback control principle can be applied to groups of transformations or logical operations. The versatility of each of these three basic operations can be enhanced by the use of "memory."

In this chapter we outline methods for improving our understanding of these basic operations and illustrate how such operations can be combined. We will see the block diagram approach in this chapter, but in Chapter 3 we will describe alternate methods that are useful in special cases.

THE TRANSFORMATION OPERATION

To improve the definition of a system over a structural description, we ask for the details of *component* operation. For example, if an order is received

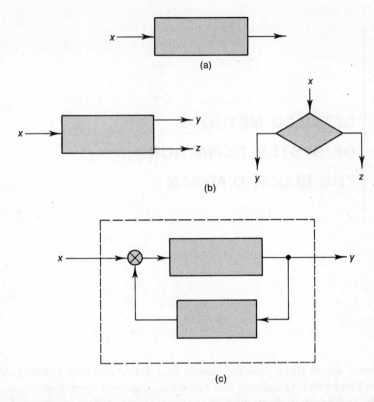

(a)

(b)

(c)

2-1 Three building blocks that can be used to construct complex systems. (a) Is the transformation block that converts an input *x* into an output *y* by stated conversion rules; the transformation block may also be used to indicate a sequence of steps in a process. (b) Shows two forms commonly used to indicate a decision block; the input *x* is tested, and produces either action *y* or action *z*. (c) Shows the common feedback operation, within the dotted lines; the input *x* is modified as a function of the ouput *y*. An analysis of the feedback block is left to Figure 2-10.

and an accounting report is issued, we may ask: "What was done to the order to obtain the accounting report?" We inquire into the details of the conversion. These steps may be simple, or complex, but if the transformation rules can be determined, we can predict what will happen to an input.

Some examples of the conversion operation are:

1. The order department receives an order, extends the items ordered by unit price and totals to obtain the total order value. This total goes to the accounting department for a credit check.
2. The cook receives 100 pounds of flour, 50 pounds of sugar, five dozen eggs, and ten pounds of butter each day. From this he makes ten cakes and ten loaves of bread each day.

3. The component amplifies an electronic signal 10,000 times when the input signal is 2000 cycles per second.
4. The operation is to find the output y from the input x, where $y = ax^2 + bx + c$.

The description of the transformation may be more or less detailed, stated in mathematics or in English, but the purpose of specifying what conversion takes place remains the same: Given the stated inputs, we must know enough to describe what kind of output will occur.

The Black Box Concept

Note that in the above examples we said nothing about exactly *how* the conversion was to be made. The accounting report could be produced by hand or by a computer, by a single individual or by a group. The cook could bake his cakes and bread in a gas or an electric oven. The electronic amplifier could be made of tubes, transistors, or some other components. Finally, the mathematical operation, the most general description, could be performed in various ways: by hand, by an analog computer or digital computer, or by any physical operation one could describe by a quadratic equation, say, the position of an object after a time x.

Thus, we can think of the transformation as a *black box*, which represents a grouping of detail. The detail is so grouped either because we do not choose to deal with further detail, or because we are unable to penetrate the black box boundary.

> *Example:* If we wished to know in complete detail why a particular dog wags his tail, we would need to destroy the dog to trace his nerve structure, to cite one form of analysis. This, however, would still not explain in complete detail why the dog wagged his tail. For the dog's owner, a black box approach is entirely satisfactory: "My dog wags his tail when I give him a bone."

How We Define a Black Box

A black box, as illustrated in the dog example, is really a system of infinite detail that encompasses the atomic structure of the dog's protein molecules and beyond. But, because of our restricted purpose—simply to make the dog's tail wag—we treat the dog as a block like Figure 2-1a. In other words, at some level of refinement, we say "enough!" and lump together what we do not know or care to discover.

The definition of a black box, then, is "operational" or "behavioristic." We do not ask in ultimate detail how a transformation takes place, but rather observe what does take place. If the input-output relationship observed is sufficiently stable to offer reliable prediction, then that reliable relationship is taken as the black box transformation. The criterion for a suitable black box definition is the same as that for a system definition. The output must be predictable, within the limits of our need, from the input.

The term black box, incidentally, originated in electrical engineering where many physical black boxes contained electronic components. (Black was the popular color for instrument panels before and during World War II.) It became convenient to provide electronic boxes with input-output specifications, connection instructions, and performance tests that did not require dismantling the hardware. Both the term and the method of treating components solely by their input-output relationships have remained and have spread to other fields. A similar trend has occurred in science, but for a different reason. "Operationalism," in physics, and "behaviorism," the corresponding approach in the social sciences, attempted to free science from ambiguous terms and from explanations that invoked supernatural beings to rescue the analyst from apparently mystical phenomena. It became popular to say that if the term could not be measured, it was undefined. Or, in our case, if no predictable relationship could be measured, the black box transformation could not be defined.[1] We shall adopt this view, indicating, where necessary, criticisms of the approach.

How We Develop the Transformation

Black box transformations come to our knowledge in three ways:

By specification

If the operation is well-known, say it is a machine for a known operation, then the specifications for operation may have been developed by others. In this case we would be fortunate to have catalogues, where we could find our component transforms at the turn of a page. At this level, the component block is clearly defined as is the transformation.

By analogy, similarity, and modification

Should the system components be less obviously circumscribed, it may yet be possible to notice processes of a familiar type—common inventory, bottleneck, allocation, or search processes to list a few business examples. Here we may be guided by existing *theoretical* descriptions, or specifications for a class of processes. Although the transformations suggested by the

---

[1] Professor Ross Ashby has been kind enough to suggest a historical note on the term black box. "I have heard," he reports, "that the original Black Box was that said by the Duke of Monmouth (who rebelled against James II) to contain the proofs of his legitimacy, which was suspect. The box, though always on the point of appearing, was always somewhere else, so it became legendary for that whose contents are quite unknown and unknowable."

more general theory may not be suitable for a particular block, the theory can often be modified suitably with less effort than if we start from scratch. Thus, if a block transformation generally involves the resolution of input-output priority problems, we may find assistance in waiting-line, or queuing, theory, and by modification of a general formula or "model" develop the particular transformation we need.

Observation and experiment

If we know nothing about the black box we have no choice but to experiment. This is done by observing various combinations of inputs and outputs, by recording them in order, and by attempting to deduce what relationship may adequately describe what we see.

Example: Sometimes we are totally ignorant of what a black box operation does, or in fact, which connections are inputs and which are outputs. In this case the combinations possible for testing inputs will not allow us to learn much about the box unless we are lucky and select an input for trial that produces a useful or interesting output. More likely we may know something about the box, its general class of performance, and the material we want to measure. To return to the order-processing example, we may not know what the department does exactly, but we can get a good idea by sending in a trial order and capturing the documents that relate to our test. With a few such tests orders, we can narrow the range of usual actions to those needed for prediction.

Experimental tests may also be necessary to confirm the black box transformations developed from theoretical considerations. Obviously, the more we know about the black box operation, the more accurately we can select experimental inputs, so any knowledge of possible theory is an aid in experimental determination of a black box transformation.

Black Box Assumptions

Let us now suppose we have attained a satisfactory black box transformation. What assumptions have been made? And, what assumptions must we make when combining black boxes? Three considerations are important:

Continued stability of transformation

The behavioral or operational definition of a black box (which rests only on observations of input-output relationships) assumes that, at least for predictions, the box must operate in the future as it has in past recorded observations. In short, we assume the black box has a fixed memory, that it cannot learn, and, specifically, that its internal operations will not change with time or strange combinations of input conditions we have not considered in our experimental trials.

Example: The classic example is a land mine set to go off after N jolts. The experimenter who applies $N - 1$ jolts may draw a deadly conclusion from his observations. He will surely be surprised when he makes the *Nth* test. The faithful cashier who after thirty years of trust and duty purloins the bank deposits represents the human analog. Metal beams have a similar ability to change with time and a variety of cumulative or fortuitous inputs: The aircraft engineer or bridge builder may treat structural members as black boxes when computing working loads and stresses; but even metal can fatigue, crystallize, and crack.

We are, of necessity, driven to black box thinking in the affairs of everyday life—even if we had no scientific theory of operationalism. We sit on a chair without thinking of its atomic structure, and make deposits and withdrawals at the bank without concern about the moral habits of the staff. We obviously cannot suspect all boxes as bombs, all employees as erratic thieves, or all physical structures as on the verge of imminent collapse. But where experience, theory, or intuition suggests the possibility of important shifts in the black box transformation, we must know more about the *internal* workings of the box. If the experimenter knew the bomb contained an N-position stepping relay that moved forward at each jolt, he could save his life. If the manager knew his clerk spent each Saturday at the races, he could take his money to the bank himself. If the designer knew how his metals fatigued under repeated stress, he could avert some aircraft failures. The need to know more about a black box than we do arises when a possible shift in the transformation we presently use can cause disaster, or substantial losses.

Typically, failures to observe the stability assumption occur when the black box is forced to operate outside its previously tested range, or under a combination of inputs not previously considered, or when a series of inputs or the passage of time alters the structure or memory content of the box.

Black box independence

Theoretically, if we knew exactly what one black box does, i.e., if we have its transformation, and if we know its manner of coupling to another known black box, then we should be able to predict what the pair will do in combination. We may then consider the combination as a new, and larger, black box.

The idea is general, as we will see in the next section. However, we are occasionally surprised not because of instability of either box, but because the boxes are not independent: Coupling the two boxes produces a change in the individual transformations.

For example, if the second box "loads" the first, or vice versa, the operation may be altered. Such effects are common in physical measurement situations in which the measuring instrument when attached to the device under measurement actually changes its transformation. Investigations of the stock market often change the market. The job may exceed the capacity of the worker. One machine may jam the operation of another.

Dependence, of course, is not always bad. Two carpenters working together can do the work of three or more men working alone, because one man can cut and hold while the other levels and nails. The division of labor gains its economies from the change in individual transformations, or methods of work, which are possible when individuals work as organized groups—a result we would not see from a straightforward combination of individual black box transformations.

When we combine black boxes, we may find "emerging" variables that are not apparent from examination of the individual parts. Chemical examples abound: Carbon, oxygen, and hydrogen have no particular taste in themselves, but in combination they can produce the sweet taste of sugar. In business, two departments when combined or related in a given sequence may produce emerging variables, good or bad, such as new product ideas, a union, or a new bowling team.

Again, for the combination of effects noted in this section, we might find an explanation if the original black boxes had been examined in greater detail. There is little doubt in the minds of most scientists that if they completely understood the amino acids that make up living protein, they could explain and synthesize living matter.

Compatibility of outputs to inputs

If we say that the output of one black box is compatible with the input requirements of the second, we mean that such an output is "suitable" for transformation by the second black box. The second black box, for example, must be able to handle the variety of the first box's output unless some loss of performance (and therefore some change in the over-all transformation of the two boxes) is not to result. We can only fill orders for items on our product list, unless we make some change in our transformation. The customer's output (his order) must be compatible with our input requirements (product line). We shall discuss this problem further in Chapter 6.

Combining Black Box Transformations

The method for combining stable, independent, and compatible black boxes is straightforward. The coupling between the blocks is specified, so that a *consistent* transfer of outputs to inputs is made. The result is a *block diagram* with a starting point (or inputs) and a terminating point (or outputs). If we have made the combination process in this way, the required couplings and connections will also be *complete*; i.e., we will have no missing links. The original structure that we observed in the flow diagram and matrix of Chapter 1 provides this connection information. The arrows in such a block flow diagram show the *variables* that connect one operation with another; the operations, or *block transformations* may be inserted when the arrows connect, i.e., where the elements were shown in Chapter 1.

The resulting block diagram shows:

1. The inputs to the system;
2. The outputs from the system;
3. The exact *sequence* of operations that take place between these terminals; and
4. The transformation of variables that takes place at each element, or operation.

Such a block diagram may itself be a sufficient system description. This is so because, given a particular set of inputs, it is now possible to trace through the block diagram and compute the outputs. A computer flow diagram is no more than a block flow diagram. (See Figure 2-2.) In what follows, however, we observe a special definition which is often useful, the transfer function of Figure 2-2a.

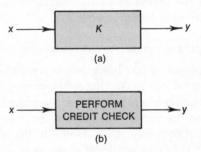

2-2   Indicating black box operations. Two alternate forms are illustrated. (a) A transformation operation. An input x is converted into the output y by the relation $y = Kx$. For such continuous conversions it is convenient to define the transfer function as the ratio of output to input, i.e., $T = (y/x) = K$. This transfer function is indicated in the box. (b) In other process operations, a complex manipulation may be performed when an arrival x comes to a given step in a process. For simplicity, this operation may be summarized in the box. The result of the operation is to produce the output y which is passed to the next process step. The latter convention is used in discrete logical systems, such as computer programs.

The transfer function

If the system has a single input and a single output, we find it convenient to reduce the over-all flow diagram to an *equivalent* black box.

We can do this most easily by defining the *black box transfer function* (from the transformation) as the ratio of the black box output to its input.

Example: If $y = kx$ is the number of dollars of an item ordered in quantity x, when the unit price is k, i.e., a transformation of units to dollars, then the equivalent *transfer function* $y/x = k$ (dollars/unit) is used to describe the black box.

Rules for black box combination

If we follow the definition of the transfer function for a black box, we obtain the output of a black box by *multiplying* its input by its transfer function. The same principle applies, by extension, to combinations of black boxes. See Figure 2-3.

1. Multiplication rule: If two blocks operate in series, we *multiply* the individual transfer functions of the boxes to obtain the equivalent over-all transfer function for the new system. The same rule applies to more than two black boxes in series (Figure 2-3a).

Example: Black box A has the transfer function $x/y = K_1$. Black box B has the transfer function $y/x = K_2$. Then, the over-all transfer function of both boxes is

$$\left(\frac{y}{x}\right)\left(\frac{z}{y}\right) = \frac{z}{x} = K_1 K_2$$

and the system may now be described by the single black box having the above transfer function.

2. Addition rule: When two black boxes operate in parallel, an addition or subtraction of variables will be required to obtain the over-all transfer function, which is defined for the ratio of output/input (Figure 2-3b).

Example: An input variable x is split into two equal signals to be operated upon separately and then recombined by addition to get an output variable. The situation is shown in Figure 2-3b. Here we follow the convention that the variable on all solid connecting lines will be the same, but that if different variables are to be combined, the summing point box is required. The combination details are shown in the figure. Note that the result shown is equivalent to *addition* of the parallel black box transforms at the summation point.

3. Transfer functions of selected output/input pairs: Although the classical black box transfer function is defined only for a single black box

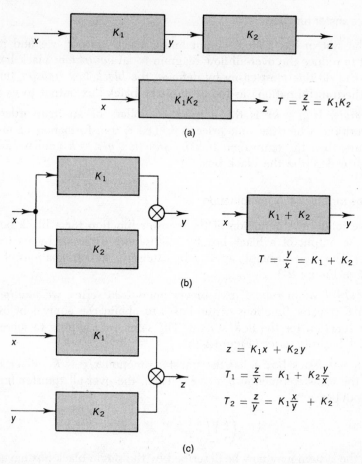

2-3   Combining blocks. The algebraic manipulations required to reduce several blocks to an equivalent single block are shown. In (c), direct reduction to a single block is not possible, although it may be convenient to speak of the conditional transfer function, as shown.

output/input, a black box with more than one input (or output) can be described in terms of the output/input ratio or transformations taken between selected output/input pairs. This is shown in Figure 2-3c. Note that here the transfer function will usually involve variables other than the output/input variables in the transfer function ratio, e.g., in Figure 2-3c transfer function $T_1 = K_1 + K_2(y/x)$.

  * *4. Many output/input variables, vector and matrix notation:* When the input to a black box must be described in many dimensions, or when the input has many attributes or variables transformed simultaneously to ob-

---

* Starred sections may be skipped at first reading.

tain a given output of many dimensions, or attributes, matrix and vector notation may be used. In such instances the above rules for combination still hold, but the rules for matrix multiplication and addition must be used.

Example: A black box describes a cost accounting operation in which three parts with costs x_1, x_2, and x_3, respectively, are to be combined into two assemblies, with total costs y_1 and y_2, respectively. The table showing the required combination of parts in each assembly is the black box transform in matrix format, where the entries in column 1 are the numbers of parts of type 1, 2, and 3 required in assembly 1, etc. As shown in Figure 2-4, the value of each finished assembly is the output vector $[y_1 = 11, y_2 = 17]$ given by multiplying the input vector by the matrix transform (in that order).

For a summary of matrix operations, see Appendix A. The rules for matrix operations are an extension of the rules given above, but allow great simplification in system notation, and therefore should be familiar to the reader.

Transformation with Time Delay

In our discussion of black box transformations in the previous sections, we assumed that the transformation proceeds without delay. This resulted in a

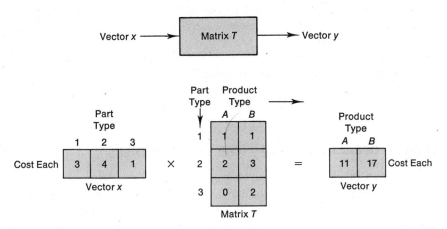

2-4 Transformation of vector inputs. An input variable *x* may consist of several classifications, or have several attributes. In this case, the input is a vector, as illustrated by cost information for three part types. The conversion operation called for is to transform part cost information into product cost information, as specified by the matrix, or table, which gives the number of parts of each kind in each product made. Multiplication of the vector *x* by the matrix *T* (in that order) gives the required result, the vector *y* with components representing the unit cost of each product. The operation of matrix multiplication is described in Appendix A.

simple algebraic treatment. However, most transformations of interest *do* show a delay: It takes time to get a given job done. When time is a factor, we cannot directly employ the algebraic methods of this section to define and combine black box transfer functions. However, the approach is perfectly general: By suitable application of the methods of Appendix B, it is possible to reduce the time-dependent case for a linear system to a simple algebraic equivalent, which may be treated by the methods discussed. Moreover, if the transformation is to be applied periodically, rather than continuously (or if a numerical approximation can be used) it is also possible to use the numerical procedure given on p. 48. We shall leave further discussion of the method to that section.

In preparation for later chapters, we should also note that any time delay in transforming an input variable into an output variable implies the black box exhibits some "memory." If the order-processing department receives an order and must transform units-ordered into total price by a unit-price multiplication that first requires a catalogue search, the order must be *held* while the search operations are being performed. Essentially the same sort of memory occurs in machines: The fly-wheel of an engine "stores" the velocity of a previous time. We should distinguish this simple memory form, which is totally deterministic or statistically stable, from delay forms that can change the black box transformation *without* our ability to predict. Clearly, in the former case analytic methods can be successful, but in the latter case they cannot. Thus, we frequently use the word *memory* in two senses. Memory, in the popular form, means an area for some vague, unpredictable storage of data and plans; e.g., "That box contains the computer memory." In the second sense, memory represents a series of delayed actions, which may be conditional, but which are nevertheless predictable, if we know the detail of operations sufficiently.

In short, *predictable* delay presents no great problems in the application of the black box methods described in this chapter.

LOGICAL OPERATIONS: LOOPS AND DECISION TREES

The decision block is a sorter. It distinguishes one input from another and takes a different action for each, like a sieve or gravel grader. The decision block can be described by the usual black box transformation methods, but because a decision block produces *conditional* changes in the over-all system transformation under specified conditions, it is commonly isolated in the block diagram as a special situation. We shall restrict our attention to the simple yes-no decision block.

The simple decision block handles statements of the following type:

1. If the customer's bank balance is negative, do not cash his check.

2. If you have not finished the assigned task, continue to work until you have.
3. If the percent of defective product is greater than 5%, use plan B; otherwise use plan A.
4. When the clock reads exactly 01:36, detonate the bomb.

We see that a choice is made between one route of action and another. The decision box makes a simple choice, called a *conditional branch* in computer flow diagrams.

Loops

Figure 2-5 shows a special case of the decision box application that is particularly important in computer programing and machine design. It represents the compute-tally-test sequence, which can multiply the effectiveness of simple instructions.

> *Example:* Suppose we have 100 numbers to total. Rather than give 100 instructions to the system to add, requiring 100 separate transformations, we give one add instruction, make the first addition, tally (increment or decrement a counter), and test to see if we have added 100 numbers. If so, we stop; if not, we *loop back* to the add instruction and repeat the sequence until 100 numbers have been added. Obviously, we can test for any given number of cycles that we may care to store in a memory device, and so the method is perfectly general.

In other cases, we may compute and test against some criteria stored in a memory device, then stop when the criteria have been met. Thus, we may continue to add until the sum of all numbers accumulated reaches 5000. The criteria can also change with time.

Combinations of counters, tests, and operations can be made. The use of various memory devices for storing test criteria and for performing operations to change test criteria will increase greatly the versatility of the system, as we shall see further in Chapter 4 and 5.

Decision Trees and Multiway Branches

The decision box can also be used in multiple sequences to provide alternate decisions for some input conditions. Sorting, classification, and ordering operations require such combinations of steps.

> *Example:* The input to a system can be 1, 2, 3, or 4. We wish to use plan A if the input is 1, plan B for 2, plan C for 3, and plan D for 4. Figure 2-6, where the input is x, shows a "tree" that will make the required discrimination.

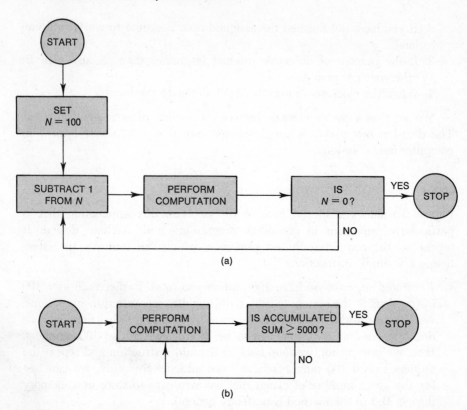

(a)

(b)

2-5 Combining operations and tests in a loop. When a system is to perform repetitive steps, it is not necessary to repeat the instructions for completing the total sequence of operations. The required number of operations may be obtained by a loop-and-test sequence which is of great importance in simplification of system design. Two typical loop-and-test sequences are illustrated. (a) A system that counts. The operation stops after 100 computations have been made. (b) A system that tests a given value in memory. The operation stops when the result of the computations produces an accumulated total greater than or equal to 5000. The tests terminating a loop may be as complicated as necessary for a given job.

Decision trees and transformation boxes can also be combined to produce many useful systems.

Example: A vending machine sells soft drinks for 15¢. The machine will accept quarters, dimes, and nickels, but not pennies. The slot is too small for half dollars. Draw a logic diagram using simple two-way decision boxes to show a possible design for such a coin device. Figure 2-7 shows the result, but other diagrams may achieve the same result and provide side benefits as well. Trace what happens in the logic diagram for various combinations of nickels, dimes, and quarters. Note that transformation boxes and logic boxes have been combined in the diagram.

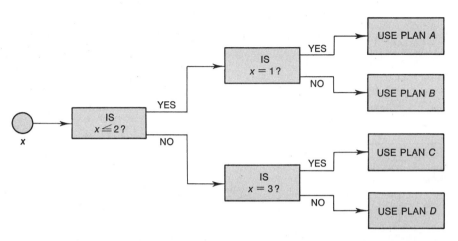

2-6 A multiway branch for logical selection or matching. The multiway branch or "tree of decisions" shown will accomplish the required matching of plan selected to input condition. In many logical systems, extensive branching of this type is used. The addition of looping, as illustrated in Figure 2-5, greatly extends the usefulness of this device.

Combining Logical Operations

Given a flow diagram showing a number of black box transformations and logical operations, we see that it is usually inconvenient or undesirable to reduce the diagram to an equivalent black box.

It may, however, be desirable for us to summarize the logical tests that must be passed by an input to produce a given output, as in complex sorting operations. *Decision Tables* are convenient display forms for doing this.

Decision tables

A tabular summary of the tests in a system, the rules for reaching a decision, and the action to be taken in each alternative may be useful in checking or describing the operation of the system. Figure 2-8 shows such a table for the coin-changer example. Decision tables are also valuable in data analysis work to describe the action taken by the system for a list of possible inputs; or, the decision table may tell what inputs to give a system to get a desired result.

THE CORRECTION OPERATION: THE FEEDBACK BOX

The third major type of block is a comparison and control box, called the feedback block. Again, this block may be constructed by an appropriate specialization of the transformation block, or transformation and logic blocks, but because of its importance, it is convenient to establish the distinction.

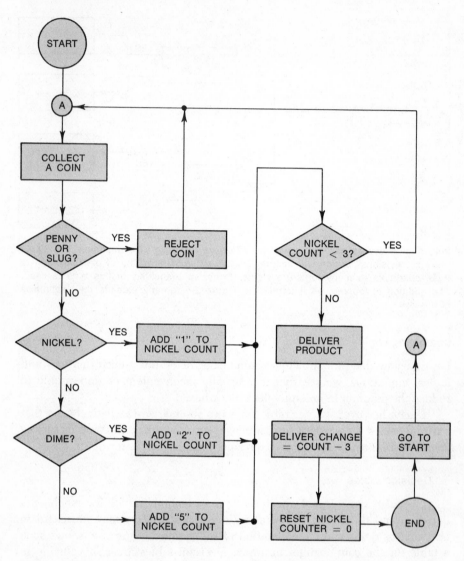

2-7 Logical flow diagram of a vending machine that accepts nickels, dimes, and quarters. The product cost is 15¢. The diagram assumes the machine is not empty and that adequate change is available. No coin return is shown.

Feedback

The general principle of feedback was depicted in Figure 2-1c. Basically, an input to the system is received and operated on by a transformation block. The results of the transformation are then monitored, and by suitable procedures the output is compared to the input standard. Any errors are

TESTS	TEST COMBINATION											
	1	2	3	4	5	6	7	8	9	10	11	12
1. COIN = 1¢ OR SLUG	Y	N	N	N	N	N	N	N	N	N	N	N
2. COIN = 5¢		Y	Y	Y	Y	N	N	N	N	N	N	N
3. COIN = 10¢						Y	Y	Y	Y	N	N	N
4. NICKEL COUNTER = 1				Y							Y	N
5. NICKEL COUNTER = 2			Y						Y	Y		
6. NICKEL COUNTER = 3		Y						Y				
7. NICKEL COUNTER = 4							Y					
ACTIONS												
1. REJECT COIN	X											
2. INCREMENT NICKEL COUNTER BY 1		X										
3. INCREMENT NICKEL COUNTER BY 2						X						
4. DELIVER PRODUCT			X					X				
5. DELIVER PRODUCT AND 5¢							X					
6. DELIVER PRODUCT AND 10¢												X
7. DELIVER PRODUCT AND 15¢											X	
8. DELIVER PRODUCT AND 20¢										X		
9. ACCEPT NEXT COIN (GO TO A)	X			X	X				X			
10. RESET NICKEL COUNTER = 0			X				X	X		X	X	X

2-8 A decision table for the flow diagram of Figure 2-7. Under the assumptions of Figure 2-7, there are four test conditions (shown as diamonds in Figure 2-7) plus start. Similarly, there are nine machine actions (shown as boxes in Figure 2-7). Note the five distinct combinations of product and change delivery shown in Action Lines 6 and 7 above. The 12 rules, shown in the columns above, result from combinations of the test conditions. The decision table is used to assure completeness and consistency in logical system design.

noted, and the error is then used by suitable procedures to correct the output on the following cycle. Such feedback may be continuous or periodic. It may reduce the error or increase it, depending upon the design of the system and its purpose. Feedback may be applied to transformation or logical blocks; but the operation of the feedback principle always requires a "loop" of action, as in Figure 2-1c.

Example: The classic example of a physical system that uses feedback is the "ball governor" invented by James Watt to control the speed of steam engines. (See Figure 2-9.) In this device the output speed of an

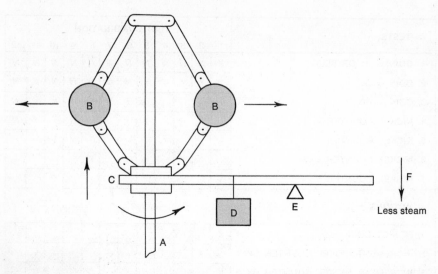

2-9 An early feedback device, the steam governor of James Watt. The action of this device is described in detail in the text. Simply stated, as the steam engine goes faster, the action of the device is to reduce the steam input, thereby slowing the engine. The purpose of the device is to maintain constant engine speed under varying load conditions.

engine rotates the shaft *A,* which causes the balls *B* to spread, raising the floating collar *C* and the weight *D.* The weight *D* provides a downward force to counter the lifting force provided by the governor as the balls spread. The equilibrium speed of the engine can be selected by changing the size of the weight *D* or by moving its position on the lever *FC.* Should the engine run too fast, the weight *D* is lifted, transmitting a movement to steam valve *F* (via the fixed pivot *E*), to shut off the steam and slow the engine. If the steam engine should run slower than desired (say when a load is applied), the process is reversed, the steam valve opened, and the speed increased. The thermostat is another classic example. Inventory control, forecasting, quality control, inspection, and similar management control procedures require the application of feedback.

It is impossible to discuss in this introduction all the variations of the feedback principle or its many applications. Consequently, in what follows we will illustrate the basic principles of application and denote the three factors which are always important in feedback systems: (1) the effective "gain" of the system, or its sensitivity, (2) the amount of feedback used, (3) the sign of the error correction applied, which is most often influenced by the lag or time delay between the time an output is measured and the time corrective action is applied.

Feedback Without Lag

To avoid complications at the outset, let us first assume that we have a continuous feedback system, as shown in Figure 2-10 in which no lag or time delay is introduced by the transformation box K or the feedback box b. This assumption allows a simple algebraic treatment of the problem.

Negative feedback, no lag

If part of the output from the black box K (b in the figure) can be adjusted to be negative when the input to the system is positive (and vice versa), we have the basic case of the feedback principle in which negative feedback is applied. Under the ideal conditions of no lag or time delay in applying corrective action, and with the negative or counteracting action, negative feedback will stabilize the operation of the system; i.e., the output of the system can be held relatively constant even though various external disturbances may tend to alter the transfer function K.

Equivalent black box transfer function for a feedback loop

The result cited above can be seen by reference to the equations developed in Figure 2-10, where the equivalent transfer function for a feed-

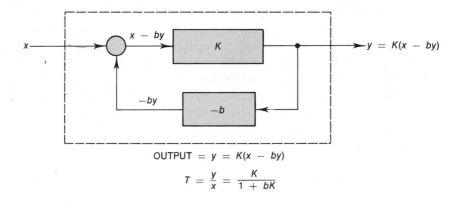

$$\text{OUTPUT} = y = K(x - by)$$

$$T = \frac{y}{x} = \frac{K}{1 + bK}$$

2-10 A block diagram of a simple feedback device showing the modification in system transfer function resulting from feedback. The input x is modified by a portion of the output $(-by)$, so that the output with feedback is also modified as shown. Without feedback, provided by the lower block, the output would be $y = Kx$. With feedback as shown, the output is $y = K(x - by)$. The transfer function for the system enclosed in dotted lines is $T = (y/x) = K/(1 + bK)$. The effect is to hold the output constant if the transfer function K of the upper box should change due to load or other environmental conditions. This illustration assumes that the process proceeds without delay. The system with delay is discussed in the text.

back loop is developed in standard form. In the derivation, an input x arrives, and without feedback would be transformed by the transfer function K into an output $y = Kx$; i.e., if the box b were omitted from the diagram or temporarily disconnected. But, with *negative* feedback (which is assumed here), some portion of y, namely, by, is fed back with a sign opposite to that of x. The transfer function of the *forward* path is K; the transfer function of the *backward* path is $-b$. When combined, they yield the equivalent transfer function for the combination; i.e., $y/x = K/(1 + bK)$, which follows from an algebraic rearrangement of terms.

Thus, the equivalent transfer function of a feedback system can be found by first finding the transfer function of the forward loop and the transfer function of the backward loop separately, then combining them by the standard method illustrated. By applying the methods given on p. 35, the forward and backward loops may consist of a number of black boxes, which can be reduced to the standard arrangement shown in Figure 2-10.

Example: To indicate the effects of negative feedback in protecting the output-input ratio y/x from possible changes in the forward transformation due to external disturbances, we now refer to formula (2) of Figure 2-10. For simplicity, assume that K and b are constants, say $K = 100$ and $b = 0.09$. Then, by substitution, $y/x = 100/(1 + 9) = 10$. Now, suppose some external disturbance causes K to drop to 50, a decrease of 50% in "efficiency" or "gain." Substitution of the new value of K and the old value of b, gives $y/x = 50/(1 + 4.5) = 50/5.5 = 9.1$. The new value of output to input has dropped only $(10 - 9.1)/10 = 0.09$, or 9%, even though the efficiency of the operation has dropped by 50%. In this way negative feedback can be used to improve the *regulation* of systems. (The reader may wish to relate this result to the operation of the ball governor when the engine receives a load, or to the amount of political pressure applied to a department head when he deviates from the budget.)

Positive feedback, no lag

We have seen that negative feedback tends to reduce deviations in the system, but what of positive feedback? From Equation (2) of Figure 2-10 we see the result is exaggeration of deviations. Thus, if the sign of bK in the denominator changes from $1 + bK$ to $1 - bK$, the ratio y/x will increase rapidly for bK near unity. As the denominator approaches zero, the system in a sense "explodes." (Oscillation is the usual result in practical systems because some limiting unstable variation about $bK = 1$ is the usual case.) Consequently, we usually try to avoid such instabilities in control systems by avoiding positive feedback where possible.

We should note that positive feedback is not necessarily harmful. Compound interest is one beneficial form of positive feedback, as are most re-investment operations. Physical devices, such as the oscillators used in radio transmitters and receivers, are other applications of positive feedback. Indeed, if the amount of positive feedback is carefully limited so that the denominator of the feedback equation does not approach zero, the "amplification" effects of positive feedback in increasing the effective value of K can be beneficial. (As an exercise the reader should, however, investigate the effect of positive feedback on regulation, as illustrated in the previous example.)

Feedback with Lag

Our introduction to the feedback principle has been greatly simplified by eliminating time delay. Although many devices may be constructed to use feedback without lag, the usual system takes time to perform an operation, or to perform a correction, thereby introducing a delay or lag in using corrective action.

When we introduce lag, the subject of feedback becomes enormously complicated. Even a survey discussion of feedback with lag is beyond our scope. Appendix B gives a brief outline of some common methods of treatment. Using the methods of Appendix B (Laplace transforms and z transforms), we could handle combinations of black boxes and feedbox loops, and reduce a complex diagram to an equivalent black box when lag is present. However, we will now restrict ourselves to an approach that is suitable for our needs, but which requires only simple tabulations. We can do this by concentrating our attention on *periodic* feedback correction and by using a numerical approach.

Our objective in the next two sections is to show that *when time delay is present in the application of corrective feedback, the character of the input variable, or signal, to the system is critical.* The examples we selected for this purpose are specific to our immediate needs but we should note that the tabular, or numerical, method employed is generally useful for a wide range of business problems, for evaluation by electronic computers, and in general, for simulation purposes. Although it is not possible to develop transfer functions for the feedback equations used here (as in the previous sections), we may develop a block diagram, show the required steps in a box, and understand that we must sequentially apply the operations indicated.

The effect of changing lag for a given feedback system input

First, we try to illustrate how a change in time delay, or lag, can change the results of a feedback operation for a given input. A rule for production planning will illustrate the point.

Example: Let the sales for week n be x_n, as in Figure 2-11. This record shows a periodic cycle, because sales fluctuate from 10 to 20 and back to 10 again, etc. To smooth production, we have devised a rule that tells us that this week we must produce an amount y_n, equal to 50% of x_n our actual sales requirements for this week's production, which we know, plus 50% of y_{n-1}, equal to last week's production. This *decision rule* can be written as an equation:

$$y_n = 0.5x_n + 0.5y_{n-1} \qquad \text{CASE I}$$

Suppose someone suggests that, instead of using last week's production in the formula, we use the value from two periods ago, so that a second decision rule might be

$$y_n = 0.5x_n + 0.5y_{n-2} \qquad \text{CASE II}$$

We begin the computation by assuming that production for all periods previous to $n = 1$ has been equal to zero. Then, by successive substitution of values, we can obtain the results shown in Figure 2-11.

We should notice several things in the table. With lag a feedback decision rule causes the system output to follow a "trajectory" of values with time. This trajectory describes the *dynamic* response of the system

		CASE I	CASE II
n	x_n	y_n	y_n'
1	10*	5.00*	5.00*
2	20	12.50	10.00
3	10	11.25	7.50
4	20	15.63	15.00
5	10	12.82	8.75
6	20	16.41	17.50
7	10	13.20	9.37
8	20	16.60	18.75
9	10	13.30	9.69
10	20	16.65	19.38
.	.	.	.
.	.	.	.
.	.	.	.
19	10	13.33	10.00
20	20	16.67	20.00
.	.	.	.
.	.	.	.
.	.	.	.
	*$x_0 = 0$	*$y_0 = 0$	*$y_{-1} = 0$

2-11 A response comparison of two feedback decision rules as defined in the text.

to the stated input. Case I eventually assumes successive values of 13.33 and 16.67, whereas Case II assumes successive values of 10 and 20, matching the input. However, previous to the 13th to 15th interval, the increasing response values represent a "transient" condition while the system is making the adjustment from no sales to the alternating values of 10 and 20. The final condition is frequently called the *steady-state* or *equilibrium* condition.

We see from Figure 2-11 that both the transient and steady-state conditions of the system may be changed by a change in the amount of lag used in the decision rule. The desired smoothing effect is obtained in Case I and *not* in Case II. Moreover, we see that *the output is determined not only by the lag and the constants in the equation, but also by the sequence of inputs.* What would happen in Case II if the input were: 10, 10, 20, 20, 10, 10, 20, 20, . . . ?

The effect of a selected input on an unstable feedback system, fixed lag

In the above example we found that both average production rates were satisfactory from one point of view. Average production equaled average sales once the system reached the steady state; in addition, neither output variation exceeded input variation.

However, we could well consider a system unstable under another input, even with a fixed delay. We could do this by selecting a decision rule that can exaggerate error, should the combination of input conditions and delay create a positive reinforcement of the input. Moreover, in the example selected, we will see that the lag and the choice of transformation and feedback values can cause sustained oscillations in the system.

Example: Consider a decision rule, with definitions as in the previous example, but with weights chosen so that

$$y_n = 2(x_n - 0.5y_{n-1})$$
CASE III

If we could ever arrive at the point where $x_n = y_{n-1} = $ constant, say 10, and if the input were held constant at that value, then this decision rule would require constant production equal to sales, because

$$y_n = 2[10 - (0.5)(10)] = 10$$

But under an input disturbance, the combination of amplification and lag can cause an unstable output from which the system cannot recover, as shown in Figure 2-12. Note that even after the input sales requirements have dropped to zero, the system continues to call for oscillating values of production.

		CASE III
n	x_n	y_n''
1	10*	10*
2	10	10
3	10	10
4	20	30
5	20	10
6	20	30
7	10	−10
8	10	30
9	10	−10
10	10	30
11	0	−30
12	0	+30
13	0	−30
.	.	.
.	.	.
.	.	.
	$*x_0 = 0$	$*y_0 = 0$

2-12 The response of an unstable feedback decision rule as defined in the text.

Feedback with lag: general considerations

Although the examples given do not describe all the difficulties and possible benefits in the use of corrective feedback with lag, they do describe the three major factors that must be checked in any feedback system.

1. The gain or amplification of the transformation to be controlled, i.e., the sensitivity of the system to input without feedback.
2. The amount of feedback that will be used for correction; and
3. The sign of the feedback correction, which, in systems with lag, is determined by a *combination* of the series of inputs to the system and the resulting lag required in the transformation and correction operations.

Thus, in any feedback system (characterized in the block diagram by a loop of action and correction) we should ask immediately: "Is there any lag in the process?" And, if so, we must determine the inputs that lead to stability, given the gain and feedback factors of the system, and those that do not.

The examples should also convince the reader that it is difficult to design a stable feedback system having a wide range of possible input conditions *if any lag is present.* Indeed, the feedback system becomes particularly impractical if the time required for transformation and correction is long when compared to the time between possible changes in the input to the system, or if the environmental changes affecting the transformation are more rapid than the system's corrective-loop response.

Usually, only two practical improvement methods are available. If the ratio of (system correction time/disturbance time) is not much less than 1: (1) Restrict possible inputs severely to those that change less frequently; or (2) change the feedback system to shorten the correction and transformation time.

PROBLEMS

2.1 The following gross description of a manufacturing system is often used. Let F be the fixed costs per year associated with production and C be the variable costs incurred per unit of product. Also, let V be the annual volume of production (and sales) in units. Then the total cost incurred per year is $TC = F - CV$. If the revenue per unit of product made (and sold) is R per unit, then the total annual revenue is $TR = RV$. The profit obtained on an annual basis is the difference between TR and TC, if that result is positive. A loss will occur if $TR - TC$ is negative. The so-called "break-even" point occurs when the volume is sufficient to make $TR = TC$. With these definitions in mind, solve the following problem.

A firm operates with a fixed cost of $1 million per year, variable costs of $10 per unit, and revenue of $30 per unit for a given product.

A. What is the break-even point?

B. Automation of the process will double fixed costs, but cut variable costs in half. What is the new break-even point?

C. If the predicted sales are 100,000 units per year, and this comes to pass, what is the profit resulting from alternatives A and B above?

D. Now suppose the sales prediction is not given as a single value but rather in terms of a probability distribution, as shown below. What is the expected value of the profit from each of the alternatives, A and B? (NOTE: For simplicity use the midpoint of the range for each interval in the probability table.)

Sales Forecast (in thousands)	20–40	40–60	60–80	80–100	100–120	120–140
Probability	0.1	0.1	0.2	0.3	0.2	0.1

E. Can the break-even computation be considered a transformation?

F. How does the break-even computation represent system structure?

G. How is the break-even computation affected by the introduction of uncertainty?

2.2   Frequently it is desirable to measure from a distance or to *telemeter* information from the scene of measurement to a safe or convenient observer's location. In this process many conversion steps are frequently used, starting with the sensor that makes the initial reading and generates the message, to the final observer location and reading point. For example, suppose a pressure reading is desired from a remote location. The following steps might be followed:

(1) A sensor converts a pressure measurement into a radio frequency.
(2) That radio frequency, which changes with pressure, is transmitted to the reading location.
(3) At the reading location, the radio-frequency signal is received and converted into an electric voltage.
(4) The electric voltage is converted into distance, as indicated by the movement of a meter pointer. This meter is calibrated in pressure.
(5) The observer looks at the meter, and interprets the result for his own use.

This sequence of conversions, or transformations, in telemetry, may be extended to other steps as may be necessary.

A. Block diagram a sequence of measurement conversions with which you are familiar. Indicate the transformation to be made at each step in English.

B. In more detail, specify in each block the transfer function of the conversion operation.

C. What is the essential characteristic of each transformation made in this sequential process?

2.3   The following block diagram is a portion of a computer program designed to read punched cards, and then to print selected cards, as determined by the condition of an indicator, called Switch A. (Switch A is simply a memory location in the computer that stores a "1" for "ON" and a "0" for "OFF".)

A. Suppose the cards fed to this program are sequentially numbered 1, 2,

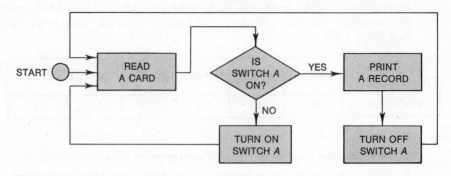

Problem 2-3

3, ... Which cards will be printed if the condition of Switch A is initially OFF? If Switch A is initially ON?

B. By what factor will the number of lines printed divide into the initial number of cards read?

C. Suppose the lines printed were instead duplicated as cards, and that these cards were again fed to the computer. By what factor would the number of lines printed on the second pass divide into the original number of cards?

D. If N is the number of passes, as described in C above, what is the relationship between the original number of cards, n, and the number of cards printed (or duplicated) on the Nth pass? (You may assume the original number of cards n is arbitrarily large.)

2.4 The diagram on p. 54 illustrates how counters and loops may be used in combination in a logical sequence of operations. (A counter is simply a computer memory location in which a number is stored.)

A. Trace the operation of this system from the start. How frequently will cards be punched? How frequently will records be printed? How frequently will input records (cards) be written on tape? (Express your answers .in terms of statements such as "every fifth card," "every fiftieth card," etc.)

B. In designing such a system, which loop performs the most work in terms of frequency of activity?

2.5 When a customer order is received, the following steps are performed, and the following tests are made. Draw a block diagram of the steps and actions taken as a result of the tests. Create a Decision Table that will summarize the results of the tests, i.e., the actions that will be taken for each combination of test results:

1. The mail is received and the letter is opened.
2. The order is edited by checking the price and stock number for each item ordered as indicated in the catalogue.
3. The price is extended by multiplying unit price by the number of items ordered.
4. The total value of the order is determined by adding the total amount for each item.
5. When the total value of the order has been determined, the following credit checks are made:
   (a) If the value of the order is less than $1000 and the customer's pay record has been good, the order will be approved for shipment;
   (b) If the value of the order is greater than or equal to $1000, the customer's credit rating is greater than $1000, and his pay record has been good, shipment will be made.
   (c) Shipment will always be made if the customer has obtained prior executive approval as recorded in the credit file.

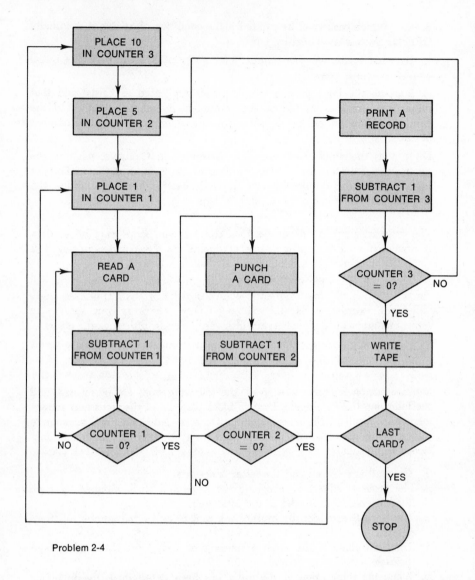

Problem 2-4

6. If the shipment is approved, a check is made against the stock on hand. If sufficient inventory is available for shipment of a given item, the amount ordered will be deducted from the current inventory balance, and an order for shipment of that item will be issued against this order number. Should the item not be in stock, a backorder will be created for this item of the order number, and a "backorder notice" will be issued to the customer for the backordered item(s).

7. Shipping papers will be created for the items authorized for shipment, and the customer bill will be prepared showing this detail as well as

the total amount due. The accounts receivable will be credited with the dollar amount of the items shipped.

2.6 In the following accounting example, a system of production, sales, and finance is described by eleven accounts.

(1) Cash
(2) Receivables
(3) Raw Materials
(4) Finished Goods
(5) Fixed Assets
(6) Production
(7) General Administrative and Selling Expenses
(8) Depreciation
(9) Sales
(10) Liabilities (Short and Long Term)
(11) Net Worth

Several documents are available from the records of this firm: A Starting Balance Sheet, a Balance Sheet for the End of the Period, an Income Statement, and a list of operations leading to these results. This material may be summarized in the Input-Output Chart of Accounts, which is also given. The format of this accounting sheet shows the interaccount transfers. The Table shows *credits* (corresponding to arrows *entering* an account block) and *debits* (corresponding to arrows *leaving* account blocks). This convention corresponds to the credits and debits in the columns and rows of the input-output table, respectively. Total debits must equal total credits both for each account and in total, as may be verified from the input-output sheet.

A. Draw a block diagram showing the interrelationship of the accounts of this company as indicated by the interaccount transfers for the period.

B. Indicate the dollar transfers to and from each account. Relate the changes in each account level to the starting and ending balance sheets.

Balance Sheet at the Beginning		
ASSETS:		
Cash	$ 500	
Receivables	2500	
Fixed	2000	
Inventory		
Finished	1000	(200 units @ $5 each)
Raw Material	500	(for 200 units)
TOTAL	$6500	
LIABILITIES:		
Short Term	$3000	
Long Term	1500	
Net Worth	2000	
TOTAL	$6500	

Balance Sheet at the End of the Period

ASSETS:

Cash	530
Receivables	1755
Fixed	1800
Inventory	
Finished	1000
Raw Material	750
TOTAL	$5835

LIABILITIES:

Short Term	1300
Long Term	1350
Net Worth	3185
TOTAL	$5835

Income Statement

SALES: 1200 units @ $10 each	$12000
COST OF SALES: 1200 units @ $5 each	6000
GROSS MARGIN	$6000

EXPENSES:

Administrative	$3000	
Selling	1500	
Depreciation	200	
Uncollectable	115	
	$4815	$4815
NET PROFIT		$1185

Other Operations:

1. Purchase of Raw Materials: $3250 (Cash: $325; Credit, $2925)
2. Administrative Expenses: $2000 cash; $1000 credit
3. Sales Expense: $1000 cash; $500 credit
4. Sales: $1200 cash; $10,800 credit
5. Wages and Manufacturing Expense: $3000 cash
6. Receivables: collected $11,430
7. Liabilities: paid off $6275

Input-Output Chart of Accounts

CREDIT → / DEBIT ↓	STARTING BALANCE	① Cash	② Receivable	③ Raw materials	④ Finished goods	⑤ Fixed assets	⑥ Production	⑦ General expenses	⑧ Depreciation	⑨ Sales	⑩ Liabilities	⑪ Net worth	ENDING BALANCE	TOTAL CREDITS
STARTING BALANCE	✕	500	2500	500	1000	2000							✕	✕
① Cash				325			3000	3000			6275		530	13,130
② Receivable		11,430						115					1755	13,330
③ Raw mat.							3000						750	3750
④ Fin. goods										6000			1000	7000
⑤ Fixed assets									200				1800	2000
⑥ Production					6000									6000
⑦ Gen. expenses												4615		4615
⑧ Depreciation												200		200
⑨ Sales		1200	10,800											12,000
⑩ Liabilities	4500			2925				1500					−2650	6275
⑪ Net worth	2000									6000			−3185	4815
TOTAL DEBITS	✕	13,130	13,300	3750	7000	2000	6000	4615	200	12,000	6275	4815	✕	✕

2.7   A company has four manufacturing departments plus a sales department: (1) Steel, (2) Laminations, (3) Metal Fabrication, (4) Foundry Operations, and (5) Sales. Let these departments be denoted by D_1, D_2, D_3, D_4, and D_5. In addition to the input of basic raw materials, each department consumes some of the output of the other departments, and conversely sends some of its own output to other departments.

Table I shows the interdepartment transfers in thousands of tons for a given year. The sales, or system output, and raw materials used, or system input, are shown for reference. However, we focus out attention on the interdepartment transfers, which show the structure of the system. Note that the total inputs and outputs are equal in Table I, both for individual departments and for the system as a whole. This simplification eliminates consideration of inventory, or assumes a constant inventory level from year to year.

We now consider the relative importance of the various inputs to each department. For notational purposes, the "from" departments are numbered $i = 1, 2, 3, 4$, and are shown as rows in Table I. The "to" departments are numbered $j = 1, 2, 3, 4$ and are shown as columns in Table I. The amount shipped from department i to department j (in hundreds of tons per year) is called x_{ij}. These are the entries in Table I. Thus, x_{12} is 300, etc. The total amount shipped (or received) by a department is X_i (or X_j), the row (or column) total. Thus, X_1, the total of row 1 in Table I, is 1000. Similarly, the total of column X_i is also 1000 for the method of measurement used.

Now consider the numbers in Table II. These represent a ratio for each column, obtained by dividing the entries in each column of Table I by the corresponding row total (or column total). This gives the fraction of each department's input that comes from other departments. For example, the total input to Department 1 is 1000 units, 200 of which come from Department 3. Thus, 0.20 or 20% of that total input comes from Department 3, etc. We perform a similar computation for each entry in Table I to obtain Table II.

As a result of the computation above, Table II consists of the ratios

Table I. Transactions

	D_1	D_2	D_3	D_4	D_5 Sales	Total
D_1		300		200	500	1000
D_2			800		1200	2000
D_3	200	100	100	100	2500	3000
D_4			600		400	1000
Raw material	800	1600	1500	700		
Total	1000	2000	3000	1000		7000

Table II. Technological Coefficients

	D_1	D_2	D_3	D_4
D_1		0.15		0.20
D_2			0.27	
D_3	0.20	0.05	0.03	0.10
D_4			0.20	
Raw material	0.80	0.80	0.50	0.70
Check totals	1.00	1.00	1.00	1.00

$a_{ij} = x_{ij}/X_i$. These fractions are always less than unity, but greater than or equal to zero. They are the *technological coefficients* that represent the structure of inputs to each department of the system. Conversely, it can be seen by inspection that, given x_{ij} and a_{ij}, X_i may be found easily, because $X_i = x_{ij}/a_{ij}$. Thus, $X_1 = x_{13}/a_{13} = 200/0.20 = 1000$, etc.

If we assume linearity and stability of the technological coefficients of Table II, we will realize that the system defined by the interdepartment transfers can be used for planning purposes.

For example, we may now ask how much production in each department would be required to obtain a given level of sales from each department. If we designate the gross output from each department (including direct sales) as X_i and the sales from department i as b_i, the input-output balance from the system provides a system of four equations in four unknowns.

$$X_1 - a_{11}X_1 - a_{12}X_2 - a_{13}X_3 - a_{14}X_4 = b_1$$
$$X_2 - a_{21}X_1 - a_{22}X_2 - a_{23}X_3 - a_{24}X_4 = b_2$$
$$X_3 - a_{31}X_1 - a_{32}X_2 - a_{33}X_3 - a_{34}X_4 = b_3$$
$$X_4 - a_{41}X_1 - a_{42}X_2 - a_{43}X_3 - a_{44}X_4 = b_4$$

In these four equations, the required sales outputs b_i would be given, the a_{ij} values are obtained from Table II, and the total department outputs X_i are to be found.

A. Draw a block diagram of the interdepartmental transfers, and indicate on each arrow the amounts transferred between departments.

B. Add to the diagram the inputs of the primary factors, or raw materials going to each department, and the sales going directly from each department to the customers.

C. Add to this diagram (in a different color) the technological coefficients showing the fraction of each department's input that comes from other departments. Note that these fractions will add to 1.00 if the fraction due to raw material from the outside is considered.

D. Suppose the sales forecast for the coming year were

$$b_1 = 800, \quad b_2 = 1000, \quad b_3 = 3000, \quad \text{and} \quad b_4 = 600.$$

Find the required production in each department. Referring to Table I or the block diagram, determine the raw material inputs required.

* E. By reference to Appendix A, note that the system of equations just described could also be written in matrix form as

$$(I - A)X = b$$

where I is a 4×4 identify matrix, A is a 4×4 matrix of the coefficients a_{ij} obtained from Table II, X is a four element column vector of the X_i's (to be found), and b is a four element column vector representing the sales forecast for each department. Solving for X gives the result

$$X = (I - A)^{-1}b$$

where $(I - A)^{-1}$ is the inverse of $(I - A)$ as described in Appendix A. Using this procedure, solve for the values of X and compare the results obtained with the answer to D.

* F. If many different sales forecasts were to be evaluated for the same technological coefficients, why would the matrix method be preferable to the usual solution methods for the four equations that have four unknowns?

* G. For the technological coefficients given, it will always be possible to obtain a solution for the values of X_i for any given set of b_i, assuming the b_i values are non-negative. Can you think of any change in the table of technological coefficients that would not permit such a solution?

* H. In the previous planning computation, no constraint was assumed on the capacity available in each department; i.e., we assumed we could produce whatever was ordered. What is the effect of constraining one or more of the variables X_i, i.e., putting an upper limit on the total production possibility of one or more departments? How could the constrained planning problem be restated?

* I. How would the planning problem proposed be affected by a change in the technological coefficients, say by a change in technology, a disaster or accident in one department, etc.

For further reference, see R. Dorfman, P. A. Samuelson, and R. M. Solow, *Linear Programming and Economic Analysis*, McGraw-Hill, New York, 1958, especially Chapter 9. Also, see the original work in input-output analysis: W. W. Leontief, *The Structure of the American Economy*, 2nd ed., Oxford University Press, New York, 1951.

2.8 Refer to Figures 2-7 and 2-8, which specify one design for a coin–changing vending machine.

A. What changes and additions would be necessary in Figures 2-7 and 2-8 to provide a coin return feature which would stop machine action, or return coins if machine is empty?

B. Could you devise another design, for example, using a counter which will only take on the values 0, 1, 2, 3, and 4? Compare your alternate proposal to the flow diagram shown.

C. In the original design, or in your new proposal, what additions and modifications would be necessary to provide change when the number of nickels and dimes in reserve was limited? Under which conditions would you prefer to give dimes for change (if available) instead of nickels?

D. In C, what further additions and modifications in the design would be necessary to handle the situation when inappropriate or no change were available?

E. In what way do the added features add to the complexity of the design? The flow diagram? The decision table?

PROJECT 2

An elevator with special timing features is to work automatically according to the rules outlined here.

A. In Motion
   1. Going up
      (a) Will stop and open doors at any floor for which the up button has been pressed by a person who is either in the elevator or on the given floor.
      (b) Will stop at the top floor automatically, open doors, and reverse direction of operation from up to down in preparation for next descent.
   2. Going down
      (a) Will stop at any floor for which the "down" button has been pressed either in the elevator or on the given floor, and open doors.
      (b) Will stop at the bottom floor automatically, open doors, and reverse direction from down to up in preparation for next ascent.
   3. In either direction
      (a) When stopping at a given floor, the register recording the stop signal for that floor is cleared.
      (b) The elevator will test for the arrival at a floor stop continuously as it moves, and having reached the floor signal location will test for the specified stop conditions in sufficient time to stop if required. The detailed mechanism of this process may be omitted. Assume that the elevator may test for a "stop" or "no stop" at any floor by proper indexing of a test register as described hereafter.

B. Halted
   1. At bottom floor doors will remain open until one of the following three conditions occurs.
      (a) A period of $t(1)$ seconds has passed, the time $t(1)$ to be set differently for different times of day (and there is at least one call for service up or down, otherwise after a wait of $t(10)$ seconds, the elevator checks for calls, moves when there is at least one, but remains at the bottom floor until that time).

(b) The weight of passengers on the elevator reaches 1000 pounds or more.

(c) The dispatcher manually initiates a start from the lobby.

2. At the top floor two conditions for a start prevail

    (a) A period of $t(2)$ seconds has passed, the time to be set differently for different hours.

    (b) The weight of passengers reaches 1000 pounds or more.

3. When going up

    (a) Will remain halted for $t(3)$ seconds with doors open, $t(3)$ also adjustable for different hours, or until the "close door" button is pressed, whichever happens first.

    (b) Will remain open while the "open door" button is pressed and will not start until this button is released regardless of previous condition (a).

4. When going down

    (a) Will remain halted for a time $t(4)$ with doors open or until the "close door" button is pressed, whichever happens first.

    (b) Will remain open while the "open door" button is pressed and will not start until this button is released regardless of previous condition (a).

5. At any door closing time

    (a) Motion will not start until test of door closure is made; should door be open, the test is repeated after a delay of one second, and continued until confirmed. This door close test is initiated after all previous conditions have been satisfied.

    (b) The "open door" button safety feature will also apply to the bottom floor and the top floor.

C. Register Updating

    1. Clear. Signal registers are cleared by the elevator, as described in Section A, above.

    2. Record. At any time a prospective or actual passenger may signal for a floor stop. This signal is held by the register, see below, until the elevator has stopped at the required floor, or until one cycle is complete, both being equal.

D. Special Instructions

    1. Do not be concerned in this analysis with the problems of acceleration and deceleration, exact floor leveling, emergency stops, and similar details. The register updating procedure may be divorced from the stop test procedure and stop timing procedure, because the register updating procedure is independent of the other two. In the registrar updating procedure, requests for a stop at the top floor are ignored when the elevator is at the top floor, and signals for the bottom floor are ignored when the elevator is at the bottom floor should these requests come from the elevator.

    2. For consistency of notation, use the representation below:

    (a) Elevator stop register. Let $R(i,j)$ be the contents of a 2×4 storage register representing respectively "up" and "down" and the four floors of a building, as shown. If $R(i,j)$ is 1, a stop is requested; if $R(i,j)$ is 0, no stop is made.

	1	2	3	4	Floor j

$R(i,j)$ Up $i = 1$
Down $i = 2$

(b) Variable timing feature. Let $t(k)$ be the time values specified in the description above, where the coding means

$t(k)$

$t(1)$	$t(2)$	$t(3)$	$t(4)$
Bottom	Top	Up	Down

These data may be adjusted according to an hourly program (not specified here), and may be assumed fixed and given, as well as available for test at any time.

(c) As a result of the notation for $R(i,j)$, the following simplified notation may be used in analysis:

$R(i,j) = 1$	the elevator should stop at floor j when in state i
$R(i,j) = 0$	the elevator will not stop
$j = j + 1$	go to the next floor above for next test
$j = j - 1$	go to the next floor below for next test
$i = 1$	the elevator is going up
$i = 2$	the elevator is going down
$j = 1$	the elevator is at the bottom floor
$j = 4$	the elevator is at the top floor
t	the time value of a clock in seconds
$t = 0$	the clock has been reset to (is) 0 (After reset, clock increments in seconds)
$t = t(k)?$	has the value of the clock reached the test value $t(k)$?

With this information:

A. Draw a logical block diagram for the tests and operations required to control the elevator in the required manner. Use the suggested notation. You will need a stop test, clear, and reset routing; a timing test, clear, and reset routine; and also a register data entry routine.

B. Can you draw your logical block diagram in any alternate ways, i.e., different logical sequences, and produce the same results? Can you simplify your logical diagram?

C. Can you suggest other representations to portray the logical sequence of events required in this control scheme?

D. If two elevators were to be coordinated so that one was generally going up while the other was generally going down, what additional modifications would be required in your diagram. (Specify, but do not make these changes in your diagram.)

3 | DETAILED METHODS OF SYSTEMS DESCRIPTION: THE FLOW GRAPH AND OTHER METHODS

The block diagrams of Chapter 2 represented operations by blocks and variables that connect operations by arrows. An alternative procedure is the flow graph approach, which is useful in describing many systems, particularly those that have "linear" operations, or those that involve detailed probability analyses.[1]

FLOW GRAPHS: A GENERAL DESCRIPTION

The flow graph is the dual of the block diagram; i.e., the same elements and relationships are shown, but in the flow graph the variables in the system become the elements or nodes, and the transformation or transfer function (usually called a *transmittance* in flow graph analysis) then becomes an arrow. This change in description greatly simplifies the network in many applications. The flow graph is most appropriate when detailed algebraic analysis is required. (Note hereafter the similarity between the block diagram and the flow graph approach to systems definition, then use the form most convenient to you.)

[1] For a comparison of block diagrams versus flow graph methods, see A. D. Hall, *A Methodology for Systems Engineering*, Van Nostrand, Princeton, N.J., 1962. Chapter 14.

Flow Graph Construction

To construct a flow graph, we first list each *variable* in the system and draw a small circle (or node) for each one listed. Each such node is labeled with its variable name, e.g., x, y, or z.

Next, we place the relations between variables (the transfer functions of Chapter 2, which will hereafter be called transmittances to conform to usual flow graph terminology) on the *arrows* connecting each "variable" node. *The direction of the arrow shows the direction in which the transmittance is applied, and so provides the input-output sequence.*

Finally, we adopt three conventions: (1) All arrows leaving a node carry the variable at the node. (2) The value of the variable at a node is the sum of all the transformed variables entering the node as "signals" from incoming arrows. (3) The transformed variable at the point of an arrow head is equal to the variable at that arrow tail multiplied by the arrow transmittance.

Example: Suppose we have a pair of equations, $y_1 = a_1x$ and $y_2 = b_1x$, which relate two output variables to one input variable. Then, we obtain the equivalent flow graph shown in Figure 3-1a. Similarly, suppose

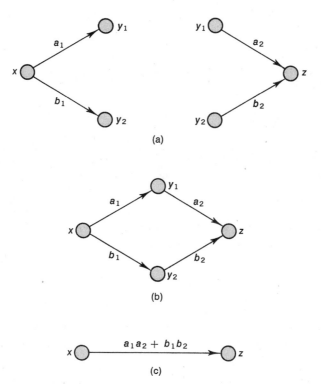

(a)

(b)

(c)

3-1 A flow graph.

we have another algebraic equation, $z = a_2y_1 + b_2y_2$, which relates two input variables to one output variable. The equivalent flow graph for this equation is shown in Figure 3-1b. Suppose now that we want to combine the three equations to show the relationship between z and x, taking these variables as the system output and input variables, respectively. Application of the above conventions will reduce the graphs of 3-1a and b to the single graph of Figure 3-1c, so that we have the equivalent transmittance (or transfer function) of the system as $z/x = a_1a_2 + b_1b_2$. (In combining the flow graphs, the intervening variables y_1 and y_2 are eliminated.) This result is the same as the result we would have obtained if we used block diagram analysis. The final result is shown in Figure 3-1d.

Flow Graph Reduction

The rules for flow graph reduction (as in the example above) follow the rules for block diagram reduction and are summarized in Figure 3-2.

Multiplication law

The transmittances of two arrows in series multiply (Figure 3-2a).

Addition law

The transmittances of two arrows in parallel (going in the same direction) add (Figure 3-2b).

Expansion law

Even numbers of arrows in series, following the multiplication law, may be replaced by transmittances of the same value with changed sign (if this is convenient or desirable for the analyst) (Figure 3-2c).

The feedback loop

This "loop" is replaced by the equivalent transmittance as defined for the block diagram in Figure 2-10. Figure 3-2d shows a variable "fed back" to itself in ever diminishing amounts; the term $1/(1 - a)$ is the sum of a geometric series $(1 + a + a^2 + a^3 + \cdots)$ for a less than one. In Figure 3-2e, the negative feedback example, the loop, as in Figure 2-10, gives an equivalent transmittance of $K/(1 + bK)$.

These graph reduction methods can be applied repetitively to simplify or reduce complex flow graphs to an equivalent transmittance.[2]

---

[2] Although repetitive use of the simple rules given is sufficient for graph reduction, advanced methods, such as Mason's Rule, can be used to speed the work in complex networks. See A. D. Hall, *Op. cit.*, p. 356.

3-2 Rules for flow graph reduction.

Examples of flow graph application can be found in many fields. For example, Figure 3-3 shows a simple flow graph used to describe an economic principle. To assure his understanding of the method, the reader should devise such examples on his own.

The Problem of Lag and Time Delay

As was the case for the block diagram, we have presented the flow graph approach for algebraic transfer functions (or transmittances) that *do not* involve time delay; i.e., we have assumed instantaneous transformation of variables throughout the system. Although this assumption does not generally hold, the block diagram and flow graph approaches have general applications, because the methods of Appendix B can again be used to

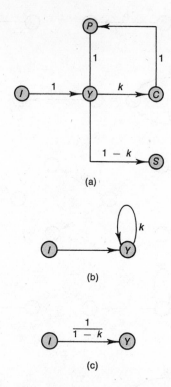

(a)

(b)

(c)

3-3 A flow graph showing Lord Keynes' theory of capital movement to illustrate flow graph reduction. (a) The theoretical relation between Investment *I*, Income *Y*, Consumption *C*, Production *P*, and Savings *S*. A certain fraction of Income, *k* in the flow graph, is devoted to consumption, so that $C = kY$. The other part of income $(1 - k)$ is devoted to Savings, as shown. If attention is direction to the relation between Income and Investment only, the flow graph of (b) results, by the reduction rule of Figure 3-2a. For this purpose, Savings *S* may be omitted from the graph. By using the rule of Figure 3-2d, we can reduce (b) to the equivalent (c). This graph is equivalent to the equation $Y = I/(1 - k)$, in which *k* is the "propensity to consume," and $1/(1 - k)$ is the well-known Keynes' multiplier.

reduce the time delay case to a form more suitable for algebraic treatment as described above.

Equivalent Matrix of a Flow Graph

The equivalent matrix of a *block diagram* (see Figure 1-8) showed the system's *black boxes* as rows and columns, and the variables connecting them as table entries.

The procedure followed to develop the equivalent matrix of a flow graph is the same as that followed for a block diagram: The network nodes are the rows and columns, and the arrows are the table entries. However, the definitions of network nodes and arrows are interchanged when we use a flow graph. Therefore, as Figure 3-4 shows, the equivalent matrix of a flow graph lists the variables as rows and columns and the connecting transmittances as table entries.

FLOW GRAPHS—STATE-DESCRIPTIVE SYSTEMS

The term *state* refers to a particular and "discrete" system condition.

Many systems can be described by discrete, rather than continuous, variables. Such cases arise naturally when the results of a decision or transformation can only be integers or whole numbers, or when the presence or absence of an attribute (e.g., red, yellow, green) is used to describe an outcome.

The outcome of a system's operation may be "use Plan *A*" or "use Plan *B*," which is a discrete result. We have one or two customers waiting, but not 1.5. A customer uses or does not use our product. An employee is in one tax bracket or another. A switch is "on" or "off." Indeed, any "continuous" system can always be described by an equivalent discrete system, if we agree to classify outcomes into a limited number of categories. Statistical measurements, for example, are often classified, or grouped, into

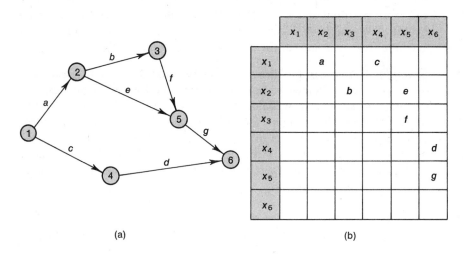

(a)   (b)

3-4 The equivalent matrix of a flow graph. (a) A flow graph with variables numbered 1 through 6 with the transmittance connecting the variables. (b) The equivalent matrix presentation. The system variables become the rows and columns of the matrix; the flow graph transmittances become the matrix entries.

10 or 20 categories, rather than handled on a continuous basis, because the resulting calculations are easier and result in little loss of precision.[3]

State-Descriptive Systems and Transitions

For the state-descriptive system, we usually want to know how the system makes transitions from one state to another, i.e., how one condition makes a transition to another.

Transitions

The coin changing logical device of Chapter 2, Figure 2-6, was a discrete logical system in which the transition of states was conditional, i.e., the transition was dependent upon a set of specifications and input conditions (the coins received). In such conditional cases the block diagram description of the system, as in Figure 2-6, is often easier to handle than the flow graph. However, there is a class of important systems for which system operation depends only upon the previous state of the system, or is conditional upon a few simple factors. In such cases the flow graph approach is the most appropriate. Two examples will illustrate the distinction and show the meaning of state transition.

Example: A machine has been designed to operate repetitively, passing through four distinct positions at successive instants of time. Let us call these positions states (A, B, C, D) and show the sequence of states by the flow graph of Figure 3-5. The deterministic "transition" of the machine from one state to the next is evident from the figure.

Example: People can be in, say, one of two states: (1) Our customers; or (2) not. If we know we have some loyal customers, some who will join us, and some who will not, we can describe this two-state system by the flow graph of Figure 3-6. The arrows show the fraction of the population that will move from one point in time to the next. (We assume in Figure 3-6 that the fractions of movement, or transition probabilities, remain constant from one period to the next, i.e., that the probabilities are stationary.)

The examples illustrate the state-descriptive cases in which the flow graph is of major use: (1) The deterministic state-descriptive system; and

---

[3] Of course, we may also be able to make a state-descriptive system a continuous system by making the differences between states progressively smaller; e.g., instead of counting our inventory of oil to the nearest 50 gallons, we might measure by gallons and fractions of gallons. The method of measurement can be an important means of system simplification. See Chapter 7.

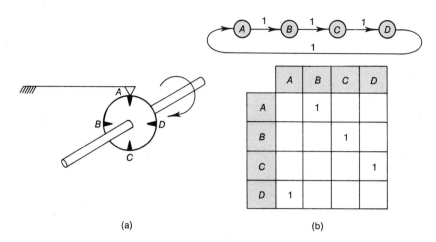

	A	B	C	D
A		1		
B			1	
C				1
D	1			

(a)   (b)

3-5 A simple deterministic state-descriptive device. (a) Shows a shaft which may be indexed to one of four positions, *A, B, C,* or *D.* The progression of movement is fixed in sequence by the physical construction of the indent and the clockwise movement of the shaft. The equivalent flow graph and transition matrix of this device are shown in (b).

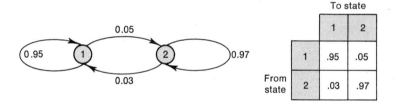

		To state	
		1	2
From state	1	.95	.05
	2	.03	.97

3-6 A simple probabilistic state-descriptive system. A person in state 1 is a customer, one in state 2 is a non-customer. The flow graph, and the equivalent matrix, show the probability that a customer will move from one state to another at the next observation, or remain where he was. In marketing applications the transition matrix is often called a "switching" matrix.

(2) the probabilistic state-descriptive system with constant probabilities of transition.[4]

The state-descriptive flow graph

The examples also show how the flow graph rules are modified to show state-descriptive systems. The nodes of the flow graph become the states

---

[4] Generalization is possible, but a comprehensive treatment is beyond the scope of this discussion. See A. T. Bharauha-Reid, *Elements of the Theory of Markov Processes and Their Applications,* McGraw-Hill, New York, 1960.

through which the system can pass, and the arrows show the transitions, either deterministic or probabilistic. For the deterministic system, all transmittances are constant and equal unity. For the probabilistic system, the transmittances become the probability of transition.

Matrix analysis of state-descriptive flow graphs

Suppose the state vector (p_1, p_2) is used to describe the probability that the system is in state 1 or state 2 at a given time, where the sum of probabilities in the vector must be 1.0. Then, given (p_1, p_2) for one time or stage, the probabilities for the next time instant can be obtained by multiplying (p_1, p_2) by the transition matrix for the system.

Example: Refer to Figure 3-6, which shows the transition matrix for the customer switching problem. Note the probability that a customer will be in state 1 at the next instant is composed of two possibilities.
1. He was in state 1 at the last instant *and*
   He remained in state 1, *or*
2. He was in state 2 at the last instant *and*
   He made the transition from state 2 to state 1.

Symbolically,

$$p_1' = p_1 p_{11} + p_2 p_{21}$$

and, similarly,

$$p_2' = p_1 p_{12} + p_2 p_{22}$$

which is precisely the same as the matrix notation

$$(p_1', p_2') = (p_1, p_2) \begin{bmatrix} p_{11} & p_{12} \\ p_{21} & p_{22} \end{bmatrix}$$

or, more compactly,

$$p_i' = p_i T$$

where p_i' and p_i represent the latter and former state vectors (probability distribution), respectively, and T is the transition matrix. To illustrate, suppose the population is split 50/50 between states 1 and 2 at time 0 so that $(p_1, p_2) = (0.50, 0.50)$. Then using the transition matrix of Figure 3-6, and following the above procedure, we would find $(p_1', p_2') = (0.49, 0.51)$ at time 1. The process can be repeated successively to generate the *trajectory* of state probabilities for each subsequent stage of observation. Such a trajectory will occur because the system has a "memory" of one time period: Its next transition depends on the former state of the system.[5]

The deterministic example (e.g., Figure 3-5) is a special case of the general transition problem with transition probabilities set equal to one. The same method of matrix multiplication can be used to trace the state transition of the deterministic system. The method is general for any number of states.

Steady-state or equilibrium conditions

Returning to the example of Figure 3-6, we would discover, upon repeated computation of the state probabilities, that after a time the state probabilities do not change from one stage to the next. Systems of the type illustrated always reach such an equilibrium, which is independent of the initial or starting condition. We can find these final probabilities by noting that the equilibrium condition requires

$$p_1 = p_1 p_{11} + p_2 p_{21}$$

$$p_2 = p_1 p_{12} + p_2 p_{22}$$

By noting that $p_1 + p_2 = 1$, and using one of the above equations, we can find a solution. Thus, for the transition matrix of Figure 3-6, using the first equation, we have

$$p_1 = 0.95 p_1 + 0.03 p_2 \quad \text{or} \quad p_2 = \tfrac{5}{3} p_1$$

and

$$p_1 + p_2 = p_1 + \tfrac{5}{3} p_1 = 1$$
$$p_1 = \tfrac{3}{8} \quad \text{and} \quad p_2 = \tfrac{5}{8}$$

In the long run, given the transition probabilities shown in Figure 3-6, the market share will be $\tfrac{5}{8}$. The method is general for any number of states.

Multidimension state diagrams

In some systems it may be desirable or necessary to define a state by two or more attributes. When this is so, a multidimensional state diagram can be useful in developing the transition matrix.

---

[5] The illustration given is a simple Markov chain, named after the Russian A. A. Markov (1856–1922) who studied such processes extensively. See W. Feller, *Introduction to Probability and Its Applications*, Wiley, New York, 1957. A series of interesting examples appears in J. G. Kemeny et al., *Finite Mathematics with Business Applications*, Prentice-Hall, Englewood Cliffs, N.J., 1962. For many interesting examples of the deterministic case, see W. R. Ashby, *Introduction to Cybernetics*, Wiley, New York, 1963.

Example: A research team is assigned two types of projects: A = applied and B = basic, as determined by the supervisor. The team may be assigned any combination of project types at a given time (including none), but at no time may the total number of projects be greater than three. We can define i as the number of projects of type A and j as the number of projects of type B assigned to the team. Thus, a given state is distinguished by the index (i, j). The number of such states is easily seen from the two-dimensional state diagram of Figure 3-7. The diagonal line $(i + j = 3)$ limits the set to the *ten* states shown. (The state probability vector will have ten positions here, and the corresponding transition matrix will be 10×10.) The concept of the two-dimensional diagram can be extended to more dimensions. However, once the concept is fixed, vector and matrix notation is usually more desirable.

Since one of the most common errors in probability analysis is the erroneous omission of a possible outcome, the state diagram is a useful tool to insure completeness of description.

Tree Diagrams and Sequences of Transition

A flow graph that shows the possible outcomes at each stage or step of a probabilistic or logical transition process as states has a branching appear-

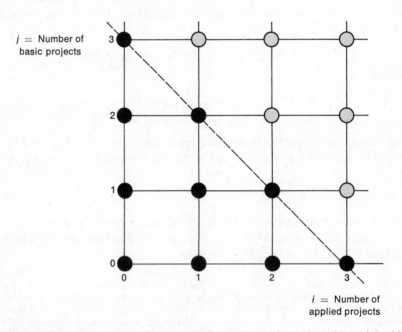

3-7 A two-dimensional state diagram. If the total number of projects (of either kind) may not exceed three, the possible combinations are limited to those shown in black below and on the dotted line $(i + j = 3)$.

ance. The number of possible outcomes or the paths leading to given outcomes increases with the number of stages, hence, the name *tree diagram*. Such diagrams are useful in the description and analyses of combinational problems, where a *sequence* of events must be traced.

Example: Consider the simple customer problem of Figure 3-6. Suppose we want to trace the possible transitions that a customer (state 1) can follow. Figure 3-8 shows the possible branching that can result.

In this example the final states (at stage 3) are states 1 and 2, but the possible routes leading to each are shown. The probability of being in state 1 or 2 can be obtained by multiplying the probabilities on the series of legs leading to a given outcome, and finally, by summarizing

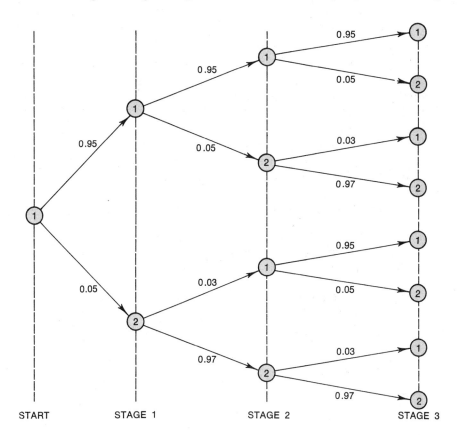

START   STAGE 1   STAGE 2   STAGE 3

3-8 A transition tree. This tree shows the possible routes a noncustomer may follow in three transitions. The probabilities of being in state (1) or (2) may be found at any stage by multiplication down the tree and an accumulation of the probabilities for each state at the last stage. This is equivalent to the matrix multiplication of the probability of being in state (1) or (2) at the start by the transition matrix three times.

for each outcome state. The probabilities of being in state 1 or state 2 at each stage are summarized below, rounded to two figures.

STAGE	STATE 1	STATE 2
0	1.00	0.00
1	0.95	0.05
2	0.90	0.10
3	0.86	0.14

The sum of the probabilities for all states at a given stage must be 1.0. (The reader should compare the tree approach to the matrix approach illustrated on page 72.) The tree diagram need not be symmetric as in Figure 3-8, because the process of transition may terminate according to rules stated beforehand. In such problems, the decision tree is useful in defining the terminal conditions of the transition process.

Example: Jones and Smith flip a coin under the following rules. A coin will be flipped, and the game will continue until a "head" appears or until four flips have been made, whichever comes first. Jones will receive $1 from Smith if "heads" occurs (and the game stops), but will pay Smith $1 if "tails" appears and the game continues, or terminates at the fourth flip. How many outcomes does this game have? What are the probability and payoff for each possible outcome? What is the expected value of the game to Jones, assuming this game is repeated a number of times?

Figure 3-9 shows the flow graph tree of the game. The probability

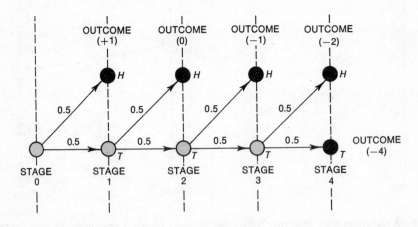

3-9 An unsymmetric tree of a game described in the text. The game terminates (black circles) when Jones wins the first "head," or when four flips of a coin have been made, whichever occurs first. Five distinct terminations of the game are possible, as shown.

of each transition is shown on each arrow, and the probability of each terminating outcome can be found by successively multiplying the probabilities on each outcome path. The amounts won (or paid) by Jones can be found by successively adding his profit or loss along each outcome path. Summarizing the results for all outcomes, we have

OUTCOME	PROBABILITY	PAYOFF	WORTH	
1	0.5000	1	0.500	
2	0.2500	0	0.000	
3	0.1250	−1	−0.125	
4	0.0625	−2	−0.125	
5	0.0625	−4	−0.250	
	1.0000		0.000	(EXPECTED VALUE)

The sum of all terminating outcome probabilities must be 1.0, and the expected value is the sum of the worth of each outcome (outcome probability times outcome payoff). Because the expected value of the game is zero, it is a "fair game." The correct construction of the decision tree permitted easy isolation of all the outcomes, and assured correct computation of the payoffs and outcome probabilities.

Tree diagrams also have other uses, such as the generation of combinations of outcomes.

Example: We plan to open a restaurant but must decide on the type of cuisine (Chinese, French, or American), the location (uptown, mid-town, or downtown), and the seating capacity (large, medium, or small). This gives us $3 \times 3 \times 3 = 27$ possible combinations (e.g., large, downtown, American restaurant and 26 other such combinations), as the construction of a tree diagram would clearly show. In complex combination or classification problems the use of the tree diagram can prevent erroneous omission of possibilities.

The stages in the transition or logical process described by a tree may relate to sequences of decision in time, or sequences of actions and consequences. In such cases, a decision causes the branching in all or part of the tree. Thus, the term *decision tree* often describes this form of graph.

Example: A decision tree, as shown in Figure 3-10, may be composed of both actions (decisions) and outcomes that may be due to chance. For example, once research is started, the outcome may be satisfactory or unsatisfactory, with an uncertain outcome. However, if the research is "satisfactory" according to stated criteria, the decision to produce now or later is not a matter of chance, but is controlled by the decision-maker. Estimates of the probability of each terminating outcome can be obtained from a diagram such as Figure 3-10.

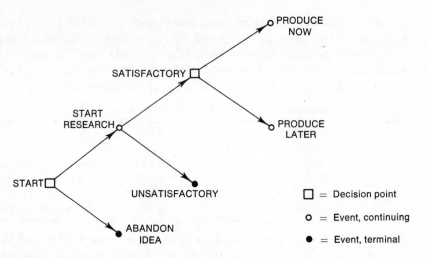

3-10 A tree composed of decisions and probability trials.

Network Flow Problems

The flow graph can be generalized to describe special flow and capacity restrictions in networks. In many of these cases the nodes of the flow graph represent points in time or space. For example, the fact that we are in Chicago, or that this is Sunday, can represent a state, and be shown by a circle. The flow graph arrows can then show the ways one can reach given states. For complex flow problems the arrows of the flow graph could show (instead of a probability) the length of time, or the distance between one point and another. For each type of system problem, therefore, special computation rules are used. Several simplified examples will illustrate the typical application.

Example: A typical system problem requires us to find the longest (or shortest) path through a directed network. For example, suppose roads connect cities *A, B, C,* and *D* as shown in Figure 3-11. Suppose also that the roads are of varying length and that the distances are shown by each arrow. What are the longest and the shortest routes from *A* to *D*? By inspection we have three possible paths.

$$ABCD = 25$$
$$ACD = 22$$
$$AD = 20$$

We see that path ABCD is the longest, and path AD is the shortest.

Example: Again using Figure 3-11, suppose the flow graph represents a network of maximum flows of a product that may occur at a given time. We may ask for the *maximum capacity* of the network to handle

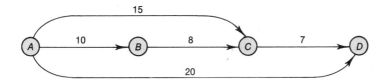

3-11 A directed flow graph used in several examples in the text.

a flow from A to D. Here, the capacity of parallel paths will add (as in the usual flow graph), but flows in series will be limited by the smallest capacity in a given chain. Application of these rules will show that the maximum capacity of the network shown is 27.

Example: Once more refer to Figure 3-11, but now let the network represent a sequence of operations and points in time. For example, let A be the starting date of a project and let D be its completion date (with B and C intermediate points in time). The arrow AB will then represent the duration of project segment AB, etc. Now, suppose that *all* project segments must be completed, and that no project segment represented by an arrow emerging from a node can commence until *all* project segments represented by entering arrows at a node have been completed. Under these conditions, we may wish to find the *minimum project time*. The minimum project time according to the restrictions stated is the same as the maximum sum of times through the network on a continuous path. The minimum project time is 25, and the so-called "critical path" is $ABCD$.

Example: To illustrate another variant, suppose we have four cities A, B, C, and D, and that Figure 3-12 shows the distances between each.

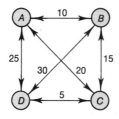

$$ABCDA = 10 + 15 + 5 + 25 = 55$$
$$ABDCA = 10 + 30 + 5 + 20 = 65$$
$$ACBDA = 20 + 15 + 30 + 25 = 90$$
$$ACDBA = 20 + 5 + 30 + 10 = 65$$
$$ADCBA = 25 + 5 + 15 + 10 = 55$$
$$ADBCA = 25 + 30 + 15 + 20 = 90$$

3-12 A two-way flow graph representing the distance between two cities. A complete enumeration of all the possible routes to City A and back is shown for reference.

For illustration, assume that the distance $AB = BA$ by the method of transportation used, so we can travel in either direction for the same cost (as shown on the arrows). If we start at, say, A, and must visit each of the remaining cities once and only once, we may ask for the cheapest route. We have a minimum sum problem (although generally, we could ask for any function of the values shown). For this case the problem may be solved by enumeration to obtain the minimum value of 55. This is a simple version of the so-called traveling salesman problem.

PROBLEMS

3.1   Using the rules for flow graph simplification described in this chapter, find the equivalent transmittance between the smallest numbered and the highest numbered variable in each of the four flow graphs given on p. 81.

3.2   Consider the following set of equations. Draw a flow graph by first making nodes for each of the three variables in the two equations. Then draw the arrows for the transmittances indicated for the first equation. Using the same nodes, now draw in the arrows for the transmittances indicated by the second equation. We now desire to find the ratio of x_3 to x_1. To do this simplify the flow graph, and find the transmittance between nodes x_1 and x_3. The equations are

$$x_2 = ax_1 + bx_2$$
$$x_3 = cx_1 + dx_2 + ex_3$$

A. Show that the ratio of x_3/x_1 is (by reducing the flow graph)

$$\frac{x_1}{x_3} = \frac{ad + c(1 - b)}{1 - (b + e) + be}$$

B. Note that in the process above, the variable x_2 has been eliminated. Compare the flow graph reduction method to the usual procedure of elimination of variables by subtraction of one equation from another. Under what conditions would the flow graph approach be most useful?

3.3   The diagram on p. 82 represents a total research and development project separated into activities (arrows) and events (circles). The diagram has been numbered so that each arrow head terminates at an event of higher number than its arrow tail. The time required for completion of each activity is given above the arrow representing that activity. (This form of project description is used in the PERT technique of planning and in equivalent forms of Critical Path Scheduling used widely in the management of complex projects.)

A. Assuming that no activity can commence until *all* of the activities before it in sequence have been completed (e.g, activity 4,5 cannot commence

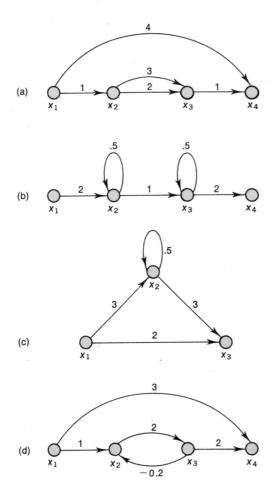

Problem 3-1

until *both* activities 2,4 and 1,4 have been completed), what is the longest sum of times through the network from event 1, the start, to event 7, the finish of the project? This is the earliest time for completion of the project.

B. Mark on the diagram the route which determined this maximum sum. This is called the critical path.

C. What happens to the earliest completion time and the critical path if the time required for activity 4,5 is reduced from 7 time periods to 1?

D. What happens to the earliest completion time and the critical path if the time required for activity 4,5 is reduced to 0 time periods?

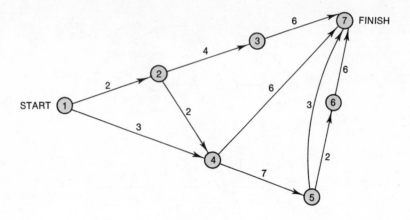

3.4 A general description of a large class of chemical processes is provided by the simple diagram below. A reactant (R) enters the system as an input. In the reactor, the chemical transformation required is produced, usually with many by-products in the reactor output ϕ. Thus, the by-products must be separated in a second processing unit, such as a distillation tower, which returns a portion of the reactor output, $k\phi$, to the reactor for additional processing. Similarly, a portion of the reactor output $(1 - k)\phi$ becomes the output of the system, which is the final product P desired. The efficiency or yield of this whole operation will, of course, depend upon a host of factors, such as temperatures, pressures, flow rates, and the like. However, a few simple questions are of immediate interest before a more complicated yield problem is considered.

A. If the fraction of output ϕ that is recirculated is $k = 0.2$, what are the flow rates $k\phi$ and ϕ if the input R to the reactor is 100,000 barrels per day (abbreviated 100 MBD)?

B. Suppose the capacity of the reactor and distillation tower is 150 MBD. What is the maximum allowable value of k and the flow rate $k\phi$ if the input R is 100 MBD?

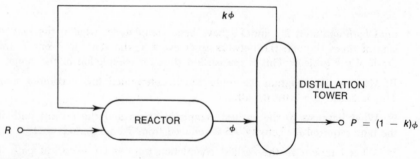

Problem 3-4

C. What general flow principles are invoked in the form of analysis made above?

3.5 A statistical control plan is described by the following table.

	O_1	O_2	O_3
S_1	0.2	0.3	0.5
S_2	0.3	0.5	0.2
S_3	0.4	0.3	0.3

That is, if strategy or plan S_1 is selected, the probability that the system will produce outcome O_3 is 0.5, etc. Due to changing conditions, an error control device selects plans S_1, S_2, and S_3 in that sequence.

A. What is the probability that the system will continue to produce outcome O_3 as these strategies are applied?

B. What is the probability that outcome O_3 will occur at least once? (Assume a single outcome selection is made according to the probability table as each strategy is applied.)

3.6 The shirt-wearing habits of an ensemble of students has been collected and tabulated, giving the following results:

(a) All students wear white shirts on Monday.

(b) On Tuesday the probability is 0.5 that a student will wear a white shirt, and 0.5 that he will wear blue.

(c) On Wednesday the Tuesday whites split 0.50/0.50 between white and blue and the blues of Tuesday split 0.50/0.50 between blue and black.

(d) Having worn a black shirt, the blacks continue to do so. The blues of Wednesday split 0.40/0.60 between blue and black and the whites continue to split 0.50/0.50 between white and blue on Thursday.

(e) On Friday, the Thursday whites again split 0.50/0.50 between white and blue, and the blues split 0.20/0.80 between blue and black.

A. On Friday what is the probability that a student will be wearing a black shirt?

B. What is the trajectory of movement from Monday through Friday, i.e., the probability distribution for each day?

3.7 A system S may be in one of three states, S_1, S_2, or S_3 which represent the position of a switch. The probability that the system will move from a present state to any one of the three choices is given by the transition matrix for S, shown below. A second system W also contains a three-position switch that may be in one of the states W_1, W_2, or W_3. The two switching systems are interconnected so that the larger system composed of S *and* W will operate if at any time the two-state description of the total system is

S_2 and W_1 or S_2 and W_3 or S_3 and W_1 or S_3 and W_3

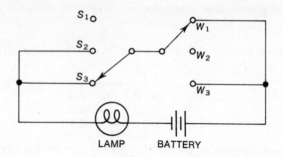

Problem 3-7

Assume that both S and W make independent moves according to their transition matrices at each new instant of time and that by this process, a "steady state" situation has been reached. What fraction of the time is the total system composed of S and W working? (Hint: find the steady-state probabilities of S and W, then use the multiplication and addition laws of probability to compute the probability that the machine will be working. For illustration, a diagram of one system meeting the description is given. In this diagram, a light bulb lights when one of the specified conditions is specified.)

$$\begin{array}{cc}
\text{Matrix for } S & \text{Matrix for } W \\[4pt]
\begin{array}{c}
\rightarrow S_1 \; S_2 \; S_3 \\
\begin{array}{c}S_1\\S_2\\S_3\end{array}
\left[\begin{array}{ccc}
\frac{1}{3} & \frac{1}{3} & \frac{1}{3}\\
\frac{1}{4} & \frac{1}{4} & \frac{1}{2}\\
\frac{1}{2} & \frac{1}{4} & \frac{1}{4}
\end{array}\right]
\end{array}
&
\begin{array}{c}
\rightarrow W_1 \; W_2 \; W_3 \\
\begin{array}{c}W_1\\W_2\\W_3\end{array}
\left[\begin{array}{ccc}
\frac{2}{3} & \frac{1}{6} & \frac{1}{6}\\
\frac{1}{4} & \frac{1}{2} & \frac{1}{4}\\
\frac{3}{8} & \frac{2}{8} & \frac{3}{8}
\end{array}\right]
\end{array}
\end{array}$$

A Possible S-W System

*3.8 The output of a system $y(t)$, a function of time, is given by the following equation, in which a and b are constants. The input to the system is $x(t)$

$$y(t) = ax(t) - b\frac{d^2y}{dt^2}$$

A. Using the Laplace transform approach of Appendix B and the substitution $1/b = w_0^2$, find the transfer function of the system, $Y(s)/X(s)$.

B. Find $y(t)$ if the input $x(t)$ is a unit impulse, i.e., if $X(s) = 1$. What does the term w_0 represent?

C. Find $y(t)$ if $x(t)$ is a step function, i.e., if $X(s) = 1/s$. Note that the appropriate partial fraction expansion is

$$\frac{A}{s} + \frac{Bs}{s^2 + w_0^2}$$

D. Find $y(t)$ if $x(t)$ is a ramp, i.e., if $X(s) = 1/s^2$. Note that the appropriate partial fraction expansion is

$$\frac{A}{s^2} + \frac{B}{s^2 + w_0^2}$$

E. Find $y(t)$ if $x(t)$ is $A \sin wt$, where A is a constant and $w \neq w_0$. Note that the appropriate partial fraction expansion is

$$\frac{A}{s^2 + w_0^2} + \frac{B}{s^2 + w^2}$$

F. In E what is the result if w approaches w_0? If t is measured in minutes and $w = 2\pi f$, where f is the frequency in cycles per minute of the input variation $x(t)$, what is the critical frequency for this system?

(In the above problem, the required transform pair is

Function	Laplace Transform
$\sin wt$	$\dfrac{w}{s^2 + w^2}$

where w is a constant representing the angular frequency in radians, or $2\pi f$.)

*3.9 The output of a system, $y(n)$, is given as a function of its input $x(n)$, and the output at previous times, $y(n-1)$ and $y(n-2)$.

$$y(n) = 0.5x(n) + y(n-1) - 0.25y(n-2)$$

A. Assuming that the time periods n are equally spaced, find the transfer function of the system in z-transform terms by using either algebraic or flow graph reduction methods. (Refer to Appendix B.)

B. What is the output response of the system if the input is a unit impulse, $x(n) = 1$, $n = 0$; $x = 0$ otherwise?

C. What is the output of the system if the input is a unit step, $x(n) = 1$, $n \geq 0$?

Note that the partial fraction expansion required is

$$\frac{A}{(1-z)} + \frac{Bz}{(1-0.5z)^2} + \frac{C}{(1-0.5z)}$$

D. Compare the results obtained in (B) and (C) with the results you would obtain by direct numerical computation of $y(n)$ for a few values. If the results of the numerical computation and the algebraic values of $y(t)$ do not agree, try again. They should.

CLASSIFICATION
AND HIERARCHIES
4 | # IN SYSTEM DEFINITION

Let us return now to the discussion of black boxes and recall that the black box represents a grouping of detail. A given black box can contain others of finer distinction, and conversely a given black box may be contained, with others, within a larger black box.

Such possibilities, particularly for a complex system, raise the question of *hierarchy*, a term taken from the Greek literally meaning sacred order, and historically denoting levels of angels, or levels of authority in ecclesiastical organization.[1] In science and logic the term applies to levels of classification, and we generally use the same term to denote layers of authority or control in organizations. For example, in logic an inclusive category or highest class is called a *summum genus*, and the lowest category, consisting of individuals only, is called an *infirma species*; each intermediate class is called a *genus* of the class below, and a *species* of the class above. Ideally, such categories in the scheme should be mutually inclusive and collectively exhaustive. From the systems viewpoint, the *summum genus* is the system itself, and the lower classifications or categories are the hierarchy of the parts of the system.

Hierarchy is the most important concept of definition in complex systems, because knowledge of the "order" of element or transaction detail

[1] "Standards and gonfalons . . . for distinction serve of hierarchies and degrees" (Milton). Hieroglyphic, or sacred carving, comes from the same ancient root.

permits the investigator to simplify or expand his system definition. Thus, when defining a system, we say that an element or transaction belongs to a given class, or may itself own or encompass other elements or transactions. Similarly, we say that several systems *belong* to the same class, or *own* other subsystems.

Although classification methods are familiar to anyone who reads or speaks (because language itself is a classification form), we will devote this and the following chapter to some of the special classification techniques of immediate interest to us as systems analysts.

DATA AND FILE ORGANIZATION

If data are formed into records, and records are formed into files, some ordering method is necessary so that we can easily obtain information when we need it. File organization has particular importance when data must be collected for system definition, or for the design of information systems with storage points for data in the information flow sequence.

File organization using codes is discussed in Appendix C. A few examples of general file structure will be useful here.

Example: Suppose we have an information file consisting of the names of employees in each department of a manufacturing firm. We may then inquire about the structure of this list. Conversely, we may have the names of a group of employees and wish to structure the list in a form representing their function, ability, or other classification group.

We could use the following outline:

I. Department
   A. Name
      1. Last
      2. First
      3. Initials
   B. Address
      1. City
      2. Street
      3. Street number
   C. Job
      1. Job name
      2. Work center assignment
      3. Rate of pay
      4. Seniority
      5. Skill level
      6. Educational level

D. Nonjob Skills
   1. Manual
   2. Hobby
   3. Language
   4. Education
   5. Other
E. Nonjob Memberships
   1. Fraternal organizations
   2. Professional or worker organizations
   3. Community organizations
   4. Other organizations

Although we recognize that this "outline" is not the only one we could have devised, it does describe the actual way the files for employees could be kept in a given organization or, specifically, the way a given personnel form has been structured.

Note that the organization of the file, like the system using it, is determined by (a) the distinct elements in the file; and (b) the relationship or ordering of these elements. Also note that we could physically arrange the data on a particular element without regard to hierarchy, but if we wish to *extract* information from a collection of records, or organize the elements in the file, we must impose a hierarchy.

For example, suppose we arrange the file described in the above outline in tabular form with the data in columns. The row of information concerning a given employee (which is a vector describing the individual's attributes) has the physical ordering of the table columns, but no necessary hierarchy of items is implied in the description. However, when we ask for an ordering of *individuals* by given criteria, say, for example, by last name, first name, and initial, then we imply a hierarchy of classification (vertically) in which the last name is more important than the first. Similarly, we may wish to extract from the file all persons who are machinists with more than five-year seniority and who belong to the Benevolent Protective Order of the Elks. The hierarchy Job Name/Seniority/Fraternal Organization is implied then in the sort required for extracting the data (Job Name would therefore be the major "key").

Similarly, records may be ordered in an alphabetical hierarchy, or in a hierarchy according to time, or in another combination of major and minor categories, as chosen by the analyst.

Arbitrary or Artificial Hierarchies

Thus, the element data in a file may be arranged in many ways, and the particular question or series of questions posed by the investigator sets the hierarchy or levels of classification. In one sense, such a series of questions may be thought of as an arbitrary hierarchy or classification that results from a particular application. The resulting hierarchy is seldom exhaustively complete.

Certain random access files are good illustrations. For example, the McBee Keysort System stores data on edge-punched cards. In the McBee Keysort System, elements with specific characteristics can be drawn from the file by the insertion of a needle, which retains the unwanted cards and releases the wanted cards, edge-punched for the appropriate key. (For further detail, see Chapter 10, Figure 10-5.)

In such files, the physical position of a wanted card in the deck of possibilities need not be known, and a wide variety of transaction sequences, or hierarchy arrangement can be produced as needed. The file hierarchy is random, until some external criteria are imposed.

Natural Hierarchies

We can contrast the random file and its artificial manipulations with a classification scheme that is designed to be complete and exhaustive and that explains phenomena or structures observations in nature. The familiar chemical and biological classification schemes are examples.

> The classical example is Mendeleev's classification of the chemical elements based on their arrangement into vertical columns and horizontal rows according to their atomic weight. According to Mendeleev's own account this idea came to him in 1868 while he was writing a textbook of chemistry. He was looking for an easy classification for teaching, rather than for serious scientific purposes. . . . Having entered the atomic weight and other characteristics of every element on separate cards, he was struck by the fact that the properties of the elements were related to their atomic weights. From certain gaps in this Periodic Table, chemists were quick to conclude that the empty spaces represented undiscovered elements, an assumption that was amply rewarded by their experimental discovery of the new elements Gallium, Germanium, and Scandium, which were found to fit neatly into the gaps.[2]

Such natural hierarchies are, in science, presumably related to actual relationships and orderings observed in nature. The more nearly a hierarchy conforms to the ideals of completeness, consistency, and realism, the more "natural" it is. In this sense, classification may be thought of as a basic tool of science, which studies the properties of classes of phenomena, rather than of particular instances. Thus, it is assumed in science that, once the results of a particular experiment have been observed, these results may be imputed to the class of experiments to which the one belongs. The ability to transfer results correctly depends upon the accuracy of classification.

[2] R. Lewinsohn, *Science, Prophecy, and Prediction.* Fawcett Publishing, Greenwich, Conn., 1962, p. 35.

Some Natural System Hierarchies

Just as a system may be defined differently for different system objectives, so may the hierarchies describing system structure. Some familiar natural hierarchies are the formal and informal organization chart, the bookkeeping chart of accounts, and the functional hierarchies of equipment and work groups. Ancestral hierarchies, or family trees, are a structural hierarchy based on heredity, and historical trees, or hierarchies of events, are also in common use, as shown in Chapter 3.

Note that a given physical system may involve several hierarchies at the same time. Thus, a given firm may have a formal organization chart that differs from its informal organization, both of which may differ from the functional hierarchy of work assignments.

Systems also exhibit hierarchies of objectives, the purpose of which, for example, may be to integrate the operations of several subdepartments to superior departments and the company, or organizational, purpose. Similarly, a hierarchy of plans for each department, classified also into immediate, short-range, and long-range categories, may be considered for a given system.

Because this wide variety of hierarchies can define a system at any given time, we should specify the classification mode to be used in a given system definition.

In the same way, we can classify a system component or *transaction* (which we will hereafter call an *entity* to denote an item to be classified) in several different categories simultaneously if we use different hierarchies to describe a given system. Thus, an employee may belong to one category in the formal hierarchy of an organization, to another category in the informal hierarchy, and to yet another category in the functional work-assignment hierarchy. Such multiple classification of the employee is consistent provided we understand to which hierarchy a given classification category belongs.

Hierarchy Changes

In complex dynamic systems, as opposed to static systems, the hierarchy of components and transactions may change with time: Employees may move from one department to another, specific messages may be passed from one level of authority to another, and one level of organization or another may assume control of the system. Such situations may require that methods of system definition, based upon updated classification procedures, supplement the block diagram and flow graph approaches. We devote the remainder of this chapter to such methods.

We sort observations into pigeon-holes or classes; we organize classes into ownership-membership hierarchies, defined for a given system.

MECHANIZING SYSTEM DEFINITION

System definition often requires massive data-processing efforts. This is so, for example, when an industrial information system must be studied, when many possible transactions occur over a period of time, or when a system contains many alternate transformations. Moreover, a number of individuals may be required to define a detailed system in a reasonable time, and, if it is to be investigated efficiently, the system must often be defined in a way that can be transferred to data-processing equipment.

The usual method of organizing such definition efforts is to employ uniform data collection and data-processing methods having rigid *format* specifications. In practice, this is usually accomplished by developing a manual of standard terms and definitions, and, thereafter, by using codes (vectors) or files of codes (matrices) to maintain a consistent, complete description method. The approach is familiar to the field interviewer and opinion-poll taker who code and edit responses to questions so that the responses obtained may be analyzed statistically on machines. The approach is also familiar to those who must define or specify large networks, such as critical path or project planning networks for a construction project. In such project diagrams, events in time, or states, are numbered and the connecting activities are designated by a pair of event numbers. Similarly, when a large hardware system is to be constructed and documented for later maintenance efforts, it is usual to code component parts or black boxes, and to code the connecting wires by color, number, or coded mechanical fittings.

A general technique for mechanizing a complex system definition can be structured either from a block diagram or from a flow graph viewpoint, using classification techniques. For illustration we will consider the block diagram approach.

Suppose we consider a system with many elements, or components, and several as yet undefined transaction types or relationships. (See Figure 4-1.) The elements may be physical components, departments, machine groups, or blocks defined to suit the purpose of the investigator.

A Data Collection Classification Procedure

A systematic method of system definition can then proceed as follows:

1. List, with an appropriate name, each element to be defined.

2. Number, or otherwise uniquely code, each element so listed. A simple serial listing is often satisfactory here, but if later grouping of elements is contemplated, a partially blocked code (*see Apendix C*) may be used to identify similar elements.

3. Develop categories for each transaction that may be encountered, and develop a code or check list for these attributes. Such a code will

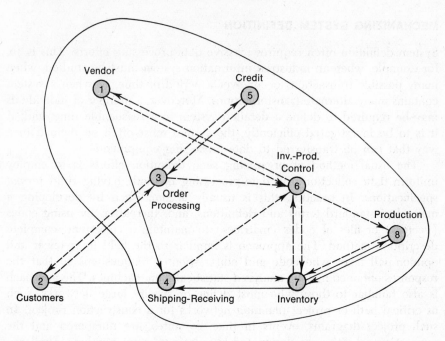

4-1 Flow diagram of a simple system, indicating material and information flows. (Solid line, material. Dotted line, information). (Taken from D. Hertz and E. Eddison, Eds., *Progress in Operations Research,* Wiley, New York, 1964, Vol. II, p. 130.)

certainly contain a space for the "From" and "To" element codes and will also contain additional information that may be useful in later analyses. It may be desirable to include some space for a transaction (or report) name in some systems. One possible code type is shown in Figure 4-2.

4. Construct, for each element, an element sheet such as the one shown in Figure 4-3. The physical form of the element sheet can range from simple cards to extensive dossiers, but regardless of the form, the element sheet should show the element name and number, and should provide space for the specified transaction data, which is arranged in a uniform format. The element sheet is usually divided into two parts: one records the structural information that relates incoming and outgoing transactions to the given elements; the other shows the detailed information on transformation procedures at the element and the detail of any files, storage, or delay that occurs at the element. An instruction sheet, or manual, containing the method of data collection and the instructions for filling out the element sheets can then be provided to a team of investigators, together with assignments to investigate specific elements. The investigators will also need to have the coded element dictionary or cross reference to fill out the transaction codes correctly.

5. Collect the information required on the element sheets. (For hardware systems, the required forms may be completed by several design groups or a team of engineers familiar with component specifications and connections.)

Data Assembly

We may now put the element sheets together as follows:

1. When they have been coded to show all transactions entering and leaving an element, the element sheets can be assembled by sorting the transaction codes. Various system descriptions can be produced, depending upon the selection of transaction code categories.

For example, for each element sheet, consider first only those transactions reported as *entering* each element. This information can be extracted from each element sheet and a summary of all transactions created. For ease in later sorting, it may be convenient to create one IBM card or *unit*

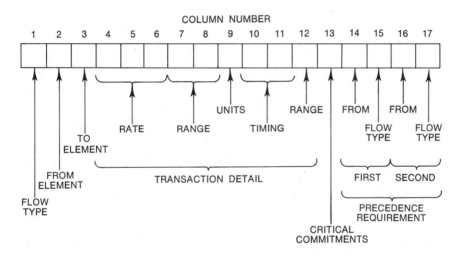

4-2 A transaction coding structure. This is one way the transactions of Figure 4-1 can be coded. The chart above illustrates the arrangement of the code digits, with description and example given below. (Taken from D. Hertz and R. Eddison, Eds., *Progress in Operations Research,* Wiley, New York, 1964, Vol. II, p. 131.)

1. Flow type, Col. 1, Material 1, Information 2.
2. From element: numbered according to diagram, Col. 2.
3. To element: numbered according to diagram, Col. 3.
4. Transaction rate between elements shown, Cols. 4–6 (units per month), Range 7–8.
5. Units of measure, transaction rate: Col. 9, receipts 1, orders 2, reports 3, shipments 4.
6. Timing of flow in days: Cols. 10–11, range, Col. 12.
7. Critical commitments: Col. 13, orders 1, approval of orders 2.
8. Precedence requirements: Col. 14, arrow required; Col. 15, flow required; Col. 16, arrow required; Col. 17, flow required. (To be used if necessary, provision for first precedence only, blank indicates no precedence requirements.)
   Note: In all cases x, xx, or xxx indicates blank.

Element Sheet

Element Name _____ Element Number _____

Transactions to and from this element: (Apply code structure in spaces below, and note any special detail below)

Special Notes:
1. Describe transformation at this element:
2. Emergency input-outputs?
3. Transformation rates?
4. Critical decisions and commitments?
5. Detail critical and normal operating restrictions
6. Special and normal resource requirements
7. Other notes: (Political, personality, quality, technical, or other problems here?)

4-3 An element sheet for organizing data collection. This sample can be simplified or expanded as needed, but it suggests a method of collecting and organizing data on an element so that the structure of the system can be developed later, either manually or by machine. Using element sheets of this type, many people can work on system data collection. (Taken from D. Hertz and R. Eddison, Eds., *Progress in Operations Research,* Wiley, New York, 1964, Vol. II, p. 129.)

record for each transaction or to place the transaction data on other similarly flexible machine-readable media.

To illustrate, suppose that, by using the conventions of Figure 4-2, the 18 transaction records of Figure 4-4 have been obtained from the field survey. (By that convention the transaction 114100101153x62xx means that a material flow occurred between element 1 and element 4; the average rate of flow is 100 receipts per month at element 4 with a range of 10; 15 days is the average time of flow from 1 to 4 with a 3-day range; no critical commitment is involved in this transaction, but initiation of this flow required a flow from element 6, which is an order.)

From these transaction data we can create many maps of the system by appropriate sorting procedures. Consider first the matrix display that can be obtained from the first three digits of the 18 transaction codes as shown in Figure 4-4. The transactions in the figure were sorted in "To"

114100101153x62xx	187004004071x62xx	236490402011x52xx	268004002000lxxxx
142050104052x71xx	216100103031x62xx	246100103011x11xx	276001003000xxxxx
147100101011x11xx	223500402031xxxxx	253500403000232xx	287004002000x6271
174050104010x62xx	232500403031x52xx	261100102031lxxxx	
178004004010x82xx	235500402010x22xx	267490102011x32xx	

4-4 Coded transactions. Note that there are 18 codes, one coded line for each arrow in the diagram of Figure 4-1. Each line contains the detail required to analyze various system properties, according to the coding structure given in Figure 4-2. (Taken from D. Hertz and R. Eddison, Eds., *Progress in Operations Research,* Wiley, New York, 1964, Vol. II, p. 130.)

element order, and spread in "From" element order. The type of transaction is entered in the appropriate From-To cell of the table, with (1) denoting material and (2) denoting information. From this matrix (Figure 4-5), we can draw an equivalent diagram of Figure 4-1 using the methods of the previous chapters. (If the transaction codes have been recorded on machine-readable media, the creation of these outputs can be mechanized. Similarly, other displays of system structure can be made by calling for other combinations of information. The procedure increases in value with a larger number of transactions and increased code complexity.)

2. Variations in the form of system construction are available once the transaction codes have been summarized. For instance, if the data have been collected correctly, each To-From transaction should match identically one From-To transaction. For example, there should be exactly two transaction codes of the form 114100101153x62xx in the transaction list shown in the example, because this transaction will be reported as leaving element 1 on the element sheet (for element 1), and also reported as entering element 4 on the element sheet (for element 4). Thus, a check is available on the consistency and completeness of the data collection. Many other questions, for example, those shown in Table 4-1, can be answered about the system.

A similar form of tabular comparison can be made from the data collected on element files and storage points. The contents of files at various elements can be compared for duplication and activity if the transaction code has been developed to show this detail. Processing load reports and cross references showing the elements affected by a given transaction are also available from the data collected.

With the basic structural information now accessible, the way is cleared for refinement of system definition along whatever lines the investigators find necessary and a consistent background is available for later analysis, simulation, or improvement.

3. In conclusion, several remarks may be useful. The procedure described could also proceed by first defining all *transaction* types of interest, and

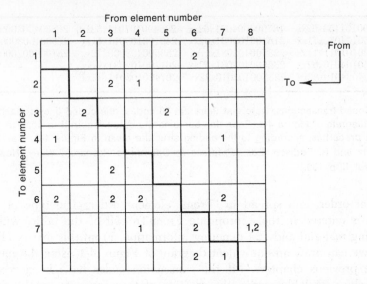

4-5 One of the many matrix displays that can be obtained from the coded transaction data. This table contains all the information available from the flow diagram of Figure 4-1, and was obtained from the first three digits of the coded transactions, shown in Figure 4-4. The code 1 in the matrix indicates a material flow; the code 2 indicates an information flow. Note that in matrix displays of this type, the number of entries across a row indicates the number of arrows coming *into* an element; the number of entries in a column indicates the number of arrows going *out from* an element. The diagonal in this type of display is usually blank, unless flows (or transitions) take place on a probability basis. (The matrix shown is the transpose of the transition matrix usually found in mathematical literature.) Entries above the diagonal indicate flows from higher- to lower-numbered elements; entries below the diagonal indicate flows from lower- to higher-numbered elements, a property which may be useful in later analysis. By using the display method described here, the code numbers assigned to elements must be unique, but need not be in any particular order. *The matrix display of data can be used in reverse to construct the flow diagram.* In particular, data collected from the element sheets, which result in one code per transaction, can be analyzed quickly for conversion to matrix form; for example, the second column of the code (Figure 4-4) indicates the *column* of the matrix entry; the third column indicates the *row* of the matrix entry. By considering each transaction code at a time, the entries in the matrix are easily obtained. From the matrix, the flow diagram may be charted easily. Using this sorting procedure, element sheets from a number of observers can be combined mechanically. (Taken from D. Hertz and R. Eddison, Eds., *Progress in Operations Research*, Wiley, New York, 1964, Vol. II, p. 132.)

by creating a *transaction sheet*. The procedure of data collection would then be to trace the required transaction types (or reports) throughout the system, recording each From-To element on the transaction sheet. This alternate approach (comparable to the flow graph approach of Chapter 3)

Table 4.1[a]   **Some Questions That Can Be Answered from the Information Contained in the Data Given in Figure 4-4**

1. Do any elements receive more information than they send? (For all transactions containing a 2 in Column 1, Search Columns 2, the "from" column, and Columns 3, the "to" column. If the frequency of entries for a particular element in Column 3 exceeds the number of entries in Column 2, that element receives more different flows than it sends. Elements 6 and 7 are in this class, as reference to Figure 4-4 confirms. Frequently such elements are decision makers, or trouble spots.

2. Are there any elements that send out more information than they receive? (Reverse the procedure above.) Elements 1 and 3 are examples in Fig. 4-4. Frequently such elements are service units, or in an inferior control position.

3. Which element in this system has the greatest variety of inputs *and* outputs? (Search Columns 2 and 3 of the transaction code. The element which appears most frequently in this search is the one required.) Element 6 here.

4. Are there any elements that deal *only* in information? (List all elements that appear in either Column 2 or Column 3 and have a 2 in Column 1. Next see if any of these numbers are duplicated in Column 2 or Column 3 of transactions having a 1 in Column 1. If not, such elements deal only in information. Element 6 is such a case in Fig. 4-4.

5. Do any elements deal only in material? (Reverse the procedure given in 4.)

6. Which flows involve critical commitments? (Pull out the transactions with an entry other than x in Column 13.) Flows 5–3, 6–1, and 6–8 are examples in the data of Fig. 4-4.

7. Is there a tightly coupled flow sequence in this flow chart? Yes, there are several if the precedence requirements are checked. (To obtain this result, it is convenient to trace backwards from an output to an input. For example, the flow from 4 to 2 is an output, but flow 4–2 requires one from 7 to 4, the flow 7–4 requires one from 6 to 7, 6–7 requires one from 3 to 6, etc., by inspection of the precedence requirements stated in the code of Fig. 4-4. Thus, the reverse of a sequence built up in this way is "tightly coupled," or must follow in the given order. For the sequence illustrated the order is 2,3,5,3,6,7,4,2. Another such sequence is 2,3,5,3,2, or 6,1,4. It may be useful to distinguish "looping" sequences from those which are not looping. The nonlooping sequence indicates a buffering in the system flow. Thus, the sequence 2,3,5,3,6,7,4,2, does not directly involve element 8, production, since the inventory element 7 acts as a buffer under normal conditions.

8. Where are the major information lags? (Scanning Columns 10 and 11 for transactions having a 2 in Column 1, we find that one to three days is the usual lag in information flow in this system. However, if we adopt the convention that a delay of zero time should be checked further, we find that information flows 6–8 and 8–7 occur with only a small frequency compared to other transaction rates. This distinction can be used to indicate periodic reports, or, an alternate code can be used for this purpose. Thus, there are no major information lags in this system, but the frequency of periodic reporting and ordering may be of interest.)

[a] Taken from Hertz and Eddison, Editors, *Progress in Operations Research,* Wiley, New York, 1964, Volume II, pp. 140–141.

produces the same result as the element sheet approach and, in addition, may be more convenient in some applications.

We should also note the advantage of having a method for defining a system *quickly*. By allowing many investigators to collect data at one time (rather than few working for a long time), a "snapshot" of the system can be obtained rather than the blurred results that could result if the system changes while the data collection is in progress. In many applications this is an important statistical advantage.

The suggested procedure also yields economies in data collection and analysis which should not be overlooked. For these reasons a number of automated procedures of the type illustrated have been developed. The best known of these is a procedure of data collection with computer analysis and display called AUTOSATE (for Automatic Systems Analysis), developed by the RAND Corporation for use by the Air Force in defining and improving paperwork systems. The method is general, however, and may be applied to systems of all kinds.[3]

CLASSIFICATION DEFINITIONS OF DYNAMIC SYSTEMS

The method of the previous section is satisfactory for defining the static status of a system (or the average status if average values are collected). However, a method of definition is often needed that will define a system on a dynamic basis; for example, so that the system can be simulated. Simulation methods will be discussed further in Chapter 12, but one popular method of system definition suitable for the purpose is appropriate here. We will consider the general class of systems that are discrete, or *state-descriptive*. A particular characteristic of these systems is that they produce changes at specific intervals of time, rather than continuously.

For such systems, an approach to system definition that uses lists of entities (elements or transactions) and their attributes allows us to produce a repetitive series of snapshots of system status leading to a "moving picture" of system operation. In the following description we use the definition of terms used in SIMSCRIPT, a computer simulation language developed for the Air Force by the RAND Corporation.[4]

The SIMSCRIPT Approach

SIMSCRIPT views a system as composed of *entities* that may be *permanent* or *temporary*, and that have attributes again *permanent* or *temporary*. For

---

[3] See, R. H. Gregory and R. L. Van Horn, *Business Data Processing and Programming*, Wadsworth, Belmont, Calif., 1963, Chapters 5 and 6; or O. T. Gatto, "AUTOSATE: An Automated Data Systems Analysis Technique," (Memo RM-3118-PR) The RAND Corp., Santa Monica, Calif., 1962.

[4] H. M. Markowitz, B. Hauser, and H. W. Karr, *SIMSCRIPT: A Simulation Programming Language*, Prentice-Hall, Englewood Cliffs, N.J., 1963.

example, an employee, John Jones, may be considered a permanent entity if he is on the regular payroll, or a temporary entity if he is a part-time worker. Jones has the permanent attribute "male" and the temporary attribute "age."

In addition to attributes, an entity may *belong to* a set or *be the owner of* a set of other entities. Thus, Jones may belong to the entity called Department 25, and Jones may own a set of entities, his personal hand tools if he is, say, a mechanic.

At any time we can describe the *status of the system* by listing all existing permanent and temporary entities with their attributes, set memberships, and set ownerships.

A change in system status, as defined above, is called an *event*. An event is said to occur, and a change in system status results, when one or more of the following changes occurs:

1. The creation or destruction of an entity.
2. A change in an entity attribute.
3. A change in entity set membership or ownership.

Events may occur due to external pressures arising "outside" the defined system boundary, in which case they are called *exogenous* events. Events may also occur due to the internal operations of the system and are then called *endogenous* events.

To complete the system definition, the analyst must define completely the rules that cause a sequence of events to occur in simulated time. The development of the event-causing rules completes the model, or system definition, by relating one list of entities, attributes, or sets to another later in time.

This listing or classification approach has the virtue that the rules of operation can be as complicated as necessary to produce realism—highly conditional rules, fixed or variable delays, random choice, and combinations of such rules are easily introduced by establishing additional lists and test procedures.

When the starting status of the system and the rules for event creation have been established, the later operation of the system has been defined, and the rules can be followed from one event to another by a computer. The memory storage of an electronic computer also permits ease of list maintenance, because the memory media are flexible: List entries can be created, erased, and rearranged in microseconds.

After "running" the defined system for a time that is sufficient to accumulate a number of events, the characteristics of the system can be analyzed statistically by reference to summaries of events, or the history of status changes. Moreover, the approach is perfectly general, so that the size and complexity of the system to be defined and simulated is limited only by the ingenuity and resources available to the analyst.

The reader will notice that the SIMSCRIPT approach to system definition is no more than a mechanization of the classification methods previously discussed. The only detail of mechanization of additional interest in this chapter is the concept of a *temporary event notice list* and an *event timing routine*. These ideas are illustrated in the following example. (Other forms of simulation timing will be discussed in Chapter 12).

The Outline of a SIMSCRIPT-Type Problem

Example: Consider a simple state-descriptive system consisting of a single work station that irregularly receives work and processes these jobs in shorter or longer times, depending upon the job to be done. (This is the classic queuing, or waiting line model.)

To define the system by the classification method, we first define three permanent entities, two of which belong to the other:

A. The system,
   1. The backlog or queue; and
   2. The work in process.

These entities and their hierarchy define the lists of system operation that will be retained. Thus, the simple system is composed of the entities backlog and work in process. These entities will, in turn, own lesser temporary entities, i.e., jobs.

We must now develop three types of event-creating rules. One type of event will be the arrival of orders (an exogenous event, because such orders enter the system). Another type is the endogenous event, which denotes a job completion. If a job arrives when work is in process, so that the incoming job cannot immediately enter the work-in-process category, the incoming job must join the backlog. Therefore, a third type of event can occur: The movement of a job from the backlog to the work-in-process category. Rules for the generation of each type of event are required.

For example, suppose we have an exogenous event generator that causes orders to occur at succeeding intervals, according to some statistical distribution. Suppose we also have a job completion generator, which determines the time required to do a given job according to some statistical distribution. (The SIMSCRIPT computer language provides for these statistical operations, but they could be constructed according to the methods of Chapter 12.) Finally, we can specify the third type of event generation by stating two rules:

1. If a job arrives and work is in process, assign that job to the bottom of the backlog list. Otherwise, go to work in process.

2. If work in process is completed and a job is waiting in backlog, move the job at the top of the backlog list to work in process.

If we assume we have these event-creating devices, the system operation can now proceed. The simulation starts, say, at time zero, with both the backlog and work in process empty. The order arrival generator, however, tells us that an order will arrive at time 5. To control the progress of the simulation, we now create a *temporary event notice list,* and note in this special list that an order will arrive at time 5. Because no other events are scheduled until then, our time recording device can jump to time 5, at which point the temporary entity, order 1, is created and system status changes.

Now we must perform several steps. First, we ask when the next order will arrive, and find from the order generator that one will arrive at time 15; we record this fact in the temporary event notice list. Next we apply the rules for the assignment of the incoming order, and assign order 1 to work in process. Finally, we ask when order 1 will be complete and determine from the order completion generator that it will be completed at time 19; this fact is also placed in the temporary event notice list, which is maintained in strict time sequence. Thus, the event notice for order 1's completion will appear after the event notice for the next order arrival.

Our clock may now jump ahead to time 15, at which time order 2, another temporary entity, is created. Again, we ask when the next order will arrive, and the input order generator gives time 23. By applying the rule for order assignment, order 2 goes to the backlog list, because work is still in process. System status now shows one order in backlog and one in process.

Having completed the cycles to this point, the clock can now be moved to the next item on the temporary event notice list, time 19, the completion of order 1, presently in process. At this time the temporary entity order 1 is destroyed, because it now passes from the defined system, and order 2 is moved from backlog to work in process. Because a new job has arrived in process, we ask when the job will be complete and find from the job completion generator time 27 for the completion of order 2. This future event is noted in the temporary event notice list in its appropriate time sequence. The simulation continues in this way, step by step, until the analyst stops the process. (See Figure 4-6.)

In the above example, many statistics of system operation can be collected as events occur and the status of the system changes. The average backlog, the standard deviation of the backlog size, the maximum size of backlog, and the average time for an order to pass through the system are available from summaries of the data generated by the simulation process. Moreover, we can use any form of distribution to govern the input and job completion generators, and with only little added complexity of formulation, we can extend the simulation to series or parallel flows.

TIME	BACKLOG	IN PROCESS	TEMPORARY EVENT NOTICE
0			Order 1 arrives at t = 5
5		Order 1	Order 2 arrives at t = 15 Order 1 complete at t = 19
15	Order 2	Order 1	Order 1 complete at t = 19 Order 3 arrives at t = 23
19		Order 2	Order 3 arrives at t = 23 Order 2 complete at t = 27

4-6 Classification method of system definition using SIMSCRIPT format. This figure summarizes system status as described in the text.

Note that by using the temporary event notice list, the simulation can proceed from one change in system status to another thereby eliminating the unnecessary repetition of computation and display that could result if system status reports were produced periodically. It should also be clear that the time scale used in the simulation can be changed to suit the analyst's needs. The SIMSCRIPT computer language provides for these adjustments and also provides the analyst with numerous, convenient instructions for handling a list creation and the timing routine illustrated above.

PROBLEMS

4.1 The following statements can be simplified, using logical classification, to give the required answer. First determine the important categories and the attributes of each category. It may help to construct a small table showing all combinations.

Here are the facts:

1. There are five houses.
2. The Englishman lives in the red house.
3. Milk is drunk in the middle house.
4. The Spaniard owns a dog.
5. The Japanese smokes Parliament.
6. The Norwegian lives in the first house.
7. Kools are smoked in the house next to where the horse is kept.
8. The man who smokes Chesterfield lives next door to where the fox is kept.
9. The man who smokes Old Gold owns snails.
10. The man who smokes Lucky Strike drinks orange juice.
11. The green house is immediately to the right of the ivory house.
12. Kools are smoked by the man in the yellow house.

13. Coffee is drunk by the man in the yellow house.
14. The Norwegian lives next door to the blue house.
15. The Ukranian drinks tea.
16. Each man has a different house, drink, smoke, pet, and nationality.

A. Who drinks water? Who owns the zebra? (There is a unique answer for each.)

B. Comment on your method of solution. Did organizing the classifications and attributes help? Did trial-and-error play a part in your solution? What other techniques did you use?

4.2 (This problem assumes the reader is familiar with the material in Appendix C.)

A manufacturer of men's clothing has developed a code for men's suits as follows:

Number Sold	Stock Number					Customer Number			Salesman
in units	*size*	*cut*	*color*	*style*	*fabric*	*region*	*city*	*serial*	
XXXX	36	R	3	21	24	1	3	6	4

1. Number sold: Units ordered. (4 character positions for digits)
2. Size: Men's suit size. (2 positions)
3. Cut: S small; R regular; L long; X extra long. (1 position)
4. Color: 1 blue; 2 brown; 3 grey; 4 black; 5 other. (1 position)
5. Style: Manufacturer's style number keyed to pattern. (2 positions)
6. Fabric: Manufacturer's fabric and price level code, first digit is price class, second digit is fabric code in price class. (2 positions)
7. Region: 1 northeast; 2 mid-Atlantic; 3 south; 4 north-central; 5 mid-west; 6 west. (1 position)
8. City: Serialized within region. (1 position)
9. Customer: Serialized within city. (1 position)
10. Salesman: 1 Herman; 2 Cy; 3 Al; 4 Irving; 5 Walter; 6 Jack; etc. (1 position)

A. Given an excerpt of the hypothetical transaction listing for this firm for a given month (see below):

1. How many longs did Herman sell on the west coast?
2. What is the distribution of shorts, regulars, longs, and extra longs by region?
3. What is the most popular color this month?
4. What should we send to Charles and Co., if the number of that store is 346?
5. If the wholesale price of 34L21121 is $39.80, what is the dollar sales of this item?
6. What region had the greatest unit sales?

B. What compromises have been made in the development of the given code structure?

C. Could you suggest a more desirable code structure that would satisfy both the need for interpretation and analysis and the need for code efficiency in terms of compactness?

D. Why is it desirable to relate the statistics by product code with the statistics by customer code? What other files should be organized around these two basic code formats?

EXCERPT FROM TRANSACTION FILE

100 32S11121 111 4	200 36S13221 221 3
200 32S11114 321 4	50 36R22121 346 5
1000 32S12136 412 1	100 36R23119 346 5
200 32S24321 523 2	1000 36L11119 152 4
1000 34R11121 132 4	1200 36L12236 441 7
75 34R22221 222 3	200 36X12634 631 1
250 34R11314 146 4	100 36X22221 663 1
300 34R22336 452 7	80 38R31323 542 2
1000 34R33419 636 6	40 38L32323 511 2
200 34R11119 171 4	75 38X33240 512 2
200 34Z21121 382 5	200 38X42236 513 2
2000 34L32236 663 6	100 40L22119 221 3
1000 34X41119 117 4	75 40X11221 646 1

4.3   In the novel *1984*, George Orwell referred to the "Office of Double-Think." This office had the function of updating the master files to suit the needs of the current administration. . . . When large-scale computer databanks are used for central distribution of information—through computer manipulations and electronic communication systems—what precautions could be taken to prevent the outcome Orwell predicted? Give an example of a situation in which Orwell's vision might come to pass.

4.4   *The Standard Industrial Classification Manual* (Bureau of the Budget) Government Printing Office, Washington 25, D.C., defines statistical categories for U. S. Industries. This 4-digit S.I.C. Code is arranged in a hierarchy. The first two digits indicate a major product group, the next digit a subclass within that group, and the fourth digit a sub-subclass. For example, Major Group 35 includes Machinery, except heavy electrical. Code 357 indicates Office, Computing, and Accounting Machines. Code 3571 indicates Electronic Computing Machines and other accounting and bookkeeping equipment, including cash registers. The detailed contents of a given category are described in the aforementioned manual which is revised from time to time as necessity dictates. Discuss the advantages of such a uniform system of accounts and the possibility of difficulties to be encountered in interpreting data reported on this basis, when used for historical or between-class comparisons. (Census figures, tax records, inter- and intra-industry transactions, geographical inventories of establishments and productive facilities, to mention a few, are maintained by the government on an S.I.C. basis. The United Nations has a similar classification for World Trade Statistics.) How do the disadvantages and advantages you have discussed relate to electronic computers and data-processing systems that use master files based on the S.I.C. codes?

4.5 A village of 5000 inhabitants is considering improving its management. Better long-range planning has been suggested as a major problem, and the mayor, who is also a real estate salesman on the side, has made up a partial list of some of the tasks his administration faces in management and control. He, however, does not have time to go into the detail presented by each of these problems, and seeks advice from you on the improvement of his administration. He has recently been elected and wants to show some progress in long-range planning by the next election, which is two years away. His list includes the following:

1. Assessment of local taxes, tax billing and record-keeping.
2. Handling zoning requests and building permits.
3. Administration of the Water Department, including billing, maintenance, construction, and repair.
4. Municipal payroll accounting, maintenance of pension and reserve funds.
5. Management of street maintenance, repair, and lighting.
6. Supervision of police activities and local court records.
7. Maintenance of capital equipment records on buildings and equipment.
8. Planning, funding, staffing, and operating the grammar and high schools.
9. Maintenance of dossiers on known undesirables and troublemakers in the community.
10. Maintenance and follow-up of files on dog licenses, as required by the state.
11. Maintenance of voter registration lists for local, county, state, and national elections.
12. Maintenance of data pertaining to the Fire Department.
13. Operations of the small but active Recreation Department.
14. Other operations, such as snow removal, tree pruning, garbage and sanitation supervision, and the like.

The mayor further explains that one of his major headaches is the projection of the possible effects of trends in the community. For example, the State proposes to build a new superhighway, which will cut through a portion of the town, and a large builder has recently acquired a tract of land on which he proposes to build 50 homes in the $40,000 class. The mayor wonders how these developments will affect his tax roster, tax evaluation, the schools, needed services, and his possibility for continued election.

A cursory examination of the offices of this small government operation, which employs a total of less than fifty individuals, revealed that files are kept on a number of the stated activities, but that they were often incomplete. Many were also located in separate locations. This village still has not automated most record-keeping functions, although the tax records (by real estate parcel) have been reduced to machine media for billing and accounting purposes.

What form of study would you conduct to assist the mayor with his problems, and what kinds of questions would you ask in setting up your study?

4.6   *Business Week,* May 14, 1966, in "Information Becomes a Hot Item," pp. 164–66, reported that International Business Machines Corp. had just formed an Information Marketing Group. The function of this group is to sell data, and its first service will be the preparation of special industrial market reports. This first service will combine Dun & Bradstreet's file of 390,000 U.S. businesses (95% of all manufacturing) and the U.S. Commerce Department's industrial input-output data, broken down into the full detail of 4-digit S.I.C. codes (see Problem 4-4). The customer gives IBM a list of its customers for specific products, sales or unit volume, and sales territories. The computer searches the D & B databank and the government data and breaks out the client's market potential and actual market share by purchasing industry, plant size, territory and other precise categories. IBM's new service is priced at $3500 to $10,000 per report, a cost estimated to be less than that for accumulating conventional, less detailed data.

A. Comment on the advantages in merging these two large databanks as indicated above.

B. What are the advantages to the client and IBM of accumulating marketing information from client requests?

C. Can you suggest any other large databanks that might be similarly merged.

D. Under what conditions might it be necessary to have a fiduciary institution control the information in a databank, rather than have the information controlled by a communication, computer, or other commercial firm?

*4.7   (Although the following problem refers to a computer programing technique, knowledge of computer programing is not necessary to understand the concept described. The reader unfamiliar with computer programing may consider the memory addresses mentioned in the following problem as numbered pigeon-holes in a post office, or sorting rack.)

Some computer programs may require us to deal with lists of variable length, which may be stored in various portions of the computer memory. If we use a special approach, the exact length of a given list need not be known in advance. Following A. Newell (Ed.), *Information Processing Language Manual,* Prentice-Hall, Englewood Cliffs, N. J., 1961. consider the following arrangement:

A computer memory is divided into a number of four-character (fixed word length) storage locations, each of which is numbered consecutively from 0001 upward, as shown in the diagram below (the italic type represents the storage address). Information stored in this memory is then arranged in *pairs* of numbers, which, let us say, will consume two four-character storage locations. The first four-character position is used for recording the data part of the list; the second four-character position indicates the storage address of the data-item that follows in the desired listing. If, in addition, we adopt the convention that "*0000*" designates the last address on the list, and that we will have a special memory location which will always be used to indicate the location of a "free" data position, we will be able to record lists of varying lengths, and add to and delete from these lists *without loss of memory spaces*. Moreover, one list may contain other lists, and so on, the degree of interconnection between lists being determined by the "next-address" portion of the records stored.

For example, see the tabulation below, which represents a series of data and next-address information stored as specified above. The list starting at address 0001 consists of the numbers 2233, 3111, 4010, and 6222, at which point the list terminates.

Note in the table that the memory locations which are "free" for data storage, namely, *0007*, *0009*, *0011*, *0013*, *0015*, *0017*, *0019*, and *0021* have already been provided with next-address links. (The *0000* next-address of data location *0021* stored in address *0022* indicates that when *0021* has been used, the data locations available have been completely exhausted. This will be so if there are no other open data locations.)

Two-part word

0001	*0002*	*0003*	*0004*	*0005*	*0006*
2233	0023	4010	0005	6222	0000
0007	*0008*	*0009*	*0010*	*0011*	*0012*
	0009		0011		0013
0013	*0014*	*0015*	*0016*	*0017*	*0018*
	0015		0017		0019
0019	*0020*	*0021*	*0022*	*0023*	*0024*
	0021		0000	3111	0003

0007

Next Available
Address
Reference

Suppose we now want to add the number 5333 to list #1 starting in *0001*.

The procedure for this would be as follows:

1. The *0000* next-address of the last data element (which was 6222) is replaced by the "next-available" empty address, stored in the special memory location indicated. To provide a new "next-address," the *0009* next-address, which is associated with next data address (*0007*), is placed in the reserved next available address location.

2. The data 5333 goes into the address location *0007* and the present link for address *0007* (namely the *0009* presently stored in address *0008*) is changed to *0000*, indicating a new listing ending.

3. To delete the data 5333 from the present list, the procedure above would be reversed, thereby making the address location *0007* available again for an alternate list.

A. Suppose, after studying the procedure above, we discovered that memory locations *0007, 0009,* and *0011* were already filled with a second list, list #2, and that the next available free address location was *0013,* as shown by the special memory box for that purpose. We again want to add the data 5333 to the list starting in memory box *0001.* What must we do to accomplish this?

B. Having completed part (A) above, we now want to add the data 7945 to the bottom of list #1, starting in address *0001.* How would this be done?

C. Suppose you wanted to add list #2, as described in part (A), to the *top* of list #1. How would you accomplish this result?

D. Why would this procedure be a useful tool for defining the system operation over a period of time?

For further illustration, see the reference cited. It contains a 31-item bibliography and several detailed applications.

PROJECT 3

A manufacturing firm has a number of files containing information about employees. A study of these files reveals much duplication in the following areas:

1. Payroll file: Contains employee's name, address, social security number, department number, special pay record, number of dependents, major medical deduction, insurance deduction, annuity deduction, state tax deduction, FICA record, pay rate class, earnings to date this year, mail address for check, if different from residence, Blue Cross/Blue Shield deduction.

2. Health Insurance file: Contains employee's name, address, Blue Cross/Blue Shield account number and status, monthly deduction, dependents by name, age, sex, date of insurance contract for each, changes in coverage with date and type. (This file found as a separate office in the Payroll Department.)

3. Life Insurance, Major Medical and Annuity file: Contains employee's name, address, major medical coverage code, account number of policy, dependents covered by major medical with name, age, sex, date of coverage, and changes in coverage. Annuity file, includes employee's name, sex, age, address, contract number, employee's contribution, tax option selected by employee, terms of con-

tract in code. Life Insurance file includes name, address, sex, age, policy number, employee contribution, beneficiary, pay options.

4. Employee Skill file: Contains employee's name, address, sex, birth date, language skills, education, special training record, record of supervisory evaluation, departments in company where assigned since date of employment, date of original employment, military service, security clearance rating and detail, skill classification code, equipment operating ability, memberships and affiliations in unions, fraternal organizations, etc., suggestion record and list of patents, inventions, etc., physical description including height, weight, color of hair, eyes, complexion, special physical problems or afflictions, accident record, absentee record, results of aptitude tests, and miscellaneous comments.

5. Credit Union file: Contains employee's name, address, telephone number, account number, credit rating, loans outstanding, monthly payments, loan record from previous loans and payments.

6. Medical file: Contains employee's name, address, sex, birth date, results of employment physical, blood type, physical infirmities, disease history, records of subsequent yearly examinations, which include blood pressure, weight, height, and other medical facts; records of visits to office for emergency treatment, medication and treatments administered, and similar clinical information.

In addition to these files, employee information enters into a number of other computations and temporary record-keeping facilities. For example, the employees are assigned to given departments, to given work centers, and to different jobs over a period of time, and this information is used by production control and cost accounting functions in order to staff projects, estimate and control costs, and to locate employees within the factory when needed. The telephone operator maintains a cross reference of employees, nearest extension, home number, and residence address. Further, several mailing lists are maintained by the company for mailing the Company House Organ, the communications of the president, and similar materials. Various statistical files are also maintained by the sales department of the firm by salesman's name, area, region, and customer.

It has been proposed that these and similar files be consolidated into a master file, or databank of information, that will answer most of the questions that could arise regarding an employee, or group of employees.

You have been assigned the task of organizing this master file. The memory media to be used must be conserved, because it is costly and because processing and search time will increase as more information is put into the master file. You realize that some compromise in the level of detail stored will be required. Thus, in addition to consolidation of common items (such as name and address), you propose several forms of summarization and levels of summarization that will make the master file as useful as possible, yet not encumber it with excessive detail.

A. Develop three alternate forms of file organization.

B. Suggest a code that might be applied to each employee that would permit fast extraction of employees, or employee groups, for statistical purposes as well as specific question-answering about a given employee.

C. Make an extensive list of the questions that could possibly be asked by the organization about a given employee or group of employees, and evaluate each proposal for file organization and each proposed code with respect to its ability to answer the proposed list of questions.

D. In making such an evaluation, would the importance of the questions that can and cannot be answered by the proposed system make any difference in the evaluation? Would the frequency of the questions asked make a difference in the file organization and code evaluation? Are there some portions of the file that should not be consolidated? What are some of the advantages and disadvantages of consolidation of the suggested files? Would the problem of access to this consolidated master file be important. If so, what provisions could be taken to provide security where required?

E. Over a period of time, the employees listed in the master file may change, the details pertaining to each may change, and the questions that may be asked about an employee or group of employees may change. Have you provided for the updating of the master file in such a way that its over-all organization is not greatly altered? Would the file organization and coding system proposed be suitable for answering questions that are not on your original list of possibilities, but which might arise in the future?

F. Suggest some long-range planning questions that might be answered by use of such a consolidated master file. Suggest some short-range control applications of the master file.

5 | CONTROL SYSTEM HIERARCHIES AND SYSTEM MEMORIES

In the previous chapters we discussed some methods for defining system structure. These methods showed the relationship between operations and developed techniques for predicting system output, given system input. We indicated that such prediction became more difficult *for the observer* as the "memory function" of the system became more extensive, because the system could then take diverse actions in response to input conditions.

This chapter elaborates upon control hierarchies so that a scheme for viewing large-scale systems will be available to us. We now consider some general system properties, which determine the "level" at which a system can predict and control. We will observe the system in this chapter from the *designer's* viewpoint, i.e., in terms of the system's purpose, which is known to us.

FIRST-ORDER PREDICTION AND CONTROL

The simplest system that can exert control is the simple feedback arrangement shown in Figure 2-10. Here, in addition to a given transformation, the system measures its output against a desired input and corrects for the *immediately* observed difference. No memory function is involved.

For example, the operation of a household furnace alone is to transform fuel into heat. When the furnace is turned on, the heat starts and continues until the furnace is turned off. The addition of a thermostat, however, introduces *first-order* feedback. The homeowner sets a desired temperature, and the thermostat, a regulator, turns the heating system on and off at temperatures above and below the desired setting, thus giving an average temperature near the set value. (A more expensive *continuous controller* could be achieved by increasing or decreasing the fuel flow to the furnace in response to temperature.) The first-order feedback system has three parts: A receptor (or sensor) to receive the temperature reading in the house in this case, a detector (or summing point) to measure the difference btween the receptor measurement and an input standard, and an effector (the furnace) to cause the change required. The response of this simple system will vary depending on the characteristics of the receptor, effector, and input standard (e.g., the furnace with a small boiler and piping system will have a quicker response than one with larger components), but a direct relationship can be calculated between these factors. The heating system is a complete slave to its design and input setting.

A control system, even at the first-order level, has the property of protecting the internal system serviced (the house) from external changes in the environment. Thus, the function of the heating system is not merely to turn the heater on and off, but to perform this act so that the householder is unaware of external temperature changes. Generally, this control system function and performance is so. The "perfect" control system would perform the job and eliminate the problems of environmental vagaries. And we would never be aware that the system was working.

Another example may clarify the point. Suppose we had to mill blocks of steel to a given thickness. One way we might accomplish this would be to set the cutter, start cutting, and not make any adjustments for the tool wear or other environmental changes until some later inspection step indicates something has gone wrong. First-order feedback can be introduced by placing a sensor just after the cutting head and measuring the cut just made. Any error so detected is fed back to an effector which alters the cutting head to the correct value. Again, because the purpose of this system is to cut blocks of a given thickness, the introduction of feedback protects the system purpose from changes in the environment.

The reader can easily suggest other illustrations of first-order feedback. In first-order feedback no explicit "memory" blocks appear. The required "memory" to correct error into direct action is built into the system structure. The function of first-order feedback is usually to hold a system at an equilibrium condition,[1] or to provide a rudimentary "following" or "tracking" ability.

The first-order system cannot predict or make a conditional choice of actions.

[1] A regulator, or controller, that produces system equilibrium is often called a "homeostat" and the process of its operation is called "homeostasis." Historically, W. B. Cannon suggested this term in his classic *Wisdom of the Body* (Norton, New York, 1932). The maintenance of body temperature, blood sugar, and blood pressure are a few examples of the many homeostatic systems in the body. Dr. Cannon's presentation greatly influenced the development of cybernetics and the interdisciplinary design of purposeful systems.

SECOND-ORDER FEEDBACK

Now, let us introduce some memory into our system. In the thermostat example, suppose we want to change the temperature setting at different times of day. These settings can be stored by mechanical, electrical, or other means—they can then be selected at the appropriate time by a clock.

Or, suppose we introduce other sensors: an outside thermometer and a wind-speed indicator. By offering it added information, these sensors enable the heating system to improve its operation by *anticipating* future heating requirements—i.e., if the system can "remember" the heat-loss formulas for a house under wind velocities and differential inside-outside temperatures— and by *evaluating* the available data for action.

This *second-order*, commercially available heating control system is obviously more complicated and more expensive than the simple thermostat. It contains not only a receptor (or more) and an effector (or more), but also *memory* storage equipment, computing or more complex transformation equipment, and coordinating ability to determine the necessary course of action, based on the input information. (See Figure 5-1.) If its components are properly balanced, the operation of this second-order system will further reduce the error between system purpose and system results. The essential ingredient of the second-order system is its ability to initiate various actions in response to changes in input conditions and to separate its actions from an immediately slavish "following" to some measure of self-prediction and control. Here the timing of response is a critical factor in determining the success of the system.

Example: To illustrate the use of memory and prediction, consider the marketing department of a firm that has developed sales plans *A, B, C,* and *D* to use under specified changes in the market, anticipated as conditions 1, 2, 3, and 4. The optimal choice of plan for each condition is

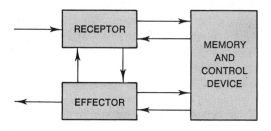

5-1 A higher order control system. This figure illustrates that a memory and control device can be used to give a receptor and effector increased ability. If conditions change, the memory and control device can provide alternate plans or direct the effector to anticipate the action required to maintain control. In advanced systems the memory and control device can also direct the receptor to be aware of alternate problem areas.

shown in Figure 5-2 by an "X" and the "decision rule" for making the best choice can be predetermined and built into the system.

If the firm has the ability to shift its operation from plan to plan *at once*, then, when conditions change, the optimal series of plans (i.e., an optimal *policy*) can be followed *automatically*.

Suppose, however, that some *time* is needed to change from one plan to another. Then, in addition to a variety of reserve plans and corresponding decision units, the marketing department must *anticipate* far enough in advance when conditions will change so that the appropriate plan can be put in effect *before* conditions change. The optimal policy can be followed *only if* the system can predict.

The classic example of the second-order control system is the "fire control" or hunting problem. If a hunter hopes to shoot a duck in the wing, he will not aim at the bird's present position—he will "lead the target." Many factors will determine where and how much to lead—target distance and direction, target velocity, wind, ballistic factors, observations of present target evasions, and often the type of duck (coots fly differently from mallards). In this example the appropriate use of prediction and control is easily tested by success in hitting the target. The hunter will be more successful, in general, as his speed at evaluation and action increases, as his memory of alternate courses of action increases, and as his ability and speed to correct for errors increases.[2]

In each of the examples above, we would say that the second-order systems described showed more "self-control" than the first-order systems of the previous section; i.e., second-order systems are more "autonomous." The second-order system is not a complete slave. It makes some decisions—based upon information and decision rules provided to the system by the designer—by itself. It can handle a greater variety of input conditions.

However, the step to the second-order system also presents additional problems of system design and system "optimization." For example, to achieve a given purpose, how much memory search and evaluation will be used before decision and action? Too much search and evaluation may slow the system response beyond usefulness; too little search and evaluation, however, may cause the system to commit gross errors. How should the economics of system operation be allocated, say between size of memory and speed of computing components, or between the precision of receptor

[2] Wartime design and use of automated fire control systems offered dramatic proof of this principle. In some systems, using combinations of radar and antiaircraft fire against fighter planes, a scheme was introduced to determine a target fighter plane pilot's flight school from an analysis of evasions after each shot. This was important knowledge, because different evasions could be explained by differences in instruction. By storing typical evasions by school and selecting the school appropriate to the target at hand (to predict future target positions) the number of successful shots was drastically improved.

Plan to use

		A	B	C	D
	1	x			
If receptor receives input type	2		x		
	3			x	
	4				x

5-2 The simplest memory of alternate plans. A change in input conditions initiates an alternate mode of operation as shown. With advanced systems, a wide range of plans, or combinations of plans, would be available to meet a wide range of alternate conditions. Compare the rigid plan selection above to the coin-changer example of Chapter 2. The wider range of alternatives available with a greater range of alternatives stored in memory will be discussed more fully in Chapter 6.

and effector components as opposed to the duplication of components required for reliability and maintainability?

Thus, the second-order and higher-order systems, which offer great benefits, also provide the designer and user with major problems not only of analysis, but also of choice, adjustment, and value. And these problems become more severe as the system becomes more complex.

MEMORY CHARACTERISTICS IN SYSTEMS

We must now digress and discuss some of the detailed properties of the memory function in systems. This discussion will then permit us to introduce the notion of yet higher-order systems into our hierarchy of system types.

Symbols and Abstractions

Although occasionally we can store actual physical items for later use (special tools, cash, inventor, personnel), memory usually implies the storage of abstractions, or symbols (a tool number, a bank balance, a stock status, a list of employees).

Sometimes we store symbols because it is convenient, other times we store symbols because another form of storage is impossible. Thus, a road map is an abstraction used for storage because we cannot keep the entire countryside in our pocket. Our abstractions differ depending on our purposes: The map suitable for the private car owner is unsuitable for the tax collector or the census taker.

In particular, as we move to higher-order systems and the components removed from receptors and effectors, we find that the operations we must perform are usually upon *symbols*.

The corporate manager seldom performs operations on a physical product —mostly he concerns himself with abstractions at various levels of detail: balance sheets, cost statements, engineering reports, correspondence, "concepts" of management, abstract values such as "opportunity cost," and social and philosophical considerations, such as community welfare and the development of alternate goals and values.

For this reason, some principles of abstraction are useful when we discuss memory. Here we restrict our attention to a few relations between symbol formation and memory ability.

Principle No. 1: Symbols used in memory can be expressed in many equivalent yet unique forms provided a one-to-one translation is possible from one set of symbols to another.

Example: Customer Jones can be called customer 123, or *ABC*, or (01, 10, 11), etc., and a translation between these formats is possible provided the symbols are uniquely related, e.g.,

$$1 \rightarrow A \rightarrow 01$$
$$2 \rightarrow B \rightarrow 10$$
$$3 \rightarrow C \rightarrow 11$$

Principle No. 2: The most convenient choice of symbols is determined by at least four factors, including (a) the memory media, (b) the operations to be performed on the symbols, (c) the size of the memory facilities, and (d) the required speed of access and retrieval.

Example: The ultimate storage of symbols in an electronic computer is in the form of electronic charges or magnetized components that can have only two states, "on-off," or "0-1." This "binary" characteristic of the storage media requires that the information to be stored be translated *into* (and for retrieval *from*) such binary numbers. Using a "pure binary" code, we could represent 64 distinct numbers from zero to 63 with five binary positions by counting in powers of two. The number 37, for example, could be represented as

$$1 \times 2^5 + 0 \times 2^4 + 0 \times 2^3 + 1 \times 2^2 + 0 \times 2^1 + 1 \times 2^0$$
$$= 32 + 4 + 1 = 37.$$

And, as a result, by observing the positions of the powers of two in the above line, we see that the pure binary equivalent of decimal 37 is 100101. (Similarly, the pure binary equivalent of decimal 63 is 11111, etc.) Pure binary is the most efficient form of encodement for the computer when numbers are used exclusively, as is often true in scientific computation.

However, when business data are processed, we use many alphabetic and special characters. For such applications, an alternative code form is often used. Six binary positions are reserved for *each* numeric and alphabetic character. Four of these six positions, or "bits," provide sixteen possible combinations, or codes, by using the powers of two from 2^3 through 2^0 (the binary equivalent of 8-4-2-1). The remaining two bits (often called B and A bits) identify four blocks, or zones, each with sixteen possibilities provided by a repetition of the four-bit 8-4-2-1 detail, as illustrated in Figure 5-3.

Zone I			Zone II			Zone III			Zone IV			Detail
Mem.	Pr.	BA	Mem.	Pr.	BA	Mem.	Pr.	BA	Mem.	Pr.	BA	(BCD)
&	&	11	−	−	10	¢	≠	01			00	0000
A	A	11	J	J	10	/	/	01	1	1	00	0001
B	B	11	K	K	10	S	S	01	2	2	00	0010
C	C	11	L	L	10	T	T	01	3	3	00	0011
D	D	11	M	M	10	U	U	01	4	4	00	0100
E	E	11	N	N	10	V	V	01	5	5	00	0101
F	F	11	Ø	Ø	10	W	W	01	6	6	00	0110
G	G	11	P	P	10	X	X	01	7	7	00	0111
H	H	11	Q	Q	10	Y	Y	01	8	8	00	1000
I	I	11	R	R	10	Z	Z	01	9	9	00	1001
?	&	11	!	−	10	≠	≠	01	0	0	00	1010
.	.	11	$	$	10	,	,	01	#	#	00	1011
□	□	11	*	*	10	%	%	01	@	@	00	1100
(		11	)		10	=		01	:		00	1101
<		11	;		10	'		01	>		00	1110
≠		11	Δ		10	''		01	√		00	1111

5-3 A six-bit coded decimal conversion chart (IBM 1401). The table shows (to the extreme right) the 8-4-2-1 binary detail associated with each character in a given line. Two additional zone bits, the same for each of 16 characters in a zone block, are indicated in four columns. In combination the zone and detail bits provide 64 characters in computer memory (first column each zone as defined for the IBM 1401), of which only 50 are usually available for printing (printed symbol shown in second column each zone). The special, nonprinted characters are used for internal control purposes. A seventh, check or parity, bit used in most computers is not shown. It is important to understand that the code "11 0001" shown as "*A*" does not necessarily mean "*A*" to the computer, but is assigned that value by people using this particular equipment. The code "11 0001"—as well as the other 63 codes shown—could just as easily stand for any other character in any 64-character set; the desired character is placed on the input keyboard and output printer in a position that provides consistent translation.

By reference to Figure 5-3, the decimal number 3 is given by the binary coded decimal form (*BCD* code) 00 0011, and the decimal number 7 is given by 00 0111. Thus, in *BCD* code, the number 37 is given by the 12-bit combination 00 0011, 00 0111. (The same decimal number, 37, coded in pure binary would have consumed only 5 positions in computer memory, as previously shown.)

Nevertheless, the *BCD* code, as shown in Figure 5-3, allows alphabetic characters, such as the letter "A," to be coded with only 6 positions, namely 11 0001, where the first two positions to the left are the "zone bits" and the four to the right are the 8-4-2-1 binary detail. Similarly, "B" would be 11 0010, and "C" would be 11 0011, and so on. If all the characters in a 64-item character set are used with equal frequency—an ideal approximated by the requirements of commercial data processing—the six-positions-per-character of *BCD* code approaches the efficiency of the pure binary scheme for numeric data. The *BCD* code also permits efficient translation of alphanumeric data from standard punch cards to internal computer storage and back again to printed output using simplified electronic circuits. Ease in handling alphanumeric data makes the *BCD* code format preferred for business data handling. Thus, a change in code format may be desirable to match storage facilities to the most common input/output or common computational requirements.

Although we used a computer example here, the problem of symbol choice and translation is general, and also applies to other media.

Principle No. 3: If part of a symbol can be duplicated or reproduced by reference to another symbol (or set of symbols) stored in memory, that portion of the new symbol is redundant.

Example: The classic example is the structure of language. Typical printed English is about 30% redundant in the sense that the reader can "fill in" the missing letters (or words) of many messages from his knowledge of the language structure. Most people will recognize

CN U RD THS TXT?

as "Can you read this text?" (This fill-in ability is the basis of the "Speedwriting" method of shorthand notation.)

Similarly, if the details of "Plan A" are stored in memory, the instruction "Use Plan A" or simply "A" need not be followed by a repetition of the details, if the user understands that reference to the stored plan is required.

Principle No. 4: The amount of information contained in a symbol can be measured and depends upon the minimum number of "most efficient yes-no" questions that must be asked to determine a missing element in a message.

In this questioning process, the minimum number of questions required will depend upon the content, size, and organization of a system's memory, and the method of symbolization used.

Example: Suppose one contestant is allowed to select (at random) one of the 32 characters in Figure 5-4, and a second contestant is to find the selected character by asking the first contestant the minimum number of questions that can be answered yes or no.

A	B	C	D	E	F	G	H
I	J	K	L	M	N	O	P
Q	R	S	T	U	V	W	X
Y	Z	.	,	:	;	!	#

5-4 A table of characters for choice game.

The least number of questions that can be asked in this game is five[3] (if the first contestant selects his character at random) and the most efficient sequence of questions is "Is the character in the upper 16?" ". . . in the right-hand eight?" ". . . in the left-hand four?" etc.

Because five questions are required to isolate the randomly chosen character from the set of 32, knowledge of the character is worth "five bits" of information, if we use the questioning measure of information content.[4]

Using the questioning measure, the reader may wish to verify that the amount of information for a five-letter group of characters randomly chosen (with repetition allowed) from the above table is 25. However, the amount of information contained in the five-letter English word QUIET is less (for the Englishman), because in English Q is always followed by a U. No guesses would be required to fill in this second character, if we knew the first was Q.

Generally, then, the amount of information received in a message (or stored in one part of a memory) depends upon the amount and kind of information already stored in a system's memory and is measured by the

---

[3] Generally, for the N-character game using random selection, the minimum number of questions is $\log_2 N$. Note that $32 = 2^5$ in this example. The most efficient questioning procedure—that which divides the universe in half at each question—is familiar to the contestant in the game of "twenty questions." With twenty most efficiently asked questions a contestant could isolate one item in a list of $2^{20} = 1,048,576$. The analyst often uses the binary questioning process to reduce system variety, as described in Chapter 11.
[4] This is the measure of mathematical information theory, developed by C. Shannon. (See Appendix D.)

total number of questions that must be asked to duplicate the message. Any knowledge of structure of the message, any reference to previously stored information, or any knowledge of the variety of the incoming information can reduce the minimum number of questions that must be asked.

To take the extreme case, suppose our contestant with the 32 character example is Jones, and by reference to our memory we know that Jones never picks any character except "A"; that is, Jones never plays at random. Then we need ask *no* questions of Jones to isolate his choice. Playing the game with him is totally redundant. It is for this reason that we find it easy to talk to persons who have a well-stocked and well-organized memory. They seem to anticipate what we are about to say. Indeed, from a mathematical viewpoint, any communication with an omniscient person is redundant.

These principles and examples (in addition to the discussion of codes and information structure in the previous chapters) teach us much about the definition and design of higher-order systems.

First, the higher-order systems will have a memory, and it will deal with symbols.

Second, these symbols can be chosen in many formats and translated from one format to another as the need arises.

Third, the higher-order system will use its memory (in combination with input information) to make predictions, and this predictive ability will require *combinations* of input and stored information, and operations upon these combinations.

Fourth, the number of system operations required for prediction, decision, and action, and the speed with which they can be performed, will depend upon the *variety* of nonredundant information that must be processed per unit time (as measured by the questioning process we just described).

Fifth, the higher-order system will have the capacity to handle a *much greater* variety of information per unit time than the variety required for *immediate* control. This ability will be gained not only by the speed of operation, but also by the storage of data and many alternate patterns to be used for swift translation, prediction, and the control of its own internal operations.

In summary, the effective, efficient ability to store, retrieve, manipulate, and act upon symbols is the initial step in building the higher-order system.

We have seen that higher-order systems typically have large, fast, well-organized memories, and that this asset provides increased control ability. We now study the organization of memory and the types of memory media.

Memory Media

The most obvious physical characteristic of a powerful control system is the size and type of memory medium used. Memory size, usually measured by the number of character storage possibilities, influences the number of different types of information handled at one instant of time and sets an upper limit to the variety of choices a system exhibits at a given time.

The type of medium used for storage usually determines the speed with which information can be stored and retrieved. One extreme is the comparison of data stored on a scroll with data stored in a card file. To retrieve information from a scroll, a sequential search pattern must be followed; however, in the card file the desired data can be located directly if the file organization is known. The same comparison can be made between a tape and a record, or between an electronic computer tape and its magnetic core storage. The song on a record or data stored in a core memory can be "addressed directly"; the tapes however, must be searched sequentially, even when the file organization is known.[5]

The speed of memory access and retrieval is often related to memory cost per character, as is memory flexibility, i.e., the ease with which characters can be erased, written, read, or moved from one position to another. Thus, the magnetic core memory used in computers is the fastest and most flexible memory media available commercially at the present time, but it is also the most expensive per character.

For this reason, in a complex system the physical media of storage are commonly arranged in a hierarchy of types, reserving the most flexible, fastest memory for information currently in demand. The mass, infrequently used information is stored on slower, less expensive media, such as magnetic tape. Thus, a modern system, such as the IBM 360 series of equipment, may employ memory functions ranging from magnetic cores operating in millionths of a second (microsecond) or even thousandths of a microsecond (nanosecond) to a reserve library of tapes and cards that must be found by a human and carried manually to the system.

We have used computer examples here, because of current interest in the subject. The reader should also realize that any medium capable of storing characters or "signals" for any period of time can also be used for memory. Symbols may be written on stone, paper, or in the sand; stored temporarily on the face of a television tube; held momentarily as an accoustic echo in a tube of mercury, or as an electronic pulse in a wire "delay line"; held in a magnetic arrangement or in a collection of colored cards; fixed in the position of electrical relays, or the chemical structure of a molecule, or the genetic code of our genes; or stored in the human mind.

The wide range of memory media available and the trade-offs possible between cost, speed, size, permanence, and flexibility provide the designer with a wealth of alternatives in the design of higher-order systems.

---

[5] For a survey of computer memory devices, see: J. A. Rajchman, "Computer Memories: A Survey of the State of the Art," *Proc. Inst. Radio Engineers*, **44**, 104, January, 1961.

Memory Organization

We have seen that complex systems usually employ a variety of memory media that can be ranked into a hierarchy of types. The same is true of memory organization, where the hierarchy is set up according to the level or pervasiveness of the information stored, when used for system control. In general, the higher level systems have the ability to exert longer range, or self-adaptive control than the simpler systems. This fact will become evident when we discuss the types of memory storage.

Types of memory storage

We may divide memory storage into three major parts for discussion.

1 *Data or Analytic Storage,* in which the information used in later operations is held (typically in a highly structured or segmented form, so that any desired part of the data elements can be retrieved at will).

2 *Routine Pattern Storage,* in which the rules for translating and combining data, i.e., the steps of a procedure of computation, are held.

3 *Novelty, Learning, or Goal Changing Storage,* which, in the higher-order systems, provides rules for revising routine pattern storage, for changing the priority of operations, or for causing a change in the memory content or of objectives of the system.

The following computer examples will illustrate the distinctions above.

Example: The distinction between data and patterns of operation must be clear before we proceed, because this distinction is essential to understanding electronic computer operation. If the steps of a procedure or program can be stored in a memory and executed with electronic speed, the total effectiveness of the machine is greatly multiplied. This is the distinction between the calculator, which requires an operator to direct its every step, and the computer, which, having a stored program of operations, is able to perform repetitive operations on its own. Thus, the stored program is the essential ingredient of modern electronic control systems.

The distinction between patterns and data is, in a larger sense, crucial, and will be discussed further in Chapter 8. The pattern of operation or structure of construction must prevail in most organizations and systems and is transmitted from one time, or one place, to another. Employees come and go, but the corporate structure remains. A story is translated from French to English, but the plot is constant. A message is written, converted by intermediate transformations to electrical, mechanical, or other symbols, and then converted back to its original form— the message structure is permanent. Many airplanes and buildings have had every part replaced with new parts, but the total design is not lost.

History and technology and their transmission to succeeding generations is a transmission of patterns as well as facts. Both are necessary. But, the recognition of patterns, the permanence or durability of pattern storage and translation of patterns without loss of structure are the essential ingredients of society, industry, science, and even personal sanity. The pattern, the structured relationship, is the essential ingredient in any system. Without a pattern, facts have no meaning, and no operation, prediction, or learning is possible.

In this example, the schematic memory box of Figure 5-5 shows two parts: on the left a series of numbers in lettered boxes (the data), and on the right a group of instructions, also in lettered boxes (the pattern of operation, or program).

The pattern of operation on the right shows what is to be done to the *contents* of the memory boxes. The operations themselves do not depend on the *contents* of the data boxes, but on the *name* of the boxes. That is, if we changed the numerical values of the data stored in the various data boxes, we would get a different numerical result, but the pattern of operation, or steps in the computation, would be unchanged.

To understand this distinction, we adopt the convention that the instruction "Add *A* to *G*" means "Add the contents of box *A* to the contents of box *G* and store the result in box *G*." We also adopt the convention that the system receives as its first instruction the contents of box *H*, and that it will proceed with the instruction in the subsequent adjacent alphabetic box unless the sequence of operations is modified by an instruction in the sequence. With these conventions, the reader may verify that the first number printed by the system shown will be

$$\{[(4+5) \times 4] + 4\} \times 4 = 160$$

Data		Instructions	
Memory location	Contents	Memory location	Contents
A	4	H	Add A to G
B	3	I	Multiply A by G
C	8	J	Add A to G
D	10	K	Multiply A by G
E	1	L	Print G
F	7	M	Add C to A
G	5	N	Go to H

5-5 The relation between data and instructions (or pattern storage) in a system memory.

If the data were changed in Figure 5-5, the sequence of operations might be extended or repeated several times, but the operations themselves would not be altered. (For example, what would be the first nubber printed if the contents of box *A* were changed to 10? Is the sequence of operations modified by this data change?)

Note that by extending the memory size (the number of memory boxes available in Figure 5-5 for data and/or instructions) the variety of data and patterns of operation can be increased. Moreover, the interconnections that can be employed between patterns increases at a geometric rate.

To show this, consider the above system if we introduce "conditions" and "imperative" instructions, i.e., pairs of "IF" and "GO TO" instructions. With this addition, the system can use its memory to switch plans of operation depending upon input data, or the results of intermediate computations, such as predictions.

Example: Figure 5-6 shows a duplicate of Figure 5-5 with the program steps altered to provide a selection of plans, depending on the data contents of box *A*; e.g., we follow the plan stored in box *L* if the contents of *A* is 1, etc. Again, if we assume the system starts with the instruction in box *H*, the system will print 20, or 13, or 5, if the data stored in box *A* is 1, or 2, or 3, respectively. (What operation will the system perform if the contents of box *A* is *not* 1, or 2, or 3? The reader may verify that the system will print the results of applying the sequence of instructions, *K*, *L*, and *M*, or 23.)

Data			Instructions		
Memory location		Contents	Memory location		Contents
A		?	H		If A is 1, Go to L
B		3	I		If A is 2, Go to M
C		8	J		If A is 3, Go to N
D		10	K		Add B to G
E		1	L		Add F to G
F		7	M		Add C to G
G		5	N		Print G
			O		Set G = 5
			P		Read New Value of A
			Q		Go to H

5-6   Memory organization that will conditionally change the pattern of system operation depending upon input data at Box *A*.

Note the important moral of these examples. *The operation, or transformation, of a system with memory can be changed not only by a change in the data entered or stored in memory, but also by a change in the stored patterns of operation in the "program" portion of the memory, and especially by the interconnections that conditionally alter the selection of operating procedures.*

Thus, with a properly organized memory, the system can not only perform repetitive manipulations of one kind, but can also take diverse actions, depending upon (1) the input information observed, (2) the data already stored, and (3) the pattern of program steps stored.

The second-order systems described in the section on second-order feedback imply a memory organization like that described above. And, with such an organization of information, the system can perform a range of operations limited only by (1) the size and speed of the memory and adjacent processing equipment and (2) the ingenuity of the memory organization designer (the programer of computer "software," to use a data processing term). Note, however, that the system must rely (at this level) upon the designer's rules. It cannot create or change its own rules without further complication of memory organization.

Thus, we come to the third general type of memory storage—the storage section that concerns the modification of existing rules and patterns, the development of new plans, or the acquisition of new data. We consider problems of invention, novelty, value, priority, allocation of resources, adaption, and goal change.

Example: Suppose the objective of the system shown in Figure 5-6 is to obtain an average output as near to 10 as possible for any sequence of inputs 1, 2, 3, ... at box A. Suppose the inputs to A are 1, 2, 3, 1, 2, 3, ... and the steps in the previous example are repeated with each change in input. The result would be an output of 20, 13, 5, 20, 13, 5, ..., yielding an average of $\frac{38}{3}$, or 12.67. This average is larger than our desired output (for the given input sequence). How could the operation pattern for the given system be altered to meet the desired objective?

The answer to this question would require analysis and correction *at a level removed one step from the routine computation.* We (or the system) would have to scan the input data, store some of it, and determine if a pattern were present. We would also have to scan the data now in memory and the present operating rules. Then we would need to develop a pattern for modifying the current operation pattern. *This analysis and correction would be performed while the system performed its routine operation.* When the higher-order considerations reached a decision to alter the present program, this change must be introduced by a swift and stable procedure.

In the present example, suppose, we store the inputs (e.g., 1, 2, 3, 1, 2, 3), search the program and previously stored data, and create the following rule: "If the incoming data pattern is 1, 2, 3,..., change the contents of box *M* to read 'Add *F* to *G*' and also change the contents of box *L* to read 'Add *E* to *G*'." This change would give an output 13, 12, 5, 13, 12, 5, . . . , and result in the desired average of 10.00. (As an exercise the reader may try to devise other modifications of the program to achieve the same result. Note also that other modifications might be desirable if the input sequence changes, say to 1123311233. . . .)

Learning and Memory Reorganization

A system that can modify itself such as the one cited above, is said to *learn*. To some extent the designer can build learning into his system by providing for higher level supervisory procedures or routines.[6] However, it is also possible to construct machines that exhibit self-learning, or self-adaptation. (See Project 4 at the end of this chapter.)

To continue with the same example, suppose the designer has provided a modication routine that makes up rules, such as the one given for maintaining the system output at 10, for different input sequences. At some time our system may confront sequences such as 3, 2, 1, 3, 2, 1 or 112233112233, or 1313121232 . . . (each sequence repeating itself statistically so that in the long run the 1's, 2's, and 3's appear with the same frequency). Then, the system may find that the same modification rule (used in the previous example) works equally well for all sequences in which the frequency of inputs 1, 2, 3 is statistically stable, and therefore conclude that a new method of analysis (statistical frequency) allows a simplification in rule selection. Thus, we (or the system) may eventually learn that the modification rule can be modified to "If the input statistically contains 1's, 2's, and 3's in equal proportions, change box *M* to read 'Add *F* to *G*' and the contents of box *L* to read 'Add *E* to *G*'." The old rule would be replaced by the new one.[7]

This example illustrates memory reorganization in learning. Some of the memory is changed. This may be accomplished in one of three ways: (1) A change in memory allocation or content, e.g., data versus patterns, or old

---

[6] A *supervisory control program* is used in complex computer systems, particularly of the real-time variety, to select appropriate subroutines, allocate memory space and control the movement of stored information between memory media, determine job priority and control the system of input-output processing equipment. For example, for the IBM 7090/94 Computer System, the supervisory control system is called the IBSYS Control System, which allows processing of a wide range of jobs in controlled sequence, the input of various compilers and translators (e.g., FORTRAN and COBOL) and library programs.

[7] By the argument of Principle 3 of this chapter, if one rule will do the job, other duplicating rules are *redundant* and need not clutter the memory.

information for new; (2) a change in the interconnection of patterns; or (3) a change in the values placed on data patterns at a given time.

Learning can take place not only by the acquisition of new information, but also by the reorganization of present information, or by a change in the interconnection and value of operating patterns as experience grows. Moreover, if memory and processing resources are limited, as they usually are, the process of learning introduces problems of resource allocation, priority of change or job performance, and innovating new procedures and, possibly, goal changes.

What new information shall we consider? Where and how shall it be stored? What will it replace? How will the new information change our rules of operation? The priority of changes? The immediate jobs? Do we have sufficient memory, or the right memory content and organization, to perform the job? Do we have any other subjects we should be considering now, but are not? Do we have the right balance between data gathering, evaluation, learning, decision, and action? Is the job we are doing now worthwhile, or should we consider other objectives and goals? An entirely different approach to problem solution?

A SYSTEM HIERARCHY

We will discuss some procedures for answering these questions in later sections, but the present observations are sufficient to suggest a hierarchy of systems, arranged by the "order" of feedback and organized memory employed.

The Simple Machine or Transformation

The so-called open-end system or simple operation is of "zero" order, because it has no memory and no feedback.

The Simple Machine with Feedback

This is the first-order system because direct feedback is present for control. No selective memory is present.

The System with Conditional Selection of Plans and Predictive Feedback

Here error correction is based on extensive memory facilities, careful memory organization, and the ability to evaluate and act on a wide range of different input conditions, often by predicting the requirements for immediate actions based on future needs. We may distinguish a range of sub-classifications for this type of system, by the sophistication of the prediction, plan selection, and plan variety. This so-called tactical system, uses second-order feedback.

The System that Learns

At this level, the system not only performs the functions above, but it can also develop new plans, new decision rules, or new predictions, or change the value of plans and methods to handle new conditions. The learning system may be thought of as a higher-order system, because it must learn while performing its lower-order functions. The corrective selection and development of plans may be thought of as a third-order feedback process. The system must perform a number of functions at once: The immediate control of receptor and effector functions, the tactical selection of plans, and the development and evaluation of new groups of plans, or strategies. This mode requires a larger memory, a richer interconnection of patterns of operation, and a more complex memory organization. Feedback can take place for the immediate control of receptor and effector, the selection of present stored plans, and in the development of new plans by reference to the system goal; hence, the term third order. This is the "strategic" system.

The Goal-Changing System

If a system can learn and, as a result of what it has learned, "consciously" develop, select, and implement new and improved goals, it has clearly reached a higher level of autonomy. We call this "fourth-order" feedback, which corrects methods of learning, develops new problems to solve, innovates, and controls goal-changing itself. Such a system must also have extensive memory facilities and be able to monitor and evaluate each of the "lower level" processes and control their change. The system must also have an increased "awareness" of data and patterns, both internal and external to the present needs of the system. The result will be increased richness of memory and memory interconnections. We may again distinguish a range of autonomy within this category: The system that can develop, select, and implement its *own* goals (and integrate the corresponding strategies, tactics, and lower operations) would be considered more autonomous than the system that could only select and implement a range of goals given to it by the designer.

To illustrate the order of system hierarchy described here, it is useful to think of a comparison, such as that shown in Figure 5-7.

The typical industrial or military organization is a composite of systems at different levels, usually arranged in a hierarchy of autonomy as suggested by our classification. (As an exercise, the reader may try to make a similar classification of computer system functions in a ranking of autonomy similar to Figure 5-7.)

System order	Functionaries responsible	
	Industrial organization	Military organization
0	Production workers and salesmen	Troops
1	Foremen and supervisors	Sergeants
2	Executive Vice President	Company Commander
3	President and Staff	General and Staff
4	Board of Directors	General Staff

5-7 A comparison of the functionaries responsible for administration of systems of various levels of autonomy.

THE USE OF SYSTEM CLASSIFICATION

A knowledge of a system's "level" of operation, in the sense just defined, is useful to the analyst and designer in several ways.

For the analyst, knowledge of the system level aids in the selection of diagnostic tools and procedures, indicates the need for possible simplification measures, and suggests questions that should be asked in determining system performance, or the location of system faults. The analyst must be aware of the variety and structure of the system he confronts, and the early classification of system level alerts him to such facts.

We know, for example, that a zero- or first-order system (a simple machine) can be approached on a mechanistic input-output basis of analyses for many purposes, but that we must know about internal memory structure before we make predictions concerning higher-order systems. We know that the more autonomous the system and the higher its level, the more we should ask about goal and value information, how memory is changed with time, and what memory now contains due to past experiences and learning, if we want to make reasonable guesses about the system's future actions in response to input.[8]

---

[8] An interesting example is the prediction of Supreme Court Decisions by an analysis of personal histories from childhood of each of the Justices. Such an approach was used by the Research Corporation of America under Leo Cherne's direction to produce a correct prediction (contrary to popular belief) on the decision establishing the constitutionality of the Taft-Hartley Law.

The designer, on the other hand, may wish to improve the operation of his system by raising it to a higher level. Again, knowing even in rough form what must be accomplished or included in the system to achieve this end is highly useful in planning design strategy, the change of designs, or in setting design goals.

We know, for example, that giving the system some memory, even though small, will greatly enhance its ability to produce a variety of outputs and usually improve its control ability.[9] We also know that improvement of the higher-order system is often most effectively attained by improving its higher-order learning, memory, and goal formulation processes, rather than by dealing with improvements at lower-order levels.

We conclude that an awareness of differences between system levels—and the steps necessary to make the transition from one level to another—can aid the analyst or designer to lift his own performance to higher levels.

PROBLEMS

5.1   In collecting a number of case histories of automation in industry, J. R. Bright (in *Automation and Management,* Division of Research, Graduate School of Business Administration, Harvard University, Boston, 1958) suggested 17 categories of the automation type listed below. These categories, which indicate increasing system autonomy, were used to classify the data collected. Comment on these categories in relation to the material in this chapter.

1. Hand
2. Hand tool
3. Powered hand tool
4. Power tool, hand control
5. Power tool, fixed cycle (single function)
6. Power tool program control (sequence of fixed functions)
7. Power tool system, remote control
8. Actuated by introduction of work piece or material
9. Measures characteristics of work
10. Signals preselected values of measurement (error detection)
11. Records performance
12. Changes speed, position, direction according to measurement signal
13. Segregates or rejects according to measurement
14. Identifies and selects appropriate set of actions
15. Corrects performance after operating
16. Corrects performance while operating
17. Anticipates action required, and adjusts to provide it.

[9] The Harvard Mark I computer of 1938–42 could store only 23 decimal digits, but this small memory, in combination with its electromechanical speed of processing, revolutionized computer system design.

PROJECT 4

[(The following experiment is adapted from an article by H. D. Block, "Learning in Some Simple Non-Biological Systems," *American Scientist*, 53, No. 1, March, 1965, pp. 59–79, where additional experiments of the same type can be found.)

Because this experiment can be completed with easily available equipment —four paper cups and slips of paper or a blackboard—the reader should try it on his own to convince himself of the "learning like" behavior of the system.]

Consider two Players, *A* and *B*. Before them is a board, as shown below.

A	B	C	D	A	B	C	D	A	B	C	D	
⬤	⬤	⬤	⬤	⬤	⬤	⬤	⬤					MARKERS
1	2	3	4	5	6	7	8	9	10	11	12	

The additional equipment needed consists of a pair of dice. Player *A* rolls the dice and generates an outcome from 2 through 12. The number on this roll indicates the number of chips or markers that will be placed on the playing board. For example, in the picture above, Player *A* has rolled an "8" and placed 8 chips on the board, starting from left to right as shown. Player *B* moves next. He may remove 1, 2, or 3 markers (removing them from right to left) from the board. Player *B* must remove at least one chip or marker, but he cannot remove more than three. .

Player *A* moves again, now taking 1, 2, or 3 markers away. This process continues with Player *A* and Player *B* alternately removing markers from the board. *The player who takes the last marker from the board loses the game.* The game thus has the name, "Last One Loses."

If this game is repeated a number of times, we can plot the results in a cumulative curve. The plot moves up one unit if Player *B* wins, and down one unit if Player *A* wins.

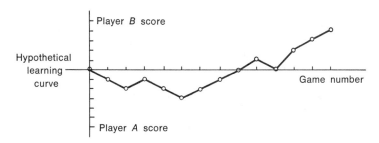

Project 4-A

Such a curve of results is in the form of a "learning curve" for Player *B*. Although Player *A* can be a thinking human being, we can create a machine to think for Player *B* which over a period of time will produce a earning curve for Player *B*, who operates mechanically without thinking.

To create a nonbiological Player B who will "learn" the winning strategy for this game, place four cups, identified as A, B, C, and D, on the table and place in each cup at the start of the series of games three slips of paper, numbered 1, 2, and 3. (Alternatively, a diagram as shown below may be drawn.)

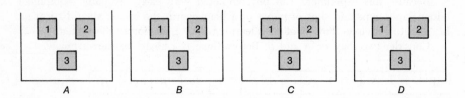

A   B   C   D

Project 4-B

Player B now observes the following rules:

1. On the first move of a given game, Player B, after looking at the number of chips or markers on the board (see picture of board), refers to the cup indicated for that number of chips, e.g., cup D for 8 chips, etc.

2. Player B withdraws a numbered slip from the indicated cup and removes the indicated number of markers from the board (1, 2, or 3 as given by the number on the withdrawn slip). He then returns the numbered slip to the cup from which it came—except under the special circumstances given in rule 5.

3. Player A makes his move, leaving a smaller number of markers on the board.

4. Player B again refers to a cup indicated by a letter above the remaining number of chips on the board, withdraws a slip, and makes the indicated removals, as in rule 2.

5. When the game terminates, and either Player A or Player B wins, a special action is required of Player B.

(a) If Player B loses the game, he discards the last numbered slip used to indicate the number of removals that lost, and does not put that slip back in the cup from which it came. That slip is destroyed and permanently disappears from the scene. This action reduces the number of slips in the cups, and also removes from a particular cup one of the numbered slips. (To avoid confusion, the player operating as Player B may wish to hold his last numbered slip before the cup from which it came until this decision has to be made. As another alternative, the slips in the cups may be numbered $A1$, $A2$, $A3$, etc., so that the cup from which a given slip was drawn will not be forgotten.)

(b) If Player B wins, the "winning" slip is preserved and returned to its own cup.

The results of these actions may be explained by reference to the terminal condition in the cups after a number of games have been played. The cups will contain slips as shown on p.133.

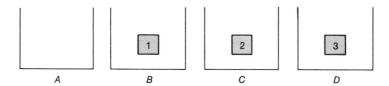

A   B   C   D

Project 4-C

Once the distribution of slips shown has been reached, it will not change. In this final configuration, Player A will win if the dice show 5 or 9, and Player B will win otherwise. The machine, i.e., the system consisting of the four cups and the slips in them, has "learned" the optimum strategy of play, which is that Player B should always leave on the board (if he can) a number of chips which when divided by four would have a remainder of one. Although this winning strategy is not always evident to the human player, the machine has "learned" this rule by a reinforcement of successful moves and a discard of unsuccessful ones.

The following questions will expand upon this experiment, and illustrate how it might be modified.

A. In the final state shown in the last diagram of the cups Player A will win (if he plays correctly) on two of the possible dice outcomes, namely, 5 and 9, and Player B will win on all the nine other possibilities. Each of these different dice outcomes has a different probability, e.g., the outcome 7 has a probability of $\frac{6}{36}$, or $\frac{1}{6}$, etc. Show that in the terminal state of the cups, Player A will win $\frac{2}{9}$ of the time and Player B will win $\frac{7}{9}$ of the time if they both use the optimum strategy. From this result show that the terminal slope of the "learning curve" for this game is $\frac{5}{9}$ and compare this figure with the experimental results for the games conducted.

B. Generalize the results of this experiment for any number of chips on the board, and show that Player B will win if the optimum strategy is used when Player A moves first and there are $4n + 1$ markers on the board to start, or when Player B moves first and there are $4n + 2$, $4n + 3$, $4n + 4$ markers to start (where n is any positive integer or zero).

C. What happens to the terminal state in the cups and the "learning" process if a mistake is made by the individual who is to follow the rules for the learning machine, e.g., say, a slip is returned to the wrong cup? How could the reinforcement rule be modified to make the "machine" less sensitive to mistakes? What will this type of modification do to the slope of the learning curve? What will it do to the rate at which the machine reaches its "steady state?"

D. In what other applications could the machine-type learning illustrated in this experiment be used? In what ways does this experiment simulate human learning and organizational learning?

E. In what way does the arrangement of the paper slips in the cups of the described experiment correspond to the arrangement and organization of information in a computer? In an industrial organization? As an extension of this exercise, flow chart and program this experiment for a computer.

[The article cited as reference for this experiment contains an extensive bibliography on machine learning. Read the original article and a selection of these references, such as W. G. Walter, "A Machine that Learns," *Scientific American*, **185**, 2, August, 1951, pp. 60–63 and H. A. Simon, "How Computers Can Learn from Experience," in W. F. Freiberger and W. Prager (eds.), *Applications of Digital Computers*, Ginn, Boston, 1963. A classic article by A. M. Turing, "Computing Machines and Intelligence," is available in two sources, originally in *Mind*, 1950, and reprinted as "Can a Machine Think?" in J. R. Newman, *The World of Mathematics*, Simon and Schuster, New York, 1956, Vol. 4, pp. 2099–2123.]

PROJECT 5

Study a machine which simulates behavior. W. G. Walter, in his classic *The Living Brain*, Norton, New York, 1953, has provided a popular study of brain waves and related subjects. However, this book also contains many interesting sidelights and diversions which will be of interest to the reader of this chapter, in particular a discussion, in Chapters 5 and 6, of learning and machines that exhibit animal-like behavior ("exploration, curiosity, free-will in the sense of unpredictability, goal-seeking, self-regulation, avoidance of dilemmas, foresight, memory, learning, forgetting, association of ideas, form recognition, and the elements of social accommodation"). The subject used for description is a small mechanical animal consisting of two receptors (a photo-cell and a switch), two effectors (two motors), and two "brain cells" (vacuum tubes), which Walter has named *Machina speculatrix* to indicate its searching ability. The construction details of this machine can be found in Walter's Appendix A, and a description of its behavior, with photograph, can be found in Chapter 5.

Obtain a copy of this book, and read the cited chapters and appendix. Do you think this machine shows life-like qualities? Why is this machine different from the programed electronic computer? In what way does it show the kind of behavior specified by Walter as human behavior? Why is the search and scan ability of this machine so important to its operation and simulation of animal behavior?

6 | VARIETY AND CONTROL: THE LAW OF REQUISITE VARIETY

We have discussed the building blocks and procedures of systems definition, and also the range of resulting system types, arranged in a hierarchy of ever-increasing autonomy. We have seen that the more autonomous system can take a greater variety of actions in response to input than a lower level system. Moreover, we have discussed the system from two viewpoints: The "outside" view of the analyst, who hopes to predict, analyze and, in short, control the operation of the system; and the "inside" view of the designer, who hopes to make the system more versatile.

Intuitively, at least, we should now realize that as a system becomes more autonomous, the analyst's outside job becomes more difficult: As the system grows in size, complexity, and variety, the analyst has more difficulty understanding and controlling it. In a sense, the analyst is in *competition* with the systems designer. The analyst hopes to control the observed system; the designer hopes to create a system that cannot be controlled against its will, but that can control other systems. The analyst faces this problem when confronting a system in nature, which may not be in direct competition with him. The more complex the phenomena, the more skilled and resourceful the analyst must be.

A formalized rule (illustrated in Figure 6-1) having many strategic implications for the analyst is embodied in *Ashby's Law of Requisite*

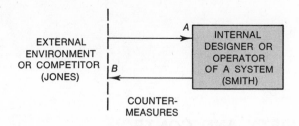

6-1   Requisite variety in a competition. If the analyst hopes to control his system in the face of competition or a changing environment, he must be able to take as many distinct actions, or countermeasures, as those available to the enemy. If the competitor can take *A* distinct actions, and the analyst-controller can take *B* distinct counteractions, the ratio *A/B* must be less than or equal to 1 for the analyst to have assured control. In the examples to follow, we shall call the competitive system "Jones" and the analyst-controller "Smith," as shown above.

Variety,[1] so named after its author. Essentially, Ashby's law states that, for an analyst to gain control over a system, he must be able to take *at least* as many distinct actions, i.e., as great a variety of countermeasures, as the observed system can exhibit. In this chapter we will examine some implications of Ashby's law.

WHAT IS VARIETY FOR THE ANALYST?

From previous chapters we recall that the definition of a system is an arbitrary selection of variables and relationships, according to the analyst's purpose. In short, the term *system* does not refer to "that thing over there," which may be described by an infinite number of systems, but to a particular list or collection of variables and relationships selected by the analyst for a particular purpose.

How can the analyst increase the list, which defines his system? How does he find the *number* that measures variety?

The length of the list, which defines the complexity of the system, depends upon the number or variety of distinctions the analyst (or controller) must make satisfactorily in order to act or to exert control. If the analyst must consider ten independent variables rather than two he will certainly find the former job more complex than the latter. The analyst must therefore count the number of distinctions that are important to him.

[1] W. R. Ashby, *Introduction to Cybernetics*, Wiley, New York, 1963. The reader will note that this chapter is directly related to the material just covered in Chapter 5 and to the material in Appendix D. Ashby's law is another way of expressing the practical consequences of the information theory of C. Shannon.

It is now necessary to clarify several definitions. Let the system have r distinct possible actions ($A = 1, 2, 3, \ldots, r$) that are important to the analyst, and let the analyst have c distinct possible actions that may be taken in response ($B = 1, 2, 3, \ldots, c$). These systems and analyst actions may be listed in tabular form, as in Figure 6-2. Note that this procedure completely defines the variety of the analyst and the variety of the system, and shows clearly the relative variety. The *rows* in Figure 6-2 are the system variety; the *columns* are the analyst's variety.

Now suppose the observed system takes an action (selects a row), and the analyst takes an action (selects a column). Then let the outcome of this composite choice be shown at the intersection of the selected row and column in the table. This outcome may be thought of as a payoff in a gambling game.

Example: Jones has a headache, a system action. Physician Smith is treating Jones. After observing Jones, Dr. Smith administers aspirin, a distinct action available to him. Let us say the outcome of this treatment is that Jones is relieved. Other system actions, treatments, and outcomes were also possible. Suppose Dr. Smith administered arsenic for the headache. The outcome of treatment would be quite different.

As in the example, we may describe for each combination of system action and analyst reaction an outcome, which may be named, or measured, and placed in the outcome table.

POSSIBLE CONTROLLER ACTIONS
(SMITH)

	1	2	3	•	•	•	c
1							
2							
3							
•							
•							
•							
r							

POSSIBLE COMPETITOR ACTIONS (JONES)

6-2 The format of the outcome table.

COMPLEXITY

We must now observe that the "complexity" of a system is not measured by physical size, but by the distinctions the analyst must take, or chooses to make. In other words, our measure of variety measures complexity.

> *Example:* An industrial organization of 100 workers, such as cottage weavers, who work independently on identical jobs, does not present significant control problems. If one weaver falls ill, the organization does not materially suffer. Indeed, the organization can easily be expanded or reduced in size. One directive will regulate all the workers. For the analyst, the total operation can be *reduced* to the operation of one weaver, multiplied 100 times.
>
> However, when ten machines operate with division of labor and a sequential flow of work with, let us suppose, ten different products that require varying sequences of demands and technological requirements, the number of possible sequences is $(10!)^{10}$, clearly beyond *complete* control of management.

Complexity, then, refers to the variety the analyst must encounter to obtain "adequate" control. Thus, to use Ashby's example, a cattle breeder may not be able to obtain ultimate control over the exact combinations of genes (which determine heredity properties) in his stock. For the breeder's purposes, however, this may not be necessary. The breeder need make only those distinctions required for his success. He need only control pairings that will increase weight, marbling, fertility, etc. He may be unconcerned with the length of the steer's tail.

REQUISITE VARIETY

The analyst, or controller, then, defines his system according to the number of distinct actions that are important to him. If the analyst's resources are limited (as they usually are), he will attempt to limit the variety of distinctions to the minimum *number*, necessary for success in the particular problem.

If such a "minimum list" procedure is followed in defining the system, what is meant by *requisite* variety? To answer this question, we will now consider a series of gambling examples in which Jones represents the system and Smith the analyst-controller.

> *Example:* To generalize, suppose Jones and Smith play the following matching game. Jones (the system) moves first and places on the table an object visible to Smith (analyst-controller). Assume Smith then places an object of his choice on the table. Jones pays Smith $1 if the

objects match, but Smith pays Jones $1 if the objects, *for any reason,* do not match. Now, as a first example, give Smith and Jones each one coin, and let either coin show heads or tails as they may. Then Smith will *always win,* because he can always match Jones. Smith has the *requisite variety* of actions, i.e., the required *two* moves, which can counter the two possibilities offered by Jones. Only one outcome is possible in this game (assuming Smith's vision is good and he plays correctly!). That outcome is "Smith wins," the outcome "a" in Figure 6-3.

Requisite variety, then, is the minimum number of distinctions or actions the analyst or controller must have to make the outcome of such a contest certain. If requisite variety is measured in this way, Jones can win *only* by increasing the variety of his actions compared to Smith.

Example: To illustrate, let Jones have not only one coin to show, but also one six-sided die. Jones may now show H or T, or one of the die sides, 1, 2, 3, . . . , 6. He has eight possible actions. If Smith still must match Jones to win, and if Smith only has one coin (but not a die to show), it is easy to see that *Jones* now controls the game, even though he goes first. Even if Jones plays at random, he will win $\frac{6}{8}$ of the time, i.e., when he shows a die. If Jones "learns" of Smith's predicament, Jones can always win (by always showing his die). Thus, Smith has lost control of the game. He cannot guarantee the outcome. The previous example's outcome is reversed, because the available variety ratio now favors the system (Jones). See Figure 6-4.

We should clarify another point before proceeding. Note that the reverse situation, i.e., giving Smith a greater variety of possible actions than Jones, is not *sufficient* to guarantee that Smith can always win. (See Figure 6-5.) Smith must not only have at least as many possible actions as Jones, but he must also have precisely the correct ones in his list of possibilities. Thus, the required number of alternatives is a *necessary* condition to exert com-

SMITH

		H	T
	H	Win = a	Loss = b
JONES			
	T	Loss = b	Win = a

6-3 An example of the outcome table for a coin game.

SMITH

		H	T
	H	a	b
	T	b	a
	1	b	b
	2	b	b
JONES	3	b	b
	4	b	b
	5	b	b
	6	b	b

6-4 A disadvantageous matching game for Smith.

plete control. The inclusion (within that number) of the precisely correct alternatives will then provide the *sufficient* conditions for Smith to win always.

The result of this discussion may now be extended to the case of many outcomes.

Example: Let us suppose that a different outcome can occur for each combination of play that Jones and Smith make in an extended matching game, defined as follows. Jones will select a number between 1 and 9 and then Smith, knowing Jones' selection, can select a letter A, B, or C. The resulting outcome, or payoff, is indicated by the lower-case letter in Figure 6-6. Note that no outcome is repeated in the same *column,* so that to obtain a given outcome as Jones moves, Smith *must* move.

Now suppose that, regardless of the particular outcome, Smith changes his objective and now wishes to minimize the variety of possible outcomes. Because Smith is completely familiar with the payoff probabilities, he can determine, in advance, his response for each move Jones makes, e.g.,

If Jones,	1	2	3 . . . 9
Then Smith,	A	B	C . . . A
Gives outcome	a	a	a . . . r

It is now possible to state that *the minimum number of possible outcomes* cannot be less than

SMITH

	H	T	A	K	Q	J	10	9
H	(a)	b	b	b	b	b	b	b
T	b	(a)	b	b	b	b	b	b
1	b	b	b	b	b	b	b	b
2	b	b	b	b	b	b	b	b
3	b	b	b	b	b	b	b	b
4	b	b	b	b	b	b	b	b
5	b	b	b	b	b	b	b	b
6	b	b	b	b	b	b	b	b

JONES

6-5 Another disadvantageous matching game for Smith. As in Figure 6-4, Jones has a coin and a die, so that he may display eight distinct outcomes. Jones also has eight distinct outcomes, provided by his coin, and, say, the Ace, King, Queen, Jack, 10, and 9 from a deck of playing cards. If the game requires exact matching of objects and attributes, it is apparent that Smith can win (match exactly) in only two cases out of the 64 possible pairs. Although Smith has the requisite variety to match Jones, Smith does not have the correct distinctions required for matching. The important point, however, is that if Smith had less than eight possible distinctions, he could *surely* be defeated by Jones. With the requisite number of distinctions, Smith has a chance—if he has the correct distinctions in his set of possibilities.

$$\frac{(\text{The number of choices Jones can make})}{(\text{The number of choices Smith can make})}$$

where the contestant making the second selection appears in the denominator; i.e., the minimum variety of *outcomes* in the contest is equal to the ratio of the variety available to the two contestants,[2] in this example $\frac{9}{3} = 3$.

We could easily prove this result in Figure 6-6 by selecting a column for each row that will duplicate successive outcomes, thereby minimizing the variety of outcomes. Suppose outcome a is chosen in the first trial. We would then select column 1 for row 1, column 2 for row 2, and column 3 for row 3 (for the outcome table given). But at row 4 we *must* introduce a new outcome, because, by our assumption, no outcome can appear more than once in a given column. The minimum number

[2] The ratio must be ≤ 1 for Smith to gain complete control.

SMITH

	A	B	C
1	a	b	c
2	c	a	b
3	k	c	a
4	m	r	p
5	l	q	r
6	q	l	z
7	n	d	y
8	r	n	x
9	d	p	e

JONES

6-6 A generalized matching game with many distinct outcomes. This game is the same as before: If Jones selects a row and Smith a column, the outcome indicated by the letter at that row-column intersection will occur. However, now there are various kinds of outcomes, not just "win" or "lose." This table is used in the discussion of the text to derive the Law of Requisite Variety.

of outcomes follows from a continued application of this procedure. So, for a table with r rows and c columns, and with no two outcomes in the same column equal, the variety of the selected set of outcomes cannot be less than r/c.[3]

By reference to the outcome table of the above example, Figure 6-6, we are now prepared to state Ashby's Law of Requisite Variety formally:

The variety of outcomes, if minimal (in the sense of the previous example), can be decreased further only by a corresponding increase in the number of columns of the outcome table.

Example: In the outcome table, Figure 6-6, Jones has nine choices and Smith has only three. Suppose the outcomes shown relate to various forms of Smith's health after an encounter with a Jones action. Suppose

---

[3] If two or more identical outcomes are allowed per column, then the variety of outcomes can be less than the number of rows, even though no column selection is made in response to a row choice. In this case, the minimum number of outcomes can be less than the ratio given above. (Consider the table in which all outcomes are a, regardless of the row and column selection.) Moreover, if the outcomes in the table are all different, the minimum number of outcomes will be greater than the given ratio, i.e., as many as $r \times c$, depending upon the table entries. See Problems 6-2 and 6-3.

also that only if outcome *a* occurs can Smith survive; e.g., all other outcomes represent death. Can Smith guarantee his survival? He cannot. Why is this so? [4]

For a variety of input conditions (Jones), only an increased variety of alternatives for the controller (Smith) can modify the variety of output (outcomes).

Only if the variety of the regulator is at least numerically equal to, or greater than, the variety of the system to be controlled, can control be a certainty.

Example: Reverting to the matching game (die-coin versus die) of Jones and Smith, we can cause Smith to win at each trial *only* by giving him the additional alternative of showing a die as well as a coin. Remember again that an increase in Smith's variety would not *necessarily* allow him to win all the time. If we let Smith play with a roulette wheel (or some other object) instead of with the required die, it would not help. The point is that, to reduce the outcomes to win alone, we must *at least* increase the number of Smith's alternatives, otherwise no improvement is possible. It is essential that Smith be given a numerically increased set of alternatives.

This is the first meaning of Ashby's law, which gives a *necessary* condition for control. The sufficient condition, which may be confirmed by consideration of Figure 6-6, is that Smith's set of alternatives contains at lease one "successful" outcome for each Jones action, or row. Thus, if *a* is the only successful outcome allowed, then the Smith alternatives must provide at least one *a* in each row of Figure 6-6. (If only one *a* is allowed per column, then at least as many columns as rows will be required, as we saw.) Thus, the minimal set of Smith alternatives to be successful must also show a winning outcome for each Jones move. This is the second, *sufficient* condition implied by Ashby's law.

REQUISITE VARIETY AND ITS CONSEQUENCES

Ashby's law tells us that control cannot be certain unless the controller has at least as many alternatives as his defined system can exhibit. This gives us a *numerical lower bound* on the requisite variety of actions the controller must have to be effective, a *measure* of the minimum requirement.

The controller must often have many more alternatives, in order that he have in reserve the appropriate set to use in a given problem area, but the controller can never have less than the *requisite number*.

[4] Because, in general, *c* must be at least $\geq r$ for Smith to gain complete control.

The derivation of Ashby's law is a property of the outcome table, and not of any particular real-life situation; it is not subject to the properties of any particular machine or system. Rather we should say that any machine or system defined by the analyst and reduced to an outcome table must inexorably obey the demands of the tabular geometry. To make the tabular presentation meaningful (see Problem 6-2) the analyst must be able to list all of the system actions that are important to him, but this is precisely what we mean by *defining* the system.

Although relatively simple in concept, Ashby's law is an elegant and powerful tool for the system analyst and designer for the following reasons:

1. It establishes an upper limit to the amount of control that can be exerted in a given case, or conversely a minimum requirement that the controller must meet.

2. It tells us there are only two major ways to adjust the ability of the analyst (or controller) to the requirements of the thing to be controlled: (1) Increase the variety of the controller, or (2) reduce the variety of the system to be controlled.

> *Example:* The biological organism is able to counter changes in the environment, such as moderate changes in humidity, temperature, and oxygen content of the air but it cannot handle all possibilities. To survive, the organism must restrict the range of its environment. Thus, we do not take baths in liquid nitrogen, reside in furnaces, or confer at the tail end of a jet engine. We eliminate impossible *rows* from the outcome table by avoiding them and thereby restricting the conditions that must be faced by the organism's control function. Or, alternatively, we add more columns to provide new actions that offer more choice in the outcome table. If we must confer at a missile launch, we do so in the block house.

3. In particular, Ashby's Law permits us to approach complex large-scale systems with a proper sense of proportion, and realistically to adjust our strategies of definition, analysis, and improvement to the particular circumstances.

4. Ashby's law also directs our attention, as students of systems, to the study of two types of techniques and methods: those that increase the possible variety of actions available to us in a given situation, and those that we use to simplify, restrict, partition, or otherwise cut system variety as the need arises.

> *Example:* The physician is not expected to cure simultaneously all of his patient's ills of every kind, social, economic, psychological, or even medical. He restricts his attention to the few critical symptoms and ills that he can control. The physician is subject to Ashby's law.

Example: The traffic director of a large city does not attempt to regulate the precise movement of each vehicle. He works to control the general traffic flow by introducing restrictions (one-way streets, limited access roads) and by increasing the variety of his control actions (the computer control of traffic lights, based on a variety of area traffic flows). He cannot do otherwise.

THE RATE OF VARIETY

We will now consider how *the rate at which variety can be handled* affects the systems analyst. We will use an informal approach in this section but we will present the subject more formally in the next section.

Example: We turn again to the die-coin versus coin game of Jones and Smith. Let us suppose that Jones can display one of his eight choices (*H, T,* 1, 2, 3, . . . , 6) *once each minute.* Then, the number of different choices Jones could make per minute, his rate of choice, is eight, and this combination of the number of distinctions possible per play and the rate of play gives us one measure of the *rate of variety* Jones can produce.

As we have seen in Figure 6-3, Smith can select, say, only H or T; suppose he also can make one play per minute, with, of course, two distinct choices. Smith's rate of variety as measured above would be two per minute. If Jones, as the first player, can only make two choices per minute, then Smith will always win, as before. He has the *requisite rate of variety* to do so.

If we compare this situation to the "one shot" example of Figure 6-3, we have the feeling that the Law of Requisite Variety should hold, if we simply replace the word "variety" with the term "rate of variety." Our intuition here is correct.

Example: To continue with Jones and Smith, let us now give *both* Jones and Smith a coin *and* a die (so that in the "one-shot" game Smith will always win if Jones goes first). Now change the rules of the game slightly as follows: Jones goes first, and a record is made of the *sequence of his choices,* e.g., *HH63T12T* . . . , for 60 minutes, so there will be a string of 60 characters available at the end of the hour (due to Jones). Because he plays after Jones in full knowledge of what Jones has done, Smith may play as Jones chooses or at any time thereafter, provided the record of choice is preserved. Now, Smith, either at the time of play or later, is allowed to see Jones' choice record, and is required to match the sequence of choices to win. Smith will be paid $1 for each character (Jones' choice) matched as before, but Smith must pay Jones $1 for each character *not* matched *for any reason,* as before.

If Smith can also make one choice per minute, *and is also allowed to play one hour,* it should be clear that Smith will be $60 richer when he quits. It is the same as if Jones and Smith played 60 one-shot games in succession.

Example: It should also be equally clear that if Smith can make only one choice every two minutes (30 per hour), Smith cannot duplicate the total exact sequence of choice Jones has made, but only half of them (and thus would win nothing). Similarly, if Smith can make only one choice per hour, Smith can duplicate in one hour only the Jones' first choice, and, by the rules will *pay out* $59.

The analogy between the controller (Smith) and the system (Jones) is exact. The controller must exhibit at least as great a *rate of variety* as the system to be controlled, for the outcome of control to be certain.

An extension of this idea, which may not be obvious, comes into play when the controller and the system are allowed to work on the basis of different time periods.

Example: Suppose in the preceeding example Jones (working at one choice per minute) makes his 60 choices in the one hour alloted to him, and quits. But, suppose also that Smith (working at 0.5 choices per minute) is given *two hours* to complete his task. Then Smith *can* duplicate all of Jones' choices exactly, and Smith can again completely control the situation.

This result does not alter the "rate interpretation" of the Law of Requisite Variety, it merely reminds us of the exact definition of "rate." By extending his variety over a longer time, Jones' rate can be cut effectively to Smith's level. Indeed, it may be more illuminating to state that the choices available to the controller must be at least equal to the possible choices exhibited by the system *in a given time period* for control to be certain. But, this is just a different way of describing the ratio requirement for rates of variety.

REQUISITE RATE OF CODED VARIETY

Consider the situation that allows the controller to work *faster* than the system, i.e., the situation in which Smith makes choices faster than Jones.

Example: Let us, as in Figure 6-4, give Jones a coin and a die, so that he has eight distinct choices ($H,T,1,2,3, \ldots ,6$), and allow Jones to make one selection per minute, or 60 per hour. Now suppose Smith has a coin, with two choices (H or T), as before, but that we now give him the following ability: He may use three choices of his coin, e.g., *HTH,* and it will be understood that such a unique selection will be translated by Figure 6-7 to be equivalent to the Jones choices.

HHH – H
THH – 1
HTH – 2
HHT – 3
HTT – 4
THT – 5
TTH – 6
TTT – T

6-7

Thus, if Jones shows a "1," we will say Smith wins if he shows the unique equivalent combination, or code, "THH," which, however, represents three selections for Smith. Now, if Smith can make selections of *H* or *T* three times as fast as Jones can select ($H,T,1,2,3,...,6$), and if the translation in Figure 6-7 is allowed, then *Smith can always win, even though his range of choices is limited to two compared with eight for Jones.*

This example is of practical importance. We find that by working faster, Smith, who has only two choices, generates as many different outcome sequences as Jones, who is working more slowly with eight choices; Smith thereby builds the requisite rate of variety. *Given adequate time, or a sufficiently fast rate, the controller can always generate the requisite amount of variety—if the above translation ability is permitted.* In the information theory terms of Chapters 4 and 5, we can illustrate this point formally by stating the equivalence in terms of the equivalent number of "binary questions" that each choice would require. Thus, with eight distinct choices, each choice of Jones contains $\log_2 8 = 3$ "bits" of information. With only two choices, each of Smith's selections contains only $1 \log_2 2 = 1$ "bit." The variety of possible distinctions will be equal; i.e., Smith can generate as much "information" as Jones if Smith can make three choices while Jones makes one, because $3 \log_2 2 = \log_2 8 = 3$.

We may now restate the Law of Requisite Variety for the rate of variety in coded form: For the outcome of control to be certain, *the controller must generate at least as many bits of information per unit time as does the system to be controlled.*

MEMORY CAPACITY AND SPEED OF PROCESSING

We have seen that to obtain complete control of a system the analyst or controller must have three abilities:

1. At least as many distinct available alternatives as the system can exhibit (or equivalently, the ability to work longer or faster with coded equivalents);
2. The precisely correct set of alternatives within the set available to counter those generated by the system (or equivalently the precisely correct translating ability);
3. The processing ability to use these distinct actions (or their coded equivalents) at a rate at least equal to the system to be controlled (or such that the information generated by the controller per unit time equals that generated by the system).

The controller can now handle a wider range of considerations or "system oppositions" if he is given both an increased reserve of possible actions and an increased processing ability, in terms of speed and memory organization. This is the same result we developed when we discussed system autonomy in the last chapter.

> *Example:* Taking a final look at Jones and Smith, suppose we give Smith, the controller, a vast array of objects to use in his matching games—dice, coins, cards, roulette wheels, and similar objects in profusion—and so organize this inventory of objects that they may be stored and retrieved in a few millionths of a second. Further let us provide Smith with the ability to distinguish one class of stimuli from another, e.g., coin observations from die observations, and a program of instructions, so that upon seeing what Jones does, Smith may retrieve the correct object and present it in its correct matching state. Let Jones have a coin and a die as before, which he may show at one choice per minute.
>
> Smith can now take on Jones with absolute certainty of success. *And in addition,* Smith can take on many other gamblers like Jones, who may be allowed to play with all objects in Smith's collection at the slower rate.[5] Within the limits set by Ashby's law, Smith can defeat all opponents. He is *in control* because of his alternate reserve resources, his ability to organize and integrate his action, and his speed of processing. Consequently, Smith can exploit Ashby's Law of Requisite Variety by using his speed, his reserve of actions, and his organized patterns of operation to counter the environment and the other gambler's system.

[5] Indeed, if Smith's processing ability is fast enough and he has the ability to use coded translations in his matching game, he can accomplish the same result with a string of equivalent yes-no choices.

We may recognize in the last example an analogy with a modern electronic computer or information processing system which, by high speed and a large store of data and programs, is able to tackle a wide variety of problems with success.

SYSTEM SIZE AND ASHBY'S LAW

Finally, note that the derivation of Ashby's law is independent of the size of the outcome table, i.e., the law is not altered by the number of rows and columns that must be considered. Conceptually, Ashby's law holds for the comparison of an analyst (or controller) of any complexity versus a system of any complexity.

Moreover, we do not care how the outcomes shown in the outcome table come about. We do not care, for example, how Jones and Smith placed their objects on the table in the matching game: Jones may have informed his butler of his choice, and had the butler place an object on the table. Smith may have dropped his choice through a hole in the ceiling. Any other procedure would have been satisfactory from the viewpoint of this chapter: The procedures by which the choices produce the resulting outcome are irrelevant to what has been said here. This fact helps emphasize the generality of what has been reviewed.

In short, to return to the purpose of this chapter, Ashby's law tells the systems analyst that he ultimately may think of a system as a set of "If— Then" combinations and their corresponding outcome table, that this form of systems definition holds for any size system, or for any procedure used in obtaining the end result. And, once the outcome table has been determined, Ashby's law prevails. To assure control, the analyst must have the requisite variety that can be measured. If he does not have the requisite variety, the analyst-controller must either simplify his system to obtain control or increase his own variety of possible actions. Ashby's law will guide us in the chapters that follow.

*ASHBY'S LAW AND INFORMATION THEORY

Before continuing, the advanced reader may wish to consult Appendix D, a brief technical discussion of information theory. In the foregoing discussion of the rate of requisite variety it was assumed that the choices made by the system (Jones) were random (all equally likely). Were this not so, the number of bits generated by Jones (called the source in Appendix D) would be less than the maximum possible, i.e., his actions would be redundant to a certain extent. To include this possibility a measure of source variety called *entropy* is defined in Appendix D.

In information theory terms, Smith may be considered a *channel*, who is to handle information from a source. Just as we measured Smith's possible variety, the capacity of the channel can also be measured in bits per unit time.

With these terms in mind, we can state Ashby's law in information theory terms: The capacity of the channel in bits per unit time must be at least as great as the entropy of the source if messages are to be transmitted without error, assuming the absence of noise. (Noise reduces the effective capacity of the channel.)

Finally, the reader should note the importance of codes in matching the source to the channel. This was illustrated when we permitted Smith to use *THH* to match the Jones choice of 1, as in Figure 6-7. The code permitted us to match Smith's faster rate, yet limited number of outcomes, to Jones' slower rate and wider choice. In general, information theory tells us that if the capacity of a channel is equal to the entropy of a source there is always some code which will provide such a perfect match between source and channel.

PROBLEMS

6.1 Compare the following procedures and comment on the benefits to be obtained using the second. *Method 1:* Attempting to teach a student a series of numbers, you ask him to memorize the following list

$$5\ 8\ 1\ 2\ 1\ 5\ 1\ 9\ 2\ 2\ 2\ 6\ 2\ 9$$

which he is to recall on demand. Record the accuracy with which the student can recall the list after one week. *Method 2:* The objective of the experiment is still the same, i.e., the student reproduces the above numbers. However, in providing the list for memorization, some structure is now added

$$5,\ 8,\ 12,\ 15,\ 19,\ 22,\ 26,\ 29,\ \ldots$$

and the pattern of generation—alternate addition of 3 and 4 to the last number—is also explained to the student. Again, ask the student to recall the numbers after a week. Compare the effect of the method of pattern presentation to that of detail presentation upon the accuracy of memory retention of a human being. Why is it easier to handle the pattern? In developing a system definition, we form a pattern of relationships from otherwise unstructured observations. How does the definition process relate to the memorization experiment above? (For further experiments, see G. Katona, *Organizing and Memorizing: Studies in the Psychology of Learning and Teaching*, Columbia University Press, New York, 1940.)

6.2 Under normal conditions we have in stock ten distinct items to ship. Items 1–5 are a deluxe version of the standard product, 6–10. Due to a temporary malfunction in the production department, items 6–10 are out of stock, but we have plenty of 1–5. A temporary decision is made to ship the deluxe version (at no increase in standard price), when the equivalent standard version is ordered. We now have a variety of only five actions to take to counter ten distinct disturbances, the incoming order types.

A. Does this situation contradict Ashby's Law of Requisite Variety? Explain in terms of the tabular presentation of Figure 6-6.

B. Because of great response to our offer, we find we can increase production runs and sell the deluxe versions at standard prices in the future. We therefore delete items 6–10 from the product line. Does this action alter the previous solution in terms of Ashby's law?

C. We now find that customers are indifferent to products 1 and 2 and 3, 4, 5, i.e., if they order either of the first two or any one of the latter they will be satisfied with any member of the given set. How would you interpret this new result in terms of Ashby's law? It appears that only 2 responses will satisfy 5 distinct stimuli. Is this a contradiction?

6.3 In Figure 6-6, where there are nine rows and three columns, suppose Smith is indifferent to the outcomes a, r, l, and d.

A. Does Smith have the requisite variety even though the rows exceed the columns in number?

B. Suppose outcomes q, l, and z are all disastrous to Smith. Does he then have control of the situation?

C. Would the knowledge that q, l, and z are all disastrous to Smith be of advantage to Jones (1) If he knew Smith's constraints of movements, i.e., the table of Figure 6-6? (2) If he did not have that knowledge?

D. How would the knowledge that q, l, and z are disastrous outcomes for Smith be of greater benefit to Jones if he also found out that Smith could not use his alternative C?

E. A knowledge of a competitor's choice constraints and the joint outcome table provides a great competitive advantage. How can this be illustrated in Figure 6-6?

F. Suppose in Figure 6-6 Smith must have outcome a occur to survive. How can he survive?

6.4 Consider a system that is supposed to perform a regulatory function. This system, as shown in diagram form below, receives in a discrete series of intervals, a stimulus S, which may be one of three inputs, A, B, or C. The input S is transformed into a "successful" or an "unsuccessful" output E, depending upon the state of input S and the then current state of the regulator R, which may take on the states 1, 2, or 3. The conditional transformation determined by R is shown in table T, in which a indicates success and b indicates failure.

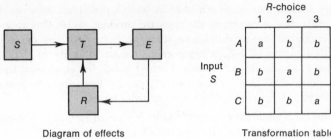

	Diagram of effects		Transformation table	

R-choice table:

Input S	R-choice 1	2	3
A	a	b	b
B	b	a	b
C	b	b	a

Problem 6-4

Let us assume further that the regulator *R* may be changed at each step of the input *S*, but that the choice of *R*'s state, 1, 2, or 3, must be predicated on the last previous effect *E* observed. That is, any possible corrective action is delayed until the next instance, so that the choice of *R*'s state must be made without knowledge of what *S* will be. The only information available is the past history of the *R* choices and the corresponding results, or effects *E*.

In this situation, which corresponds to most discrete industrial control situations, such as industrial quality control which monitors product variables, regulation can never be perfect, because of the one-step delay and the lack of knowledge of what causes a result. (The regulator "sees" only the output state *a* or *b* but does not know what input state caused this result—even though the transformation table *T* may be completely known.)

We now wish to evaluate two policies for *R* in which a policy will be defined as a sequence of *R* choices. We assume input *B* is most likely.

Policy I: Remain at regulator action 2 always (based on the fact that input "disturbance" *B* is most likely), or

Policy II: Try actions 1 or 3 at random, if two consecutive *b*'s occur, under the assumption that these disturbances, or alternate inputs, are equally likely. If two such trials (or 1 or 3) fail to get an output *a*, this policy calls for a return to regulator state 2. The corrective cycle is to be repeated after return to state 2 according to the random rule if two more *b*'s occur.

A. Which policy is superior (*b* outcomes less) if the disturbance, or input sequence is

$$B\,B\,B\,A\,B\,A\,A\,B\,C\,C\,B\,C\,A\,B\,B\,B\,C\,B\,B\,B$$

B. Would it be helpful to know that disturbances *A* and *C* are not equally likely? How would the statement of Policy II change if the probabilities of these alternate disturbances were known?

6.5   This problem illustrates the "bit" as the measure of variety. Reference should be made to Appendix D before making the computations in this and the following problem.)

A manufacturer has four customers: *A, B, C, D*. If the orders arrive at random (i.e., are independent, customer to customer):

A. What is the entropy of the source of information, i.e., how much information is gained by knowing an order comes from a particular customer, if all customers are equally likely to send in an order?

B. If the probabilities are, respectively, 0.4, 0.3, 0.2, and 0.1 for customers *A, B, C,* and *D*, what is the entropy of the source?

NOTE: $\log_2 = 3.32 \log_{10} N$; therefore,

N	$\log_2 N$
0.1	-3.32
0.2	-2.32
0.3	-1.74
0.4	-1.32

C. If 100 orders are received during the week, what is the total amount of information received by discovering, as each order arrives, the customer from whom it came?

D. Two hypothetical machines, Model I and Model II, are designed for display of customer credit standing. Both machines work with a magnetic belt formed into a loop sequencing the customers in the deterministic transformation

$$A \rightarrow B \rightarrow C \rightarrow D$$

The tape is advanced by pushing an "advance button" which moves the tape ahead one customer at a time. The current customer status is displayed on a cathode-ray television tube. In both machines, the operator indicates credit disapproval or approval by means of a keyboard, and in the latter case updates the receivables outstanding. However, the two machines differ as follows: In Model I the approval or disapproval of credit leaves the present customer's record in view, whereas in Model II the picture is automatically reset to customer *A*'s display. Compare the two models by computing for this application the expected number of operations of the "advance button" per order. Assume the orders are handled as they arrive, i.e., are not presorted, and that each order must be checked on the machine.

E. Why is Model II preferable in this application, and why is the number of pushes required of the "advance button" less in both cases than the entropy in bits computed in B? How could this machine be improved?

6.6   In this hypothetical example, a CIA employee is to receive a coded message via the notes of a song which he receives over the regular Voice of America transmissions, 8:00 P.M. Monday nights, his time. The tunes are composed especially for the occasion and always start with the same note repeated three or more times, the first change indicating the start of the message. Rhythm is not part of the message. Seven preselected major tones (A–G), regardless of scale, are used in the compositions, with middle C and C above middle C being considered equivalent. The basic melody used in the code is usually obscured by extraneous background arrangements. A piano is used to transmit the message. The coding of the message uses the transition between a *pair* of notes to indicate a given alphabetic or numeric symbol, as shown in the proposed matrix of 49 cells (see below). Thus, a transition from D to C yields the decoded letter X and so on. However, of the 49 available cells, ten are not presently used.

A. How could the unused spaces be used to the greatest advantage to improve the secrecy of the messages?

B. The composer now suggests also using the sharps and flats in sending messages, because this would permit a greater variety of composition. What principle should be followed in laying out the decoding table to maximize secrecy?

C. The agents now decide to extend this coding/decoding procedure by using several transformation tables of the type shown, but with different letter arrangements, thereby converting the single transformation to multiple transformations selected by an input. The choice of table is to be by the name of the composer of the selection played just preceding the actual message. This song is played at 7:55 P.M. just before the station break, and is used as background music for the announcer concluding the program for that half hour. When this is done, comment on the complexity of the decoding equipment that must be available to the agent in the field.

	SECOND NOTE						
	A	B	C	D	E	F	G
A	A	B	C	D	E	F	G
B	H	I	J	K	L	M	N
C	O	P	Q	R	S	T	U
FIRST NOTE D	V	W	X	Y	Z	.	?
E	1	2	3	4	5	6	7
F	8	9	0	#			
G							

\# = space

D to C equals X, etc.

DECODING TABLE

7 | DIRECT SIMPLIFICATION METHODS

As we saw in the last chapter, the systems analyst must have at his disposal at least as great a variety of possible actions or resources as the system he wishes to control. This requirement raises the important question of system simplification, because quite often the analyst will not have the requisite resources to define, analyze, and control the system he confronts.

Indeed, the act of system definition itself raises this question, for in selecting the elements and relationships he will use for his system in a given case, the analyst will always face that infinity of possibilities we discussed in Chapter 1.

What is the analyst to do? As we remarked in Chapter 1, we have no universal theory of systems simplification that can be used to select elements and relationships in a particular problem. We can outline some useful approaches, however, which will arm the analyst with at least a strategy of systems simplification. This chapter and the next will outline a few such strategies.

THE COST OF SIMPLIFICATION VERSUS THE COST OF PROCESSING ABILITY

The meaning of "simplification" has changed with our ability to process information swiftly and inexpensively. For many years investigators attempted to create *elegant* theories, descriptions, and systems definitions that relied upon few assumptions or that required few steps to complete a demonstration in logic or mathematics. The aim was to obtain a neat, apt, fastidious selection. (The Latin root of *elegant* means to choose, or select.) This was a reasonable objective in view of the later difficulty in making manipulations with "inelegant" models. Man-years and lifetimes were devoted to the creation of more elegant proofs, more elegant theories, and more elegant methods of analysis. We are still impressed by the Principle of Parsimony, expounded in the fourteenth century by William of Ockham. He suggested that, when in doubt, we should accept those conclusions that follow from the least number of propositions, assumptions, and steps in reasoning.[1]

Such a philosophy is inappropriate when the costs, time, and resources required for manipulating relatively cumbersome definitions, data, or procedures can be greatly decreased by using electronic computers and similar devices. If we take into account the *total* effort of defining a system *and* analyzing it, we usually find that the optimum approach is to treat the research process itself as a system and to balance the effort expended in defining the system with the corresponding effort and cost of analysis. By approaching the system in this way, many forms of system definition and analysis that would otherwise be inelegant are, when modern data-processing equipment is available, the most efficient ones. Thus, a lengthy step-by-step *algorithm* (or set of rules for solving a problem), although mathematically inelegant compared to a "simple" formula, may be more efficient than the "simple" formula when a computer is used for the analysis of a system problem. The listing or classification approach to system simulation discussed in Chapter 4 is an example. It is aesthetically untidy, but highly efficient.

From another viewpoint, the drastic elimination of detailed assumptions, computing steps, and relationships to be handled can be harmful if we enforce simplicity for its own sake. The concept of elegance conflicts with the facts of life in many systems, which can be inherently messy. To eliminate such "messiness" in the name of simplicity destroys one of the essential characteristics of the system to be defined. The required prediction or control ability may be lost by stripping away the burdensome filigree.

The purpose of simplification as discussed here is to create a balance between the variety of the system to be handled by the analyst and the analyst's resources. As such, simplification of system definition is necessarily related to the analyst's objectives *and* resources, not to some historical concept of elegance, or neatness.

[1] M. Bunge, *The Myth of Simplicity*, Prentice-Hall, Englewood Cliffs, N. J., 1963.

We should also distinguish between intellectual and physical simplification. Simply because an analyst views a system in more or less detail does not mean he must necessarily engage in a physical simplification of the system (although this may be the result of his investigation). The two ways of eliminating detail should not be confused: Because the housewife simplifies her view of an automobile to a key, an accelerator, and a brake does not mean that she must have the motor removed. We will now discuss such mental simplification.

DIRECT SIMPLIFICATION METHODS

For our discussion, we can divide simplification methods into two main categories: First-order methods, which *directly* reduce complexity; and higher-order methods (see Chapter 8), which simplify a system *indirectly*, through a series of steps. This split conforms to our discussion of system hierarchy in Chapter 5.

The Strategy of Direct Simplification

Direct attempts at system simplification usually involve the actions of *elimination* and *grouping*, either of which directly decreases distinctions that need to be made in a system definition. Let us first consider a few general examples that illustrate the strategy and then examine some specific methods.

In defining a system for a given purpose it soon becomes apparent that large blocks of detail are irrelevant and should be eliminated. Such elimination implies the analyst has imposed implicit *constraints* in his system definition. In fact, no system definition could be made if constraints were not introduced, because without constraint the system would have no structure.

A set of such constraints, if increased, acts as a *filter* to narrow the set of possible elements and relationships that will be considered. To illustrate, consider again the research team of Chapter 3, which could take on projects of type *A* or *B*.

Example: If no limit were placed on the number of each kind of project the research team could take on, there would be an infinite number of combinations of *A* and *B* type projects allowed. By restricting the total number of projects to three or less, however, a limit of *ten* possible combinations results. The stated restriction filtered out, or eliminated, all other possibilities.

To continue with the same example, suppose we also required the research team to have in process at least one project (of either type) at all times. Then, the state (0,0), which corresponds to complete idleness, would be excluded, and the number of combinations allowed would be cut to *nine.* Similarly, if we required the research team to have in process at least two projects, but not more than three of either type, the number of allowed combinations would be *seven,* and so on, as may be seen from the two-dimensional state diagram of Figure 3-8.

The need for careful specification of constraints should now be clear. Without *any* constraint, the system to be considered becomes impossibly large, because it would then include all elements and relationships that even remotely bear on the objective of the system definition. On the other hand, it is also possible to constrain the system so that *no* elements or relationships remain.

Thus, in the example above, if we required the research team to work on three jobs or less, and at the same time required the team to have at least four projects of type *A* or four of type *B, no* state would satisfy the requirements *and* the restriction, and the system could not be defined. We would say that the constraints chosen were *inconsistent,* because no "feasible" system would result from the specification.

Thus, choosing suitable constraints reduces the complexity of a system definition, because the distinctions made in that definition can be reduced by *elimination.*

Grouping system distinctions also directly simplifies a system definition.

Example: Again, in the example of the research team, suppose we grouped the distinctions between projects of type *A* and type *B,* and just called them "projects" without regard to kind. With the possible choices now in one dimension, rather than two, the imposition of a constraint will leave fewer distinctions than before. Thus, if the research team is limited to three projects or less, only four possibilities (0, 1, 2, or 3) can result, and not ten as when the two dimensions (*A* and *B*) were considered.

We may now ask: "How do we choose suitable constraints and ways of grouping? Two approaches are used: The exploitation of "real constraints and "obvious" grouping boundaries, and the imposition of "artificial" constraints and grouping methods.

"Real" constraints and "obvious" boundaries

Many systems have relatively obvious physical, social, or similar existing constraints and groups. For example, a given machine has an upper limit to its hourly output. The architect may find a stream runs through his client's property. Legal requirements or constraints may demand or prohibit certain acts. The design of chairs, a system, is constrained by the physical size of sitters. An antiaircraft gun control system is constrained by the physical construction of its weapon, and depends upon the fact that targets do not move at perfect right angles. A certain range of temperatures and pressures is required to cause a chemical reaction. A driver must stay on the road, maintain a headway greater than zero, and not run out of gas.

Similarly, we find herds of animals, clusters of people, banks of machines, political factions, component sections or modules, repetitive tasks, and organizational departments that naturally suggest not individual notation or distinction, but group treatment.

When such natural constraints and groups appear, they may be exploited to reduce the variety in the system to be defined. Such constraints and groups are not only helpful in reducing system variety, but are also an essential part of the system definition.

"Artificial" and "arbitrary" constraints and groups

In addition to natural constraints and groups, the analyst may choose to introduce those of his own making. Thus, the analyst may wonder what will happen if he constrains all production equipment in a shop to work at 60% efficiency. The architect (or his client) may prefer colonial architecture to all others. A driver may want to travel from New York to Chicago, but not use a turnpike. In the same way, we may arbitrarily create artificial classes and groups, stratify data for ease in computation, or eliminate distinctions by reference to a higher, broader mode of classification. Do we really need to know the number of males and females in Louisville, or would knowing the total population be sufficient? Couldn't we deal with *small, medium,* and *large,* rather than with the exact garment size? Would it not be possible to report the output of the department in dollars, rather than by dollars for each distinct product line? Why not build in modules, or blocks?

If we follow this same train of thought, our next question might well be: "When do we use elimination methods, and when do we group?"

From the examples above, and those to follow, we see that elimination methods, which result from the application of constraints, reduce detail by reducing the area, region, or set of points to be investigated or contained in the system definition. In this way, the system definition includes elements and relationships that are important within or at the boundary of the constrained region. Thus, the resulting system definition is useful for detailed investigation and analysis of variations *within* or *at the border* of the defined region. *We simplify by elimination when the system objective requires optimization, isolation, and search of detailed action.*

Conversely, it may be desirable to make comparisons or tests *between* large blocks of elements and relationships. *We simplify by grouping, classification, and consolidation of detail when the system objective requires estimation, comparison, and test between blocks of detail.*

Some combination of grouping and elimination is the rule in most system definitions, but the distinction between the approaches is strategic when we plan direct simplification procedures.

With this background, we will now consider some detailed examples of elimination and grouping techniques.

Elimination Methods

Many of the approaches to elimination and grouping are similar, but for our present purposes we will discuss three general methods of elimination currently used: (1) Restricted ranges of measure, or interest, (2) logically or statistically restricted combinations, or patterns of acceptance, and (3) threshold and discrimination methods.

The first approach seeks to put a small box about a continuously described area, which will be of later interest. The second approach attempts to reduce the number of points that must be considered within a box. And, the third approach, usable only when observations can be ranked or scaled, uses "adjustable" elimination, so that the analyst can experimentally *partition* a large system into smaller subsystems. The approaches may be used alone, in combination, or in conjunction with other simplification procedures.

Restricted ranges of measure or interest

The definition of a system can be greatly simplified, if we restrict the range of variation that system variables can take.

Usually, by limiting the range of system variables, many secondary elements and relationships can be eliminated because they would be important only under extreme conditions.

Example: Suppose a system output z, is related to the system inputs x and y by the equation

$$z = x + \frac{1}{y^2}$$

If the variable y is constrained to be $y >> 1$, then $z \cong x$, and the definition of the system is not only simplified by the elimination of y, but also linearized.

Similarly, if we know something about the form of the typical output of a system, even though a detailed description is not available, experimental development of the required system definition may be simplified.

Example: Figure 7-1 is a rough sketch of the ouput z of a system known as a function of the input variables x and y. Suppose we know a "global" maximum value of z is in the range $a \leq x \leq b$, $c \leq y \leq d$. If we

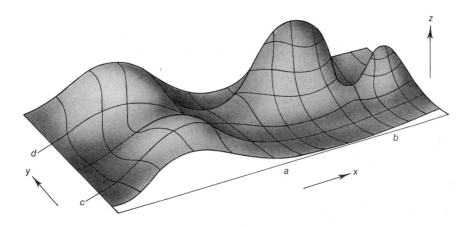

7-1   The output of a system *z* as a function of inputs *x* and *y*.

know this much, our search for the maximizing values of x and y is greatly simplified, because the search area is restricted, and alternate, nonglobal, maxima are excluded from consideration. In short, if you are looking for the highest mountain in the world, to know that it is somewhere north of India is helpful.

In many systems major discontinuities in system performance occur as system variables move from one level to another, even though the variables themselves may be continuous.

Example: The familiar break-even chart shown in Figure 7-2 may be linear until the capacity of one-shift operation is reached. When two-shift operation starts, added fixed costs of supervision and commitment jump at the limit of one-shift volume. Systems of this type are simplified if they can be considered piece-by-piece, thereby avoiding jumps and discontinuities in the restricted definition.

Similarly the area of system interest may be limited by *trial boundaries,* which limit the area within a larger system for which a detailed system definition is required.

Example: A production problem arises concerning poor output quality. The industrial engineer for the shop obtains a flow layout, showing the position of the machines on the factory floor. The engineer then checks off areas on the floor, or major blocks in the process that *do not* appear to be the source of trouble. He then carefully investigates the area remaining within these trial boundaries.

Thus, one direct method of system simplification is to consolidate the area that needs further detailed system definition or search.

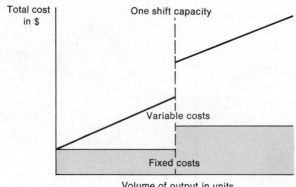

7-2 A break-even chart showing a jump at the limit of one-shift capacity.

Logically or statistically restricted combinations

System simplification can also be obtained by restricting attention to specified combinations of conditions, or to patterns of operation of interest to the analyst, and by eliminating all others. (Elimination of the unwanted patterns is equivalent to selection of the wanted patterns: The approach to the final result is a matter of convenience.)

In many sequential or combinatorial system problems, most possibilities that *could* be considered can be eliminated because they are impossible or illogical on technological, procedural, or similar grounds.

Example: A production operation consists of assembling a bolt (B), a lockwasher (L), and a flat washer (W) *in that order,* as shown in Figure 7-3. Theoretically, the number of possible sequences of three things is 3!, or 6. But, on physical and technological grounds, only *two* of the possible sequences are suitable. We can assemble *L-W*, and then insert B; or, we can reverse the process, holding B and assembling L and W on B. All other combinations are either physically impossible or contrary to specification.

Example: A sequence of order-processing operations involves (1) receipt of mail, (2) order editing, (3) credit check, and (4) product ship-

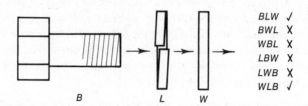

7-3 An assembly operation.

ment. Theoretically, the number of possible sequences is 4! or 24. Because none of the operations can start before the mail is received, and because a credit check is needed before product shipment, the remaining practical possibilities concern only whether to provide a credit check before or after order editing. There are therefore only two real possibilities, not 24.

If a large set of different system elements or relationships, each of which is described in many *dimensions,* must be simplified, a smaller set can be obtained by sorting out, or *extracting,* those items with the desired combination of dimensions. Moreover, by increasing the number of dimensions in the sort, the simplified set may be reduced to any desired size.

Example: From a deck of 52 playing cards, we may extract 26 that are black, 13 that are spades (and black), three that are black spade face cards, and only one black ace of spades. (There are no blue cards, so that it is possible to specify a dimension, or set of dimensions, that will produce no set members. In general, however, an increase in the number of dimensions required in the extraction will decrease the number of items extracted.)

Example: A personnel file consists of 1000 names. If we ask for male employees, we extract 600 names. If we ask for males over 40, we get 300. If we ask for males over 40 who have attended four years of college, we get 50. And if we ask for males over 40 who have attended four years of college *and also* speak French, we get 2.

It is frequently useful to relate items extracted in such a logical elimination procedure to a space or time scale, using maps, graphs, or charts. Because highly specific human and physical characteristics tend to *cluster* in place or time, the mapping procedure may suggest added dimensions, or combinations for extraction, that will aid in further system simplification.

Example: A criminal investigator wishes to define the system of operations of a criminal who has committed robberies in a given mode of operation in small jewelry stores on several occasions. The physical locations of the crimes, when plotted on a map, are found to cluster in a given locality *and always to occur on one-way streets.* The investigator now narrows his field of interest to small jewelry stores on one-way streets in the area, simplifying his stake-out problem. Moreover, by searching the historical files for similar crimes, he can extract a smaller list of suspects than he could without the one-way street dimension.

Many systems will be simplified if their operation is considered only at the logical *extremes* of activity.

Example: Given a complicated equation for a system description, a mathematician might first ask "What happens when x becomes very large, or very small, ∞ or 0?" In this way he can bypass much of the complexity of the equation and greatly simplify his approximations. Such approximations give the limits of system operation under extremes of system input.

Similarly, the mathematician might ask "Under what input conditions will the system output be very large, or very small, ∞ or 0? In this way simplified approximations may reveal critical combinations of inputs that can cause extremes in system output. For example, in the feedback equation $[(y/x) = k/(1 + bk)]$, when the product of system amplification and the feedback factor equals minus unity, the denominator becomes zero, and the system "explodes" or breaks into oscillation. The point at which such breakdown occurs may be the main point of interest in the system definition.

Using this same form of argument, we can show that some systems operate under *optimum* conditions *only* at the extremes of activity set by specified constraints. The possible or feasible modes of system operation in these systems may be numerous (or infinite), but the number of "optimum" combinations of conditions is drastically limited, even for highly complex systems. Linear programing is a specific method for exploiting this method of system simplification.

Example: Figure 7-4 shows a simple system with two inputs x and y representing the units of two products that may be manufactured in a given shop. *Both* products require time on *both* machines A and B, and, because time on machines A and B is limited, an increase in x means a decrease y, and vice versa. The equations defining the machine restrictions are shown in Figure 7-4, and assume 400 hours available per week for each machine type. The "feasible area," representing possible combinations of x and y, shown shaded, is a consequence of the linear restrictions imposed by machines A and B. The assumption, of course, is that to complete two units of x (or y) takes twice as long, or consumes twice the specified machine time, as the manufacture of one unit of x (or y).

Suppose we obtain $50 profit for each x and $75 profit for each y, which is a linear measure of system output. The point of maximum profit will lie on the outer perimeter of the feasible region, a logical consequence of the straight line geometry defining the system. The optimum conditions for the product mix of x and y may be obtained by progressive evaluation of the corners of the feasible region (maximum profit of $3500 occurs at Corner No. 3) by substitution of the corner values of x and y in the "objective function" $z = 50x + 75y$ at each of the possible

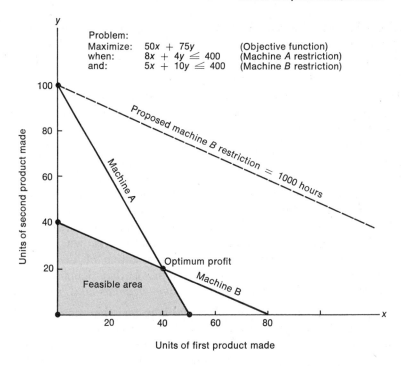

y

Problem:
Maximize: $50x + 75y$ (Objective function)
when: $8x + 4y \leq 400$ (Machine *A* restriction)
and: $5x + 10y \leq 400$ (Machine *B* restriction)

Units of second product made

Proposed machine B restriction = 1000 hours

Machine *A*

Optimum profit

Feasible area

Machine *B*

Units of first product made

7-4   A simple linear programing example illustrates the principle of logical elimination.

corners of the feasible region. The *Simplex Method* of corner evaluation, which indicates the order in which corners should be evaluated, further limits the number of corners that must be evaluated.[2]

The important point here, however, is that the system of possible combinations of *x* and *y* has been immeasurably simplified by exploiting the geometry of the linear system in combination with the linear objective of optimization. Moreover, by changing a constraint, the set of possible optima can be further reduced. Suppose the time available

---

[2] The Simplex Method is an algebraic algorithm, or set of procedural rules for computation, for finding the optimum solution to a linear programing problem of the type illustrated in Figure 7-4. The virtue of the method is that it is computationally efficient, produces the optimum (if there is one) in a finite number of steps, and requires fewer evaluations of extreme points than a complete enumeration and evaluation of all possibilities. The method is described in J. G. Kemeny *et al.*, *Finite Mathematics with Business Applications*, Prentice-Hall, Englewood Cliffs, N.J., 1962, pp. 384–392. A complete treatment, with theory, may be found in R. P. Dorfman, P. A. Samuelson, and R. M. Solow, *Linear Programming and Economic Analysis*, McGraw-Hill, New York, 1958. The Simplex Method provides a general solution to problems having linear constraints and a linear objective function, and is not limited by the number of constraints or variables. In particular problems and computational tasks, the number of variables or constraints imposed may be limited by the capacity of the computing equipment available, not by the procedure.

on machine A is increased to 1000 hours, with the resulting restriction shown by the dotted line in Figure 7-4. The number of corners of the feasible region is now reduced from four to three, so that the search for optimum conditions can be correspondingly simplified.

The importance of linear programing as a logical form of elimination is greatly enhanced as the complexity of the system increases, and consequently, this approach is often used in routine searches for optimum conditions in linear systems with several hundred variables and thousands of restrictions.

Statistical sampling procedures also offer a way to filter system elements and relationships, while retaining the basic pattern of system operation.

When we draw a *random sample* from a population, we select a portion of a larger set (eliminating the remainder) so that each member of the sample is drawn from the population with equal (or known) probability. The members of the sample are then representative of the population, or larger system, and may be used to simplify further definition, because we can now deal with fewer representative elements and relationships.

Example: Suppose the system objective is to find the minimum cost sequence of operations when 100 jobs must be sequenced on one machine. The number of possible sequences is 100!, a number too large to evaluate.

However, suppose a random sample of 1000 possible sequences is constructed by choosing the order of jobs at random for 1000 cases. The 1000 sequences thus generated are representative of the much larger system—they are scattered throughout it—and the probability is high that one of the random sequences, when the cost is evaluated, will be very close to the cheapest sequence. Indeed, there is a finite probability that the sample will include the minimum cost sequence. Thus, although the simplified system is only an approximation to the real one, it allows us to proceed, where otherwise we could not.

Threshold and discrimination methods

In many systems the elements and relationships present can be *ranked* or *scaled* by characteristics such as the frequency of interaction, importance, size, amplitude, or probability of occurrence.

After being ranked or scaled, relationships and elements can then be selected (or rejected) if they are above (or below) a set value, or *threshold*. This ability to discriminate provides an efficient method of system simplification that deserves special attention.

Example: Suppose we measure the frequency of paperwork transactions between different departments in an organization. Usually, we will find a wide range of frequencies. Some transactions will occur much more frequently than others; e.g., routine order processing will be more voluminous than emergency requests. A complete system describing all possible transactions in the paperwork system would be complex. However, if we do not consider transactions that occur less than ten times a week—because they are less frequent than the threshold set—the major flows in the daily paperwork will stand out clearly, and the system of flows will be simplified.

The ability to use threshold discrimination methods successfully in systems simplification is based upon several facts, observable in most systems.

First, as was the case in our mapping of clusters produced by logical elimination, clusters of frequency, intensity, size, or other measure are usually found in most systems.

Second, the efficient isolation of such clusters by threshold methods is a result of the highly nonlinear distribution of most system measures throughout the system to be simplified. For example, if there were an equal transaction frequency for all types of paperwork in the above example, simplification by invoking a threshold would not work. But, distributions of this type are *not* uniform; they are highly skewed. A few, frequent, large, important events, transactions, variables, or relationships *and* many of lesser measure exist.[3]

Finally, as a consequence of the clustering effect and the nonlinear distribution of system activity, *it is possible to use threshold techniques not only to simplify a system by eliminating many elements and relationships from consideration without materially affecting the major patterns of system operation but also to split, or partition a larger system into a number of smaller systems which thereafter may be treated independently.*

Because threshold methods in system simplification are important, some evidence of the *distribution* of system measures is of interest to experienced systems analysts. A few examples will clarify the generality of threshold application.

Example: From studies ranking words in English (and other languages) by their frequency of use, we find a distribution that declines rapidly (in a roughly "exponential" fashion). One hundred short words (a, and, the, when, . . .) constitute 50% of typical English text. Another few hundred words constitute the next 30%, and so on, for all the words in the dictionary.

This fact, investigated extensively, by G. K. Zipf,[4] provides a basis for proposals for a Basic English vocabulary so that language instruction may be simplified. Speed courses in typewriting and shorthand, and training

[3] According to General Maxwell D. Taylor's records (*The Uncertain Trumpet,* Harper & Row, New York, 1960, p. 91), between October 6, 1955 and March 31, 1959, the Joint Chiefs acted upon 2977 issues. Of these, 2954 issues were unanimously agreed upon; thus, only 23 were left in disagreement. These, however, were the "blue chip" issues.

[4] G. K. Zipf, *Human Behavior and the Principle of Least Effort,* Addison-Wesley, Cambridge, Mass., 1949.

in similar repetitive jobs have often been structured to exploit this frequency distribution.

The nonlinear distribution of word use is typical of a wide range of systems involving human actions that exhibit what Zipf calls "The Principle of Least Effort." Zipf's law states that individuals tend to minimize their expected expenditure of effort, thus producing the observed nonlinear distribution of activity.

Certain activities are performed more frequently than others—and, in general, the most frequent activities are those the participant estimates to be the easiest. Whether this activity distribution is due to habit, physical factors, or other causes, the experimental evidence remains. We take many more short trips than long ones, place orders for a few items more frequently than orders for many items, tend to buy a few things more frequently and in greater volume than others, tend to live near people with whom we frequently do business or converse, make more short telephone calls than long ones, and talk to the same few people most of the time. Most people even find their mates within a few blocks of their residence. The distribution of almost any measure of human activity falls off as the amount of "effort" increases.

Let us see how this experimental fact can be exploited to eliminate undue system complexity.

Example: The number of orders placed, the value of inventory, and the number of units consumed of various stock items in a total product line follow the nonlinear distribution predicted by Zipf's law. Of all the repair parts sold by Sears Roebuck, 70 to 80% are for home appliances, such as washers and dryers. A few parts account for most of the activity. This fact is the basis of industrial *ABC* systems of inventory control (Figure 7-5), in which extensive control is applied to the few Class A items, with less detailed control applied to the B and C categories.[5]

Example: To improve operation efficiency we first consider the few activities that consume the most time or the largest number of dollars over a day or week. By considering such activities first, any improvement in efficiency will be multiplied many times, due to the repetitive nature of the work.

Example: In police work, the force available must cover criminal activities so numerous, that they usually exceed the ability of the force. The usual expedient is to rank or scale possible criminal activities by their frequency and seriousness. Generally, petty thefts and minor crimes

---

[5] For a discussion of multiple item inventory problems and the ABC approach, see M. K. Starr, *Production Management, Systems and Synthesis,* Prentice-Hall, Englewood Cliffs, N. J., 1964, p. 321, or M. K. Starr and D. W. Miller, *Inventory Control: Theory and Practice,* Prentice-Hall, Englewood Cliffs, N.J., 1963, pp. 93–164.

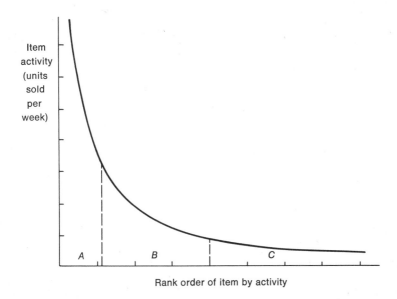

7-5   The nonlinear distribution of item use in a typical inventory list is an example of Zipf's Law. In *A-B-C* systems of inventory control, different control methods are used for high, medium, and low use items.

outnumber such serious crimes as murder and grand larceny. A threshold, or priority is established so that attention is first directed to the few crimes that are the most serious offences against society.

In New York City, for example, police do not begin a detailed investigation of a burglary until the theft exceeds $10,000 and in most operations an emergency code is assigned each call to give a priority to calls currently outstanding.[6] In this way, activities that are less important to the system at a given time (i.e., activities below the "seriousness threshold") are screened out. Action is taken on the few serious crimes.

Example: The design and analysis of power, transportation, and communication systems is often based on "peak load" requirements. We know that, if the system can handle the few peak loads, it can also handle the lesser demands of off-peak times. Thus, major attention is placed on a study of the few peak load conditions, and on actions for controlling or altering the few peak requirements.

[6] Susan Black, "A Reporter at Large: Burglary," *The New Yorker*, (Part I) December 7, 1963, pp. 63–128; (Part II) December 14, 1963, pp. 89–152. This fascinating report provides many examples of criminal modes of operation which illustrate clustering, threshold effects, and the observation of constraints in burglaries by both criminal and police.

In human activity, it is often possible to exploit the nonlinear distribution of activity, or clusters of activity intensity to create system simplification.

Physical measurements and sample estimates also exhibit a well-known nonlinear property that can be exploited by threshold methods. The field of statistics is largely concerned with this fact.

For example, the Central Limit Theorem in statistics[7] states that the averages of sample measurements taken at random from a given population will tend to be "normally distributed" about the true mean of the population. The normal probability distribution (like the exponential distribution) is nonlinear, although symmetrical: The probability of extreme deviation of a sample average from the population average is much smaller than for a small deviation. This fact is exploited in the statistical control chart.

Example: One example of a statistical control chart is the x-bar chart used in industrial quality control work. In this application, measurements are made of a product characteristic for random samples of four or five units, and the average of these measurements is plotted on a chart. Upper and lower control limits are then placed above and below the over-all, or grand, sample average, which is the best estimate of the mean of the population being studied. The control limits are set such that only a small percentage of the observed results would fall outside the limits due to *random* causes. Attention is then directed only to "out of limits" measurements. Trouble-shooting and action-taking may then be limited to rare, exceptional cases that are most probably due not to chance, but rather to some *assignable* cause. Arbitrary forms of "exception reporting" are also constructed this way.

Similarly, many standard statistical procedures, such as regression and correlation analysis, are often used to eliminate variables and relationships that do not contribute significantly to system description. In other words,

---

[7] The Central Limit Theorem, according to A. M. Mood, is the most important theorem in statistics from both the theoretical and applied points of view. "And it is one of the most remarkable theorems in the whole of mathematics. A great many eminent mathematicians (De Moivre, Laplace, Gauss, Tchebysheff, Liapoundoff, Levy, Cramer, and others) have contributed to its development. The theorem is this:
If a population has a finite variance σ^2 and mean μ, then the distribution of the sample mean approaches the normal distribution with variance σ^2/n and mean μ as the sample size [n] increases.
The astonishing thing about the theorem is the fact that nothing is said about the form of the population distribution function. Whatever the disribution function, provided only that it have a finite variance, the sample mean will have approximately the normal distribution for large samples. The condition that the variance be finite is not a critical restriction so far as applied statistics is concerned because in almost any practical situation the range of variation will be finite, in which case the variance must necessarily be finite." (From *Introduction to the Theory of Statistics*, 2nd ed., p. 136, by A. M. Mood and F. A. Graybill, Copyright 1963, McGraw-Hill Book Company, New York. Used by permission.)

these techniques eliminate factors below a statistical significance threshold, which is set by the analyst.

Example: A marketing manager hopes to build a "model" that will predict sales of his firm. He has data on monthly sales and also data on several other possible factors, say, box-car loadings, construction starts, and the like. He may propose a model of the form

$$y = a_1x_1 + a_2x_2 + a_3x_3 + \cdots + a_nx_n,$$

where y represents his monthly sales, the a's are constants (to be determined), and the x's are the values of the available statistical factors. If the statistical regression analysis shows that a given ax term does not contribute significantly to the value of y, then that factor will be eliminated. Because formal statistical methods, such as regression and correlation analysis, are easily automated for computer evaluation, we can often use such elimination methods to develop predictive system models, when we have volumes of historical data.

Many physical systems, because of their design or method of construction, also produce nonlinear measures that may be exploited by threshold methods. Such results can occur, because a system is designed to work with varying efficiency over a range of input conditions, because of a few instabilities, or because of isolated design or construction weaknesses produce malfunction.

Example: Hardware systems[8] are usually designed to work at their best under their conditions of most frequent use. A common practice is to eliminate the many inefficient operating conditions by setting threshold specifications above and below which a system should not be operated, and conversely to simplify design by making these limits as narrow as possible.

Example: Hardware systems also often have a few specific conditions under which operation is unstable, within the desired operating range. If the few serious instabilities can be screened out by threshold methods and stabilized, the system will usually work satisfactorily under the other required conditions.

Example: A television repairman receives a portable television set of a certain make that has the following symptoms: shrinking picture, intermittent static, and flashes on the screen. He immediately investigates, by inspection and test, the operation and condition of the selenium

---

[8] We often call mechanical and electrical systems used in industry and in military service (e.g., computers, electronic control systems, etc.) *hardware* systems to distinguish their physical equipment from the organized instructions and data flows handled by them, which are called *software* systems.

rectifier in the low-voltage power supply section of the set. He does this because of his previous experience with such equipment, or from a manufacturer-supplied trouble-shooting list (based on probabilities of collected histories), relating the symptoms with the most frequently occurring causes of the specified trouble.

Now, we have seen how threshold methods can be used to eliminate the many system distinctions that do not exceed a set threshold. But what happens when the threshold level for a given measure is applied to *all* the elements or relationships in a complex system?

As the acceptance threshold is raised for a given system measure, many elements or relationships, important at finer description levels, are eliminated. For example, by raising the threshold on a relationship measure, we discard the connecting links between system elements as we move to higher threshold levels, and disconnected groups of elements and relationships remain. When this effect can be produced, the disconnected subsystems may be treated as if they were independent, thereby greatly reducing system complexity.

Example: The traffic patterns between five cities have been studied, and the number of trips per week between each of the five cities has been tabulated, then mapped as in Figure 7-6. The complete tabulation of two-way trips involves five elements and twenty relationships (if traffic within the same city has been omitted). Suppose these data are screened by a threshold, so that only traffic flows that exceed 1000 trips per week in a given direction are shown. The new map is not only greatly simplified, but also broken into two parts, representing two

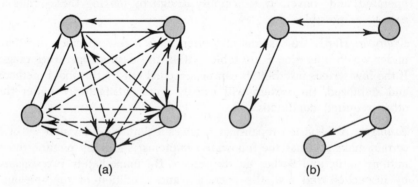

(a)   (b)

7-6 The traffic pattern between five cities. The solid lines in (a) represent 1000 trips a week or more, the dotted lines represent less than 1000 trips. If the less-than-1000-trip relationships are eliminated, as in (b), the larger system separates into two independent systems.

major traffic patterns. At the new level of discrimination, the two patterns may be considered independent, and treated as two simpler systems.

In numerical data displays, we can accomplish partitioning of this type simply by rounding or truncating to fewer significant figures.

Note also that more complex forms of threshold applications can be applied when a measure contains several dimensions. We can apply selected thresholds to each dimension of such measures to achieve a desired effect.

Example: In radio communication work using *amplitude modulated signals,* such as those heard on the common table radio, the signal heard may be characterized by *two* dimensions: frequency and amplitude. A range of radio stations across the dial may thus be illustrated as in Figure 7-7, which is a plot of amplitude versus frequency at a given time.

In the usual home receiver we tune the set to a given station by using a form of "slit discrimination," which effectively eliminates stations above and below the *frequency* to which the set is tuned, yet passes the signal within the slit, as shown by slit A. It is also possible to discriminate in terms of *amplitude.* For example, if we establish a *lower threshold* on the amplitude, we could eliminate low-level background interference. Similarly, if we establish a *higher threshold,* we could eliminate high amplitudes that produce violent static crashes. This complicated setup would allow us to hear only signals that passed the conditions defined by the small box at the intersection of the vertical frequency slit (A) and the horizontal amplitude slit (B) shown in Figure 7-7. Most professional communications receivers have controls for

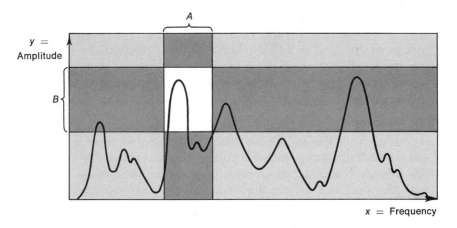

7-7 The representation of an amplitude modulated radio signal (the wiggly line) by the dimensions of frequency *x* and amplitude *y*.

adjusting the width and position of such discrimination slits independently, so that only the desired signal may be heard. Although this procedure is performed electronically in the radio receiver, the same process can generally be implemented by adjusting statistical "slits" for acceptance and rejection. As before, the process is more effective if the data are widely variable and nonlinearly distributed for the dimensions used.

Grouping Methods

Let us now discuss the second form of direct simplification—grouping methods. We again cite three major approaches: (1) Statistical grouping, (2) logical and arbitrary grouping, and (3) the use of prototypes, or a multidimensional cluster of characteristics or measures, to represent a larger complex group. We shall see how the prototype (as described here) may be used as a building block in more complex system definitions.

Statistical grouping and the use of descriptive measures

A common grouping technique is the description of mass data by *statistics,* such as the *average, range, standard deviation,* or *total.* Such forms of "data reduction" are compact—many elements and relationships occurring at different times or at different places, or of somewhat different types, can be described by a number or two. And, although the identity of particular elements and relationships, as well as their location in time or place, is lost in the grouping, that detail may not be needed.

Example: Suppose the sales for five days in a week are 100, 200, 300, 400, and 500, *in that order.* The total sales for the week is 1500, and the use of a total as a statistic reduces five distinct observations to one. Although the trend is lost, it is not needed to compute the dollar sales for the week. For other purposes, such grouping of data will not be appropriate, as we shall see in the section on Elimination and Grouping Problems.

Example: In village *XYZ* live 1000 men and 1500 women. The average age is 42 for males and 48 for females. Suppose we were interested in male-female comparisons in the village. The statement, "In village *XYZ* the average female age is six years greater than the average male age," provides one such relationship and reduces 2500 distinctions to two. There is no "average" male or female to be found, but the fictional male and female may be more useful for our purposes than a detailed comparison of each of the 2500 citizens of the village. We may not need to know that Mary Jones is now 18.

Logical and arbitrary grouping

We can simplify a system by defining certain observations, which may be distinctly different, so that they belong to a more general class. In effect, we thus gain simplification by a *reduction in dimensionality*.

Example: An automobile fleet owner wants to get a quick picture of the maintenance problems of a new fleet of cars for comparison with previous fleets. In the description of the system of new cars, such problems as cracked distributor, broken timing chain, failure in high-tension lead, replaced points, replaced plugs, replaced condenser, replaced coil, and the like are all grouped under the category "ignition problems"—a logical collection. Although he may later wish to explore the details further, the fact that one fleet type has a much greater percentage of ignition problems than another may be all the information currently needed by the fleet owner.

We may also achieve simplification in many cases if we arbitrarily *convert a continuous variable to a discrete variable,* which may assume several levels, or attributes.

Example: A list of customers giving the exact dollar amount of purchases made during the past year is being prepared. Each customer is ranked by the exact number of dollars-and-cents he has spent for purchases. Because there are 1000 customers, the list is sizable. A simplified approach would be to classify the customers arbitrarily into small, medium, and large purchase categories, then display the number of customers in each class.

An extension of the variable-to-attribute method of simplification is to use "zones of indifference." By blocking unimportant variations we get approximate, yet greatly simplified, economic computations, simplified displays of complex data, and simplified systems definitions.

Example: An analyst begins a study of truck routing, only to find a wide range of trip lengths to be considered. Thus, a vast amount of detailed data must be collected on the cost of a distinct trip length. Suppose the analyst finds his resources inadequate to the task of such detailed observation, and moreover, estimates the results of his study would not justify the cost of processing such detail. He may therefore decide to divide the area under consideration into ten cost indifference zones that will estimate roughly the cost of trips from the main warehouse. The resulting simplification—similar to the cost zones illustrated by a parcel post map—allows the analyst to make an appropriate cost comparison of alternate dispatching rules. The analyst can adjust the cost of data collection and processing either by the precision of his analysis, or by increasing, or decreasing, the zone widths.

The use of indifference zones may be extended to the construction of *contour maps* or *indifference curves* that relate a category or class of measure to *xy* or other coordinate systems. Such displays are familiar in topological maps, showing spaced contour lines of equal depth; weather maps, showing isobars; and economic diagrams, showing iso-profit, or iso-cost lines, and the like.

Example: The use of lines of value (iso-lines) produces an area of indifference in which variations within the band between two lines are not detailed, but may often be inferred. The variation will at least be less than the interval between contours. For example, in the map in Figure 7-8, the *detailed* distribution of soot fallout in New York City is shown at the 80 tons per month and the 70 tons per month contours. Although

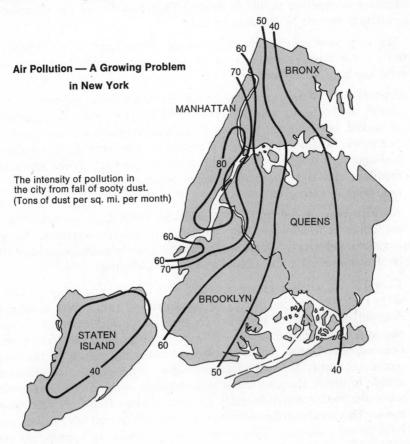

Air Pollution — A Growing Problem in New York

The intensity of pollution in the city from fall of sooty dust. (Tons of dust per sq. mi. per month)

MANHATTAN BRONX QUEENS BROOKLYN STATEN ISLAND

7-8 A contour map in which lines connect points of equal value of a system measurement. Here, we see the intensity of soot "fallout" in New York City. (*N.Y. Times,* Sunday, June 27, 1965, page 12E.)

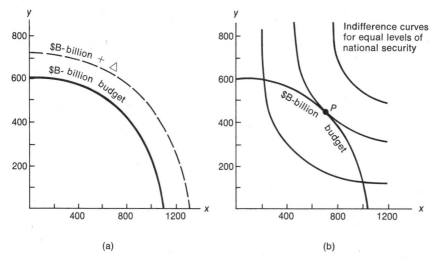

(a)   (b)

7-9   An example of trade and indifference curves in a military application. (Adapted from Hitch and McKean, *op. cit.,* pp. 110–112.)

we may infer a steady decrease in fallout as we move away from the 80 to the 70 tons per month lines, such detail is not part of the system shown. Figure 7-8 also shows how the contours may be related to other system features. We may ask why the high intensity contour covers the East River, over the East Side of Manhattan. A plot of the location of power plants operated by Con Edison, New York City's utility company, would place many X's in the high intensity area.

In economics, similar plots, showing contour lines on *xy* or other coordinate systems are often used to illustrate the possible trades between alternative activities (which, if combined, would give a fixed, equivalent result), or to indicate combinations of equally preferable outcomes, so that we may be "indifferent" to the actual combination chosen. A hypothetical military example will illustrate this point.[9]

Example: Figure 7-9a shows a curve representing the trades possible under the *most efficient conditions* between *y*, the offensive potential (i.e., expected number of targets a strategic bomber force could destroy after D-Day, as an offensive operation) and *x*, the defensive potential (i.e., expected number of attacking bombers an air defense force could destroy in certain circumstances). For a given budget of $B-billion, we

[9] Compare this example to the linear programing example of page 164. The example shown is adapted by permission of the publishers from Charles J. Hitch and Roland N. McKean, *The Economics of Defense in the Nuclear Age,* pp. 110–112. Cambridge, Mass.: Harvard University Press, Copyright, 1960, by The RAND Corporation.

assume that the amount allocated to the strategic bombing force was spent most efficiently to maximize offensive potential, and that the amount allocated to air defense was spent most efficiently to increase defensive potential. The sacrifice in defensive potential to obtain an *increment* in offensive potential is shown by the "production possibility" curve in Figure 7-9a. For a larger *total* budget, the production possibility curve would move up and away from the origin, so that we may think of a family of such curves, or contours, connecting the maximum efficient combinations of offense and defense that can be bought with $B-billion, or $2B-billion, or $3B-billion, and so on. (The curves shown and their scales are hypothetical; the determination of the points on such curves would be a matter for detailed quantitative analysis. The equal "trade-off" contour, however, illustrates the system relationship connecting (1) offensive target destruction, (2) defensive kill potential, and (3) the size of the *total* combined budget for both operations, with the assumption of most efficient use in either example.[10]

We now ask how we might find the "optimal" combination of offensive potential and defensive potential, as defined above?

If it were possible to find a common measure, a commensurate measure of effectiveness, to scale offensive potential and defensive potential as desirable alternatives for a given national security level, we could plot the trade, or indifference curves, representing equally valuable alternatives *for that given national security level*. Such objective indifference curves, for a nonlinear system of this type, are usually convex when viewed from the origin—as we relinquish more of our defensive potential, we demand proportionally more offensive potential in return, and vice versa. A family of such objective indifference curves may be plotted, representing various contours or connected points of equal objective value to us, as in Figure 7-9b. For a fixed budget of $B-billion, the optimum combination of *x* and *y* (defensive potential and offensive potential) is the point *P*, which is on the production-possibility curve for $B-billion, and *at the same time* on the highest national security indifference curve possible.

This example of nonlinear programing does not illustrate the techniques of solution, but rather shows how indifference can simplify a system definition.[11]

[10] The production possibility curve shown is a nonlinear constraint. Any combination of *x* and *y* below the constraint is *feasible*. On the curve, each combination is said to be technically efficient in that an increase in offensive potential necessitates a decrease in defensive potential. The question of finding the "optimum" efficient combination remains. This problem is conceptually similar to the linear programing example of page 164, but is used here to illustrate a nonlinear case, and to show the usefulness of widely spaced, or simplified, lines of indifference.

[11] The reader will find an extensive discussion of examples of this type together with mathematical techniques of solution in Hitch and McKean, *op. cit.*, especially the Appendix "The Simple Mathematics of Optimization" prepared by Alain C. Enthoven of the RAND Corporation.

Prototypes

If the dimensionality of the elements or relationships to be described is inherently so large that grouping under a more general category will not provide the needed detail, we often use a *prototype*, i.e., a typical block of elements and relationships we can use instead of many distinctions.

Example: A manufacturer has a number of distributors throughout the country. He knows they differ. The New England distributors are a different breed from those in the South and West. He wants to devise a system of distribution to include these differences, but knows he cannot have a different system for every distributor. He asks for a picture of the typical New England distributor as compared with the typical distributor in other regions. He wants a few *prototypes* on which to base his decisions, not a detailed description of all his outlets.

Example: The insurance salesman who meets many customers daily cannot afford the time to learn every detail about each customer, nor can he have a distinct insurance plan and a distinct sales strategy for each customer. He looks for prototypes in the individuals he meets. He has a few distinct sales plans and approaches to match his current needs. The sly, wealthy financial analyst gets one treatment; the extrovert middle-class grocer gets another.

The high cost and time required for data collection compels us to use prototypes when the elements and relationships to be identified, described, and grouped become numerous, scattered geographically over a wide area, or require the services of expert analysts for their description.

Example: For a six-year study of heart disease The University of Michigan selected Tecumseh, Michigan (pop. 9500), as a *typical* U.S. City.[12] Settled in 1824, Tecumseh has several industries, a typical heartland Main Street, and a fringe of farms. In this community, 8600 residents, nine-tenths of the population, were persuaded to participate in the lengthy medical investigation, which required blood tests, urine samples, electrocardiograms, X-rays, and complete medical examinations. To collect such refined data on a national basis—even for a statistical sample of individuals—would have been economically infeasible, as well as possibly misleading due to variations in data collecting conditions in different field locations.

---

[12] *Time,* July 23, 1965, p. 59.

Example: For similar reasons, test markets, used in experimental market research, are used as prototypes. To maintain secrecy, to permit the use of control locations in experimental design, to cut cost and time, and by the nature of the experimental treatment (block advertising), such typical, or prototype, blocks of elements and relationships must be used.

Frequently we wrongly represent a prototype by a set of statistically *average* conditions or measurements—often neglecting possible instabilities or gross variations about the average. Or, we construct our prototypes, regardless of the field of analysis, by trying to remember and visualize *a specific and striking example*—a most unforgettable character—that epitomizes a range of elements and relationships, forgetting that the prototype chosen for dramatic effect may not be the prototype useful for prediction.

Because the prototype, or simplified model, is the result of combinations of system simplification by elimination *and* grouping, it is important that we conclude this chapter with a survey of the assumptions and pitfalls encountered in using the first-order simplification methods discussed thus far.

ELIMINATION AND GROUPING PROBLEMS

Elimination and grouping, as methods of system simplification, make certain assumptions we should discuss further. We will not repeat existing works[13] on logic or statistics, but will review two major data-collection and prediction problems: stability and variability.

[13] A basic library list of over 300 references is provided by the Committee on the Undergraduate Program in Mathematics of the American Mathematical Society, P.O. Box 1024, Berkeley, California 94701, covering statistics, probability, logic, and other mathematical areas. From this list, the reader may wish to select (1) W. Feller, *An Introduction to Probability Theory and Its Applications*, Vol. 1, Wiley, New York, 1957, and (2) E. Parzen, *Modern Probability Theory and Its Applications*, Wiley, New York, 1960, (3) A. M. Mood, and F. A. Graybill, *Introduction to the Theory of Statistics*, 2nd ed., McGraw-Hill, New York, 1963, (4) W. Quine, *Mathematical Logic*, rev. ed., Harvard University Press, Cambridge, Mass., 1951, and (5) D. Kalish and R. Montague, *Logic; Techniques of Formal Reasoning*, Harcourt, Brace & World, New York, 1964 as standard works in probability, statistics, and logic. At a more introductory level, J. G. Kemeny *et al.*, *Finite Mathematics With Business Applications*, Prentice-Hall, Englewood Cliffs, N.J., 1962, provides an introduction to discrete probability problems and other topics of interest to students of business, with flow charts and diagrams. P. G. Hoel, *Introduction to Mathematical Statistics*, 3rd ed., Wiley, New York, 1962 may be used at the same level. E. Mendelson, *Introduction to Mathematical Logic*, Van Nostrand, Princeton, N.J., 1964, is also introductory. At the level of application, in handbook format, there are a number of useful works. For practice in statistics, M. R. Spiegel, *Theory and Problems of Statistics*, Schaum Publishing Co., New York, 1961, provides 875 solved problems of a standard type, E. L. Grant, *Statistical Quality Control*, McGraw-Hill, New York, 1952, provides numerous applications of statistical control; O. L. Davies (ed.), *Design and Analysis of Industrial Experiments*, rev. ed., Hafner Publishing, New York, 1956, discusses the construction and analysis of experiments; and A. J. Duncan, *Quality Control and Industrial Statistics*, Irwin, Homewood, Ill., 1959, is a one-source handbook of techniques and further references. A number of specialized texts are available for given applications (design of stratified public opinion samples, estimation, factor analysis, etc.). However, for these sources the reader should consult library entries for the special topic of interest or the bibliographies provided by the works cited above.

Stability

For our system definition to work—for it to predict system output, when given system input—we must assume an underlying stability in the system described, regardless of the level of complexity or the degree of systems simplification achieved by *any* method.

If we could *not* assume such stability, then the elements and relationships relevant for our system definition *now*, would at a later date or at a different place, be *irrelevant*. Like Alice, we would be in a Wonderland, where every new event was a surprise.

The basic assumption of scientific investigation and practical action—the assumption of stability—becomes more important as we begin to eliminate or group detail: Inherently we assume the *few* elements and relationships remaining in our system definition—the few left after elimination, or the few left after grouping—will *continue* to be representative and predictive for our system. Even though our system definition may be a gross approximation, we want it to be a *robust* definition, firm under minor changes in conditions, and permanently useful.

This desired stability may be found in deductive systems or logical systems *by definition*. For example, we may define the fact that when we turn on switch *A and* switch *B*, light *C* will illuminate, but not under other conditions. From a series of such statements, the logical consequences of system operation may be deduced with logical certainty. And, we may find some unfailing regularities of this type in nature—in astronomy, in physics, in the operation of an electronic computer—if we do not push the precision and reliability of our predictions too far.

But, in all real world systems there *is* variability and the question of "statistical stability" remains.[14]

[14] Statistical stability implies that causes of variation which can be assigned to specific factors have been taken into account or removed from a system, so that the output of that system can be predicted within given limits, the remaining variation being "random," in the sense that we cannot find other causes. Although, in any practical experiment, it is not possible to prove or demonstrate that a given sequence of observations is random, a number of tests can be devised to determine if the sequence of results behaves as if it were random in the theoretical sense of being drawn independently and "at random" from a given population, or distribution of possibilities *which does not change with time or the sequence of observations*. A basic exposition of this important point is given by W. A. Shewhart (W. E. Deming, ed.) *Statistical Method from the Viewpoint of Quality Control*, The Graduate School, Department of Agriculture, Washington, D.C., 1939, a reference which is in many libraries. Although statistical tests can be used to monitor sequences of data collected for analysis, and although many standard statistical procedures assume random variation as a requirement for their results, it is true that many applied statistical studies have failed—even worse, given totally erroneous results—because experimental probabilities, averages, standard deviations, and other statistical measures have been computed from sequences of data which are *not* statistically stable. Since this error in application occurs so frequently, the reader should be ever on guard for its appearance in his work. A number of other statistical errors and logical fallacies are noted in M.R. Cohen and R. Nagel, *An Introduction to Logic and Scientific Method*, Harcourt, Brace & World, New York, 1934, pp. 316–332 and pp. 376–403, some of which are summarized hereafter.

Briefly, statistical stability requires that variation in a system measure must be "random" regarding time or repetition; i.e., a system measure must not exhibit trends, cycles, or other "assignable causes" of variation important to our system objective, but unaccounted for in the system definition Figure 7-10.

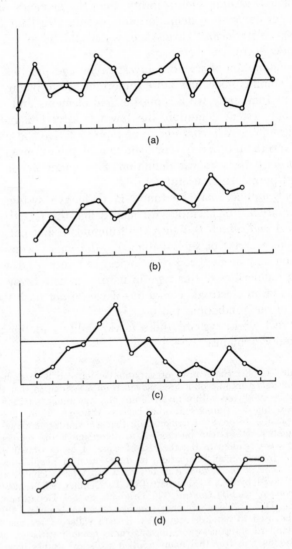

(a)

(b)

(c)

(d)

7-10 Time-series of observations that do and do not show statistical stability. In (a), a statistical pattern of random variation gives statistical stability. The presence of a trend in (b), a season pattern in (c), and a highly improbable deviation in (d) must be removed (or accounted for) to obtain statistical stability.

When such "causes" of variation have been removed or taken into account, the "scatter" that remains is presumably due to so many different factors acting independently and in combination that we may consider the variation random, and the measure used to describe a system element, relationship, input, or output, "statistically stable."

Although there are many possible tests for statistical stability (such as the control chart example, page 170), the most important requirements are that the statistical measure used, its range of variation, and its "pattern" of variation remain statistically stable, in the sense just defined.

The stability requirement for the statistically described system corresponds to the "single-valued" outcome requirement for the deterministic, or logical system, and is a straightforward concept if the predictive nature of a system definition is kept in mind. In short, if a deterministic system is not single valued, or if a statistically described system is not statistically stable, we must redefine the system until these requirements are met.

The Size of Statistical Variability

In addition to the requirement of statistical stability, if we are to compare system characteristics for various times, places, or conditions, we worry about the *magnitude* of statistical variation present in a system measure— even if that measure is statistically stable.

For sharp comparisons we require that the within-group variation for the measures to be contrasted be substantially less than the between-group variation. We can state this somewhat differently in the language of experimental design. The variation between payoffs for alternate courses of action (different strategies, or test "treatments") must be greater than the variation between different subjects tested, or repetitions of the test under the same treatment conditions (Fig. 7-11).

Rather than repeat textbook examples to illustrate the effects of instability and inappropriate within/between class variability, we will study several data collection and data organization examples that will illustrate the two basic requirements. In the following discussion, the reader will be aided by understanding that many possible inconsistencies in field data collection result in statistical instabilities, for the reasons we are about to illustrate. It should also be understood that statistical categories for data collection are chosen depending upon the variability of the cases that are observed and the comparisons that must be made. These points are clarified in the next two sections.

Consistency and Statistical Stability

Our classification and grouping of observations and cases should be consistent, so that a correct statistical count or measure will result for each group or class defined.

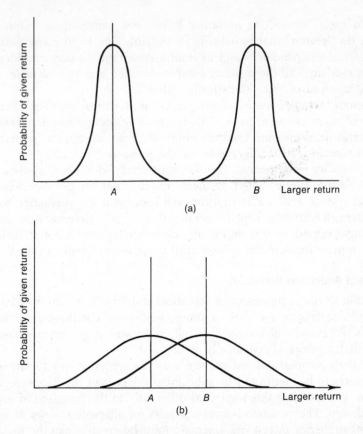

7-11 An illustration of within-group and between-group variations. In (a) the various observations are scattered tightly about alternatives A and B, and the alternatives are widely separated. Thus, comparison of the alternatives is easy—every example of B is better than A. But, in (b), the scatter about alternatives A and B is large, and the alternatives are not widely separated. Then, some outcomes of alternative A could be better than some outcomes of alternative B, and there is no clear preference for A or B.

Obtaining a consistent grouping is difficult because inconsistencies can arise from so many sources (i.e., cases presumed to be alike can differ in so many distinct ways or dimensions) that the investigator is unable to control all of them. A few of the major trouble areas will illustrate the usual precautions we can take.

If a variety of different individuals and investigators, estimators, or measuring instruments must be used in data collection, these sources should be checked for classification, estimation, or measurement consistency. Technically, standardization and calibration describe the required equalization of understanding or reference.

The problem of multiple-agreement—even *under identical circumstances* —becomes more difficult as the number of distinct dimensions to be measured or classified increases, because the separation of distinct cases into one class or another becomes more difficult for the individual or instrument. Even in straightforward applications, such as the assignment of code numbers to a list of inventory items in stock according to clearly written directives, many misclassifications can be expected. Training programs and strict standards help overcome this problem, as does use of automated measuring and input devices, where this is possible.

If data to be grouped take a long time to collect, the underlying conditions giving rise to the observed results may change *while the data collection is going on.* When this happens, the data grouped together will not be consistent, because the observations at different points in time come from different underlying cause systems. Sequential examination of the data during collection, or preservation of the exact time of the observation for later test should be required during lengthy investigations.

For the same reason, a check of consistent category definitions used for data collection and grouping is essential regarding historical data, because the exact definition of a class may not have been consistent over time. The definition of terms used in government reports, for example, are revised periodically to meet changing needs and conditions, and the reconciliation of such definitional changes is usually a major, but necessary, task.

A similar argument, of course, holds for data collected at different places. The response to identical observation methods may not be consistent in different locations: The question may not be understood, the environment may cause an unexpected bias, the observations may not be made at simultaneous times at each location, and so on.

Example: A computer manufacturer wished to develop a historical record of equipment sales and rentals so that this information could be used in future planning. A ten-year record was to be collected of all transactions, classified by stock number, customer number, terms of sale, age of equipment, and the like, including foreign sales, rentals, exchanges, and trade-ins. Clear, written instructions and personal visits by marketing experts of the firm initiated the project, and soon a master file began to grow in the home office. It became apparent, however, that major inconsistencies were present in the data. Sales were reported for nonexistent stock numbers and customers; customer numbers were not applied consistently; mergers, "spin-offs," and similar customer reorganizations were not handled uniformly; equipment modifications requiring a change in code were not recorded; in describing customer types, because each foreign office seemed to have a different classification concept, the classes were blurred, and wandered from year to year. As a result, much of the data had to be collected again or completely re-edited (mostly by hand, although the source data had been transferred to magnetic tape). Two years passed before the master file was up-to-date and reasonably consistent. (Minor errors, however, are still being found.) More than 80% of the development cost of the master file—which grew to nearly one million source documents—was spent on establishing consistency and stability checks, and on studies of file simplification methods that would correctly produce comparative summary reports and files. Such an experience is common when data must be obtained from many people, over a period of time, from many places.

Statistical tests can check the desired stability of observations over time or place, or conversely point out the observations unlikely to be equivalent. However, they must be used with a full appreciation for the stability and variability of the underlying system. For example, contrary to popular belief, the application of standard statistical formulas for computing a "sample size" does not produce a helpful (or correct) answer unless stability of the cause system being sampled can be assumed: There is always a trade between too large a number in a sample group on the one hand (to gain simplicity and precision of description), and too small a number on the other (to assure stability and consistency in grouping), a balance not included in the standard formulas.

Because it is impossible to collect every fact about every system element or relationship, the possibility exists that one or more important distinctions will not be collected, and drastically different data will be grouped erroneously. Moreover, in many field data collections, it is impossible to return to the observation point in time or place to enlarge the distinction list, so that the collected data may become worthless, if the inconsistent results *are* found, or, perhaps, worse if the inconsistencies are not found. A strategy to avoid this unfortunate impasse is to pretest data-collection methods and preanalyze the data collected on a small scale before initiating a large-scale data collection effort.

Stratification and Variability

When we choose a category and its boundaries for computing a statistical measure (or for logical comparison) we have seen that we should have small within-class variation compared to between-class variation, particularly if we are to compare classes. The same rule holds, of course, in the selection of a prototype, or element-relationship block. The more tightly variations from the prototype cluster about the prototype description, the more useful the prototype is. In practice, however, how do we develop class boundaries?

Example: Suppose we wish to create a prototype of two villages, using age and income. Table 7.1 shows the average value and range about the average for villages *ABC* and *XYZ*.

Table 7.1

VILLAGE	ABC		XYZ	
	Average	Range	Average	Range
Age, male	35	1 mo.–45 yrs.	42	25–80 yrs.
Age, female	37	1 mo.–60 yrs.	48	18–90 yrs.
Income, family	$5000	$2000–$100,000	$6000	$5000–$7000

Although we might compare the villages by saying the typical citizen of *ABC* was younger than the typical citizen of *XYZ*, we could not talk fairly about a difference in average income for the typical citizen. The income within *ABC* ($2000–$100,000) varies so much more than the variation shown between classes *ABC* and *XYZ* ($5000–$6000), that it would be difficult to make a meaningful, or statistically acceptable, test for differences in average incomes. Moreover, the facts that some very high-income individuals live in *ABC*, and that income in *XYZ* is narrowly distributed about the average, are likely to be very important if the purpose of our system definition is, say, selling insurance or deciding how to stock a store. Average age and average income would not be good prototypes of these villages for purposes of comparison.

The solution, which increases the complexity of the system definition because we have grouped too much, is to *stratify* the data, or break it up into finer comparisons, to take into account the *atypical,* high income families in ABC.

Example: Returning to the age-income comparisons of the villages, suppose we were able to consult the census figures for each, and found the distribution of income by age as shown in Table 7.2, which gives percent of population in each category.

Table 7.2

VILLAGE	AGE		INCOME			
			<$5000	$5000–9999	$10,000–14,999	≧$15,000
ABC	<	35	60	40	0	0
	≧	35	10	60	20	10
XYZ	<	35	20	80	0	0
	≧	35	30	70	0	0

Then, it would be reasonable to stratify or create a class boundary at, say $10,000, and represent each of the two villages in a two-way table (Table 7.3) summarizing age and income.

Table 7.3

			INCOME	
			< $10,000	≧ $10,000
ABC	Male	35	100	0
	Female	35	70	30
XYZ	Male	35	100	0
	Female	35	100	0

It would now be fair to report the average income and range in each strata.

Unfortunately, the ease of stratification or classification illustrated in the village comparison is not typical of more complex comparisons. Seldom will we know enough about a system to select the most efficient categories, dimensions, class intervals, or prototypes at the outset. Data may be unavailable, or only partially available, and not in the form desired. Trials and experiments are usually necessary to discover class breaks that will serve the system purpose.

In the village comparison example, we started with a model that was too simple, based on our variability criteria, and made it more complex by adding dimensions until the result was satisfactory.

For complex systems, where some computing and data-processing facility is available, we can work the other way, i.e., start with a system definition, which for experimental purposes, has too many description categories. In such a simplification, the techniques discussed in this chapter may be used in combination.

Example: We want to describe the element and relationship blocks in the U.S. population into which individuals fall for the purpose of predicting the detailed opinions of the population regarding a political candidate. Initially, we decide on description of a population element in seven dimensions, each dividend into the levels shown below.

Table 7.4

Dimension number	Dimension name	Number of levels	Levels considered
1.	Political party	3	Democrat, Republican, Independent
2.	Religion	5	Protestant, Catholic, Jewish, Other, None
3.	Region	6	East, South, Midwest, Southwest, West, Border states
4.	Sex	2	Male, Female
5.	Residence	3	Rural, Town, Urban
6.	Occupation	5	Professional, White-collar, Blue-collar, Nonlabor family, No class
7.	Race	4	Caucasian, Negro, Oriental, Other

The total number of possible classifications is the product of the seven level numbers ($3 \times 5 \times 6 \times 2 \times 3 \times 5 \times 4$), or 10,800. Clearly, adding more dimensions or levels rapidly increases the number of possible combinations beyond reasonable bounds, certainly for visual tabulation purposes, and for most data-collection budgets. For example, suppose we add preference for candidate *A, B, C,* or *D* as dimension No. 8, and media exposure to TV, Radio, Newspapers, and Magazines as dimension No. 9. Then the number of possible combinations is $10,800 \times 4 \times 4$, or 172,800.

Although the storage of this type of mass data is not impossible, it would be cumbersome for analysis and prediction, and we would want to reduce the number of classes. We would proceed in the following way:

Step 1: Although all the combinations suggested are possible, there are many very *improbable* combinations, or combinations representing so small a portion of the total population that they would contribute little to our prediction of candidate popularity. These category-combinations can be eliminated. For example, there may be one or two *Negro-Jewish-Professional-Males* in the *Rural-South* who prefer *Candidate C,* are *Republican,* and primarily read *Newspapers.* However, that event is so unlikely and so unimportant in the total, that the specific combination is dropped. Continuing with more enthusiasm, we note that the number of *Professional* workers in *Rural* areas is so small that the entire block of possibilities containing this combination of levels may be eliminated. Proceeding in this way, we may reduce the possible number of combinations to a much more limited number.

Step 2: With our now smaller list, we begin to ask questions about the usefulness of some of our dimensions and levels—are they really *all* necessary? Suppose we know the combination *Urban-Catholic-Negro* is highly correlated (in terms of political preference) with *Urban-Catholic-Caucasian* opinion. Need the racial distinction be made here or in similar types? Obviously not, if our purpose is to predict political opinion by extrapolating from the opinions of blocks, or prototypes, of population segments. We may group the possible combinations, because the variation between them is so small in terms of our system objective. For example, we may eliminate Race as a dimension entirely, except for the few critical areas where it may be important, say *Urban-Negro-East.* Just as we used our knowledge of the census data in Step 1, we would use our knowledge of political science, sociology, and past voting data to effect a further elimination of distinctions that were *highly correlated,* by grouping them into a more general class. (We would make certain, of course, that the correlation was stable, by examining the stability of past history.)

Step 3: As a final step we would test the prototype blocks of population remaining in our reduced system to confirm that individuals represented by the prototype (a) varied only little in their political opinion *within* their specific class, and tended to move in opinion with their category neighbors; (b) that there was a sufficient difference of opinion and movement of opinion *between* the remaining classes, so that further grouping would not be desirable; and (c) that the stability of our final class definitions could be assured in field data collection that would bring to our files the opinion trends necessary for updating our simplified system.[15]

*OTHER DIRECT SIMPLIFICATION METHODS

In addition to elimination and grouping, at least three other direct forms of system simplification find wide use. These approaches are (1) The substitution and transformation of variables, relationships, and parameters, (2) the exploitation of system symmetry, and (3) the tabular rearrangement of data rows and columns into partitioned blocks. We will briefly review each approach in turn. (Many other forms of direct simplification can be found in specialized fields. When such methods are found useful in the reader's work, he should note them down as an addition to our present, abbreviated list.)

*Substitution and Transformation

We can often use substitution of variables, relationships, and parameters to simplify a system description. These forms of simplification are also useful to bring an unfamiliar model into a familiar form or to ease analysis.

Example: We often use a simple substitution of parameters to simplify equations. To illustrate, suppose we wish to solve the equation

$$(p - q)x^2 + (p + q)x + \frac{u + v}{r} = 0$$

in which p, q, u, v, and r are constants, for x. The equation is cumbersome, and we may not recognize it as a standard form. However, by substituting

$$a = (p - q) \qquad b = (p + q) \qquad c = \frac{u + v}{r},$$

the original equation becomes

$$ax^2 + bx + c = 0$$

---

[15] For a popular treatment of this form of simplification, see Eugene Burdick, *The 480,* McGraw-Hill, New York, 1964. The number "480" refers to the 480 population categories used by political scientists to analyze opinion for the Democratic Party in the Kennedy campaign of 1960. The Appendix to Burdick's book gives a description of the 480 categories remaining after the simplification procedure described above.

the familiar quadratic equation with the well-known solution

$$x = \frac{-b \pm \sqrt{b^2 - 4ac}}{2a}.$$

We may now resubstitute the original values, and obtain the solution in terms of p, q, u, v, and r.

$$x = \frac{-(p + q) \pm \sqrt{(p + q)^2 - 4(p - q)(u + v)/r}}{2(p - q)}$$

In less obvious cases an ingenious rearrangement of terms and careful choice of values for substitution may be needed. Several examples of this type appear in the derivations of Appendix B.

The substitution of variables and relationships according to a consistent rule leads to a transformation in which we convert one *set* of variables and relationships into another set. The mathematical transformations discussed in Appendix B are examples of this method of simplification.

The one-to-one transformation, which maps each possible system in one scheme to a unique set of systems in another is of major interest, because it is reversible, and we can thus obtain solutions in the original framework. Figure B-1 illustrates this transformation-inversion procedure.

One of the major questions that arise when we transform a system from one scheme to another is which system properties remain *invariant* under the transformation. Thus, if we draw a circle on a plane and then transform that plane into a cylinder (by rolling up the page until its edges touch) we preserve many properties of the original circle. The circle's area, circumference, and radius will be the same as before if we measure these values along the cylinder's surface. However, points on the circle's circumference are no longer equidistant from a perpendicular drawn through the center of the circle. This fact is certainly of interest to a sheet metal worker who attempts to fit round pipes together; a round pipe of the original diameter would not fit the hole in the cylinder. We would also be interested, as systems analysts, in how alterations of the circle in the plane correspond to alterations of the circle on the cylinder and vice versa.

The use of logarithms provides a more direct example. When we take the logarithm of two numbers, say 8 and 16, the difference between the original numbers is not preserved, e.g., $\log_2 8 = 3$ and $\log_2 16 = 4$, a difference of 1 instead of 8. Moreover, operations on the transformed numbers are transformed, too. The addition of the logarithms is equivalent to multiplication of the original numbers. This knowledge is important because if we consistently apply the corresponding operations to the original and transformed numbers, the results of those operations will be identical, e.g., $\log_2 8 + \log_2 16 = 3 + 4 = 7$, and the antilog of 7 to the base 2 is $2^7 = 128 = 8 \times 16$. Thus the ability to perform easier operations on the transformed system is of great value in simplifying systems analysis.

We will leave further discussion to Appendix B, but cite a famous problem to illustrate the power of the transformation to aid analysis.

Example: The famous Swiss mathematician Leonhard Euler presented the following problem and its solution to the Russian Academy at St. Petersburg in 1775.[16] In the town of Königsberg in Prussia there was an island called Kneiphof, marked A in Figure 7-12a, with the branches of the river Pregel flowing about it as shown. Seven bridges, marked a, b, c, d, e, f, and g connect the island to three land areas, B, C, D. The question: Can a person plan a walk in such a way that he will cross each bridge once but not more than once? The townspeople amused themselves trying different routes; some claimed it could be done, others denied the possibility. Euler solved the problem in general as well as for the specific case by converting the map to a flow graph.

Let the node of a graph represent each of the four land areas, $A, B, C,$ and D. Let the arcs of the graph represent each of the seven bridges connecting the nodes appropriately. Figure 7-12b shows the result. The bridge problem is the same as that of transversing the graph from a given starting point over each arc only once and returning to the start. Call a node or vertex of the graph *even* if an even number of arcs lead to it, and *odd* otherwise. Euler proved in general that the required route is possible only for graphs that have all *even* nodes. If the graph has no more than two odd nodes, all arcs may be covered in one journey, but it is not possible to return to the starting point. In general, if the graph has $2n$ odd nodes, where n is any integer, it will require exactly

[16] Adapted from L. Euler, "The Seven Bridges of Königsberg," reprinted in J. R. Newman, *The World of Mathematics,* Simon and Schuster, New York, 1956, pp. 573–580.

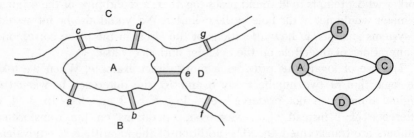

7-12 The Seven Bridges of Königsberg. At left, a map showing four land areas and seven bridges. At right, an equivalent graph.

n distinct journeys to traverse it.[17] These general deductions were possible by study of the graph, although they were not obvious from the map.

*Symmetry

Another important simplification principle is to invoke the concept of symmetry, or to exploit symmetric system structure if present. Although we use symmetry to indicate "beauty" and "fine form" in common language, we refer more specifically to bilateral symmetry, exemplified by right- and left-hand similiarity, mirror images, or the geometrical symmetry of a circle about a diameter or a sphere about a plane through its center.[18]

As a simplification procedure, symmetry permits us to extend analysis of a smaller part of a system to a result for the system as a whole. Thus, if we know a hemisphere has a volume of two cubic feet, we know at once that a sphere made of two such hemispheres will have a volume of four cubic feet. In systems analysis this principle is important in handling complex decision trees, probability problems, and structural analyses. The device is greatly enhanced if we can find symmetries within symmetries. Although extensions of this idea abound, one simple example will suffice here.

> *Example:* If a stick is broken in half at random, what is the length of the smaller piece? Solution: "Breaking 'at random' means that all points of the stick are equally likely as a breaking point (uniform distribution). The breaking point is just as likely to be in the left half as the right half. If it is in the left half, the smaller piece is on the left; and its average is half of that half, or one fourth of the length of the stick. The same sort of argument applies when the break is in the right half of the stock, and so the answer is one fourth of the length." [19]

[17] For the full proof, which is a simple and direct argument, the reader must consult the reference cited. However, to disprove the Königsberg possibility, we give the following from Euler, which sets the pattern for his later proofs. Suppose you start at A and begin to traverse arcs, recording the route as A, B, A, C, . . . , etc. A pair of capital letters indicates an arc is crossed, e.g., AB or BA indicates that one of the two arcs between A and B, is crossed. Since five bridges lead to A, the letter A must appear at least three times in the sequence describing the route. Similarly, the letter B must appear twice, since three bridges lead to B; similarly D and C must each occur twice. "That is to say," Euler concluded, "the series of eight letters that represent the crossing of the seven bridges (with A as a starting point) must contain A three times, and B, C, and D each twice; but this is quite impossible with a series of eight letters. Thus, it is apparent that a crossing of the seven bridges of Königsberg in the manner required cannot be effected." Euler's argument and later generalization is most easily visualized by inspection of the flow graph.

[18] See H. Weyl, *Symmetry*, Princeton University Press, Princeton, N.J., 1952, reprinted in abbreviated form in J. R. Newman, *The World of Mathematics*, Simon and Schuster, New York, 1956, pp. 671–724.

[19] F. Mosteller, *Fifty Challenging Problems in Probability with Solutions*, Addison-Wesley, Reading, Mass., 1965, p. 63. This small book contains many problems illustrating symmetry.

*Partitions

If a system is very large it may be possible to break it into several smaller independent subsystems. This principle was illustrated in Figure 7-6 when we discussed threshold methods of simplification. However, we provide some matrix illustrations here for emphasis.

First, tabular data, particularly data that represent input-output relationships, may be collected in a form that does not indicate any independent structure. Such matrix representations may come from the development of sets of simultaneous equations, from observation of system transactions, or from other sources. At the outset, the arrangements of the rows and columns, set by the arbitrary numbering of system elements, may produce a "random" looking result. See Figure 7-13, where an "X" indicates a table entry and a blank a zero.

However, by judicious rearrangement of the rows and columns of the matrix, we may arrange the data in blocks, or in practical cases into near block form. In Figure 7-13a, for example, the rows and columns are numbered 1, 2, 3, and 4. If we rearrange both rows and columns in the order 1, 3, 2, 4, we obtain the blocked result shown in Figure 7-13b. This revised result would indicate relationships between elements 1 and 3 as a subsystem and between elements 2 and 4 as another subsystem. The two subsystems are independent because no entries relate 1 and 3 with 2 and 4. This ideal may be approximated in many cases, either by rounding, by using a threshold cutoff, or by a row and column rearrangement that recognizes larger table entries as more important than small. The rearrangement will be more obvious with spare matrices, i.e., those with many zero entries. When perfect blocks of table entries cannot be found, approximate blocks will be useful to indicate approximate subsystem divisions and the important relations which link them in the over-all system.

The ability to partition data in this way also has many computational advantages. If a table can be broken up into smaller blocks as shown below, the segments of the table can be handled separately. When this is done it may be possible to handle a very large single computation as a series of smaller computations. The ability to eliminate zeros or insignificantly small

$$
\begin{array}{c}
\begin{array}{cccc} 1 & 2 & 3 & 4 \end{array} \\
\begin{array}{c} 1 \\ 2 \\ 3 \\ 4 \end{array}
\left[
\begin{array}{cccc}
x & & x & \\
 & x & & x \\
x & & x & \\
 & x & & x
\end{array}
\right]
\end{array}
\qquad
\begin{array}{c}
\begin{array}{cccc} 1 & 3 & 2 & 4 \end{array} \\
\begin{array}{c} 1 \\ 3 \\ 2 \\ 4 \end{array}
\left[
\begin{array}{cccc}
x & x & & \\
x & x & & \\
 & & x & x \\
 & & x & x
\end{array}
\right]
\end{array}
$$

$$(a) \qquad\qquad\qquad (b)$$

7-13   Data arrangement for partitioning.

numbers from the computation reduces computation time and the memory space required for storage if an electronic computer is used. Thus, given fixed computing facilities, a large "impossible" computation can be handled by treating that single problem in stages.

Example: Consider the multiplication of a 4×4 matrix by a column vector as shown below.

$$\begin{bmatrix} 2 & 4 & 0 & 0 \\ 1 & 2 & 0 & 0 \\ 0 & 0 & 3 & 2 \\ 0 & 0 & 1 & 2 \end{bmatrix} \times \begin{bmatrix} 1 \\ 2 \\ 3 \\ 4 \end{bmatrix} = [10, \quad 5, \quad 17, \quad 11]$$

Compare this result with the two multiplications of the 2×2 blocks partitioned from the original matrix by 2 two-element column vectors.

$$\begin{bmatrix} 2 & 4 \\ 1 & 2 \end{bmatrix} \times \begin{bmatrix} 1 \\ 2 \end{bmatrix} = [10, \quad 5]$$

$$\begin{bmatrix} 3 & 2 \\ 1 & 2 \end{bmatrix} \times \begin{bmatrix} 3 \\ 4 \end{bmatrix} = [17, \quad 11]$$

The original result can be obtained by recombining the two smaller results, but all of the multiplications by zero have been omitted, and the number of positions used for storage of the problem has been reduced.

Thus, partitioning has wide use in the analysis of large scale systems, both to simplify interpretation and to reduce computation. The study of input-output economic relationships and the manipulation of such data provide obvious applications, as does the analysis of other forms of transaction and interaction data. (For several input-output readings that will illustrate the simplification of large-scale systems defined in tabular form, see Problem 7-7.)

In this chapter, we have discussed a number of direct simplification methods. In Chapter 8, we will study system simplification methods that may be applied indirectly, or at a higher level of system hierarchy.

PROBLEMS

7.1 Following the diagram of Figure 7-4, in which the problem was to find the maximum value of

$$\text{Revenue} = 50x + 75y$$

while observing the restrictions

$$(1) \quad 8x + 4y \leqq 400$$
$$(2) \quad 5x + 10y \leqq 400$$

suppose additional restrictions were added as follows:

$$
\begin{align}
(3) \quad & 7.8x + 4.3y \leq 400 \\
(4) \quad & 4.8x + 10.2y \leq 400 \\
(5) \quad & 8.5x + 4.3y \leq 400 \\
(6) \quad & 5.2x + 9.8y \leq 400 \\
(7) \quad & x + y \leq 80 \\
(8) \quad & x \leq 50 \\
(9) \quad & y \leq 50
\end{align}
$$

A. Make a plot, similar to that of Figure 7-4, but including all of the additional constraints. Is the feasible area of solution substantially changed?

B. Which of the constraints could be *eliminated* without affecting the maximum value of revenue? (That is, which could be thrown out as irrelevant?)

C. Which of the constraints could be grouped, thereby reducing their number, without materially affecting the solution?

D. Why is the simplification of the "system" in this way a useful process for the analyst?

E. A computer program used to find the point of maximum revenue (and the corresponding mix or combination of x and y) takes a length of time which is approximately proportional to the number of constraints imposed. Comment on the economic balance between the cost of computation required to find the precise solution to the system containing nine constraints as opposed to the loss of precision in the solution that can be obtained more quickly and inexpensively if the problem is simplified to only the first two constraints? Why would such simplification procedures be of interest to the analyst who confronts a large-scale problem, i.e., one with a very large number of constraints?

7.2   Consider the problem defined in three variables by the following:

$$\text{Maximize Revenue} = 50x + 75y + 100z$$

where

$$
\begin{align}
(1) \quad & 8x + 4y + z \leq 400 \\
(2) \quad & 5x + 10y + z \leq 400
\end{align}
$$

A. Realizing that the two constraints represent planes in a 3-dimensional space, draw a diagram representing the feasible area that the values of x, y, and z can take on. Mark the extreme points of this feasible area. (You should have four, plus the origin, 0, 0, 0.)

B. Why is the knowledge that the optimum revenue must occur at one of the extreme points a simplification procedure?

C. By observation, or evaluation, what is the maximum revenue?

D. Could you have deduced this result from observation of the objective and constraints—without drawing the figure?

7.3 The game of tick-tack-toe is played on a 3 × 3 table, or matrix, by two players. The first player selects and marks one of the nine squares. The second player selects and marks one of the remaining eight squares. The first player then selects and marks one of the seven remaining squares, etc. ("X's" and "O's" are usually used to indicate the choices of the first and the second player, respectively.)

The game ends when either player succeeds in marking three squares so that they form a straight line, horizontally, vertically, or diagonally. The game may also end in a tie, in which all the squares in the table have been filled, but neither player has achieved the winning result.

A. If the matrix of play is numbered in the usual matrix format, so that each of the nine squares in the table is designated by a particular subscript pair (i, j) from $(1, 1)$ through $(3, 3)$, how many distinct patterns of play would be available to the first player—if the game were not terminated by the "win" rule above? The second player? What effect does the win rule as a constraint have upon the number of possibilities for each player?

B. At the outset, the first player has nine possible square-choices, if the matrix notation (i, j) is used. If we invoke the principle of symmetry as a simplification procedure, how many basic choices does the first player have on the first move? What are they?

C. How many basic choices does the second player have on the second move, if the first player *has chosen the center square* on the first move?

D. Why is the principle of symmetry a powerful simplification procedure when it can be used?

E. Suppose the first player *does not originally select the center square*. How many basic moves are there for the second player if the first player (1) selects a corner square, (2) selects a peripheral midsquare? Why is the power of symmetry as a simplification procedure reduced in these cases?

7.4 Suppose you are making a study of United States real estate prices with the objective of buying 50,000 acres or more for residential development. As a start you propose to make a map of the United States that will show in different colors the average price per acre across the country.

A. If your time and resources required the completion of this preliminary study in 30 days, how could you simplify the data collection and data display?

B. How would you locate the required price information in an efficient and inexpensive manner?

C. How could you simplify the storage of your basic data so they could be updated with new price trends?

D. In making a more detailed study of "interesting" areas, how could you simplify the cross-reference problem for the many local factors that might be used to compare one region or tract with another?

E. How might local factors cause you to review your original picture?

7.5   As Fanny Hill once observed, there is a certain repetition in life. Fortunately, Fanny was right.

A. Why is statistically stable repetition an essential requirement for statistical simplification?

B. Would definition or simplification of a system be possible if there were no repetition of events?

C. We often hear a conflicting quotation, attributed to the pre-Socratic philosopher Heraclitus, who observed: "You can never step in the same river twice," and ". . . the only constant is change." If this world view is true, does it conflict with the concept of statistical regularity and stability required for system definition? If not, how are the two extremes compatible?

D. The late Billy Rose made one of his fortunes by a statistical analysis of popular songs during the thirties. He found a large proportion of "ooh" sounds in the popular lyrics of the time and thereupon composed a number of songs according to that formula, such as "Barney Google With The Goo-Goo-Googley Eyes." What assumption about the market made this approach reasonable, and, as it turned out, very rewarding?

7.6   In the payoff matrix below, three strategies, S_1, S_2, S_3, are proposed. The payoff for each of four possible outcomes, N_1, N_2, N_3, N_4, (whichever occurs) is given. Strategy S_1 is a *dominant strategy*, because it has a larger payoff under all possible conditions than S_2 or S_3.

	N_1	N_2	N_3	N_4
S_1	8	6	5	10
S_2	7	5	5	9
S_3	8	4	3	8

A. Why is the search for a dominant strategy a simplification procedure?

B. What is the danger in developing an incomplete list of possible strategies? What is the danger of developing an incomplete list of possible outcomes?

7.7   As an exercise, read the following articles from *Scientific American* magazine. Note the data handling and simplification methods used by the authors. Also note how the structure of the tables may be interpreted and how portions of the tables may be partitioned. The reader will benefit more from these articles if he has learned how to invert a matrix, as described in Appendix A.

W. W. Leontief, "Input-Output Economics," *Scientific American*, October 1951.

W. W. Leontief and M. Hoffenberg, "The Economic Effects of Disarmament," *Scientific American*, April 1961.

W. W. Leontief, "The Structure of Development," *Scientific American*, September 1963.

W. W. Leontief, "The Structure of the U.S. Economy," *Scientific American*, April 1965.

A. P. Carter, "The Economics of Technological Change," *Scientific American*, April 1966.

(A complete set of these articles in reprint form, together with a large multicolor wall chart showing the complete input-output table of the United States Economy with latest figures is available from Director of Research, *Scientific American*, 415 Madison Avenue, New York, N. Y.)

8 | HIGHER-ORDER SIMPLIFICATION METHODS

The detailed methods of definition and simplification discussed thus far are most suitable for the study of relatively simple systems. Detailed flow charts, tabulations, lists, equations, and logical rules are the paraphernalia of a systems analyst working to improve a procedure or process that is both limited in scope and stable in character—or one abstracted sufficiently to produce those desirable conditions.

Theoretically, of course, the same approach and the same tools could be extended without limit to the large, complex, goal-directed system. Yet, a number of practical difficulties suggest an altogether different approach and set of tools.

If a system is able to formulate its own goals and plans, to switch goals and plans at will, and to adjust internally its own allocation of resources and priorities of action, knowledge of current structure is less useful for prediction and control than knowledge of the guiding goals and values which integrate and guide the total system. Moreover, for very large systems, a detailed definition may not be feasible, even if it were useful. In short, the analyst's resources must be redeployed and his thinking shifted to a different level if he is to make headway in an environment of true complexity.

As a consequence, we now shift our level of discussion from that of detailed system definition and direct simplification to the higher level consideration of system goals, objectives, values, and measures of effectiveness —both present and potential.

A RESORT TO HIGHER-ORDER DEFINITION

A statement of a system's major goals, objectives, values, and measures of effectiveness, together with a few major constraints, allows the analyst to approach the "controlling structure" of the system at the outset, rather than after collecting detail about operations. Because the list of goals, objectives, and measures of effectiveness a system uses will diminish in length as we go up the organization hierarchy, the analyst may, by this approach, limit himself in his definition to a smaller number of important relevant points, yet retain those factors that have pervasive and lasting effects upon system operation. He may, indeed, find the higher level definition a more stable and predictive way to define the system than the use of detail.

The Simplifying Effects of Higher-Order Definition

The higher-order approach to system definition simplifies by working with the system's control structure hierarchy. This more general, higher order method provides a definition less time-dependent than the detailed structure definition, and covers more special cases, thereby reducing the variety of definitions that would otherwise be required for numerous special cases. We give up something in specificity of prediction, but we gain in generality of coverage.

The higher-order approach stresses *relevance* rather than completeness or precision. Just as the design for a building may be an elaboration of the outlines of an architect's sketch on a dinner menu (as was the case with Eero Saarinen's design for the futuristic TWA Air Terminal at New York's Kennedy Airport), the analyst's detailed system of definition may originate from the relevant insights gained from the higher order "sketch," which, by its very simplicity, projects these points. For this reason we speak of "this view from the top" as a simplification method.

The higher-order approach is also concerned with the system's potential for improvement, growth, change, and optimization. In planning and control terms, it is a strategic approach. We want a trade between one form of effort and another, between one measure of effectiveness and another. We arrange our definitions to produce this result.

Goals and effectiveness measures

Before continuing, let us define goals and effectiveness measures.

A *goal* is a desired state or result we hope to reach. For example, to hit a given target, or to come as near to it as possible, is a goal; to achieve the maximum possible profit, or the minimum possible cost, under given constraints is a statement of a goal. (Other synonyms, such as objective, purpose, and aim, may be used.)

An *effectiveness measure,* sometimes called by mathematicians an "objective function," allows us to measure how well we are doing with respect to the goal, and in this way specifies in detail what we mean by the goal's accomplishment for a particular problem.

For example, suppose our goal is to maximize profit in a given operation. This is a vague idea until we specify that profit is to be calculated as $50x + 75y$. The statement Maximize Profit, where Profit $= 50x + 75y$, is now complete. We know what we want to accomplish (maximize) and we know that we must measure the result of any combination of x and y in terms of that objective. The effectiveness measure provides us with a rating scale and allows us to compare alternate courses of action (say, various combinations of x and y) by their relative effectiveness measures.

One alternative (or set of alternatives) is called more effective, or "better" than another (or another set) if it receives a higher effectiveness measure score (higher profit in this maximizing problem).[1]

We see that the most effective choice of alternatives possible (or feasible) is the "optimum" choice. This is specifically what we mean by "optimum": Not some vague notion of the "best" result, but rather the highest score on an effectiveness measure scale that clearly defines how the best shall be measured.

The effectiveness measure thus leads us to the "best" choice or choices of alternatives, i.e., those having the highest score or equally highest scores on the scale *we have defined* or accepted as our yardstick. We can readily see the importance of clearly defining the effectiveness measure for a system, when we realize that changing the scoring method will change the game.

If a touchdown in football were worth less than a field goal, i.e., if we computed the final score by giving more points for a field goal than for a touchdown, the team activities would change accordingly. The team would attempt more field goals and fewer touchdowns. Similarly, in the maximizing example, if Profit $= 75x + 50y$ (instead of $50x + 75y$), we could generally expect a shift in the optimum combination of x and y. Moreover, the relevant points of system definition change, too. The constraints on field goals and the constraints on the production of x become relatively more important than the constraints on touchdowns and the constraints on the production of y.

Later in the chapter, we develop the implications of the effectiveness measure. We should note, however, that effectiveness is not necessarily the same as efficiency. *Effectiveness* means to produce the desired result, to

---

[1] Similarly, should the objective be to minimize cost, we would seek a low score, or minimum measure. Other goals and effectiveness measures are obviously possible.

accomplish the correct end, or to secure the relevant outcome. Efficiency in its generic use means to accomplish any stated objective without wasting resources. Thus, we may find the most efficient route from New York to Memphis in terms of time, cost, or other resources, but this solution would not be effective (or relevant) if our objective were to go from New York to Los Angeles.

To the economist, efficiency has a more precise meaning. For the maximizing problem given above, a choice of x and y would be called "technically efficient" if, for a stated value of x, we had made y as large as feasible or possible, so that our potential ability to increase y had not been wasted. (Under such conditions, a change in x requires a change in y and vice versa.) In this technical sense, we may have many "efficient" combinations of x and y, namely those combinations that force us to the limit of our limited abilities or resources. To look for technical efficiency is insufficient. Each efficient combination of x and y may have a different effectiveness measure, and only one combination (or a few) may be able to achieve the maximum effectiveness score.[2] We must have a clear effectiveness measure before we can select the optimum course of action.

With these preliminaries, and hopefully with a higher motivation and interest in the specification of clear and workable effectiveness measures, we will now discuss the more complex system, consisting of a hierarchy of subsystems, subdivisions, or departments we hope to define by our higher level methods.

The definition of conflicts

Conflict in decision making arises when the outcome of a choice can be valued from two or more viewpoints. For example, suppose that in a deterministic system strategies S_1 and S_2 are proposed and that from one viewpoint the values of the outcome for each strategy are $S_1 = 10$ and $S_2 = 20$. Then, the highest value strategy is S_2. However, if from another viewpoint the values are different, say $S_1 = 18$, $S_2 = 9$, the choice is reversed. Thus, to select the highest value strategy, the user must agree on the method of evaluation, and if he cannot, conflict results.

One method of resolution is to seek a "higher" method of evaluation which encompasses two (or more) methods of evaluation as subsets. To illustrate, suppose the values shown for S_1 and S_2 by the above two methods are additive, and that we agree to abide by the total result, a new value which includes both. Then the new values are $S_1 = 28$, and $S_2 = 29$ and the

---

[2] The reader may like to compare this discussion with the problems illustrated in Figures 7-4 and 7-9, and to follow up the point by reading the first few chapters of R. P. Dorfman, P. A. Samuelson, and R. M. Solow, *Linear Programming and Economic Analysis*, McGraw-Hill, New York, 1958, and C. J. Hitch and R. N. McKean, *The Economics of Defense in the Nuclear Age*, Harvard University Press, Cambridge, Mass., 1960.

conflict is resolved. To resolve the conflict in another way, we might simply suppress one scheme of evaluation or the other and abide by the simplified result.

Although simplified operations research and systems analysis studies often use one of the resolution approaches above, practical resolution of conflict in most important choice problems presents serious evaluation difficulties. Questions of additivity, scaling, utility—and whether measurements of certain values can be made at all—are not easily resolved. Such questions, however, have a direct bearing upon the outcome of a choice procedure and thus, if incorrectly answered, can seriously distort a system definition and its use.

Therefore, in the higher level of definition of a complex system, we seek conflicts in the goal structure of the system's organization of goal-directed efforts. We take this approach because system difficulties usually show up in the way the system rates or measures the success of its major subdivisions, or departments. The analyst will usually select as a guide a level of hierarchy detail that will reveal the major conflicts between functional departments or blocks in the work flow.

In earlier chapters we have seen that the configuration of a system's transformation blocks and the transactions between them provides the detailed capabilities of the system, and allows us to predict system output for a given input. Such a definition can usually be obtained for the relatively simple system.

If the system is of a higher level however, it will contain various choice points. The various blocks, or subsystems, may adopt alternate response patterns to alternate goals, either because this ability is built into the system design, or because the subsystems have learning or innovating abilities.

Our design problem then is to coordinate the subsystems into an organization that will enhance the over-all purpose(s) of the *total system*. We want to predict the effect of goal-directed activities of the departments on total system performance.

The most likely trouble-spot in the design of a complex system, or the operation of an existing complex system, is not that the individual blocks do not operate "efficiently" or even effectively regarding their own stated goals, but that the goals guiding these operations do not, when combined, result in either efficient or effective operation of the entire system.

Example: Consider a typical industrial organization consisting of three functional departments or divisions: Sales, Production, and Finance. We hope to goal-direct the output of the subsystems to avoid random action. Let us suppose that the departments will execute efficiently any goal we set. We must then select an effectiveness measure for each department, for the use of their managers and staffs.

For example, suppose we decide to base a salesman's commission on a fixed percentage of individual gross sales. Then the "best" salesman would be the one with the highest gross sales, or the "best" Sales Department would be the one with the highest total gross sales.

Similarly, we may rate the Production operation on a "production cost per unit" basis. Then the "best" production manager or the "best" Production Department would be the one that, in a given period of time, produced a given unit output at least cost.

And, if we use maximum cash liquidity, or minimum bank charges, or minimum bad accounts, as a criterion for financial excellence then the financial officer, or the Finance Department, will adjust operations to achieve these goals, and different financial officers and departments may be scaled accordingly (Figure 8-1a).

In short, if a given goal or objective has been recognized and judged accordingly by the subsystem (or individual in the subsystem), let us assume that the decision-making apparatus of the subsystem (or individual) will select available alternatives. The chosen alternatives should improve the "success measure." Moreover, the subsystems will attempt to alter the structure of operations, the resources available, and the restrictions present in order to attain "higher scores." By design, psychological direction, or other motivations, we can usually accomplish this result.

At first glance, we may be happy with our accomplishment. The departments and individuals know their functions and purposes, they are performing them efficiently, and they are learning, by our measure, to improve their performance.

Trouble will arise, of course, if while improving its own success or effectiveness measure, the goal-seeking actions of one department (or individual) thwart, frustrate, and defeat the goal-seeking actions of other departments (and individuals).

For example, the subobjectives of maximum gross dollar sales, minimum production cost per unit, and maximum cash liquidity seldom produce a harmonious operating result for a system of three functions (Sales Department, Production Department, Finance Department) that hopes for maximum profitability.

The product mix sold to achieve maximum gross sales may not be the most profitable, or cheapest one, to make. The cheapest product mix to manufacture may not be the salable one. The methods and equipment required for the cheapest manufacturing cost may require major capital investments, thereby detracting from financial liquidity.

Worse, we may find that rating each individual solely on gross sales produces less total gross sales than the Sales Department could otherwise achieve! The lack of cooperation among individual salesmen

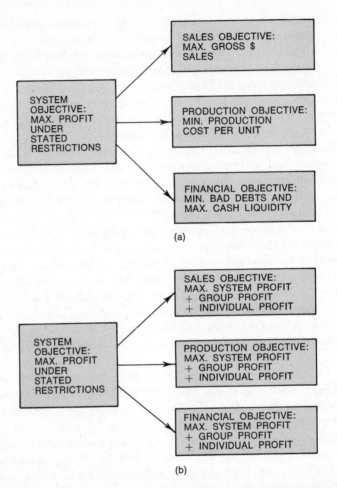

8-1 Two structures of systems and subsystem objectives. In (a), as described in the text, obvious conflicts of interest are generated between the departments by the way in which subgoals have been set. In (b), the subgoals have been modified. The measures of effectiveness are more complex, but attempts to maximize the rating score computed from the mere complex measure will force greater cooperation between the departments.

engendered by our strict gross sales commission policy could cause conflicts within the Sales Department itself.

The same argument also applies to Production and Finance. There is no guarantee that the same success measure applied to individuals and groups will produce the desired over-all result. Furthermore, there is no assurance that the goals set for individual departments in light of their functions will, when combined into a system of subgoals, produce the desired result for the system composed of these parts.

Thus, in the complex organization, usually consisting of many goal-directed subsystems, subsystem conflict is the primary problem. The analyst is concerned with clarification of goal conflicts in a total system's organization of subsystems not only because it may simplify his definition problem, but also because the identification and resolution of such goal conflicts can have a profound effect upon the total system operation. Many analysts use this higher-order definition at once because they have found that only by this route can they achieve heroic improvements in total performance.

Suppose, as in Figure 8-1b, we attempt to remove some of the obvious conflicts in the organization by proposing a new rating method for each department. Because we want cooperation between the departments (so that the total system operation may be improved), we devise a rating measure that rewards group and total system achievement as well as individual excellence. Moreover, we arrange our rating scales by profits rather than by gross sales, production cost, or bad debts, so that we have a uniform scale of measure and a uniform maximizing objective for all departments in the system.

In the new system, our objective is to maximize the stated effectiveness measure (which is now the more complex formula containing weighted contributions of system, group, and individual profits). Although we have difficulty determining the exact formula to use in each department (e.g., the formula to balance individual and group incentive and motivation), a change from the first to the second scheme can strongly affect decision-making habits of the departments in question, and weighting factors in the effectiveness formula can manipulate system response. The analyst's problem is to know the effects of the present subgoals, and to be aware of alternate goals that may be evaluated by experiment or computation.

With this first example in mind, let us now turn to a more complicated case involving not only the problem of defining effectiveness measures, but also the problem of changing the definition of effectiveness as the organization grows.[3]

Example: The problem of system growth raises the question of reorganizing subgoals and may be illustrated by the small industrial organization that becomes large. Suppose the XYZ Company initially manufactures only one product, and uses three machines in the shop: a drill press, a lathe, and a metal saw.

Cost may be conveniently estimated by organizing the three machines into cost centers: a functional Drill Press Department, a Lathe Department, and a Saw Department.

---

[3] With larger multiactivity organizations, we usually improve the total system if we organize activities on a product-line, project, or mission basis, rather than on a functional or department basis. See J. G. March and H. A. Simon, *Organizations*, Wiley, New York, 1958, p. 29. For some military arguments for this approach, see Maxwell D. Taylor, *The Uncertain Trumpet*, Harper & Row, New York, 1960.

After watching the load on the three machine departments, the owner decides he could possibly fit another product into the line by using the idle capacity of the various departments, and he puts this plan into effect.

Business increases, and the owner adds additional capacity to the three departments by buying more drill presses, lathes, and saws, which in turn generate the ability to add to the width of the product line, which he does. As business grows, the owner finds he needs a greater variety of equipment; as a result, he adds new departments: a Plating Department, a Painting Department, an Assembly Department, a Shipping Department, a Credit Department, etc.

Unfortunately, as the operation grows in size and complexity, the owner has difficulty finding the cost of making his different products—because of scheduling, machine leading, and other problems (not to mention the accounting problem of overhead distribution). He can never seem to pin down the responsibility for a given product or given order, so that costs rise, lead times extend, and misquotes are made. He begins to lose orders, and his staff always seems at odds over who is responsible for a delay. Massive inventories build up in-process between departments. So that schedules and plans can be meaningful and not subject to crises each hour, the cost of communication and control systems and devices increases.

In short, the owner finds his total system effectiveness measure (which he may have defined as, say, net profit before taxes per dollar of gross sales) is declining.

Moreover, the owner has trouble finding the cause of the difficulty. So many of the operations required for a given product's production are entangled, enmeshed, and merged with the operations required for the production and coordination of other products that the problem of analysis and control seems insuperable—even though, for example, the machines in the shop are being used at nearly 100% of capacity, or "efficiency." The owner has lost control of the total operation. Although he uses the individual productive facilities efficiently, the organization is not as effective as it could be.

At this point in his growth, the owner (which may now be a corporation) may decide that a net increase in effectiveness, according to the measure adopted, may be improved by reorganizing the components of the total system on a product-line, project, or mission basis (Figure 8-2).

The owner may not only reassign supervisory responsibility along a product-line basis, but also physically separate the production equipment and reorganize it into a product-flow, rather than a functional grouping.

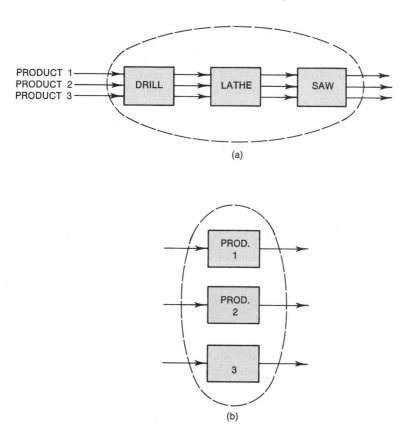

(a)

(b)

8-2 A shift in organization as a manufacturing system grows in complexity. In (a), the small shop passes each product through common operations. When the variety of products is small, there is efficiency in shared operations. However, as the variety of products and operations grows, the costs of coordination, machine interference, in-process inventories and bottlenecks increase, and it is frequently more efficient if the operations are regrouped on a product-line basis, even though there is duplication of productive facilities. The gain comes from the improved control ability and predictability obtained in the latter case. The growth history of most large industrial and military organizations follows this pattern.

In the new arrangement, the efficiency of the individual productive facilities may not be as great as before, probably less for the "decentralized" operations. Yet the over-all control cost, the inventory size, the lead-time length, and the cost estimate error will have been reduced, thus providing an increase in the total system's effectiveness measure. If we consider all product lines, the over-all effectiveness of the total organization will have been increased.

In the new physical and supervisory arrangements, the effectiveness measures of the new "blocks" in the system will also have been changed.

The owner would now be concerned with the profit before taxes on each product line per dollar of sales, a measure that allows *comparison* of products by their profitability. Indeed, to allow present product lines (and product-line divisions) to be compared to alternate investments, the owner may change all the effectiveness measures to "return on a five-year investment period," which may have further reorganization effects upon the system structure.

Questioning current effectiveness measures and the effects of possible alternate effectiveness measures, as we have seen, can have substantial repercussions in the operation of the total system and its parts.

Multiple goals

Just as the divisions of a system may have conflicting goals that restrict the full attainment of a clear over-all system objective, it may also be possible that the system as a whole, or one of its subsystems, has conflicting *multiple goals*. Such a system (or its part in conflict) like the house "divided against itself," usually finds itself in trouble. For this reason, multiple, yet conflicting goals are of interest in system definition.

Note that this form of goal conflict is different from the functional or operating conflicts discussed above. In the previous section, for example, the goals of each subsystem were clearly understood and followed. Furthermore, the total system goal was clear. Problems arose because the clearly followed subsystem goals caused conflict *between the subsystems,* and because the combination of such goals did not promote the clearly understood total system goal.

In multiple goal conflict, the system or its parts may not clearly perceive a set of goals consistent with themselves. For example, an industrial concern may state its objective as maximizing total gross dollar sales, and simultaneously maximizing net profit. In most large-scale industries that manufacture many different products and distribute to widely dispersed locations, these two goals are inconsistent: The gross sales objective argues for maximum sales without regard to profitability, and the profitability objective argues that items in the product-customer mix should be promoted selectively, with reference to individual profitability rather than to total gross sales.

Specifically, the production and marketing decisions, and the results obtained, will usually be different if the firm seeks one objective *or* the other. It is impossible to achieve both objectives simultaneously, except under the relatively trivial case in which the profit margin on all items is the same, and in which the marketing and distribution cost for all customers is the same (as would be so with one product sold to one customer). We often find such self-contradictory objectives when we have several trouble symptoms. First, the system may be aware that it cannot yield allegiance to two disparate goals simultaneously. To resolve the problem, the system may attempt to follow one goal at one time and another goal at another time. This solution may be tolerable if the alternate goal choices are not grossly opposed to each other. However, oscillation between extremely disparate goals can reduce the system's operation to total confusion, breakdown, or immobility, particularly if the conflict between goals is so severe that no goal or set of consistent goals can be selected. Such extreme results are common in the psychiatric literature concerning human breakdown, and are also evident in the operation of many large organizations and hardware systems.[4] Clearly, planning is difficult or impossible under these circumstances.

Similarly, the system may attempt to adopt other strategies to rid itself of the multiple-goal problem. It may appeal to a "higher" goal, which subsumes the conflicting goals and permits use of a new effectiveness measure. It may arbitrarily restrict its list of multiple goals to a consistent set, or it may "lock" on such a set and refuse to consider others (even though conditions have changed and the old goals are no longer appropriate for the growth or survival of the system). It may attempt to weight conflicting objectives and thereby artificially create a new single objective and effectiveness measure. Or, it may select and follow a simple goal or set of goals and leave the satisfaction of the remaining conflicting goals to the guidance of stated operational constraints. For example, it would be consistent to maximize gross dollar sales, while requiring the component actions to produce a profit contribution not less than 10%. This constraint would allow the simple objective to be followed, while modifying it to satisfy partially the requirements of the alternate, conflicting objective.[5]

As in the previous section, the resolution of multiple goal conflict can produce marked system improvement. Yet, regardless of how we resolve the goal conflict, our first step must be to define the goals and early attention to this systems analysis problem will simplify later ones.

Constraints, risks, and commitments

We have just seen that a constraint can modify a system objective by limiting or requiring a certain level of performance. In addition to stated

---

[4] It is unnecessary to cite a roster of goal-conflicts that may be found in any complex society, and therefore in its systems. Any observer can create his own list of Hamlet-like dilemmas. However, as a point of discussion, the reader may consult R. S. Lynd, *Knowledge for What?*, Princeton University Press, Princeton, N.J., 1939, especially Chapter 3, "The Pattern of American Culture," pp. 54–113.

[5] For a more complete discussion see: the Appendix "The Simple Mathematics of Optimization," in C. J. Hitch and R. N. McKean, *op. cit.*

constraints, which are introduced arbitrarily to eliminate goal-conflict problems, most systems also have physical constraints that have the same effect.

Thus, in a higher level definition it is desirable to look for the major physical constraints that may grossly affect system operation. Such constraints may be material- or information-processing abilities, or the time delays and response-time characteristics of the system.

Similarly, most systems have critical choice points at which major portions of the system's resources may be committed. When such decisions to commit the system to action risk failure, resulting in a substantial portion of the systems resources being lost or ineffectively used, knowledge of such points and types of decision must be included in the higher level system definition. This knowledge is necessary because decisions involving large commitments may not have the same effectiveness measure as those for more routine decisions; i.e., the utility scale may change.[6]

> *Example:* Suppose an industrial firm has the objective of maximum gross sales with the constraint of not less than 10% profit contribution on any sale. A salesman obtains a large order that will not only increase gross sales, but will also meet the profit criterion. However, that order represents a large percentage of the total productive capacity of the system. Thus, the risk of cancellation in midstream, the effect upon other customers due to delay in their deliveries, and possible expansions in productive capacity required to meet the over-all demand are all important factors to consider in the decision to accept the new, large order. Once the new order is accepted, the firm is committed and the point and manner in which the commitment is made become important factors in the higher-level system definition. Here, the utility of the dollars received for the new order may be less than for the usual order, and the firm may decide to handle it differently.

A Device for Higher-Level System Definition

One device for summarizing the facts of a higher-level system definition is an *Information Inventory Sheet*, as shown in Figure 8-3. The example shown refers to the processing and distribution of frozen chicken by a purchasing-manufacturing-distribution system.

The outline presentation can be drawn on a large sheet of paper. At the top we draw a rough block diagram showing material flow and informa-

---

[6] For a clear explanation and examples, see D. W. Miller and M. K. Starr, *Executive Decisions and Operations Research*, Prentice-Hall, Englewood Cliffs, N.J., 1961. To illustrate, most people will bet a quarter on any proposed lottery, but if $100 is the minimum stake, they begin to compute the odds against them in relation to the prize that can be won.

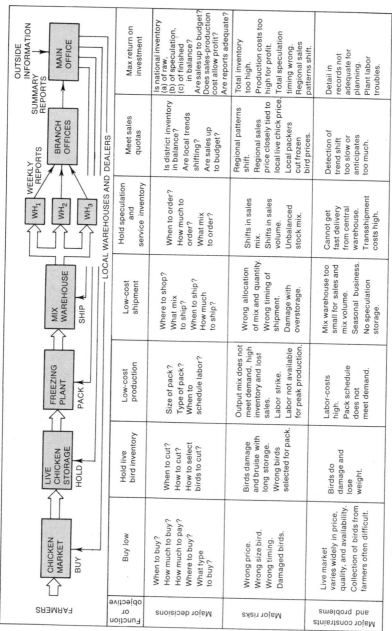

8-3 Data collection and analysis chart. A helpful tool in deciding where to start inventory investigations is a complete list of decisions, risks, and problems, under function, on a single piece of paper. In this form, the inter-relationship of problems can be seen, and work can be ranked in order of importance. The example shown refers to frozen chicken production, inventory, and sales.

tion flow. A column is provided for each major operation block, and each column is then divided into rows in which we may write the objectives, constraints, decisions, risks, and problems for each block. (Because of space requirements, Figure 8-3 is necessarily simplified. In practice, a larger sheet would permit more detail.)

This sheet may be completed by interview with the supervisor and staff at each block, with the detail of the sheet meeting the needs of the situation. Typically, when such a sheet has been filled out for each block, a review of the information collected (with all the information displayed at one time for the supervisors to view and discuss in conference) will produce additional entries, revisions, suggestions, and comments.

Moreover, all the information displayed at one time for the supervisors to view and discuss provides a common ground for understanding the total organization's objectives and problems.

Example: In the frozen chicken example of Figure 8-3, different problems arose. There were labor troubles at the processing plant, because of erratic scheduling. Field inventories of the product (chicken breasts, legs, wings, pies, whole birds, etc.) were unreasonably high, and unbalanced. Although the stock was sufficient, the right item was not at the right place at the right time; consequently, shortages, distress sales, and frequent expediting were the rule.

Because orders could often not be shipped from the mix warehouse as they were ordered from the field, the local sales people (at some 90 warehouse locations) tended to hoard what they thought would be needed, to pad orders to the factory, and to estimate local trends erroneously. The erratic production schedules existed because the mix warehouse was small compared with field storage capacity and production had to be geared to emergency orders.

A commitment to deliver a given pack could not be reversed, nor was it easy to reverse a decision to send a shipment to a given field warehouse location, because transshipment costs would represent more than the profit on the product. Worse, the chicken market is highly seasonal, placing peak loads on the buying and production operations.

The Information Inventory Sheet consolidated these facts with the stated objectives and constraints of each block, or department. Although this system definition is simplified (the details of processing activity and distribution activity are omitted), the Information Inventory Sheet has the advantage of displaying the "over-all" picture, so that the relation of the block objectives, constraints, risks, and problems can be seen by all.

It became apparent here, that the stated individual block objectives could not be achieved with a tightly coupled system. The need to make major production and distribution commitments early, caused largely by the small capacity of the mix warehouse, seemed to be the source of many of the difficulties. By enlarging this mix warehouse, which formerly was only a marshalling area to make up carload lots, and by changing its purpose to that of providing a buffer storage and speculation storage (rather than leaving this purpose to the field warehouses), the commitments on production runs could be scheduled without the interference of emergency requests.

Moreover, the commitment resulting from the shipment of large blocks of production of a given pack to a given field location could be postponed, and shipments could more nearly meet market demand. (Here the grouping of variability of demand and the ability to forecast over a short lead time are definite advantages.) These changes in capacity and objective served to "decouple" the production and distribution operations from unpredictable changes in the retail market, and furthermore, to decouple the production operation from the live chicken market. When the production operation could be planned for labor stability and divorced from immediate shipping and sales requirements, more attention could be devoted to handling the raw material efficiently.

The changes in purpose and capacity did not completely solve the stated problems of this organization, but they did provide major improvements in a time shorter than what would have been possible if the system definition had proceeded from the detailed to the general, rather than from the general to the specific.

Although our information inventory example was taken from a processing industry, the reader can, by extension, see the usefulness of the method in other systems definitions problems.

THE SIMPLIFYING EFFECT OF CHANGES
AT A HIGHER ORDER

Earlier in this chapter we saw that a change in system effectiveness measures together with planned reorganization could simplify a system definition (e.g., the case in which the functional organization was changed to a product-line organization). We now pursue that subject further.

Suppose an investigator were assigned the task of finding the quickest way to control a new job in a large-scale organization. (This is the task confronting a new administrator unfamiliar with the details of an organization.) Suppose further that, after cursory examination, the organization itself is found to have many of the goal-conflict problems we have described, as well as numerous political factions, operating difficulties, wasteful practices, and technical inadequacies. How should the investigator begin? What questions should he ask? How could he cut through oceans of data without losing perspective? If he is to supervise, how does he obtain control of his job and his organization?

For this assignment, our investigator will certainly start with the higher-level approach. He will use his knowledge of the conflicting department objectives, the critical decision and commitment points, and the procedures by which the organization exercises control.

Although he may be expected to find only a handful of powerful individuals in even the largest organizations, and also to realize that his main coercion sources lie in the power of the budget and the power of appointment, he may choose at first to shun these individuals or devices and view the organization at "arms length."

So that he may not be confused by too close a view, or be swayed by the briefings or political charm of the organization's present department heads, or waste time in a continuous series of conferences, he may prefer to formulate and to ask a series of pertinent questions in writing, and to delegate the responsibility for answering them to particular individuals, with particular deadlines.

Our investigator will receive some answers, but not others. Subsequently, he will spot deficiencies in the organization and locate conflicts of interest, duplication, omission, and critical commitments. (He may correlate these facts in an Information Inventory Sheet, or other convenient means, such as marginal cross referencing on the reports received.) One of his more important questions will be to request the evaluation reports by which the organization judges its performance (the documents and methods that implement measures of effectiveness in practice). Frequently he will find these reports of performance are contradictory, misdirected, unused, or lacking altogether.

He may then proceed to define his system by a synthesis of this material (if it is satisfactory), or he may choose to simplify the system by manipulating its objectives, effectiveness measures, and methods of reporting performance.

Note that to control the system our investigator may *of necessity* simplify his definition of the system or the system itself. It should also be evident that usually he cannot accomplish these simplifications by a detailed specification of changes in operating practices, detailed instructions to each individual in the organization, or detailed intervention in each exceptional case, nor can his present definition include these facts. He can, however, simplify system structure, operating practices, and decision-making, if he restructures the system's goal hierarchy and monitors performance against the new goals.

This high-level change may involve reorganizing the budget, changing the objectives of key personnel (or replacing them with others who will operate under the new objectives), and changing the format of reporting procedures and the communication flow. In other words, the investigator may combine system treatment or improvement with the definition of his system, bypassing the morass of detail he cannot control directly.

Although we have only sketched this approach to higher-order simplification through redefinition or manipulation of the system, we now present two dramatic examples that illustrate our point more fully.

Example: In 1961, four weeks after he became Secretary of Defense, R. S. McNamara dispatched drafts of questions, and sought not answers, but suggested information sources and possible deadlines for obtaining answers. On March 1, 1961, he issued the formalized drafts of his famous 96 questions (known as "McNamara's 96 Trombones") with a deadline and a man assigned to answer each question.[7] The answers, often returned to the author with requests for more specific information, pinpointed the duplication effort (the Pentagon had 3000 committees), contradictory estimates and plans (the separate intelligence services of the Army, Navy, and Air Force had different measures of the missile gap and peril), and omissions in organization (the Defense Department had no division charged with examining the organization and procedures of the armed services, although that was its task; instead, each service had its own department supposedly performing that function internally).

First, the obvious duplication was immediately eliminated (e.g., more than 400 committees were abolished in the first six months), and the missing divisions were added (the Defense Intelligence Agency and the Office of Organizational Management were created). McNamara then reorganized the budget and comptrollership operations and set the effectiveness measures by which the organizational complex was to evaluate itself (and be evaluated at the higher level). In vindication of General Taylor's position, these measures were adjusted to a mission, rather than to a functional or service basis, with the over-all objective of increasing the flexibility of the services instead of staking everything on the concept of massive retaliation, which had been fostered in the past, mostly by the Air Force. The widely reported changes in the Defense Establishment are an outgrowth of these early actions, which for the first time made the system manageable by a civilian authority, and did so, not by changing the practices of the military directly, but by changing the measures and questions by which their sources would be evaluated.

[7] T. H. White, "Revolution in the Pentagon," *Look*, April 23, 1963, pp. 31–44. This extremely complete and well-written article gives the background and procedure of McNamara's reorganization and results in more detail. For a later example at the city level, see S. V. Roberts, "Mayor to Set up Top Planning Unit," *New York Times*, July 27, 1966, p. 1. This article refers to the application of Defense Department Methods in New York City.

Example: O. W. Wilson, Police Superintendent of Chicago since 1960 (and, like McNamara, a former university professor) came to office after a major police scandal in which patrolmen acted as lookouts for criminals and transported stolen goods in police cars. He found his force riddled by corruption, racked by political pressure and patronage, and lacking the barest rudiments of efficient operation. Precincts were often organized along the boundaries of a political ward, with the ward boss dictating justice; some patrolmen had to purchase their own carbon paper to prepare reports.

In reorganizing the force, Wilson, like McNamara, gained control by working at arm's length. Although he occasionally talked to the press to create public confidence in his activities, he usually avoided the public and political visitors, and simply asked questions of his force.

He found, for example, that no organized reporting method existed for evaluating the performance of officers and patrolmen. Crime reports were often lost or not recorded, and seldom evaluated if available. Moreover, no assignment priority existed: Noisy parties received the same attention as murders in progress.

Wilson defined his system by creating the reports and communication practices required to give the men practical effectiveness measures.

All crime reports by citizens were recorded, coded for computer storage, and dispatched on a priority basis from a centralized control center via a 12-channel communications network to radio cars. In reporting the disposition of the case, the patrolman could no longer radio in that he had resolved the problem; he had to complete and file a written report which was matched against the original report in the computer. This action discouraged laxity, bribe-taking, and preferential treatment of offenders. It also allowed statistical analysis of crime rates, locations, and methods of criminal operation.

Wilson drastically improved the operation of the force by a combination of measures involving redefinition of the system and the introduction of new communications equipment, more radio cars, and adequate supplies. However, the most powerful force in this improvement was in the redefinition of the system, by providing it with effectiveness measures that allowed Wilson to control the system, not be a subject to its chaos, political rivalries, and criminal intrigues.[8]

THE PROBLEM OF PRESENT AND POTENTIAL CAPABILITY

The higher order approach to system definition simplification is often directed to an evaluation of alternate possible operations under changed

[8] Numerous authors have reported on the Chicago Police reorganization. The most recent: J. Starr, "Chicago Shows Way to Police Reform," *Look*, October 19, 1965, pp. 43–49. See also, O. W. Wilson, *Police Administration*, 2nd ed., McGraw-Hill, New York, 1963.

objectives, effectiveness measures, and constraints. For complex systems, this form of long-range definition demands the analyst's highest skills, and usually requires a multidiscipline approach for satisfactory results.

Thus, we may ask for a definition, not of present system operation, but of *potential* system operation. For example, the potential actions of a complex system are of prime concern to a military or industrial intelligence officer, who must anticipate future opponent actions.[9] He seeks to simplify his problem by ruling out opponent actions unfeasible or unlikely owing to constraints in the opponent's system.

Such constraints may be physical constraints (the available equipment), environmental constraints (prevailing terrain, weather, raw materials), informational constraints (available technical talent, educational resources, communication networks), and goal and value constraints (the rigidity of goal and priority selection, which limits possible goal and value choices in the system).

Example: A system has a wider range of possible actions at its disposal and can take them faster if it has a large number of uncommitted resources. A shop with substantial idle capacity on a variety of productive machine tools can take on a variety of new production orders quickly; but, a shop with a small variety of totally occupied equipment cannot easily do so without a time lag for the acquisition, installation, and planning required for new facilities.

In addition, a system is likely to make a more precise selection of appropriate actions and to implement them more swiftly if it devotes a substantial portion of its available resources to long-range activities. The supervisory control program of a modern computer installation physically occupies much of the high-speed memory of the machine, as opposed to the area required for the execution of a current calculation. However, the memory resources devoted to this "long-range" control permit the machine to select appropriate subroutines rapidly, and to execute a sequence of different calculations rapidly, thereby increasing the system's effectiveness for a wide job mix. Similarly, the military intelligence officer unconcerned with the anticipation of possible changes in enemy organization and goal choices and preparation for them is unlikely to perceive the many alternate courses of enemy action, or to have resources available to cope with them.

The objective of this form of definition, of course, is the exploitation of long-range enemy weaknesses, or the strengthening of long-range weaknesses in the friendly system.

Example: On the national level, industrial, input-output tables that show by transfers of productive output how industrial segments of the

---

[9] See the interesting discussion of international intelligence system organization and operation in S. Kent, *Strategic Intelligence for American World Policy*, Princeton University Press, Princeton, N.J., 1949. For a discussion of industrial intelligence operations, see W. Fair, "The Corporate C.I.A.," *Management Science*, July, 1966, pp. B489–B503.

economy are related, both totally and geographically, are commonly prepared.[10] Thus, a certain portion of the steel industry's output (which is relatively stable under normal conditions) is consumed by the steel industry itself, some by the automotive industry, some by the electrical industry, and so on. A change in the total output will then pervasively affect the entire economy, because of the needed output transfers.

We may then ask from such a presentation: (1) "What are the critical industrial segments of our own economy that if improved would have the greatest effect on total production?" and (2) "What are the critical segments of the enemy economy that if destroyed would have the most damaging effect?" The military implications of such questions are obvious when we think of the selection of bombing targets, and it was this form of analysis that selected the German ball-bearing industry for destruction in World War II. From a domestic viewpoint, we may want to rephrase the questions geographically. For example, "What would happen to the capability of the United States economy if an atomic bomb were dropped on Cleveland, Ohio?" Most nations engage in such long-range capability analyses of their own and foreign countries, but the same approach is clearly appropriate for anticipating the effects of casualty losses, strikes, or improvements at the firm level.

In the assessment of long-range growth, we are interested in the *rates* with which constraints and goals of a system can change, as well as their direction of change. Such questions, of course, also involve the speed with which a system can reorganize its present resources for alternate application in response to changed goals. For example, from a military viewpoint, "How quickly can the typewriter industry shift its productive output to machine guns?" From an industrial viewpoint, "How quickly can a competitor change his present product line?"

It is important to realize that the analyst can define a system by its goal and constraint structure, and measure quantitatively or estimate quantitatively the amount of surplus resources available for a given system. Moreover, it is usually possible to measure or estimate the rate with which change in these resources and their use could be effected.

Example: A small shop provides the easiest example. At any time, given the number of shifts worked, the number of available hours by machine type is known, or can be estimated within narrow limits (allowing for breakdown, tool setups and changeovers, and the like). Similarly, it is possible to find both the average and the instantaneous loads on each type of equipment, so that a slack figure giving surplus hours available

[10] M. K. Wood, "PARM, An Economic Programming Model," *Management Science,* May, 1965, is a recent example of this form of definition and analysis. V. Leontieff, *The Structure of the American Economy,* Oxford University Press, New York, 1951, is the basic monograph on the approach.

for alternate use may be computed. Next, the speed with which the equipment can be alternately used can be estimated from planning and tooling lead times, the mix of equipment, and the skill of management coordination. Finally, it is also possible to estimate the time necessary to supplement existing machine resources by acquisition of added equipment, overtime work, subcontracting, and similar alternatives. With such quantitative estimates available, evaluation of alternate production possibilities in response to alternate production goals may proceed on a quantitative basis, too. In this way, alternate production possibilities can be ranked by an effectiveness measure and alternate production facilities (different firms, say) can be ranked by their effectiveness for a given task. This type of definition and analysis has both industrial and military significance, and many such studies are performed in planning large purchases, or selecting military contractors.[11]

The steps in a capability study

In developing a long-range capability study, three steps are involved: description, report, and speculation.

Development of present constraints will show that many are permanent. For example, the terrain, roadway, rail, communication, and basic raw material constraints of a nation, as well as the moral and social characteristics of the population, population clusters, educational levels, and demographic characteristics do not change rapidly. In industry, the physical locations of the plants, warehouses, and major tools do not change on a day-to-day basis, nor do the basic skills of the employees, the products, or the characteristics of the workers. The development of this background information may be called the *descriptive element* of the long-range definition.[12]

Some constraints, however, change with time: leaders, current technology, and available technical talent, exotic tools, and equipment. As a result, basic description must be updated constantly if the analyst is to make revised projections of capability. This is the *reportorial element* of the long-range definition.

Finally, projections must be made from both past and current information so that long-range potential and the effectiveness of alternate system actions may be evaluated, or so that the probability of alternate opponent actions may be estimated. This is the *speculative element* in the definition process.

---

[11] Similar capability measures can be made on social systems, using the skills of the political scientist, sociologist, and anthropologist. See K. W. Deutsch, *Political Community at the International Level*, Doubleday Short Studies in Political Science SSPS-1, Doubleday, Garden City, N. Y., 1954, who (in Chapter 4) lists 14 selected measures for defining the characteristics of nations and communities.

[12] The terms used here are those of S. Kent, *op. cit.*, who provides extensive examples of each phase of the definition.

The suggested steps are equally appropriate for the long-range definition of the industrial organization, the political sectors of a country (municipal, county, and state), and the long-range improvement of hardware systems by redefinition and redesign.

It may appear initially that the projection of system capability and action does not simplify the analyst's burden, but rather creates data that further complicate the analyst's job. The next section shows that this is not so.

THE DATABANK

In application, the execution of the descriptive step often results in the creation of massive dossiers, files, and other collections of documents. (The *New York Times*, for example, in an attempt to anticipate the background needs of breaking news, maintains bibliographical dossiers on 1.3 million individuals, 500,000 corporations, 100,000 places, 100,000 ships, and 10,000 maps.[13]) With modern electronic computer equipment much of the descriptive step may be reduced to a databank or master file of information organized so that information may be retrieved quickly and inexpensively in response to selected questions by the analyst.

For example, in the industrial application, the master file may contain an inventory of all the products made, keyed by part number, together with such identifying factors as price, inventory level, orders outstanding, manufacturing specifications, marketing data, competitive products, alternate choices of materials or vendors, alternate manufacturing practices, and other selected information, with cross-references to the background files less frequently consulted.

In the municipal file, data may be keyed to the street address of land parcels, so that tax rosters, crime statistics, street repair statistics, municipal lighting statistics, and similar information may be readily available to answer long-range questions, such as "What will be the effects on the tax roll, police demands, educational requirements, utility capacity, and economic structure of the community if a new high-rise apartment is built at 1234 Main Street?" [14]

Since 1960, the electronic computer has made the mechanization of

[13] R. Kahn, "The House of Adolph Ochs," *The Saturday Evening Post*, October 9, 1965, p. 32. Many intelligence operations are modeled after the organization of a large newspaper.

[14] "Public Automation," a monthly newsletter published by Public Automated System Service, Chicago, contains reports of rapidly expanding municipal, county, and state applications in long-range planning using this approach. The interested reader should also see E. F. Hearle and R. J. Mason, *Data Processing System for State and Local Governments*, Prentice-Hall, Englewood Cliffs, N. J., 1962. Databanks also present dangers to the individual. For a current political discussion see "Data Center Held Peril to Privacy," *New York Times*, July 27, 1966, p. 41, a report of Congressional debate over proposals to merge data on citizens from 20 Federal Agencies into one master databank.

the databank both technically and economically feasible for wide use. Because the computer has improved the density of information storage as well as the speeds of updating and retrieval by orders of magnitude, the technical feasibility of handling large files of data that may be searched in complex extraction combinations is available at low cost today.[15] Moreover, much of the databank information can be used for servicing routine applications, such as inventory status reports, customer billing, short-range production planning, and development of market statistics—applications which justify the creation of a basic databank that when supplemented can be used for long-range planning by the industrial firm. The direct benefits in government, such as tax billing and control, inventory and asset control, and work scheduling can also justify the creation of databanks.

In addition, the recent development of electronic remote input data-sets (such as those provided to the airline reservation clerk or savings bank teller for "on-line, real-time" updating of seat and dollar inventories) together with their associated communication systems further raises the ability of "management information systems" to provide *current* updating of master files, a previous stumbling block in accurate file maintenance and control using the databank.

Thus, it is both technically possible and economically feasible today to maintain large-scale inventories of information, which can be updated with current information. The implications of this ability should not be overlooked by the analyst who seeks to make long-range projections, because the availablity of this resource greatly simplifies his job.

Historically, for example, the time and cost spent on systems analysis, particularly for long-range projections and evaluation of alternatives, was devoted in an 80/20 ratio or more to data collection and "purification" as opposed to analysis and projection. The application of most of the techniques of statistics and operations research also bore the burden of onerous data collection. With the steps of description and reporting reduced to a mechanized format, this ratio is readily reversed.

Thus, recent technical and economic improvements in data collection, storage, and retrieval permit the analyst to concentrate on question generation, analysis, and speculation. For the large-scale system, particularly, the control advantage of this new asset is overwhelmingly important for the analyst. Indeed, many forms of analysis, such as statistical analysis of "real-time" data inputs, would be unfeasible without these developments.

How capability problems and intelligence questions arise

Future capability problems and substantive intelligence questions usually arise in one of three ways: (1) As the result of reflection by men

[15] Marvin Camrus, "Information Storage Density," *IEEE Spectrum,* July, 1965, pp. 98–105. This article is of additional interest, because effectiveness measures for various forms of storage media are developed in it.

employed to anticipate problems, (2) when surveillance or systems tests notice something unusual, or (3) from the direct request of the consumer of the system analyst's product. These routes may combine to generate questions.

For example, questions may arise from the "desk" of an intelligence officer assigned a geographical area or an industrial product group, as he surveys both the background information and incoming information in his area. A surprising fact, or a contradiction between incoming data and background history, may prompt a question. The introduction of a new product, the plans for new facilities or equipment, or needs of an executive may initiate questions, as was the case with McNamara and Wilson.

The following examples illustrate some of these sources. They have been arranged to illustrate questions regarding constraints, then questions concerning goals and goal response.

First, an inventory of assets presently available to a system frequently indicates that the relative value of the asset mix has changed with time, often without appropriate utilization changes.

Example: As the result of a proposed computer installation on a "total system" basis, a large oil company made a list of its assets, such as producing facilities, real estate, station leases, chemical equipment, crude reserves, financial resources, credit card lists, present computer equipment, and similar items. Although the firm was formerly production oriented, and adjusted its objectives to the maximum utilization of productive potential, it soon became apparent that its 6-million credit card holders were an even more important asset than the refining facilities. The firm changed its effectiveness measure from a production to a marketing orientation and thus focused attention on the exploitation of the credit card holders. Items other than gas and oil were added to the product mix because they had greater profit margins: Consumer items, insurance, and motel rooms, were made available on credit, both at stations and through the gas and oil bills mailed monthly. The change in objectives produced by an analysis of asset potential markedly improved the profit and loss statement of the firm.[16]

Similarly, an analysis of capabilities may reveal that some assets are, in fact, liabilities.

Example: When Billy Prince became President of Armour, the firm's objective was to be the largest meat packer in the United States by sales volume.[17] An inventory of the firm's assets, by their profitability, showed

[16] For other examples of this type, see T. Levitt, *Innovations in Marketing*, McGraw-Hill, New York, 1962.

[17] Two articles separated by three years provide a before and after comparison. See F. Lincoln, "Billy Prince's Somewhat Silver Spoon," *Fortune*, January 1956, p. 126, and R. Lubar, "Armour Sees Fat Years Ahead," *Fortune*, October 1959. p. 117.

that many facilities were operating not at a profit, but at a loss. The Chicago stockyards were one example. On the other hand, several meat by-products produced a comfortable margin, and thus provided a route to increased profit potential. This analysis led to a change in objectives that toned down the meat-packing operations, dispensed with unprofitable yards and packing plants, and supplemented by-product operations that were to increase net profit. The net income of the firm increased noticeably with these changes in objectives, which resulted from a profit potential analysis.

Again, an analysis of capabilities, potential, and constraints may reveal that an apparent liability can be exploited by changing the objective of an operation.

Example: When the Matson Lines investigated the constraints limiting cargo shipments from the West Coast to Hawaii, they found a maritime regulation that prohibited the combination of "dangerous" cargo with other cargo on one vessel. Automobiles, a major item, were dangerous because they contained batteries and gasoline. So, when automobiles were shipped with other cargo, batteries and gasoline had to be removed, with consequent heavy loading and unloading expense by hoist. By exploiting the rule, a conversion was made to all dangerous cargo ships. With gas and batteries in place, stevedores drove the cars on board and parked them like parking-lot attendants, speeding turnarounds, drastically cutting dock costs, and effectively increasing ship capacity. This efficient utilization of space resulted in effective use of the fleet. Although the ships sailed partially empty on some runs, they more than compensated for this loss by making more frequent trips and incurring smaller dockside charges.[18]

Unusual facts about the utilization of productive potential often raise questions about long-range changes.

Example: The striking fact that in 1960 only 57 of Chevrolet's 7000 dealers provided night maintenance for customers raised questions about the potential service charges, potential new sales, and potential tie-in sales that could be exploited if this limitation were removed.[19]

Similarly, analyzing current input information against a background of management standards, technical performance specifications, or historical trends often allows questions to be raised before a problem becomes serious.

Example: Following the example of the military services, such as the management control system installed by General C. LeMay for SAC

[18] F. L. Weldon, "In-Company Operations Research," (Abstract), *ORSA Bulletin*, **10**, 1, May, 1962, p. 13.
[19] Levitt, *op. cit.*, p. 57.

and other Air Force operations, many commercial aircraft carriers, such as TWA, display current status of performance, equipment failures, and current operating difficulties in a central briefing room, connected by private line telephone to the major national airport installations. A daily survey of this information, presented to operating executives in verbal, graphical, and statistical form, stimulates questions that may be answered by the telephone hookup, or by special investigation. By using this approach, an epidemic of part failures for example, may be detected by statistical observation and action taken to prevent serious loss. Indicators of long-range difficulty may also be derived from all parts of the system by using the communication facilities and the summary properties of the briefing room display. (The radar-room scenes of television and the films are familiar examples of the briefing room approach in combat situations. The electronic computer, with its databank of information and electronic input devices, permits more sophisticated use of the briefing room approach to question stimulation. But, frequently, in complex situations, the ability of the human brain to correlate and synthesize facts comes to its greatest usefulness in developing questions. Man and the computer cooperate in this situation to produce results better than either could produce alone.)

Let us turn now to a few examples that refer more to the political scientist, sociologist, anthropologist, and psychologist than to the engineer, mathematician, or accountant.

In addition to the potential capability that *could* be exploited, which we have just discussed, we must often determine if that potential *will* be exploited by an opponent's or one's own system. We are all aware of the individual with great talent, who is insufficiently motivated and therefore does not use it, and, conversely, of the individual with more limited resources who uses all of them to the limit of his abilities. In fact, the latter individual may be more productive than the former. But, *if* the former could be goal directed to exploit his greater assets, his potential capabilities would produce more results than the capabilities of his limited friend. Furthermore, both individuals and organizations have the ability to grow and learn, so that we may also ask to what degree a possible change in goals and values would cause a change in the potential capabilities of the system. The following examples, for these reasons, have a direct bearing on studies of potential.

The disparity between a present level of achievement (using a given effectiveness measure) and the level perceived as an "optimum" or satisfactory objective may, if known, be used to assess the pressures causing change in the system performance.

The so-called reference group of sociology is based on the idea that an analyst can measure the "relative deprivation" perceived by an individual or a group between a present state and the one held as a goal. When this measurement can be accomplished, the analyst can gain some long-range insight into trends of opinion and action. We would call this form of definition a goal capability study.

Example: During World War II, morale studies were made of the troops.[20] Analysts expected Negro troops in the South to have a lower morale than Negro troops in the North; yet upon investigation they found the contrary result. The Negro recruit related his current Army status and pay to that of the local Negro community, not to an absolute scale. Army Negroes in the South had more available funds to spend than the local males therefore they were able to afford more luxuries and attract the local Negro women. The lot of the Army Negro in the North was worse, by comparison to the industrially employed Negro male. In the North, the industrially employed Negro enjoyed the advantage of relative luxury and female admiration. The relative deprivation of the Northern Army Negro lowered his morale.

To extend the example, the human being, group, or organization can be expected to have pressures for change toward a goal if (1) the goal is within the potential capability of the system's resources, and (2) if the goal has not yet been reached. The greater the disparity between achievement and objective, when resources are available, the greater the pressures to change.

Example: The concept of the "reference group" has been widely exploited as a motivator of change in the marketing of consumer products. For example, if a salesman can locate the individual or family considered a reference group ("The Joneses") in a given community, he may attractively induce a sale to this "thought leader" and exploit the social pressures so generated. Aerial time-lapse photographs of air-conditioner installations show remarkable epidemics of sales radiating from the motivating air-conditioner installed in the corner house with children, or in the prestige apartment inhabited by a professional worker.[21]

Conversely, for systems in which the disparity between present achievement and the ultimate objective is great, the analyst may look for a change in goal patterns, values, and actions if system capability is insufficient to achieve the presently perceived objectives. If the system cannot change its objectives to meet its capabilities, or cannot relieve the constraints

---

[20] S. A. Stauffer, et al., *Measurement and Prediction* (Vol. IV in Studies in Social Psychology in World War II), Princeton University Press, Princeton, N. J., 1950.
[21] W. H. Whyte, Jr., "The Web of Word of Mouth," *Fortune,* November, 1954, p. 140.

that limit its operation, the analyst can expect revolt, system breakdown, or erratic system behavior. The dealings of Louis XVI with the various groups and estates of the French people, which resulted in the French Revolution and his own execution, provide an example of the failures of the king and his government in this area.[22] In a mechanistic sense, the electrical motor severely overloaded beyond its inherent capabilities, burns out or blows its own fuse.

A similar approach can be applied at the higher level to the analysis of the goals a system conceivably can assume. Again, for human beings (or for a society), tradition, historical training, and habit usually limit the conceivable or acceptable goals (in addition to setting the satisfactory level of achievement in response to those goals). This knowledge is strategic in projecting the relative success of alternate proposals for action.

> *Example:* Since the time of the Trojan Horse (and perhaps earlier) one of the principles of warfare has been to mystify and mislead the enemy. The art of deception is largely based on knowing what the enemy wants to believe, and therefore, will accept. Thus, in a correct and highly acceptable mass of data the deceiver places an incorrect but acceptable, extremely important fact. The strategy (as Pooh-Bah observed) provides ". . . corroborative detail, intended to give artistic verisimilitude to an otherwise bald and unconvincing narrative." [23]
>
> "Operation Mincemeat" of World War II, is such a "Trojan Horse" example. In this deception, a corpse disguised in every detail as a British officer was floated to the shores of Portugal from a submarine. The German intelligence, which valued factual corroboration highly, carefully checked the identity of the "Man Who Never Was," and was deceived by the careful preparations (which included medical procedures that masked the time of death). They then accepted as true the false invasion plans, which were carried by the corpse as a cover for the Allied invasion of Italy via Sicily.

As we discussed in Chapter 7, the rigidity of goal and constraint patterns

---

[22] Deutsch, *op. cit.*, p. 21. Similarly, the lifetime observations of the noted psychiatrist H. S. Sullivan led to the conclusion that an individual's self-evaluation was the most important predictor of his evaluation of others. The greater the disparity between his own ambitions and his level of achievement toward them, the less he would think of others. See H. S. Sullivan, *Conceptions of Modern Psychiatry*, Norton, New York, 1953, and *Interpersonal Theory of Psychiatry*, Norton, New York, 1953.

[23] The quotation from Winnie the Pooh is used in Lieut. Commander Ewin Montagu's book *The Man Who Never Was*, Bantam Books, New York, 1965, p. 22. Commander Montagu originated and directed the "Operation Mincemeat" scheme, described above. His now famous description of those events was originally published by Lippincott, New York, 1954, after German files on the case had been made public.

in systems of individuals often causes them to *cluster,* in terms of geographical locations, in interaction patterns, or in unified actions. This fact is also strategically significant in long-range planning.

Example: To illustrate, consider the following problem, a prototype of the political action study which is seldom published in detail for obvious reasons.

The conflict of special interest clusters often thwarts public projects, such as construction of new schools. In small New England Communities, for example, dramatic conflict often arises between two highly clustered centers of value and power.

On the one hand, we have a familiar cluster represented by the old-line Republican, country club member, who is usually Protestant, a relatively wealthy land and business owner, conservative in attitude, a long-time, well-educated resident who associates with similar types.

On the other hand, we have another familiar value cluster, the Democratic, Catholic, liberal, labor-class, relatively poor member of the Elks, Moose, Eagles, Legion, or other fraternities, often with relatively less education, without extensive property or business holdings who also associates with similar residents.

Although the former group usually holds the economic power of the community, the latter holds the political power, being more numerous. Thus, a proposal on public issues by one side—such as the construction of a new public school, or the bussing of parochial students at public expense—is often defeated, on principle, by the other side.

The size and extent of each power group can be defined by the methods described in Appendix E, "Suggestions for a Study of Your Hometown," or by the prototype and stratification techniques discussed in Chapter 7. More important in this example, we can often isolate individuals or small groups with critical power positions by graphing or sorting their associations, transactions, memberships, and other possible relationships. Joint memberships in given organizations, joint transactions in daily life, and joint opinions on key issues can thus be displayed in tabular or flow graph form. The individual or group with any compatible transactions to and from each major cluster often has the power to move both.

For example, in one New England community, which must remain nameless, a group of investigators isolated a key individual. She was a wealthy Irish manufacturer's widow, who belonged to the country club, made frequent trips to the bank, but who was also Catholic, Democratic, and who, from her husband's background, enjoyed the confidence of labor leaders, minority groups, and dissident thought leaders in the community. She was not active in politics at the public level, and her power was not well known. She hardly recognized it herself.

Yet, her quiet recommendations to both sides were often sufficient to stimulate compromise and cooperative effort.[24]

Thus, in this example, the mechanical study of interest clusters, mutual associations, and transactions helped redefine the community power structure. Long range questions of community capability to achieve given goals, and the methods for achieving them can often be clarified by the approach described.

THE CIRCULAR PROCESS OF DEFINITION, TEST, AND TREATMENT

The foregoing examples should show that long-range capability studies are higher-order forms of system simplification. A definition that works with goals and constraints allows us to concentrate selectively on system features that are now relevant and on features that will probably be relevant in the future.

We have also seen that the definition of a large-scale system will change with time, certainly in its detailed description. The higher level approach may thus provide a more stable overall system definition, as well as a simpler one, and may furthermore guide the analyst in his prediction of future system change and growth—thereby simplifying the analyst's future problems.

We now come to our final topic for this chapter and this section. Just as the system to be defined can change with time, it is also true that the analyst will later alter his system definition with time, seeking constantly to improve it.

In short, the job of system definition never ends for the analyst of the complex system. He will make a preliminary definition, test it, perhaps make a system change, treatment, or improvement. Then, from his experi-

---

[24] The success of the Kennedy family in politics illustrates more dramatically the principles developed in this example. For another illustration, the reader should consult K. W. Deutsch, *Nationalism and Social Communication,* MIT Press and Wiley, New York, 1953, especially Figure 1, p. 18, which graphs the growth of a national elite in the United States, 1750–1795, according to the late Robert K. Lamb (also the author of Appendix E). In this diagram, the political power of Alexander Hamilton during the stated period stands out clearly. He was military secretary to George Washington, protegé of Elias Boudinot, Director of the Mint, and William Livingston, Governor of New Jersey, was related by marriage to John Van Rensselear and Philip Schuyler, and as Secretary of the Treasury was associated with William Duer, and a wide range of other prominent individuals, and institutions, such as the bank of New York. His personal, family and business ties to the colonies of Virginia, Pennsylvania, New York, and Massachusetts gave Hamilton key policy, decision-making, and persuasive powers in the early development of the United States. Many of the key power clusters shown in the referenced diagram persist to this day as the result of continued hereditary, institutional, and social associations within the power clusters defined in the Colonial period.

ence and observations, the analyst will be able to improve or correct his original definition, and repeat the cycle of definition, analysis, and treatment again.

This sequence of events may be compared to the so-called "helix of science," the repetition of definition of theory, experiment, and correction that continuously produces improvements in knowledge. In practice this helical improvement pattern may not progress smoothly; there may be regressions, jumps, and similar fits-and-starts in the analyst's work, particularly in unfamiliar situations. Nevertheless, the concept of dynamic correction in the system definition, as a result of what is learned in analysis and treatment, is an important motivator for the analyst.

In this light, we now turn to the next major section of this book, Systems Analysis.

PROBLEMS

8.1 Following the illustration of a linear programing problem provided in Figure 7-4, consider the following problem.

Maximize the objective: $50x + 75y$ = Gross Income

where x represents the number of units of Product A and y represents the number of units of Product B. Observe the following restrictions:

$$8x + 4y \leq 400 \quad \text{(Machine I Restriction)}$$
$$5x + 10y \leq 400 \quad \text{(Machine II Restriction)}$$
$$y \leq 30 \quad \text{(Market Restriction)}$$

A. Show that the maximum income possible under these conditions is $3500.

B. Specify the values of x and y for this optimum.

C. How would this solution be affected if the objective were restated as
Maximize the objective: $75x + 50y$

D. How does the new result affect the idle time in the shop; i.e., compared to the original solution, is there a change in the difference between machine capacity and market potential used and available?

E. Someone proposes that instead of maximize income, the objective should be minimize the cost of production, given as $15x + 25y$. Is this a reasonable proposal? If not, how could the problem be restated to make the proposal reasonable?

F. Instead of minimizing cost or maximizing revenue, the proposal has now been made to maximize profit. Given the figures above, what can be done to reach the new objective?

G. The Sales Manager insists that the market price for product B be reduced to $50 to build acceptance for that product. What would this requirement do to the maximum revenue figure obtained in A?

H. The production manager insists that the maximum number of units be manufactured under the original constraints, i.e., that the problem should be to make $x + y$ maximum. What result would then be obtained in terms of x and y? What is the maximum number of units that can be produced?

I. Under the original conditions in A, an additional hour of capacity on either Machine I or Machine II is possible. Which should be preferred in terms of the maximum revenue objective? Would this preference change if the objective were changed?

J. Having found the solution to I, how many added hours of machine capacity, of the type selected, could be added before the restriction set by the other machine or market restriction is encountered?

K. In A, suppose the income from Product B were fixed at $75 per unit, but that the income from Product A could be increased by increasing the price per unit from the present $50. How large would this price have to be before the original values of x and y, obtained in B, change to more production of Product A?

L. We have now considered the objectives relating (a) maximum income, (b) minimum cost, (c) maximum profit, and (d) maximum number of items produced. Can you think of any other objectives that might be proposed? From this list of possible objectives, how would you select the one to use? Why is the potential of unused capacity of interest to the planner, whatever the objective selected? Why is it also of interest to know where capacity is no longer available? Why is it of benefit to know the marginal increase in a given objective that can be obtained by providing additional capacities of various kinds? Why are these questions, which consider only the objective, function, and constraints imposed by the system, highly useful for planning—even though we have not described in any detail the exact operations of the machines? Can you think of any other situations, other than the shop illustration provided here, in which the same form of thinking would be valuable?

8.2 In developing a new management information system, there are two general ways to proceed. In the first, all presently used input paperwork forms, files, and output reports are examined. Then the new system is devised to consolidate the files and to simplify the reports so that an integrated operating system results. On the other hand, it is also possible to proceed by first making an analysis of all the decisions and operations that require information, then by designing a system to satisfy these needs. Comment on the disadvantages of each of these approaches.

8.3 From time to time the Federal Reserve Board changes the prime interest rate used by the banking system of the United States.

A. Why is this a higher level form of system control?

B. What structural changes could be expected from a change in this control variable?

C. How do system lags and anticipations enter into the control picture when such higher level control variables are used to change the system of commercial transactions?

8.4   Again, consider the tick-tack-toe game described in Problem 7.2. Suppose the first player selects the middle square as his first choice. Suppose also that the second player selects a corner as his following move. A strategy that will permit the second player to guarantee that the game will end in a tie (so the first player cannot win) exists.

A. What is the winning strategy for the second player? (Note that this may be found by a check of the appropriate strategy to use for each possible basic move of player one on his second choice.)

B. Write your procedure in learning the tie strategy for the second player.

C. Could you devise a machine to carry out the strategy you have learned?

D. Could you devise a machine that would "learn" what you have learned about the tie strategy for the second player? (As a start, assume a machine without knowledge of the game—which corresponds to a player who has not played the game before. Assume also that random moves will be made to any feasible square at each stage and improve this strategy depending upon the win, loss, or tie results for player two.)

E. In what way does "learning" impose constraint upon action for the second player in this game?

F. Why does learning generally impose constraint upon action in highly structured situations of the type illustrated by tick-tack-toe? Is such constraint a general result of the learning process?

8.5   Frank is hurrying home late, after a particularly grueling day, when it pops into his mind that today is Kitty's birthday! Or, is it? Everyone is closed except the florist's. If it is not her birthday and he brings no gift, the situation will be neutral, i.e., no payoff, or 0. If it is not and he comes bursting in with roses, and obviously confused, he may be subjected to the Martini test, but he will emerge with a position of strong one-upness—which is worth 1. If it is her birthday and he has clearly remembered it, that is worth something more, say 1.5. If he has forgotten it, he is down like a stone, say -10.

A. What should Frank's strategy be if he assumes that the outcomes (birthday or not) are equally likely?

B. How could Frank's decision be changed if his probability estimate is off?

C. If his estimates of "payoff" are not correct?

D. If he refuses to accept the outcome -10, without regard to the probability of its occurrence?

SYSTEMS ANALYSIS AND DIAGNOSIS

9 | SYSTEMS ANALYSIS: A SURVEY

From what we have seen, the definition of a system will be a circular process—with definition, analysis, and treatment following sequentially until the objective of the system definition has been reached.

THE PURPOSES OF SYSTEMS ANALYSIS

In developing the system definition we therefore reach a stage at which the investigator introduces tests and diagnostic procedures designed to assure him that his provisional definition is reasonably good, or definitely bad, and to note specific strengths and weaknesses in the system. This stage in the circular process is called systems *analysis*.

SIX QUESTIONS

Of course, we have many specific reasons for testing a system or what we know about it, but six general reasons may be advanced, and it is useful to review these to indicate the range of test types that may be needed. (The range of test types needed by the investigator, following our previous discussion, determines the complexity of the system definition.)

Curiosity—What Is It?

In the previous chapters we have assumed that something is known about a system we want defined specifically and selectively for a given purpose. However, this is not always so. Suppose we are presented with a system, which may be thought of as a black box with various input and output connections, various knobs and dials, and various bumps and corners— and that we have no idea what the thing is, or what it is for. Indeed, the "system" need not be mechanical or electrical. Suppose we encounter some strange item on a beach and wonder what it is and what it does. Or suppose we walk into a strange social organization and wonder what goes on there. How shall we answer such questions?

The solution, of course, is to test it. Have we seen anything like it before? What happens when we poke it, or turn it over? Does it move or does it lie still? Can we distinguish the inputs from the outputs? Does it have any observable structure, or any regular operation pattern that can be seen? Does it respond to a few random tests?[1] Does it respond as we predicted it would when we subjected it to a specific test? If so, some of our curiosity is removed, and we may proceed with our definition, im-

9-1 An "unknown" black box. An "unfamiliar" system may be presented to the analyst who may not even know which connections are inputs and which are outputs. The small squares indicate the system may have a few "windows," which permit inspection of the inside workings from outside the system boundary. Tests must be made to gain further information about the system.

---

[1] If we know absolutely nothing about a system, a series of random tests will do as well as anything else in giving some preliminary knowledge. (See Ashby, *op. cit.*, p. 88.)

proving the predictability of the system model in response to a wider range of tests.

How does it operate?

As we continue our tests, we may want to know how the system operates. What are its input-output specifications, even though at first they constitute only a crude listing? Can these specifications be refined more, so that the system definition can be more specific? Will any tests tell us how the system works internally, so that we can specify operations for internal blocks and relationships?

Does it work as predicted?

In a later stage of refinement, we may have a system definition and want to know if one or more examples of the system definition in the "real" world agree with predictions made from the system definition.

Predictive tests are used in two senses: (1) The test of a system definition for realism and logical correctness, i.e., the *test of the definition* because it may yet be imperfect; and (2) the test of a specific example to see if it conforms to the standards represented by a given systems definition; i.e., the *test of the example* under the assumption that the definition itself is correct and fixed.

We may have a case that should have been predicted by our system definition (a given input should have given a specified output because the case met all the conditions and assumptions of the system definition), but was not—here, the definition is faulty. Conversely, our manufacturing specifications and proved designs may provide a firm system definition, but we may have an instance that does not meet the specifications—here, the instance is faulty concerning the fixed definition. Generally, these two views of system prediction correspond to research and development testing and to production testing.

Example: An engineer designs a radio to work on a 9-volt battery. He draws a blueprint stating how to make the radio and provides specifications under which his design will work. (a) Suppose a prototype, made according to these instructions and supplied with a 9-volt battery, fails to work. We would suspect the engineer's design. (b) Suppose the design has been perfected, and several "successful" units now work as predicted under the specified conditions. If a consumer uses the radio with a dead battery, he cannot expect it to work; nor could it work if plugged into a 115-volt house current plug. These conditions are contrary to specification. Similarly, the radio cannot work if it were not constructed exactly according to the design specification.

This outcome in no way invalidates the design, or system definition, but rather is a faulty example of it. (c) Finally, the radio may work when supplied with a 6-volt or a 12-volt battery, or if the girl who makes it accidently introduced a few "incorrect" parts. This means the operation or construction specification is not so critical as the system definition states: The definition may be broadened to cover the less restricted cases.

In this way the system definition is improved by testing until we know what it can and cannot do. The final definition of a system may be stated operationally in terms of the specific input-output predictions possible.[2]

Why does it fail to work as specified?

Continuing in the same way, we may need tests that will tell us why a system does not work, or fails to predict, and will give us this information as specifically as possible. Exactly what component in the structure is faulty? What specific addition or deletion from the system definition would solve this particular problem? Tests for diagnosis and trouble-shooting are part of this process.

Can it be improved?

Even though a system definition works within the specifications set for it, we may want to "improve" the system. For example, we may want to achieve the specified result faster, at lower cost, or with less use of scarce resources. If the system does not work according to specification or design, we want to repair or correct it. How can this be accomplished?

What are the effects of treatment and change?

Finally, we may want to predict the effects of proposed changes and treatments, so that we can prepare for the results, or so that we can

---

[2] Operationally, a system definition is said to be increasingly *realistic* as the range of test outcomes it will predict increases (including all tests to date and those that may be applied in the future). See P. W. Bridgman, *The Logic of Modern Physics*, Macmillan, New York, 1946, pp. 55–59; and K. W. Deutsch, "On Communication Models in the Social Sciences," *Public Opinion Quarterly*, 16, Fall, 1952, pp. 363–364. The most realistic total system definition would predict all possible outcomes under all possible conditions—an impossibility for any abstraction or simplification from the real thing. Thus, a practical system definition is always constrained and limited, and a clear statement of the constraints must become part of the complete specification of the system definition. Research and development testing and production testing provide a continuing refinement of the definition, and permit correction, narrowing, or broadening of the system constraints to fit the objective of the system definition and the observations made from its use.

evaluate alternate proposals. We can regard such problems as analyses, rather than system definitions, because we presuppose a firm starting point from which to evaluate.

OUTSIDE TESTS

In distinguishing tests for the foregoing purposes, it is helpful to distinguish between the extremes represented by *outside* tests, as opposed to *inside* tests. The boundary chosen for the system under consideration sets this distinction.

Outside Tests versus Inside Tests

We may want to apply outside tests, which concern only system outputs for selected inputs, either for convenience or from necessity.

Outside tests are always necessary when we are unable to penetrate the system boundary, or when we are able to do so only with difficulty. Outside tests may also be more convenient than inside tests even when the latter can be applied.

> *Example:* A physical examination is certainly less painful, safer and easier, than, say, a bone-marrow test, or exploratory surgery. Therefore, on the human patient outside tests are usually performed before the more difficult and dangerous inside alternatives. Similarly, in testing a TV set, it is certainly possible to open the box and poke around with various instruments. However, it is far simpler to look at the picture under various trial conditions, and to obtain a diagnosis by this means.

The outside test, then, is usually a *response test* in which the output response of the system to selected inputs is checked against previous experience or design specifications. Such response tests may be conducted rudimentarily by using one or two test cases, by applying a battery of test cases, or by continuously changing input conditions over a specified range.

> *Example:* Several authorities have proposed a simple response test to detect hearing deficiencies in newborn infants. One seemingly crude but highly effective proposal is to subject an infant in the hospital nursery to a tone or a hiss produced electronically through a loudspeaker at controlled volume.[3] If the infant wakes up, or if the awake

---

[3] M. P. Downs and G. M. Sterritt, "Identification Audiometry for Neonates: A Preliminary Report," *The Journal of Auditory Research,* 4, 1964, pp. 69–80.

infant responds by movement, sound, or other sign, he is clearly able to hear. If he does not respond, the infant may have some hearing difficulty, and is therefore carefully watched. The simple response test permits early detection of difficulty, which is important because vocabulary skills and verbal comprehension (dependent upon hearing ability) develop most rapidly in the child's first two years.[4]

Like the hearing test, outside response tests offer a convenient "screening" method, which measures an individual's response against known or specified standards or norms. The response test may also be used to collect more information about a system's ability.

Example: Let us continue with the hearing example. The family pediatrician may, in later months, subject the infant to the sound of a drum (low note) or a bell (high note), or a clap of the hands to determine the infant's range of audible sounds. If necessary, when the child can speak and understand simple instructions, an ear specialist can administer more complex tests with varying sound frequencies and varying sound levels to plot the complete frequency response for each ear. Such additional testing more clearly defines what the child can and cannot hear.

Response tests are frequently preferred to inside testing procedures when the internal operations of the system are not clearly understood, or when inside tests may alter the operation of the system itself. Thus, we may subject a complex system to a series of tests to aid our understanding of its operation, because an attempt to define it by other means may be beyond our ability. Yet, to know that the response of the system to input A is always ouput C, and to input B always ouput D—regardless of how these relationships are produced—tells us something useful about the system, and may be sufficient information.[5] Similarly, we prefer outside tests when we know that probes of the system are likely to alter its usual

---

[4] *Pediatrics and Disorders in Communication*, Reprint No. 835, The Alexander Graham Bell Association for the Deaf, Inc., Washington, D.C., 1965.

[5] The response of a *linear system* to a sinusoidal input is particularly interesting (see Appendix B), because knowing this response, we can predict the response to any time-varying input. If the input to a linear system is a sine wave, the output from that system will be a sine wave of the same frequency, but of possibly different amplitude, and possibly displaced from the input wave by a time t or, equivalently, by a phase angle ϕ. If we can determine the complete amplitude and phase response of the linear system experimentally for an input of constant amplitude ranging over all possible frequencies, then we can determine the equivalent transfer function for that linear system in mathematical terms (by appropriate curve fitting methods). From this point, it is possible to evaluate and predict the response of other forms of input to the system description. For this reason engineering texts place major emphasis upon response texts and the development of transfer functions for linear systems, either by experiment or by mathematical consolidation of block diagrams or flow graphs.

operation. In such "sensitive" systems selected outside tests may often provide the information wanted without disturbing the on-going operations. Thus, in political and intelligence studies, the outputs of communication services (radio, press, TV) and other publicly available indicators of system response to the input of current developments are monitored, so that knowledge of a foreign country may be obtained without the risk, danger, or disturbance introduced by the presence of internal probes or tests, such as agents, wire taps, or insurrections.

Let us conclude this section with a short discussion of outside tests universally used in many fields: The tests for "response time," input-ouput "balance," and the "correctness" of inputs.

An important fact about a system may be the time required to translate a given input into a given output.

Example: The answer to this question is often obtained by "tagging" an input and waiting for the tagged output to appear. The customer may test the response time of his vendor by issuing an order for a given shipment and recording the delivery date of the shipment. The salesman may enter a motel and take a shower. He could test the response time of the hot water system by measuring the time between a turn of the "hot" faucet and the appearance of hot water.

The response of a system to an input may be a single output, delayed by the response time of the system, or the output may be distributed over a length of time (a series of outputs will be initiated by a single input).

Example: Two interesting examples involve the use of radioactive tracers in medicine. The first involves study of the human circulatory system, the second involves the operation of the human heart.

To test circulation a small quantity of sodium chloride solution, tagged with the radioactive isotope Na^{24}, is injected into a vein of the patient's forearm. A Geiger-Müller counter, which detects radioactivity, is then placed in contact with one of the feet. If the blood circulation is normal, the presence of radioactivity is very soon detected in the foot; it increases rapidly and reaches a maximum value within an hour. If there is a circulatory impairment of some kind, however, the radioactivity will increase slowly, showing that the blood has difficulty reaching the foot. By moving the counter to different parts of the body, the position of the restriction can be located and the necessary treatment can be applied.

To test heart pumping action radiosodium chloride can again be injected into the bloodstream. A counter attached to a recording pen is placed over the heart. As the radiosodium enters the right side of the heart the count rises, then drops as the venous blood enters the lungs; a few seconds later, the radiosodium appears with the arterial blood in the left side of the heart and there is another rise and fall of the count. By studying the resulting curves, the pumping action of the two sides of the heart can be compared and abnormalities can be discovered.[6]

The response time of a system may also be distributed statistically about a mean value, rather than be a single fixed value, or single fixed sequence of outputs.

Example: Suppose several people appear at a library during the day and make book requests. If, for each customer, we record the response time between request and delivery of a book we would have, at the end of the day, a distribution of response times that would characterize the library operations.

When the normal response time, or response time distribution, is known for a given system, wide variation from the norm would indicate some internal change in the system.

Input-output "balance" calculations are often made to check system operation. The various Conservation Laws of physical science, roughly stated, tell us the physical output from a system must either flow out, or be stored, or discarded in measurable amounts (although such measurements may be difficult in practice). Similar physical laws hold for the conservation of energy and momentum, and by analogy, for such applications as cash flow and accounting balances.

Example: If N people enter the library during the day, N people must leave—unless they are lost in the stacks somewhere!

We may also ask: How much *"useful"* output is there compared to the input? Most physical systems cannot, for example, completely convert one form of energy to another. The potential energy output of coal is not completely converted to an equivalent output of electrical energy by the steam generator—some energy is lost to friction, leaks, and incomplete conversion, or waste. The ratio of output to input here is called the "efficiency" of the system, a number less than or equal to 1.

Conversely, some systems produce more useful output of a given kind than the useful input provided. The profit-making corporation must operate on this basis: The dollars received for sales must exceed the dollar input for materials, labor, and overhead, the difference representing profit. (The apparent gain in dollars, of course, is equivalent to the intangible "value" of skills, organization, and other abilities invested in the transformation effort.) Here the "efficiency" is greater than 1.

[6] From S. Glasstone, *Sourcebook on Atomic Energy*, copyright 1950, D. Van Nostrand Company, Inc., Princeton, N.J., p. 461. Both examples are from the same source and page. See especially Chapter XVI, "The Uses of Isotopes," for other examples in many fields from biology to industrial trouble-shooting.

Similar outside response tests can be made for systems that transform information inputs, rather than physical inputs, although the same conservation laws do not apply, because an input of information may be lost (and in the long run generally is).

We may ask, for example, if an input message is transformed *without loss of variety* by a system, regardless of how the message is transformed. Thus, if the input to a system is A, B, C, and the output is 1, 2, 3, there is no loss of variety because the transformation is "one-to-one." On the other hand, if the input is A, B, C, and the output is 1, 1, 2, there *is* a loss of variety because the system codes *both* A and B into 1, and only C uniquely into 2. From such observations we may develop notions (and measures) of distortion, fidelity, and other response measures for the characteristics of information transformation systems. (The Second Law of Thermodynamics applies to information systems. See Appendix D.)

Outside testing can also check that the assumptions of the system definition with regard to input conditions are met in practice. This is not a response test, but assures us that the response obtained is for the correct input conditions.

Example: The raw material inputs to a manufacturing process are usually routinely inspected to assure their conforming to specification. Such a test is common for the input supply voltage to electronic equipment, for the data used as input to a mathematical computation, and for inputs to human patients, such as the triple checks of prescription correctness by some pharmacies. Such checks of input conditions may often be conducted routinely by the system itself, as for example, in data-processing operations, where inappropriate inputs are rejected. If the system itself does not reject inappropriate inputs, however, the analyst should ascertain that the inputs to the system under study meet his assumptions or specifications.

The Danger in Using Outside Tests

Unfortunately, although inside tests are more likely to cause unwanted system change than outside tests, outside tests can have the same effect if the system has some memory ability. The classic example of this danger is the land mine, discussed on page 32. The investigator who applied outside pokes to the mine might conclude it was harmless, only to have his tests themselves move the internal position of a firing mechanism. In the same way, a series of inputs to a system can modify the system itself by altering its memory content, its internal connections and conditions of response, or its goal-changing functions.

Such internal changes may be harmful or beneficial to the system (or the analyst), depending upon the kind of change generated by the tests and the purpose of the analyst. For example, testing itself may improve the system's operation: Teachers hope their instruction and tests will benefit the students.[7]

Our point, of course, is that the application of outside tests without any knowledge of internal structure and function may produce surprising results, and outside tests must therefore be used with caution, even though they are the only, or the easiest way to proceed. We do not normally "see what will happen when we push the A-button" unless we know something about the internal workings of the system under test.

Systems Analysis

Tests or Questions

OUTSIDE	INSIDE
Response Tests	*Structural Tests*
Frequency	Omissions
Overload	Compatibility
Stability	Coupling effects
Fidelity to specifications	Alternates
Reason	*Reason*
Prediction	Check definition
Limits of operation	Understand structure
	Troubleshooting
	Improvement

9-2 A brief outline on systems analysis. The outside tests treat the system itself as a black box. The inside tests probe within the system mainly to ask questions about structures, malfunction, and improvement. (Taken from D. Hertz and R. Eddison, Eds., *Progress in Operations Research*, Wiley, New York, 1964, Vol. II, p. 136.)

INSIDE TESTS

When it is possible to probe the system so that we can make internal specifications and test them, a wide range of point-to-point checks become available to us. Indeed, some inside tests may be easier to make than outside tests.

The Probe

In many systems internal inspection and test are relatively easy, and

---

[7] The teacher is also aware that he instructs at his peril, as one anonymous Arab pedagogue lamented: "I teach you to write poetry, and you defile me with your verse; I make you an archer, and you slay me with your bow."

probing will not in any way affect the internal structure or condition of the system.

For example, the continuity and correctness of flow or connection between system elements may often be observed or tested without damage to the elements.

> *Example:* Suppose we know the system flows should occur in a certain sequence or between specified elements and not between others. Such specification may be summarized in a "from-to" matrix, as previously discussed on page 97. Each possible from-to connection specified may then be checked against the flows or connections observed. Flows that should be present and are not and, conversely, flows that are present and should not be can be checked in detail. Automation of such "continuity" and "short" tests in checkout of electronic equipment, such as the point-to-point check of IBM circuit modules by computer, is current practice.[8] Detailed checks of paperwork and material flows are a similar example.

Moreover, it may be possible in some systems to get an over-all view of the internal workings of the system from the "outside" without disruption of the system. For example, after removing the protective cover from a piece of machinery, visual inspection may reveal components that are melted, discolored, worn, disfigured, or damaged, due to extremes of environmental conditions, wear, breakdown, or abuse. Some "outside" measuring techniques, such as X-rays and the techniques of radiography and thermography, allow internal inspection of system construction or operation without damage to the system. When such forms of inside inspection are innocuous they may allow the analyst to proceed with extensive inside testing at will. In the same way, nondestructive readings of documents, computer memory content, dated parts, and similar obvious internal checks can often be made without altering or modifying the system operation.

Frequently, although it is impossible to view the entire internal workings of the system without difficulty, "windows" in the system may allow partial inspection.

> *Example:* The human eye, for example, is such a window, allowing the physician to "see" a selected internal portion of the body without violating its boundary. The physician can look in while you look out. The physician uses this ability to check the effects of elevated blood pressure (an outside measurement) upon the internal capillaries by direct observation into the depths of the eyeball. Many famous discoveries have

---

[8] See the quotation given as CASE III, Problem 9.1.

been made when such a "window" has been found in an otherwise black box.[9]

Selection of Probe Points and Probe Types

When inside testing becomes difficult or dangerous, or when inside tests may disrupt the system, we must carefully select the probe points and probe types. In addition, because the possible probe points and probe types in testing a complex system usually exceed the capacity of the analyst or his need to employ them, and because tests consume effort and time, the strategy of test selection becomes an important issue for inside testing. The same argument holds, of course, in the selection of outside tests to present to the system, but the increased difficulty, cost, and danger of inside testing heightens the problem.

The effects of internal probing for information, usually referred to as the "probe effect," provides one guide to the choice of probe points and probe types. In most inside system tests (and in some outside tests) the presence of the measuring or testing medium (whether it be an instrument or a human observer) changes to some extent the character of the system under analysis. The question is "What will be the effect for different probe points, and for different types of probes, or methods of questioning?"

Example: To take an obvious example first, suppose we propose to purchase a small business at the request of its proprietor, who tells us the firm's assets (cash, inventory, fixtures, etc.) have a total value of $X, broken down into the various accounts. Being reluctant to accept this statement at face value, we insist the proprietor employ a Certified Public Accountant to audit the books of the firm, assess the value of the inventory, and so on. This auditor charges $Y for his services, a sum paid from the current assets of the firm. If $Y is a large percentage of the assets $X, the act of auditing will have substantially changed the firm's asset condition—the measurement and test will have altered the system. But, if $Y is a small percentage of $X, the probe effect will be small. The analogy in hardware systems is when a measuring instrument "overloads" the system's capability, thereby producing erroneous results.

In the detailed analysis of social and human systems, the probe effect is increased. Thus, crude interviewing techniques or the known presence of

---

[9] In the 1820's an American Army Surgeon, William Beaumont, nursed to health and for years took care of a Canadian hunter, Alexis St. Martin, whose stomach had been permanently opened by a gunshot wound. "The remarkable chance occurrence made possible an exploration of digestive processes in the stomach, at will, in many different circumstances. In admirably careful observations on his famous patient, Beaumont performed experiments which made history in science." W. B. Cannon, *The Way of an Investigator,* Norton, New York, 1945, p. 29.

an "observer" in a group meeting usually alters drastically the pattern of social interaction, and the analyst may unwittingly or purposefully be deceived.[10] Field or clinical observations by psychologists, psychiatrists, sociologists, anthropologists, and political scientists are subject to this probe effect, and some writers have observed that little should be expected of quantitative analysis in these areas as a result.[11]

Consequently, the analyst must select a probe point and type that will not produce a distorting effect. At the same time, he hopes to find a probe point and type that will reveal to him, for his time and effort, the most information concerning the test system. Although a balance between these factors is easier to call for than to obtain in practice, the analyst can frequently select a "critical" test point and test type to exploit, even in very complex systems.

Example: In 1954, the CIA received a report pinpointing a terminus of telephone wires serving East German military and civilian officials—a conglomeration of wires that would handle simultaneously 432 calls. This "find," if it were true, provided an excellent probe point into the East German Communication system: It would produce voluminous results if it could be tapped.

Further investigation by mapping and surreptitious inquiry revealed that the connection point was five feet underground below the village of *Alt-Glienicke* on the Soviet side, yet only 600 yards from the American Zone border village of *Rudow*. With this information available, a "cover" operation was put into effect. An Air Force radar station was constructed at *Rudow*, while a tunnel to the connection point was dug. Dirt and debris removed from the tunnel were carted away in small containers disguised as various Air Force equipment. When the tunnel was completed (in record time and under conditions of utmost secrecy), the lead-covered telephone cable was tapped, and the 432 wires were connected to 432 tape recorders. For a year complete interception of conversations was made until the tap's discovery on April 22, 1956.

[10] Many anthropologists have been embarrassed to discover after years of study that the "Old Chief" of the tribe had been spinning yarns, rather than relating facts, in the belief that his friend the anthropologist wanted to hear something interesting.

[11] "In other words, in the social sciences we have to deal with short statistical runs, nor can we be sure that a considerable part of what we observe is not an artifact of our own creation. An investigation of the stock market is likely to upset the stock market. We are too much in tune with the objects of investigation to be good probes. In short, whether our investigations in the social sciences are statistical or dynamic—and they should participate in the nature of both—they can never be good to more than a very few decimal places and, in short, can never furnish us with a quantity of verifiable significant information which begins to compare with that which we have learned to expect in the natural sciences. We cannot afford to neglect them; neither should we build exaggerated expectations of their possibilities. There is much which we must leave, whether we like it or not, to the un-"scientific," narrative method of the professional historian." N. Wiener, *Cybernetics,* 2nd ed., Wiley, New York, 1961, p. 164.

The discovery of the probe clearly altered the operation of the observed system, but previous to its discovery the delicacy with which the probe had been inserted and the critical nature of the probe point provided a major intelligence triumph.[12]

An interesting feature of this wiretap example is the number of measures taken to disguise and alleviate the effects of probing into the East German Communication System. We are not told the technical details of the electronic skill required by the successful wiretap, but the expensive and laborious efforts to disguise the tunnel itself are evident.

Thus, in the insertion of probes for sensitive inside tests it may be possible to devise counteracting treatments for the system to disguise the probe or the probe effect. For example, preparations that will allow a probe to he made in such a way that the subject will not be perturbed, embarrassed, scared, upset, disheveled, hurt, or injured are essential to the work of analysts in individual and group problems. The office environment of the physician or legal counsellor is designed to insure privacy of interview, as are the laws of disclosure. The interviewer gauges his attitude to inspire confidence in the respondent or to place him off guard. The surgeon employs anesthetics to mitigate the pain and apprehension caused by an operation. The psychologist observes a group of children at play through a one-way mirror. Each of these artifices represents an attempt to reduce the probe effect.[13]

Similarly, the ability to transform variables or to correlate measurements aids in reducing the probe effect.

One of the more difficult higher order inside investigations (and from what we have seen in previous chapters, one of the most valuable) is the determination of long-range system goals and system values. In fairly simple systems, an inspection of system structure, memory content, and possibly goal formulation procedures may reveal the system's needs, but in more complex systems such direct probing is not likely to produce the desired results. In such systems the device is often to change the probe type to one which is not alarming, yet which has results highly correlated with the desired, but offensive question.

Example: "Using the 'indirect' procedure, questions are asked, for example, about how radical or conservative certain magazines or men in

---

[12] A. Tully, *CIA: The Inside Story,* Morrow, New York, 1962, pp. 2–6. According to the author, the Soviets opened the Rudow tunnel as a tourist attraction until June 9, 1956, when an announcement was made that "40,000 Worker Delegates from East Germany and the Soviet Union have seen this triumph of American espionage."

[13] For some interesting interviewing approaches, see I. F. Marcosson, *Adventures in Interviewing,* John Lane (Bodley Head), London, 1920. Other interesting examples may be found in M. Jahoda, M. Deutsch, and S. W. Cook, Editors, *Research Methods in Social Relations, Part Two: Selected Techniques,* Dryden, New York, 1951.

public life are. The respondent who calls them all conservative indirectly reveals his own 'radicalism' and conversely with one who rates them as radical." [14]

Scientific measurements that would otherwise be destructive or difficult may also be conducted by measuring a variable that can be transformed mathematically or physically into the desired quantity. For example, the measurement of the moisture content of a sample of raw material may be difficult or impossible. Rather than attempt the direct measurement, some moisture-measuring instruments measure the amount of radio-frequency (microwave) energy absorbed by the sample, a quantity that can be related mathematically to moisture content. The latter measurement is easy and nondestructive. The field of scientific instrumentation abounds with similar examples, and the ability to make such "mathematical" transformations allows measurements to be taken at a distance and "telemetered" back to the observer, who may be miles from the measuring point.

PARTIAL INFORMATION

In most systems we encounter, we are not driven to the extremes of outside tests alone, or inside tests alone. We have at least partial information concerning the internal operations of the system, so that we may select outside tests more intelligently, and we may have at least a few easily made inside tests.

For example, if we recognize a system to be a member of a larger class of systems, we know something about it although not perhaps the complete details of its operation. If we have a history of the particular system at hand we know something about its present condition, although perhaps not everything.

Such partial information greatly narrows the range of possible tests that may be needed and permits us to make a good guess (or a logical or probabilistic choice as in Chapter 11) of the next test procedure.

Moreover, if we can make some inside tests in addition to outside tests, based upon our partial knowledge of internal system structure, our variety of possible testing procedures is greatly increased.

For example, with the combination of outside tests and a few internal probes we may check the response of selected *parts* of the system, rather than its over-all response and thereby isolate the system part that may be improved or corrected to improve or correct over-all system response.

Similarly, it may be possible to inject an input internally, and then by

---

[14] A. Kornhauser, "Constructing Questionnaires and Interview Schedules," M. Jahoda, M. Deutsch, and S. W. Cook, *Research Methods in Social Relations*, Dryden, New York, 1951, Vol. 2, p. 452.

outside testing to define internal system structure more clearly. (Combined strategies of this type are discussed in Chapter 10.)

Example: The physician may inject dye into the bloodstream so that specified portions of the circulatory system will appear on an X-ray picture. Although the physician penetrates the body to make the injection, such penetration is seldom dangerous or particularly harmful to the patient. *Angiograms* and *arteriograms,* which reveal clearly the details of selected circulatory functions, are made routinely by this method in the analysis of human circulatory problems. In one medical refinement of this technique it is possible to move the X-ray camera during exposure so that only one plane through the patient's body is "in focus" and, further, by repeating the process with different camera motions, to take photographic slices through the patient's organs without injury or discomfort to him. Similarly, the "signal tracing" of tagged documents and similar system inputs to an organization may be detected at selected internal test points. By selecting the inputs carefully, specific paperwork functions may be tested. The latter approach may also be used in the diagnosis of hardware systems. (Techniques of this type are discussed more fully in Chapter 10.)

With the objective of combining outside and inside tests, a physical system may be designed so that selected inside measurements can be extracted at "test points" or output terminals from the equipment. Thus, certain monitoring points are built into a chemical processing facility with readings displayed on a control panel. Check answers in a computer program are often printed out during the progress of the program's execution. To reduce the cost of maintenance, trouble-shooting and repair, many electronic systems are constructed so that inside tests can be conducted from outside terminals, inspection points, and meters "inserted" for this purpose. Although this design approach increases the initial cost of the system's design and construction, such action can drastically decrease maintenance and trouble-shooting difficulty, and is usually necessary for detailed "on-line" control of a complex system.

Thus, the analyst usually has partial information about a system—either from experience, as the result of specific test procedures, or by design—and his ability to use this knowledge greatly increases his diagnostic and control ability. What, we might ask, would happen if the analyst had "complete" information concerning the system under study?

COMPLETE INSIDE INFORMATION ABOUT STRUCTURE AND FUNCTION

If we are totally knowledgeable about the inner workings of a system (at a given level of detail), even greater flexibility in testing is available to us.

First, if we could conduct independent and nondisruptive internal tests, we could check the transformations at each stage or component of the system. More detailed isolation of faults would be possible, and several relatively simple tests, such as the correctness of subsystem output on a point-to-point basis for a given system input, might be possible. A detailed examination of internal memory content, or system status, at a given moment or step in a process is another example of internal tests, when we have complete knowledge of the system.[15]

Conversely, with complete knowledge of what the system should do internally, which may, for example, be known from design criteria, it may be possible to devise a series of outside response tests that will sequentially check selected system functions in a "diagnostic routine" of test problems.

The logic of such diagnostic routines will be explored in Chapter 11. However, in simple terms, as shown in Figure 9-3, if we can find independent blocks in the system, and if we can find input tests that will require the correction operation of one combination of systems blocks at one time and another combination at another time, we may be able to check correct block-by-block operation by logical selection of the block combinations to be tested. In computer design, for example, system blocks are often constructed so that diagnostic routines may be developed for them. Even if a complete diagnostic checkout is impossible or unwanted it is still possible to develop specific diagnostic routines for differential diagnosis of a selected set of symptoms.

Examples of this approach—based on outside tests and a knowledge of system structure and block transformations—can be found in many areas. For example, an accounting system may be audited electronically by a "test deck" of trial conditions entered into the electronic computer. This diagnostic routine checks the accounting system, its files, and the computer function.

Example: Suppose we wish to test an accounting system, which, converted to an electronic computer, computes a payroll for a large number of employees. If we define when we should pay each employee, and thus define all other conditions as "illegal," we can compose a sample list of employees, state the conditions under which they worked, and feed this list to the system for evaluation. Some tests might include the

---

[15] The "failure" of the airborne computer in the first Gemini V space launch may not have been a failure of the computer at all according to NASA reports. Although the computer was working satisfactorily, something had altered the contents of the computer's nondestructive readout core memory unit. Although no reasons for this change have been advanced, the ability to isolate the change was based on a complete knowledge of what should have been in memory at the time of test. See J. Mercer, "Gemini Malfunction, Was It the Computer?" *Control Engineering*, July, 1965, p. 24. (Later investigation showed astronaut switching procedures had placed the computer on battery power for too long a period, depleting the battery and causing the unexpected memory change. *Control Engineering*, August, 1965, p. 32.)

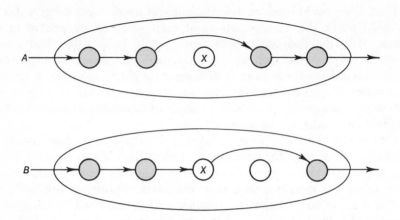

9-3 The principle of a diagnostic response test. Selected input *A* requires the correct operation of the sequence of elements shaded in the upper diagram. Selected input *B* requires the correct operation of the sequence of elements shaded in the lower diagram. If input *A* gives the correct output result, but input *B* does not, there is a high probability that element *X* is defective. Progressive tests of this type can reduce the probability that elements in the common shaded chain are causing the fault. (Taken from D. Hertz and R. Eddison, Eds., *Progress in Operations Research,* Wiley, New York, 1964, Vol. II, p. 138.)

names of employees not on the payroll, employees who were on the payroll, but just quit, employees assigned to the wrong department or with erroneous wage rates, employees who supposedly worked an "impossible" number of hours during a week, and so on. Should any of these people be paid (on paper, of course) a fault in the system will be indicated and probably isolated. The same procedure can also be applied to other accounting and record-keeping functions, such as accounts payable, accounts receivable, cash disbursements and receipts, inventory, and capital accounts.[16]

In the remainder of this book we will discuss in more detail several testing, trouble-shooting, and diagnostic procedures. We will see that test selection is, by analogy, the same as the initial selection confronting the analyst when he first defines his system, and that the methods of systems simplification discussed in Chapter 7 and 8 are also applicable here. Once the system has been specified, however, and its definition "frozen" or temporarily agreed upon, that framework guides our further analysis. We will now turn to methods of system simplification.

[16] Dept. of U.S. Air Force, *Guide for Auditing Automatic Data Processing Systems,* Government Printing Office, Washington, D.C., 1961.

PROBLEMS

9.1   Several response tests made from the outside of a system were cited in the text. This is the most widely used form of testing, one we use in everyday life when we converse with others, turn on an electric light, or start a car. It is, however, important to understand when this form of testing is likely to be most successful and when it must be used with care.

To illustrate this point, here are three cases in which outside response tests are proposed. What are the advantages and dangers of outside testing in each case? Where is the outside approach necessary? When is the usefulness of the approach greatest? In which case would your confidence in the results obtained be the greatest? Why?

CASE I: From a book by Theodor Reik (Adapted from *Listening with the Third Ear,* by Theodor Reik, by permission of Farrar, Straus & Giroux, Inc. Copyright 1948 by Farrar, Straus & Giroux, Inc. and *The Inner Experience of a Psychologist,* by Theodor Reik, by permission of George Allen and Unwin Ltd. Copyright 1949 by George Allen and Unwin Ltd.), p. 23, we have the following quotation: ". . . [the hunch of psychoanalysis] is that men reveal themselves—all their emotional secrets—when they talk freely about themselves; not just when they talk about their secrets, but about everything concerning themselves." Later, on p. 126, we find a similar, although apparently contradictory, quotation. "Mahler once remarked, 'The most important thing in music is not the score.' In psychoanalysis, too, what is spoken is not the most important thing. It appears to us more important to recognize what speech reveals and what silence reveals." (The outside test here is the analyst's remark, or silence, and the response is the patient's verbal output, or silence.)

CASE II: In an attempt to automate the auditing of financial and accounting systems implemented by electronic computer, many industrial firms and government agencies (e.g., Department of the U.S. Air Force, *Guide for Auditing Automatic Data Processing Systems,* Washington, D.C., Government Printing Office, 1961) have proposed the development of a series of "test decks" of cases for input to an accounting, or other form of data processing system. (Indeed, the use of test decks is a standard procedure for testing newly designed programs, and the experienced programer or systems analyst spends many hours devising the most difficult and extreme cases his system can encounter to test its operation under these unusual, as well as usual, conditions.) The purpose of the test deck is to determine if these diverse inputs are responded to in the appropriate, conditional manner by the system. Presumably, if the range of response tests is great enough we may assume the system is free from error, as well as from purposeful fraud. (The test deck approach is currently a highly controversial auditing method for accounting systems, but it is gaining acceptance in many areas. Why this diverse opinion?)

CASE III: From an IBM press release dated October 12, 1965, we have the following quote: "Endicott, N.Y.—Microcircuit assemblies for IBM

System/360 travel through a computer-controlled final test line. The three-station machine, controlled by a specially modified IBM 1410 data processing system, can perform more than 1000 short-open tests, scores of impedance tests, and hundreds of logical integrity tests on every assembled card. The tests, at an average rate of one card a second, represent the last step in the production at Endicott of the printed circuit cards used in System/360." (Similar approaches are used in final missile check-out, and are proposed for automative testing in the field. See Problem 9.3. Although special test probes are often brought out for response testing purposes, for the purposes of this question, consider this application an outside test.)

9.2 Consider the following example of a diagnostic routine. The Allen Electric and Equipment Company manufacturers a small computer (in the $7500–$10,000 price range) that hooks up electrically to an automobile with eight leads in five minutes. The machine performs up to 80 diagnostic tests on the car's ignition and carburetion systems in ten minutes or less. The sequence of these tests and the standard specifications of the manufacturer of the car are set by an IBM-type card inserted into the computer. (See cut of a card for 1966 Chevrolet, below.)

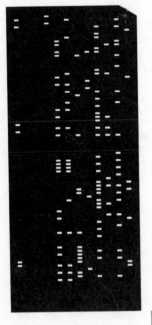

4660   121-A

© 1966 UNIVERSAL TESTPRODUCTS, INC.

#	Test	Condition	Spec
1	NO LOAD BATTERY VOLT	Vehicle electric power off	Min 12.40 VOLT
2	BATTERY UNDER LOAD	Test result 1 must be good	Min 10.50 VOLT
3	POINT RESISTANCE	Points must be closed	Max 0.080 OHMS
4	COIL PRIMARY RESIST	Connect H.V. jumper to jack	01.40 - 02.10 OHMS
5	BATTERY TO COIL RESIST	Turn ignition key on	Max 01.60 OHMS
6	COIL SECONDARY RESIST		05.40 - 09.10 K Ω
7	COIL POLARITY		
8	CONDENSER SERIES RES	Remove H.V. jumper - open pts	Max 0040
9	CONDENSER CAPACITY		0.180 - 0.230 MFD
10	CONDENSER LEAKAGE		Min 03.00
11	AVAIL SECONDARY VOLT	Remove dist H.T. wire	Min 025.0 KV
12	PRIMARY RESIST BYPASS	Turn key to start	Max 0.400 VOLT
13	SOLENOID CURRENT DRAW	Crank starter	Max 024.0 AMPS
14	SOL CABL & CONTAC DROP	Crank starter	Max 0.300 VOLT
15	STARTING CURRENT DRAW	Crank starter	Max 0130 AMPS
16	CHGE CKT OUTP W/O AIR	HT wire in - start - 2000 RPM	Min 033.0 AMPS
16A	CHARGE CKT OUTP W AIR	HT wire in - start - 2000 RPM	Min 057.0 AMPS
17	REGULATOR CUT-OUT REL		NA
18	BOUNCING POINTS	2000 RPM — by cylinder	
19	ARCING POINTS	Idle — by cylinder	Max 0040
20	DWELL ANGLE	Idle	031.0 - 034.0 DEG
21	DWELL VARIATION	Idle — by cylinder	Max 004.0 DEG
22	INIT TIMING (STD TRANS)	Idle — vac off — timing light	002.0 - 004.0 DEG
22A	INIT TIMING (AUT TRANS)	Idle — vac off — timing light	007.0 - 009.0 DEG
23	DIST ADV - CRANKSH DEG	2000 RPM - vac on - timing lt	045.0 - 049.0 DEG
24	DIST CAP & ROT LEAKAGE	Idle — plug wire out by cyl	Min 025.0 KV
25	DIST ROTOR AIR GAP	Gnd plug wire @ dist by cyl	Max 003.0 KV
26	SECONDARY VOLT REQUIR	1500 RPM - dist wir in - by cyl	006.0 - 010.0 KV
27	PLUG WIRE CONDITION	1500 RPM — by cyl	Max 018.0
28	FOUL OR SHORTED PLUGS	1500 RPM — by cyl	Max 0040
29	CYLINDER BALANCE	1000 RPM — by cyl	Max 070.0%
30	FAST IDLE CARB SETTING		NA
31	IDLE RPM — STD TRANS	Idle - air on - comp valve clos	0450 - 0500 RPM
31A	IDLE RPM — AUTO TRANS	Idle - air on - comp valve clos	0450 - 0500 RPM
32	REGUL CHARGE VOLTAGE	2000 RPM	13.80 - 14.80 VOLT
33	COMBUSTION EFFICIENCY	Idle — attach exhaust probe	070.0 - 080.0%
34	FUEL PUMP PRESSURE	Idle — insert transducer	03.00 - 04.50 PSI
35	FUEL FLOW	Varied speeds and load	GPH
36	FUEL CONSUMPTION	Dynamometer — 60 MPH	MPG

CHEVROLET 66 194" TRANS AUT-STD CARB 1 BBL F.O. 1-4-5-2-3-6

Corvair 6 Cyl 180 H P

⑤ ⑥ ①
④ ⑥ ②

Test results showing "good" or "bad" and test notes are printed on another card, which becomes a record for the customer and the shop. (See second cut, below.) The computer tests can be expanded to include other auto systems, such as cooling and exhaust, as these test functions become economically feasible. The test unit was inspired by units used to check the jet propulsion systems of missiles at Cape Kennedy. (This machine is described in more detail in "Computerized Engine Analyzer Could Revolutionize Car Care," *Motor Age*, February, 1966, p. 101.)

A. Under what conditions could such a diagnostic routine of tests be applied to other systems?

B. What are some of the advantages of such an approach to auto maintenance for the car owner? For the shop owner?

C. Could such a testing approach be used if the specifications of auto performance under different conditions were not completely known?

D. What are some of the dangers, if any, in the use of such equipment?

NAME_____MAKE_____

ADDRESS_____YEAR_____

CITY_____MILEAGE_____

DATE OF TEST   **No.**

FORM 100-A

		GOOD	MARG	FAIL
150.	RETRACTABLE HEADLIGHT OPERATION		MARG	
149.	HEADLIGHT CANDLEPOWER L. H. HIGH BEAM		MARG	
148.	HEADLIGHT ALIGNMENT L. H. HIGH BEAM	GOOD		
147.	HEADLIGHT CANDLEPOWER L. H. LOW BEAM			FAIL
146.	HEADLIGHT ALIGNMENT L. H. LOW BEAM	GOOD		
145.	HEADLIGHT CANDLEPOWER R. H. HIGH BEAM			FAIL
144.	HEADLIGHT ALIGNMENT R. H. HIGH BEAM	GOOD		
143.	HEADLIGHT CANDLEPOWER R. H. LOW BEAM	GOOD		
142.	HEADLIGHT ALIGNMENT R. H. LOW BEAM		MARG	
141.	WHEEL ALIGNMENT — CAMBER — L. R.		MARG	
140.	WHEEL ALIGNMENT — CAMBER — R. R.			FAIL
139.	WHEEL ALIGNMENT — TOE-IN REAR	GOOD		
138.	STEERING WHEEL SPOKE POSITIONING			FAIL
137.	WHEEL ALIGNMENT — L. CASTER	GOOD		
136.	WHEEL ALIGNMENT — R. CASTER			FAIL
135.	WHEEL ALIGNMENT — L. CAMBER			FAIL
134.	WHEEL ALIGNMENT — R. CAMBER	GOOD		
133.	WHEEL ALIGNMENT — TOE-IN		MARG	
132.	MAXIMUM ROAD HORSE POWER	GOOD		
131.	AUTOMATIC TRANS. SHIFT PATTERN & OPERATION		MARG	
130.	CLUTCH PEDAL FREE TRAVEL & OPERATION	GOOD		
129.	OBSERVED REAR WHEEL BALANCE		MARG	
128.	Rear Wheel Drive Speedometer Test at 60 M.P.H.	GOOD		
127.	Rear Wheel Drive Speedometer Test at 30 M.P.H.	GOOD		
126.	CARBURETOR POWER VALVE OPERATION	GOOD		
125.	INTAKE MANIFOLD VACUUM — LOAD	GOOD		

9.3   In several types of systems situations, the analyst prophesies either at his peril or to his advantage. For example, a *self-defeating prophecy* is one in which the analyst's predictions are defeated by a reaction of the system to the analyst's statements. If an analyst predicts that the prices for hogs will be very low next year, farmers who hear this prediction may well constrict the production of hogs, thereby raising the price of pork. Thus, the analyst's prophecy is *made* erroneous, because he made it public. Conversely, suppose an analyst predicts that the sales of automobiles will be greater next year than the previous year. If this prediction is incorporated into the sales quotas of the distribution organization, the prophecy may well come true, because the salesmen will work harder to achieve the goals set for them. The prophecy becomes *self-fulfilling*.

A. Can you think of any other examples of *self-defeating* and *self-fulfilling* prophecies?

B. Realizing that effects of the type described do occur, how could you use prophecy to manipulate a system?

C. How could the investigation of a system act as a prophecy, as viewed by the system?

D. For what kinds of system would an optimistic or a pessimistic prophecy be irrelevant?

10 | SELECTED SEARCH PROBLEMS AND TECHNIQUES

One of the most general problems encountered in systems analysis is that of search. If, for example, the system does not work or if it fails to work according to specification, we must search for the fault or cause of malfunction. In general, there may be multiple faults or causes of malfunction, and this considerably complicates the problem. We may have the problem of locating a given item in a file. If the desired item (or items) is not uniquely described, as is the case in many information retrieval problems, the search problem is complicated. A similar search problem occurs when we attempt to find a designated target, such as a mineral deposit hidden in the earth or a life raft tossed about at sea, for which only partial coordinate information (or no information) is available. Yet another example of the search problem is that of determining optimal policies or conditions for maximizing or minimizing a given objective function.

Thus, in general, the problem of search is another way of describing a selection process in which we attempt to pick out or isolate in a system a given point or set of points with specified characteristics (e.g., a faulty component, a desired document, a physical location, an optimum adjustment). Much of what has been said about system simplification is relevant to this problem, and it is worthwhile to pursue the subject further, because it is also central to the problem of systems analysis.

In what follows, we will survey a group of typical search problems that point up several, generally useful, search strategies. Although each field has its specific techniques, our illustrations are representative of the thinking that can be applied in a broad class of problems. Because of their specific interest, formal techniques of logical and probabilistic diagnosis have been left for Chapter 11. We now take up, in order, trouble shooting, information retrieval, random search, and optimizing search.

TROUBLE-SHOOTING METHODS

Problems of maintenance, repair, and fault correction in systems require that a given difficulty (or difficulties) be found and corrected. To speed this process we employ various methods, each of which attempts to isolate a defect in an orderly, progressive manner. Although the following examples are taken from current maintenance and testing practices in the hardware field, they have general applicability.

Detection at a Glance

Observation, in addition to revealing various symptoms of malfunction (which may be used as described in Chapter 11 to isolate faults logically), may also reveal the solution. If, for example, physical damage (such as a melted component, a severed electrical connection, or a hydraulic leak) is present when the investigator looks at a hardware system, it often provides a direct clue to the system's failure. Because this form of inspection is often the easiest, it is usually the first trouble-shooting method employed.

Similar forms of diagnosis are often possible when the system has been provided with measuring instruments, such as meters, trouble-lights, or other automatic detection equipment. For this reason many electrical and mechanical devices have metered outputs. The automobile has a gas gauge; the radio transmitter has one or more current and voltage meters; the hydraulic system has metered pressure and temperature points.

We often employ senses other than sight in such direct diagnostic steps. The sound of the motor tells the mechanic much about its internal operation. The electrician looks for overheated components by touch or by smelling the acrid charred shellac of electrical insulation. The physician uses even more complex forms of physical examination, before he makes other tests. He, for example, observes the patient's pallor, the slight shuffle in his step, the sound of his voice, the perspiration on his brow, and uses these direct observations as his first diagnostic signals.

We emphasize these relatively obvious observation methods not only because they are the easiest to employ, but also because they are frequently the source of effective screening decisions that greatly affect the later course of diagnosis. Because major decisions are frequently made at the outset of a diagnosis, such decisions should be made to discriminate as grossly as possible. And if the initial physical observation is made well, the investigator is often led to the solution of his problem at once, or with very few confirming tests.

Short and Continuity Checks

In hardware systems of any complexity, the system structure may not be as desired, either due to faulty construction, or due to deterioration, damage, or unplanned changes in configuration which occur with time. In such cases it may be relatively easy to make point-by-point checks of desired structure against actual structure, and to perform such tests in a methodical way.

Example: Suppose a system consists of N components that may be connected in various specified ways. We can summarize such a system of interconnections in matrix form, as shown in Figure 10-1, and test the presence or absence of each matrix entry by observation or measurement. Two faults may occur in such an interconnected system. First, a required connection may be absent, so that the required flow continuity is not possible. Such a defect would show up if a required cell in the specification matrix did not also appear as an observed combination. Second, a required flow between two given points may, in fact, be observed to connect two other points. In electrical trouble-shooting, special misconnections of this type called "short circuits" provide a name for the frequent observation of a long flow path that is shortened incorrectly during manufacture, by component or insulation failure, or

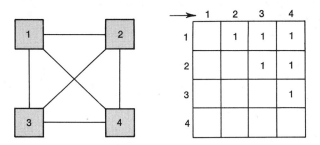

10-1 Short and continuity testing using matrix specification. The figure shows a four-component system which allows connections between each component. When no distinction is made between the direction of flow, and when there is only one connection between any two blocks, the number of connections is $(N^2 - N)/2$, in general, and six here, as shown. In the matrix, the cells to be tested are above the main diagonal. Extensions of the method can show multiple cell entries, or make two-way flow distinctions.

by damage. In many cases, tests of this type can be automated, because they are simple, numerous, and repetitive.

The matrix approach to orderly testing may be extended easily to two-way flows, or to multiple connections of different types, either by using multiple interconnection matrices, or by delineating the flow distinctions within each matrix cell. Thus, the components may be connected electrically and hydraulically, or there may be multiple electrical or hydraulic connections between each system block. The testing procedure is not altered by this additional complexity, although the number of tests to be made obviously increases.

Similar tests for system structure are also possible for paperwork, information flow, and logical systems.

Signal Tracing and Signal Substitution

Another large class of test procedures examines the correct transformation of a system's blocks in response to a standard test input. This procedure is known as *signal tracing,* and is illustrated in Figure 10-2. For illustration, consider a system composed of four blocks connected in series to provide a succession of input transformations. A standard test input is applied at the input to Block A. It is assumed that the correct transformation is known at each step of the process, i.e., that the variables that should be observed at the outputs of B, C, and D are known. Assume we also have available a probe that will not distort the measured signal at each point, so that the observation itself will not affect the quantity measured by overloading, or by other forms of the "probe effect." Then, by progressive comparison of the specified output versus the observed output at each system block, as we move away from the input, we can always isolate a defective block *if the blocks are independent in their operation.*

> *Example:* Four light bulbs are connected in series, so that all must work if the string is to light. The string does not light, and the defective bulb (or bulbs) is sought. To do this, the string is plugged in to provide a test voltage. We make successive probes continuing from the first bulb along the string until the first defective bulb is found by the absence of the test voltage. When the defective bulb is found, it is replaced. The string then either does or does not light. If it lights, the testing stops. If not, we continue the same procedure until the last defective bulb has been replaced and the string lights. Although this straightforward signal-tracing procedure can be made more efficient (as we shall see), the first-to-last approach is often used because little thought is required in the selection of test points.

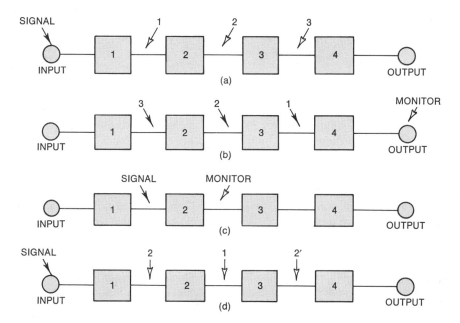

10-2 Isolation methods using signal tracing and signal substitution. The dark arrows indicate the application of a test signal. The white arrows indicate the application of a monitor or signal detector. (a) Signal tracing with successive probe points. A signal applied to the system input is traced for correctness away from the input. (b) Signal substitution. A monitor is applied to the system output, and the correct signal is inserted in progressive steps away from the output. (c) Use of signal substitution and tracer probe to test a single system block for correctness of transformation. (d) Signal tracing with binary selection of probe points. Either probe point 2 or 2' will be used, depending upon the results obtained with probe 1. The same procedure can be used with signal substitution. Binary probe point selection results in fewer probes for isolation.

Clearly, the procedure just described can be reversed by the use of *signal substitution,* as illustrated in Figure 10-2b. In this approach, a test probe is applied at the output of the system. The input to each system block that will produce the standard output is assumed known. Then, the required input at each block is inserted, block-by-block, progressing *away* from the output location until the defective block (or blocks) has been found, as described above. Again, the method will always provide isolation if the blocks are independent, and if the test inputs do not cause probe effects.

As a final example, the combination of signal substitution and signal tracing may be used to test the performance of selected system blocks, as shown in Figure 10-2c. Here a single system block is tested by appropriate signal substitution and corresponding monitoring of the block output. Again, we assume that this insertion and probe combination can be made without altering the system operation or the signal and its detection.

Creating Independence

In systems in which the blocks do not operate independently, which frequently happens when feedback loops are present, it is sometimes possible to create forced independence by disconnecting the feedback loops and performing tests specified for that condition. In the extreme, we could possibly remove the component blocks from the system and test each block separately, according to separate test specifications. In many cases, particularly in complex systems, components that tested "good" in isolation will not perform correctly in the system. In such cases, additional devices, to be described, may be required.

Binary Splits

Some thought will reveal that the progressive method of signal tracing or signal substitution just described is not the most efficient procedure possible. We could reduce the number of probe points or insertion points by strategic selection of test points, rather than by progressive selection.

We can achieve an improved selection by logically cutting the system in half at each successive probe insertion (or substitution). By a logical or binary split, we mean a choice of probe points that will divide the system into two parts at each stage, such that the probability of finding the defect in either part is one-half, or as near to that fraction as possible.

> *Example:* Continuing with the four-light-bulbs problem, again assume series connection, so that all bulbs must work for the string to light. Assume that we know only one bulb is defective, but we do not know its location. Then, after applying a test voltage across the string, the first point for binary detection is between the second and third bulb, under the assumption that all positions for the defective bulb are equiprobable. With only a single bulb defective, this probe will isolate it as being either bulb 1 or 2, or bulb 3 or 4. Next, by using one more probe between bulbs 1 and 2 *or* between 3 and 4, we can isolate the faulty bulb. This procedure thus requires a maximum of two steps, rather than the maximum of three required by the sequential procedure previously described. (See Figure 10-2d.) It is interesting to compare the maximum number and the average number of steps needed by the output-to-input and binary methods to isolate a fault in a system of N components connected in series, with the fault's position equiprobable in each of N locations.

Example: For illustration, consider $N = 4$. Then both the maximum number and average number of probes using the binary selection method will be $\log_2 4 = 2$. The maximum number of probes using the sequential method will be three; the average number of probes will be $\frac{1}{4}(1 + 2 + 3 + 3) = \frac{9}{4} = 2.25$. Thus, for this case, the binary selection method is better in reducing both the maximum number and the average number of probes necessary for isolation. The disparity in favor of the binary method greatly increases as N increases. For example, if N is a power of 2, then both the maximum number and the average number of probes using the binary selection method will be $\log_2 N$ (or at most the next integer larger than $\log_2 N$, if N is not a power of 2). However, the maximum number of probes for the sequential approach is $(N - 1)$, and the average number of probes is, using the sum of an arithmetic series,[1]

$$\frac{1}{N}\left[\frac{(N - 1)N}{2} + (N - 1)\right],$$

both of which increase must faster than $\log_2 N$ with N.

	Binary		Sequential	
N	Maximum	Average	Maximum	Average
2	1	1	1	1.00
4	2	2	3	2.25
8	3	3	7	3.38
16	4	4	15	7.96

The binary splitting approach is thus preferred with N large, when nothing is known about the fault's location (i.e., all possibilities are equiprobable), and the system can be halved at each testing stage. The same argument holds when a single fault may be expected with *known* probability at one of N locations. In this case, the system is split into parts having equal probability of containing the defective item, or as near to this desired split as is physically possible.

Example: Consider four components in series, one of which is known to be defective. The probability of failure for each component in the string is given (from past experience) as

---

[1] The sum of the arithmetic series $1 + 2 + 3 + \cdots + N = N(N + 1)/2$. In the problem above, $N - 1$ sequential tests are made, and it is assumed that the last probe either locates a defective bulb (in which case the Nth is good, if there is only one defective) or not (in which case the last bulb *is* defective). Thus, a maximum of $N - 1$ probes (not N) may be required for sequential isolation of a single defective. To compute the average number of probes, the $(N - 1)$st probe is counted twice, as illustrated for the case of $N = 4$ above.

| | Probability of a fault (for this system,|
Component	assuming a single defective)
1	0.4
2	0.3
3	0.2
4	0.1
	1.0

The first probe choice that will most nearly divide this system into parts having equal probability of containing the single defective is between components 1 and 2 (assuming the components are connected in the string 1-2-3-4). This choice divides the system into part No. 1 (containing component 1 with a probability 0.4 of being defective) and part No. 2 (containing components 2, 3, and 4 with a probability of 0.6 of containing the defective). This probe isolates the defective either in part No. 1 (in which case the search is finished) *or* in part No. 2 (in which case the search must continue). If the search continues, part No. 2 is probed between components 2 and 3, because this gives an equiprobable split for the remaining system. Again, this second probe isolates the defective either as component 2 (and the search is complete) *or* as lying in the set of components 3 and 4, which requires a third probe (between components 3 and 4) for final isolation. In this case, the actual number of probes required will depend upon the location of the defective component, and may be one, two, or three, as can be confirmed by enumeration of the four possible conditions (component 1, 2, 3, or 4 defective). The maximum number that may be required, three, is greater than $\log_2 4 = 2$, because a perfect binary split was not possible at each testing stage. From the table below, it is easy to compute the average number of probes required as 1.9.

| | Component | | | | | | |
	1	2	3	4			
					(1)	(2)	Expected
Probability defec-					Probes required	Prob-	value =
tive in string	0.4	0.3	0.2	0.1	to isolate	ability	(1) × (2)
First bad	X	0	0	0	1	0.4	0.4
Second bad	0	X	0	0	2	0.3	0.6
Third bad	0	0	X	0	3	0.2	0.6
Fourth bad	0	0	0	X	3	0.1	0.3

Expected Number of probes = 1.9

The expected number of probes (1.9) is less than $\log_2 4 = 2$ because the probability of finding the fault is clustered at one end of the string. Indeed, in this case, the binary split procedure is equivalent to the sequential search procedure that starts between components 1 and 2, although this would not generally be the case.

Consider the alternative series arrangement in which the string is composed of components in the order 4-1-2-3. Then, upon rearrangement of the probability table above, we would find that the maximum number and average number of probes needed for isolation would be two, and that the binary approach is superior to the sequential approach, as is usually the case for single fault detection.

These examples illustrate that although the binary search procedure may be logically preferred as an optimum method under the stated assumptions, it may not be possible or desirable to implement the procedure in every case. For example, it may not be possible to find the logically required probe points, or these points may be difficult to reach physically, so that another method is desirable. The probability of a single failure may not be known, or if known, it may not be possible physically to split the system into equiprobable halves at each stage. Moreover, if many of the N components in a system are defective at the same time, the power of the binary splitting approach over the sequential signal tracing approach diminishes, as may be seen by considering the four-component system with three of the four components defective. Finally, in complex systems with multiple failures, the binary search procedure may be more cumbersome to organize and to control than a somewhat longer, yet more obvious progressive signal-tracing scheme.

As a result of these observations, many probe schemes strike a compromise between what can be gained by the binary approach, and what is physically possible. Often complex systems will have natural junctions, which can be used to split the system into segments. If available, these points are used for isolation tests, and good system design practice always calls for the inclusion of such isolation points between major subsystems.

Intermittent Failures

Thus far, we have assumed that a fault, if present, will remain present during the course of the isolation search. Unfortunately, this convenient state of affairs is not always realized; the fault may be intermittent and thus it may or may not be found at a given search step.

In such situations, which, in terms of time and effort, are by far the most troublesome for the investigator, the isolation procedures just described are still useful. However, the application of a probe at a given test point must cover a sufficient period of time to include at least one observation of the intermittent fault. For this purpose, it is often desirable to use multiple and simultaneous probe measurements, rather than a detailed series of measurements.

For example, suppose a system consists of N components in series, as before, and that the system shows an intermittent failure pattern which may lie in any one of the N components with equal probability. To isolate the intermittent failure, we again apply a standard test signal to the input of the system, but we now continuously monitor both the output of the system (which is correct most of the time) and a test point at the "middle" of the system or as near this point as is physically possible. As the monitoring proceeds, the intermittent fault appears in the output of the system. Two outcomes are possible for the midpoint probe: Either the intermittent difficulty will show up there or it will not. If it does show up, we know that the first half of the system is at fault, and a new test point nearer the input to the system is selected for continued monitoring. If not, we move the test point nearer the output of the system. The procedure continues until the source of the intermittent failure has been found. (If multiple sources are suspected, a progressive sequence of probe points from input to output may be preferred, as before.)

Although the search procedure described may be slow and, if the intermittent failure is of short duration, may require the investigator's careful attention, we may be assured that the continued application of the approach will eventually provide the required isolation. The search obviously may be speeded by the use of multiple simultaneous probe points to provide (at a greater expense for test equipment) a saving in investigation time by obtaining all probe measurements at once. In addition, the investigator may substitute continuous recording instruments for his own continuous observation and (again at a still higher cost for test equipment) lessen his own effort in locating the intermittent fault.[2]

When such equipment is unavailable, or when continuous measurement is impossible, more drastic procedures, such as those described below, are often used to reduce an intermittent failure to a permanent failure, which may be isolated quickly by less expensive means.

Stress Methods

It is generally true that most systems will, under extreme duress or stress, break down at their weakest point. In a particular system, such "breakdown" is frequently associated with the intermittent observation of a symptom, a probe point deviation, or extraneous mode of operation that is more persistent than under ordinary circumstances. At the extreme, the intermittent fault may be permanent.

---

[2] One of the shortcomings of the local repair shop in locating intermittent failures in hardware systems is that most field facilities are not equipped with the variety or number of recording test instruments that could be useful in these difficult cases. This is another example of the law of Requisite Variety.

Stress may be applied to the system as a whole or to its suspect subsystems. In hardware systems, stress if often applied by variation of the supplies required for system operation (stuffing or starving the system), by extreme variation of environmental conditions (temperature, humidity, pressure, vibration), or by requiring extremes of input and output (alternate overloading and "coasting"). Similar forms of stress are often applied to human organizations for similar reasons.[3] Thus, automobile torture testing, military survival exercises, and marginal testing of electronic components are aimed at the isolation of components, individuals, or subsystems that are likely to fail or to show unwanted symptoms in the future or that presently show such signs of failure rarely or intermittently. The objective is to convert the improbable event into the highly probable event on an experimental basis.

Clearly, the amount of stress applied to a system or to its parts must be calculated with some care; otherwise permanent system damage of an unwanted type may occur. For example, although it is desirable to locate a weak component in a system, it is not desirable to so stress the system as a whole that all its components are permanently ruined. We may stress a mechanical or electrical system by vibrating it strenuously, but we do not usually drop it from a 100-foot cliff and expect any diagnostically useful results.

In addition to stress methods often being used for their own sake in "sensitivity analyses" of various forms (to evaluate the stability of a system's transformation properties under duress), they may also be used in conjunction with the continuous probe point monitoring described in the previous section. Thus, if a system contains a suspect component, this component may be subjected to stress while the probe points are monitored. If no specific suspect is available, stress applied to the whole system while the probes are monitored may accentuate the intermittent failure or increase the frequency of its occurrence. For example, components of an intermittent hi-fi amplifier may be subjected to alternate heat and cold (by application of a soldering iron and pinpoint sprays of liquified refrigerant gas under pressure), while one or more probe points are monitored against a standard specification.

It is interesting to note here that systems designs often create "stress points" inadvertently, and that if these points are known or can be isolated in the design, potential trouble sources can be forestalled. Field

---

[3] For example, see Problem 13.1, page 439. Stress methods are often applied in personnel interviews, in group and individual survival experiments, and in organizational evaluation by purchasing agents and prospective customers. This form of testing is also found in the folklore of most societies. Remember the many young men who completed "impossible tasks" to win the hand of a princess. The extermination of dragons, heroic wood-chopping, the location of rare prizes, the placation of family rivalries, and similar hurdles have been the substance of stories from Homer to Horatio Alger.

tests and torture tests of new products have this objective. Similarly, analytical and laboratory techniques are often planned for the same ends, as, for example, in mechanical stress analysis in structural design problems.

An analogy is of interest to the administrator of human organizations.[4] If the work flow in an operation has been analyzed, so that its organization of cooperative endeavors is known, it may be possible to find stress points created by the organizational design.

For example, in a series of operations requiring cooperation, as in a system with division of labor, each subgroup attempts to develop a stable pattern of interaction, or work, both within the subgroup and between the other subgroups in the system. When these stable patterns break down, or cannot be built up, the individuals involved experience stress or an uncomfortable feeling of pressure and dissatisfaction. "A breakdown in the flow creates opposition as the individuals struggle to restore it. The expected responses from the individuals in the sequence prove inadequate, and new coordination problems arise." [5]

Thus, at points where the work flow cannot be stabilized and controlled, (e.g., when a sequence of jobs required for the completion of a task or mission is not under the control of a single supervisor), stress points may be expected between the work groups. If the supervisors of the different work groups are attempting to meet different organizational needs, they cannot adjust to the requirements of any single manager, unless he controls or supervises all of them. Typical conflicts arise between the functions of sales, production, and finance, between maintenance and production, and between material handling and inspection. The more tightly "coupled" the suboperations must be to complete a given task, i.e., the more closely one operation must gear its actions to those before and after it, the greater the likelihood of trouble, unless the total system is coordinated to the given task.[6]

In short, "significant irregularities in the rate of flow and significant changes in the interaction of the individuals concerned indicate a point of organizational stress." [7]

In terms of the previous discussion, it should be clear that organizational stress may be induced for experimental purposes by restricting operating capacity, time, and resources for a given work load. Usually organizational stress points become clear as such restrictions are applied.

Block Substitution

Another standard fault-location procedure serves to illustrate how systems

---

[4] See E. D. Chappel and L. R. Sayles, *The Measure of Management—Designing Organizations for Human Effectiveness*, Macmillan, New York, 1961.

[5] *Ibid.*, p. 37.

[6] Compare this discussion with that of Chapter 8.

[7] E. D. Chappel and L. R. Sayles, *op. cit.*, p. 39.

analysis and systems treatment can be intertwined or accomplished at the same time.

For several reasons, it may be desirable to locate and to correct a fault in one step by substituting a new system component or module for a suspected defective.

First, this procedure may be easily and swiftly used in systems constructed on a modular principle, as are most modern systems designs. Either binary or progressive substitution may be used, depending upon the modular construction and the number of modules presumed defective. Thus, if a system can be divided into two parts, A and B, and if the corresponding spare modules are available, direct substitution can isolate the defective part. Subsystem A *or* subsystem B, *or both* subsystem A *and* subsystem B must be defective. The three possible forms of substitution, using the spare subsystem, will not only isolate the fault, but also correct it in the process. Although this procedure is fast, it requires the availability and substitution of large modules, which, in extreme circumstances (both subsystem A and subsystem B bad), could result in total system substitution. (Duplicate facilities are often maintained on standby for just this purpose.)

The same procedure would be possible with systems divided into more numerous modules, if sufficient spares were available and if the effort required in the substitution process were minimal compared to that required in extensive diagnostic tests.

For example, returning again to the four light bulbs connected in series, suppose the string failed to light as before. Then, if sufficient spares were available, we could first replace half the bulbs with new ones, say bulbs 1 and 2. If the string then lights, we could replace one of the new bulbs with one of the old bulbs, say in position 1. If the string lights with the old bulb, then the remaining old bulb is at fault. If the string does not light with the substituted old bulb, then that bulb is at fault. (A similar sequence would be followed if the string did not light with the substitution of bulbs 1 and 2 at the first stage. If so, and if we had sufficient new components, we could renew bulbs 3 and 4, then resubstitute old bulbs until the defective or defectives turn up. The procedure works best when the probability of multiple failures is small.)

A substitution procedure with exactly the same logic may be used by starting with two identical systems, one operative and the other inoperative, or equivalently by complete substitution of all modules in the inoperative system to make it work at the outset. To find the defective module, the modules from the inoperative system (or the old modules taken from the "rebuilt" system) are resubstituted on a binary split or progressive basis until the working system *fails* to operate. The procedure of resubstitution is continued until the single defective module or modules have been isolated. This approach has some appeal when it can be used, because the working system provides evidence that the "new" modules are all in working order at the time of substitution.

The reader will realize that the block substitution procedures just described are essentially different ways of implementing the signal-tracing and signal-substitution methods already discussed. For example, the substitution of a "good" system from the input to a given point applies a correct input to that point, and is equivalent to synthetic signal substitution. Conversely, substitution of a "good" system from a given point to the system output is equivalent to probe insertion at that point, as required for signal tracing. The approach chosen is thus a matter of physical convenience.

In this section we have considered a number of fault-search methods widely used in hardware systems for trouble-shooting. These methods, however, are of general use, and, as an exercise, the reader should attempt to cite examples of the general procedures in specific fields. Under what conditions, for example, can the signal tracing procedure be successful? When is block substitution preferred to signal tracing? What additional information might improve the trouble-shooting sequence? How can these data be organized? How could these trouble-shooting procedures be automated? Consideration of such questions will considerably improve the reader's appreciation of the approaches cited.

It is also worthwhile to note that even rudimentary training in the suggested procedures often leads to great improvement in the trouble-shooting ability of maintenance and "special project" personnel.

INFORMATION SEARCH PROCEDURE

Information retrieval is another example of the search problem in systems analysis. In this section, we present a brief survey of the procedures used, and note that the forms of search indicated may be expressed also in the Boolean Algebra format of Chapter 11.

The Item-Characteristic File

Information files are composed of a list of *items* (such as books, articles, land parcels, and individual names) that have certain *characteristics* (such as topics covered, key words, attributes, and skills).[8]

For example, a file consisting of eight documents described by six key words (which either appear or do not appear) represents a simpli-

---

[8] For a more detailed discussion of the organization of files, see R. S. Ledley, *Programming and Utilizing Digital Computers*, McGraw-Hill, New York, 1962, Chapter 11, "Searching, Sorting, Ordering, and Codifying."

fied file. For simplicity, the documents will be numbered (coded) 1–8, and the key words will be coded *A–F*. (The codes used may be structured to have meaning, as indicated in Appendix C and the reference below.) The associations of characteristics with items, i.e., key words with documents in this file, may be displayed as in Figure 10-3, which is a term-document or characteristic-item matrix for the hypothetical eight documents and six key words. A "1" in a given row indicates that that document can be described by the indicated key word. Similarly, a "1" in a column indicates that that term describes the indicated document.

Item Retrieval

Documents having the desired key words (or items having the desired characteristics) may be retrieved or extracted from the file in various ways.

If we can operate on the rows or columns of the term-document matrix *C* of Figure 10-3, which may be possible if the matrix is not too large, we can find the documents directly by two procedures, which we will illustrate by example.

Example: Suppose that documents containing both key words *A and B* are desired. Then if the elements of columns *A* and *B* of Matrix *C* are multiplied together cell by cell using logical multiplication ($1 \cdot 1 = 1$, all other combinations equal 0), the required documents will be indicated by the 1's that remain in the calculated result. Thus,

Documents	A	B	C	D	E	F	Key words
1	1	0	0	1	0	0	
2	1	1	0	1	0	0	
3	0	0	1	1	1	1	
4	0	1	1	0	0	1	= Term-document matrix *C*
5	1	0	0	1	1	0	
6	0	0	1	0	1	0	
7	0	1	0	1	0	1	
8	1	1	1	0	0	0	

10-3 A typical term-document matrix *C*. In this format, documents are coded numerically and key words alphabetically. Each row refers to a document and its associated key words. Each column refers to a key word and its associated documents. (It is equally possible to work with the transpose of this matrix by the interchange of row and column operations described in the text.)

Documents	A	B	(A·B)
1	1	0	0
2	1	1	1
3	0	0	0
4	0	1	0
5	1	0	0
6	0	0	0
7	0	1	0
8	1	1	1

and documents 2 and 8 are the ones desired. (In Chapter 11, this form of manipulation will be expanded to include other forms of logical combination of characteristics, which will then be called logical statements having the value True or False.) The procedure provides a direct matching of key words with documents.

Example: Another simple procedure that provides a count of the number of matches between the desired key words and those present for each document uses ordinary matrix multiplication by a column vector composed of 0's and 1's to indicate the desired key words. For example, if documents having key words B, C, and F were desired we could form the column vector q, for key words, which has 1's in positions B, C, and F and 0's elsewhere as shown below. Multiplication of the term-document matrix, C, by q, in that order, produces the column vector r, which describes the number of matches for each document.

$$[C] \times [q] = [r]$$

		Key word			Document	
$[C]$	$\times$	A	0	$=$	1	0
		B	1		2	1
		C	1		3	2
		D	0		4	3
		E	0		5	0
		F	1		6	1
					7	2
					8	2

In this example, document 4 matches the three key words specified and is uniquely selected. However, other documents match one or two of the specified key words, and may therefore be of some interest. In efficient retrieval systems in which the keywords are precisely applied, documents which have the highest value in the computed column vector r will be the most relevant. (In practice more complicated computation forms are often used to give a relevance score for each document in the set, as discussed briefly hereafter and extensively by Salton.[9])

Three File Search Methods

Three forms of search are often used in extensive files, namely, (1) search by item for given characteristics, (2) search by characteristic for items so described, and (3) search by short tables of characteristic with cross references. Each of these methods which we will illustrate by using the term-document matrix data of Figure 10-3, is suitable for computer use.

Example: A file may be organized by listing items as a heading, and sublisting the characteristics. This produces an item-characteristic file. A search on the item, or document in this case, can be made down the document list. If the desired key words are present for a given document, that document number is extracted. Such a listing of documents need not be in any particular order, but the search for all relevant documents must encompass the entire list. Physically, such a file organization and search procedure corresponds to the search for items by examination of every item on a computer tape, or, in the manual file, to the search for a sub-set of desired items from a set of edge-punched (McBee) cards. (See Figure 10-4a.)

Example: Conversely, a file may be organized by listing characteristics as a heading and sublisting items having that characteristic. Again, with our previous definition, this produces a characteristic-item file. In this file, the characteristics (key words) must appear in a given order. Here we assume an alphabetical order of key-word codes for efficiency. To find the required documents, we first place the specified key words in alphabetical order. Then, we consult the first specified key word and note the relevant documents. Next, we consult the second key word and retain the relevant documents for this key word (if any) that also match the relevant documents for the first key word. This procedure continues until all the specified key words have been consulted, and the common relevant documents are isolated. This procedure has the advantage that only the specified key-word categories need be consulted, not the entire list. However, a strict ordering of the key words in the file is required so that they can be found easily. Physically, this method corresponds to the manual use of "peekaboo" cards, illustrated in Figure 10-4b.

---

[9] See G. Salton, "Progress in Automatic Information Retrieval," *IEEE Spectrum*, August, 1965, pp. 90–103. This review article contains an extensive bibliography.

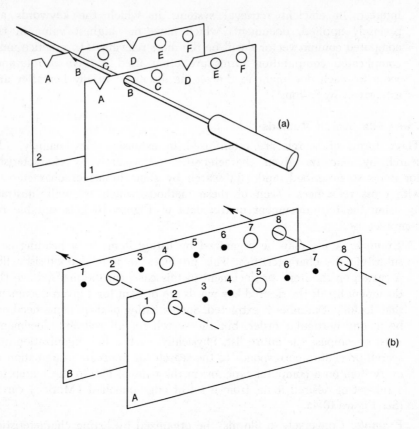

10-4 Edge-punched item cards and peek-a-boo characteristic cards. In (a), one card is made for each item (document) in a file, and the characteristic (key word) is punched at specified edge positions. Items 1 and 2 of Matrix *C,* Figure 10-3, are shown. To extract all items with a given characteristic, a needle is inserted in the edge position (hole or notch) for that characteristic (*B* is shown). All items with that characteristic fall out of the file. In (b), one card is made for each characteristic, and items having that characteristic are indicated by punching out a hole in a designated item position. Characteristics *A* and *B* of Figure 10-3 are shown. To find items with given characteristics, the desired characteristic cards are aligned. Light will pass through the item holes that have all the specified characteristics, here documents 2 and 8.

Example: A third form of file organization and search (known as the Tabledex Method) is a tabular combination of the previous procedures, which drastically reduces search time at the expense of file complexity. The file is organized by creating a table for each characteristic, or key word in the present case, and listing in order as subheadings the items (documents) described by the given key word. So far the organization is similar to the previous example. However, we now expand the table by listing for each document shown all of the pertinent characteristics *greater in order* than the characteristic, or key-word code, of the table at hand. To accomplish this we use the alphabetical ordering of key words and numerical ordering of documents shown in Figure 10-3 for the term-document matrix C. Figure 10-5 shows the complex Tabledex file organization for the data of Figure 10-3. Note that the characteristic tables are arranged in alphabetical order, that the documents in each table are in strict numerical order (where they appear), and that the characteristics for each document so listed in a table are in alphabetical order and contain entries of higher alphabetical order than the table designation (again, where they appear).

To search for documents described by a given set of key words (or items described by a given set of characteristics) we first put the desired characteristics in ascending (alphabetical) order. We then scan the Tabledex file for the table corresponding to the lowest order of the desired characteristic. We next scan the document list in this table for documents (if any) showing the remaining key words. If we find such documents, they are the desired ones, and our search ends. We need only consult one table in this method of search.

For example, suppose we wanted the documents described by key words B and C. Because these key words are in order, we consult the

Table A		**Table B**		**Table C**	
Documents	Key words	Documents	Key words	Documents	Key words
1	D	2	D	3	D,E,F
2	B,D	4	C,F	4	F
5	D,E	7	D,F	6	E
8	B,C	8	C	8	(None)

Table D		**Table E**		**Table F**	
Documents	Key words	Documents	Key words	Documents	Key words
1	(None)	3	F	3	(None)
2	(None)	5	(None)	4	(None)
3	E,F	6	(None)	7	(None)
5	E				
7	F				

10-5 A tabledex file organization for the term-document data of Figure 10-3. One table is prepared for each key word (coded alphabetically here). The tables are ordered alphabetically (by the code) as shown from left to right down the page above. To find a document associated with a given set of key words, the keywords are first ordered by their code. Then the table for the first keyword is found. Documents described by the other key words specified (if any) will appear in that table and may be found by inspection without recourse to other Tables in the file.

Tabledex File and find Table *B*. The documents described by *B* are listed. We next scan the key-word listing for each document shown containing *C*. The only documents satisfying the request are documents 4 and 8.

A manual Tabledex file may be constructed as a book of pages, with one page for each key-word table, and the remaining detail printed on the page. (A computer can be programed to produce such a book if desired.) Then, to locate a given document, we turn to the page representing the lowest order key word, and find the request (if it exists) on that page, by following the above method.

Searching with Relaxed Conditions

With any of the above procedures, the search for a given item (or document) may possibly not lead to *any* items having the specified characteristics (or key words) if the characteristics required are too numerous. In such a case, the number of requirements must be reduced to find some items that are reasonably desirable.

This relaxation of conditions raises questions about which of the characteristics to discard and which to retain in a further search. First, a combinatorial problem arises. For example, if, say, five key words are used in the search for a document and the search fails, we might think of using only four key words, and then repeating the search. However, the number of ways four key words can be selected from the original five is five, the number of ways three keywords can be selected from five is ten, the number of ways two key words can be selected from five is ten, and so on.[10] We may have to perform a series of searches of this type before finding any relevant documents. The situation worsens severely as the original number of desired key words increases.

Fortunately, several methods combat this combinatorial difficulty. For example, the search procedure described on page 274 will give the number of matches that do occur for the specified key words, and therefore serves to rank the documents in the order of relevance (by the number of matches) even though no perfect matching document can be found.

Example: Suppose, using the data of the term-document matrix [*C*] of Figure 10-3, we desired to find documents described by key words *A*, *B*, *C*, and *D*. Without knowledge of what is in the file, we may thus form the column request vector *q*, and multiplication of the term-document matrix *C* by the request vector *q* (in that order) will produce a column vector *r* which, in effect, evaluates the documents in the file in terms of the request. Thus, for the four key words suggested:

---

[10] Recall that, in general, the number of ways *r* things can be selected from *n* is

$$n!/[(r!)\,(n-r)!].$$

$$[C] \times [q] = [r]$$

	Key word		Document	
$[C] \times$	A	$\begin{bmatrix} 1 \end{bmatrix}$	= 1	$\begin{bmatrix} 2 \end{bmatrix}$
	B	1	2	3
	C	1	3	2
	D	1	4	2
	E	0	5	2
	F	0	6	1
			7	2
			8	3

The results show that no document is described by all four specified key words (because there are not four matches), but that two documents show three matches (documents 2 and 8), and several show two matches. One order of preference would be to inspect the documents in the order indicated by the number of matches.[11]

The concept just illustrated is easily extended to the case in which some of the key words are more important in the search than others. In such a case, the original request vector *q* may show weighted values for each desired key word (instead of the binary indication of the previous example), and the process can be repeated. For example, suppose we still want key words *A*, *B*, *C*, and *D*, but that the key word *C* is thought twice as important as the other key words. Then we have

	Key word	Weighted Request		Document	Weighted Matches
$[C] \times$	A	$\begin{bmatrix} 1 \end{bmatrix}$	=	1	$\begin{bmatrix} 2 \end{bmatrix}$
	B	1		2	3
	C	2		3	3
	D	1		4	2
	E	0		5	2
	F	0		6	2
				7	2
				8	4

[11] Ledley, *op. cit.*, pp. 506–510, indicates an alternate sorting procedure to achieve the same result.

which now prefers document 4. Although such weights may be arbitrary, depending upon the investigator's choice it is also possible to generate weights based on the possible correlation of key words and documents in the file, and such methods are often used in automated retrieval information systems.[12]

Finally, there may be forms of search in which certain key words (or characteristics) *must* be satisfied, and other key words, although desirable, are not necessary. In such cases, the search can proceed by first partitioning the file (and therefore the corresponding term-document matrix) by sorting out the documents with the mandatory key words, and then continuing as before.

Example: Suppose that for the file described by matrix C of Figure 10-3 we wish to find documents described by key words A, B, and C, but that term A is mandatory. Then, by a sort on key word A (and deletion of key words D, E, and F, which are now irrelevant to the search), we have a reduced term-document matrix C_{NEW}, which may now be searched for key words B and C as before.

$$[C_{\text{new}}] \times [q_{\text{new}}] = [r_{\text{new}}]$$

Document	Key word B C		Key word		Document	Matches
1	1	0	B	$\begin{bmatrix}1\\1\end{bmatrix}$	1	1
2	1	1	C		2	2
5	1	0			5	1
8	1	1			8	2

$$\times \qquad = \qquad$$

The new term-document matrix contains only rows 1, 2, 5, and 8, because these are the only documents in the file having the mandatory key word A; it contains only columns B and C, because these are the only pertinent key words remaining for the search. The result shows that documents 2 and 8 meet all three requirements, because we know the documents have key word A (by virtue of the original sort) and because two matches indicate that both key words B and C have been matched.[13]

Indexing

In the preceding, we have assumed that the items or documents filed have associated with them definite characteristics which are clearly recognized

---

[12] See Sarton, *op. cit.*, pp. 94–95.

[13] It is useful to note that the matrix by vector multiplication used in the examples above is equivalent to making a count, for each document in succession, of the number of 1's that appear in the columns selected by the request q, or the computation of a weighted sum, if q is not a binary vector.

and which can be attributed to a given item when the file is made up. For example, suppose a file shows product assemblies as items, and the attributes of these assemblies are their specific parts. Then the relationship of part to assembly is clearly defined by product specification, or blueprint, and no ambiguity should occur in the assignment of "characteristics" to items. A similar situation obtains in highly structured information systems, such as the chart of accounts: The characteristics that should cause a given cost to be posted to a given account are defined, so that the association defined by the item characteristic table is clear.

More generally, however, the job of assigning key words to documents, or characteristics to items, which is called indexing, is not so clear-cut. For example, suppose we have a technical article that refers to (1) aircraft, and (2) manufacturing, and that these key words are assigned to that document. The article in question will not be found if a request is made for all articles described by the key words (1) airplane and (2) production. This problem is distinctly different from the cases described above for the assembly file and the cost accounting file, where the specification of a few rigidly prescribed terms will locate a unique item, or set of items. In the more general information retrieval problem, a given item or document can be described in an infinite variety of ways and shades of meaning which places an unrealistic burden on the indexing, processing, and request operations. For the rigidly indexed file, the terms used by the indexer and the requester must be complete and absolutely consistent to provide the desired result.

A number of devices are used to alleviate this somewhat unrealistic requirement. Some intermediate device or step is required to overcome inconsistencies and incompleteness which often arise as the popularity of descriptive terms changes, as personnel changes, and as the scope of the master file increases.

Dictionaries

Acceptable term dictionaries are often provided, so that the indexer and the requester can use similar words in the input and output operations. Frequently, this approach is expanded to include a *thesaurus* of terms to which a common code may be applied. For example, aircraft, airplane, and other synonyms for the same type of flight equipment may be coded to a single identifier, say subject 3.16, which is thereafter used as the indexing and search code for filing and retrieval. Similarly, concepts and operations may also be given a code number, and a dictionary or thesaurus of concepts arranged in a hierarchy of generality may be developed, so that a given specification can be related to more or less general specifications, as the need arises. Again, the same idea may be used to develop phrase dictionaries, in which, say, the terms "cost" and "accounting" are combined into the more useful descriptive term "cost accounting" to be coded and used for index and search.

Such devices are usually employed in automated information retrieval systems, so that minor variations in indexing and request formats can be handled. Another approach, also used in automated information systems, is to compute the statistical correlation between terms used in the file, and between items that have similar descriptions. This can be accomplished for a given file, and revised by recomputation as the contents of the file changes. The computation may also be arranged in stages to suggest alternate terms for search, or to provide an automatic weighting for the terms used in a request, and for those terms generated automatically from the request.

For example, in a given file we may find that the term "aircraft" appears frequently with, and therefore is highly correlated with, such terms as "airframe," "fusilage," "propeller," "acceleration," "jet," and "supersonic." However, the terms associated with "aircraft" may also be associated *in the file* with the term "airplane," which may be thought of as a second-order term. Thus, the analysis of the contiguous modifying terms for one more general term, may in turn lead to one or more synonyms for it as those synonyms are employed in the file itself. By this procedure, the term "airplane" could automatically be added to the initial request for documents pertinent to "aircraft." Thus, the original request for an item may be expanded or contracted by the information processing system, and weights may be computed for evaluation of document pertinence along the lines previously described.

As we shall see in Chapter 11, the information search procedures we have discussed here can be expanded to many applications, including the search for causes of system difficulty, when we are given a set of observed symptoms.

SOME RANDOM SEARCH PROBLEMS

Let us now turn to some search problems, which, although they involve isolating one or more specific items from a much larger, and perhaps infinite, population, accomplish this not by logical sequencing but by random sampling.

Locating a lost object, target, or an optimum point from many possible alternate points presents a problem in which a "random" search procedure may be useful. Although it would not seem to at first, a random search method has many appeals. If, for example, a systematic search procedure is chosen, and the desired item is not associated with the choice of the specific procedure used, the item will not be found.

Example: Suppose a particular item belongs to a set of odd-numbered categories. If the investigator selects an examination or testing procedure which considers only even-numbered items, that procedure is doomed to failure. It will not find the desired item, and this failure is a property of the chosen search method.

Similarly, a random search procedure is, on the average, one which cannot be defeated by opponent strategy.

Example: Suppose the police search for crimes in progress by following a systematic surveillance route: The radio car makes a systematic tour of the community at specified hours. If this search pattern becomes known to criminals in the community, they will surely take advantage of the systematic pattern and commit their crimes when it calls for nonsurveillance. The same argument holds for both space and time. And so, many police forces make random tours of surveillance.

In addition, the use of a random search procedure often gives the investigator a limiting condition for item isolation, which can be used as a standard against which other search methods can be compared.

Example: Any knowledge of the probability distribution of an item's location improves the probability of locating it. But it may be desirable to determine how much this information is worth. By comparing the probable return that can be achieved from a given amount of search effort by one means (assuming some knowledge of a pattern of operation or location) as opposed to a random search method (which requires no knowledge), the value of the alternate search procedure can be assessed.

We now give several examples to illustrate these points.

Random Search in an Area

One of the classic military search problems is the location of a target, which may be in an unknown position (and therefore at random as far as the investigator knows) in a given area A, e.g., the problem of locating an enemy ship in the ocean.

In this situation, an evaluation of the probability of the target's detection is often useful if a random search procedure is used.

To develop this point, consider an area A, as shown in Figure 10-6, which contains a target X located at an unknown xy location. It is proposed to tour the area A by means of a random path of length L. Let us further suppose that the target X will be detected by the search procedure if the search path passes within a distance $W/2$ from the target's location (i.e., the search path sweeps out a band of width W symmetrically centered

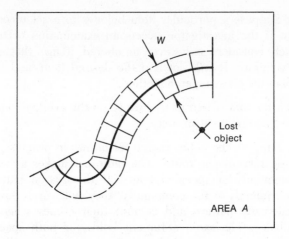

10-6 Random search in an area. In the bounded area, there is an object of Search X. A random search path of length *L* is made through *A*. It is assumed that the lost object will be found if the area of width *W* about *L* covers *X* in the random search. The total area swept out by the search path is *WL*, which is a fraction *WL/A* of the total area under consideration. To derive the equation shown in the text, the area swept out by the search is divided into a number of small boxes of area *WL/n*, each having a probability *WL/nA* of containing the lost object *X*.

over the search point, and target detection definitely will occur if the band includes the target location, and will definitely not occur otherwise). Our purpose is to compute the probability of detection as a function of *L* and *W*, in comparison to the search area *A*.

We first divide the length of sweep *L* into *n* equal parts; in effect we divide the area *WL* of the path swept into *n* small boxes of dimension $(W \times L/n)$. The probability of detecting the target in one of those small boxes is given by the ratio of area $(WL/n)/A = WL/nA$. The probability of detecting the target after traversing all the small boxes along *L* is

$$p = 1 - \left(1 - \frac{WL}{nA}\right)^n$$

which follows from the probability that the target will *not* be detected in the sequence of *n* boxes (considered to be independent, because of the random form of search and the random location of the target) being one minus the probability of detection at an individual box raised to the *n*th power.[14]

[14] If the target is not detected after *n* tries, it must not be detected on any of them. Thus, by virtue of the multiplication law of probability, the probabilities of failure are multiplied to get the sequence probability of failure, and the probability of detection is one minus this amount.

If we now let n become very large (i.e., let the area of the small boxes approach zero) we have the limiting condition[15]

$$p = 1 - e^{-WL/A}$$

where e is 2.718. This result shows that as the length of the search path L increases, the probability of target detection approaches 1.0. This effect can be quickened by increasing the width of the detection band W.

It is interesting to note that if the area WL swept by the search path is so small compared to A, that there is little chance of overlapping, the probability of detection becomes simply $p = WL/A$, the ratio of the two areas. The higher-order terms, which in the limit produce the exponential, take into account the overlapping that may occur with longer search paths, which will in effect produce sampling with replacement. Either of the above formulas tells us that more effort at random search (larger L) produces a situation of diminishing returns. An added unit of effort in search does not progressively produce the same added increment in the detection probability, but rather a progressively smaller one as the search continues.

We may now ask how much effort is worthwhile in a given search by this method? This question may be answered by evaluating the cost of a unit effort of search and the benefit to be had if the target is found. Thus, assuming that the benefit from target detection is \$$c_1$ and that the cost of search is \$$c_2$/mile of L, we may write an equation for the total expected benefit from a search of length L as

$$\text{Total Expected Benefit in \$} = c_1(1 - e^{-WL/A}) - c_2 L.$$

This equation is a function of L and may be maximized in a number of ways. For example, if we take $W = 1$ mile, $A = 100$ square miles, $c_1 = \$1000$, and $c_2 = \$5$/mile, successive substitution of trial values of L will reveal that the optimum length of search L is, for the assumed conditions, about 70 miles.[16]

Because in the random search method described above, the target may in fact have been "discovered" more than once, we may ask for the probability that the target has been found exactly m times in a tour of length L. If we call the ratio $WL/A = \phi$, the "coverage factor" of the search to the

---

[15] The series of terms generated by $(1 - WL/nA)^n$ equals $e^{-WL/A}$ if $n \to \infty$; i.e.,

$$e^{-x} = \lim_{n \to \infty} \left(1 - \frac{x}{n}\right)^n.$$

The same result may also be achieved by other means.

[16] Tabulated values of e^x and e^{-x} may be found in standard works, such as R. S. Burington, *Handbook of Mathematical Tables and Formulas*, 4th ed., McGraw-Hill, New York, 1964.

total area A, the probability of discovering the target exactly m times is given by the Poisson distribution[17]

$$P(m, \phi) = \left(\frac{\phi^m}{m!}\right) e^{-\phi} \qquad \left(\phi = \frac{WL}{A}\right).$$

The coverage factor ϕ may be specified in various ways, depending upon the problem, but for random search, the basic relationship holds. In general, ϕ will represent the expected number of sightings made.

For example, suppose that in the area A there are numerous targets, not just one. Then the target density is given by the number of targets N divided by the area A, N/A. The average number of targets sighted in a tour of length L will be $m = (WL)(N/A) = \phi$. The probability of "discovering" exactly m targets in a random tour of length L is given by the Poisson distribution and the new value of ϕ (where, of course, the assumptions of random scattering of the targets in area A, random search, and certain detection within $W/2$ of the path L are maintained as before).

> *Example:* Suppose a ship passes through a mine field in which there are N mines in a given area A. Suppose also that the mines have an effective range $W/2$ for the ship (i.e., a mine will attack the ship if the ship passes within $W/2$ of it). Then, $\phi = WLN/A$ as before, the number of mines encountered in a path of length L is given by the Poisson distribution, and the probability that the ship will encounter at least one mine in its tour L is $(1 - e^{-\phi})$. The "mean free path" or average distance between mine encounters is $1/\phi = A/WLN$.

Although more general treatment must be left to the references, it is worthwhile to consider one application of this result that gives a clue to the range of possibilities for further analysis.

> *Example:* Suppose a pack of S submarines may operate in one of two ways: either independently, or as a group. For simplicity, we assume the same detection and search rules as above (i.e., definite detection within a band $W/2$ of the random search path). The probability that a ship passing through area A will be detected at least once (by one or

[17] Derivations and extensions of this form of search theory may be found in P. Morse and G. Kimball, *Methods of Operations Research,* Technology Press and Wiley, New York, 1951, and in four articles by B. O. Koopman, all in *Operations Research* (The Journal of the Operations Research Society of America): "The Optimum Distribution of Effort," **1**, 2, 1953, pp. 52–63; "The Theory of Search: Part I, Kinematic Bases," **4**, 3, 1956, pp. 324–346; "The Theory of Search: Part II, Target Detection," **4**, 5, 1956, pp. 503–531; "The Theory of Search: Part III, The Optimum Distribution of Searching Effort," **5**, 5, 1957, pp. 613–626. This form of analysis was widely used during World War II.

more of the submarines) is $(1 - e^{-SWL/A})$. If F ships per month pass through the area, the expected number sighted (at least once) is[18]

$$D = F(1 - e^{-SWL/A}).$$

Suppose that the submarines fire torpedos upon sighting, and that the probability of sinking the target after sighting is P. Then the expected number of ships sunk per month with S submarines operating independently in area A is

$$H_i = F(1 - e^{-SWLP/A}).$$

Although the value of D (expected number of the F ships sighted as a function of the effort expended) saturates rapidly as the number of submarines S and the length of tour of each L is increased (because multiple sightings increase), when the probability of sinking upon sighting is small, the number of ships sunk H_i does not saturate so quickly with increased effort, because the multiple sightings provide multiple tries at sinking the same target.

When the submarines operate as a group instead of attacking separately, all will respond to a sighting made by one. Assume all the S submarines will be able to "home" on the first one and get their chance at sinking the ship. In this case the probability that the ship is sunk is $1 - (1 - P)^S$ instead of the value of P which it had if only one submarine attacked. Thus, the expected number of ships sunk by the group method is

$$H_g = F(1 - e^{-(SWL/A)[1 - (1 - P)^S]}).$$

The relative advantage of group action over independent action is given by $R = H_g/H_i$. If this ratio is tabulated against the number of submarines S, for various ratios of WL/A, it may be seen that, if WL/A is large, the number of submarines in the optimum group moves toward 1.0, but if WL/A is very small (vast area to cover), continually increasing the size of the group is beneficial.[19] For example, data on Japanese shipping indicated that about three U.S. submarines per group would give optimum results in the Pacific. After the analysis and perfection of the group tactics by practice, the yield per submarine in a group of three was about 50% greater than the yield per independent submarine, confirming the analysis.

---

[18] This number should not be confused with the expected number of "ship-sightings" made per month by the submarines which can exceed F and which is given by $\phi = SFWL/A$. The number of ship sightings would follow the Poisson distribution with the given ϕ.

[19] See plot, Figure 1, Morse and Kimball, *op. cit.*, p. 89.

In conclusion, many of the calculations involving search in an area depend upon more complex detection and attack rules than the simple ones used for illustration here. For example, the use of alternate detection equipment (e.g., radar, sonar, the human eye, or other devices) can change the probability that a target will be sighted as a function of the distance from the point of search. A rule for visual detection often indicates that the probability of sighting falls off with the cube of the distance between the target and the detector. More complex rules hold when the relative movement of the target and the detector are known.

To illustrate the effect of the detector upon the search process, consider the following practical problem of exploration in which a two-stage search process is used. This problem has been simplified somewhat for presentation, but it contains the essential ingredients of the industrial exploration process and the important concept of using several levels of search detail.

Example: A valuable prize is located in one of two areas. (As a prize, consider a mineral deposit, an oil or gas deposit, or a similar valuable

Area 1	Area 2

asset.) Although it is known that there is one and only one prize in the total area, no information is available on the exact location of the prize (i.e., the correct area, or box, is not known). Two search methods are available (1) an inexpensive method, which costs $10,000 per look, and (2) an expensive method, which costs $1 million per look, and which must be used (e.g., drilling for oil) for prize acquisition.

An obvious way of locating the prize with certainty is to use the expensive method, with a random choice for the first look.

METHOD I (for certain location in one stage)

$$\text{Total Cost (in millions)} = (1)(0.5) + (2)(0.5) = \$1.5,$$

because if the prize is not found on the first expensive look, the process must be repeated in the remaining area (i.e., two holes must be drilled to locate and acquire the prize).

We now ask whether or not a two-stage search and acquisition procedure would be less expensive. However, the inexpensive detection method is not certain. Moreover, the method gives spurious readings, which indicate the presence of the prize when it is not there, and also occasionally fails to detect the prize when it is there. For example, these chances are usually characteristic of the detection equipment used: Electronic or other detection equipment carried in a truck over rough terrain or in an aircraft through turbulent atmosphere can issue false signals due to vibration, random noise, and the like—as well as provide true signals for only a fraction of the prizes passed over.

Nevertheless, suppose we decide on the following plan (which for illustration is simple to avoid mathematical complexity): Two looks will be taken in each of the two areas, and any positive signals obtained by the inexpensive method (true or false) will be recorded. If one area scores higher than the other, the certain method of detection and acquisition will be used first in the high-score area. Should the area scores be tied, we will revert to the random use of the expensive method exclusively. In either case, if the first expensive look does not yield the prize, the expensive method will be used on the remaining area, to acquire the prize with certainty.

We now turn to a cost evaluation of the second method. Let us assume the following data for illustration.

λ = the probability that the inexpensive look will yield a false positive reading = 0.1 per look.

p = the probability that the inexpensive look will yield a true positive reading when the prize is there = 0.2 per look.

With these data available, we can now compute (1) the probability that the prize will be acquired on the first expensive look, (2) the probability that the prize must be located by random application of the expensive look, because the scores are tied, or (3) the probability that two expensive looks will be required, because the inexpensive look gave a false positive reading.

To summarize these computations, suppose the prize is actually in Area 2 of the diagram below, so that the probability of getting a signal (false) from Area 1 is λ per look, and the probability of getting a signal from Area 2 (true or false) is $\lambda + p - \lambda p = \alpha$ per look. The actual scores generated by these two basic probability values, which we assume to be constant regardless of the number of looks, will have the binomial distribution. Thus, for two inexpensive looks in each area, we may summarize the nine outcome score combinations possible in the table below, which also shows the correct probability values for each possibility.

Area 1	Area 2
Probability of a signal = λ	Probability of a signal = $\lambda + p - \lambda p = \alpha$

PRIZE IS HERE

Note: In Area 2, a signal may arise either because the prize is there, with probability p, or from spurious causes with probability λ. Because only one signal is obtained per look, both causes do not occur together.

Case	X_1	X_2	$P(X_1, X_2)$	Appropriate formula
1	0	0	0.41990	$(1 - \lambda)^2(1 - \alpha)^2$
2	0	1	0.32659	$2(1 - \lambda)^2\alpha(1 - \alpha)$
3	0	2	0.06350	$(1 - \lambda)^2\alpha^2$
4	1	0	0.09331	$2(\lambda)(1 - \lambda)(1 - \alpha)^2$
5	1	1	0.07258	$4(\lambda)(1 - \lambda)\alpha(1 - \alpha)$
6	1	2	0.01411	$2(\lambda)(1 - \lambda)\alpha^2$
7	2	0	0.00518	$\lambda^2(1 - \alpha)^2$
8	2	1	0.00403	$2\lambda^2\alpha(1 - \alpha)$
9	2	2	0.00078	$\lambda^2\alpha^2$

TOTAL   0.99998 (or 1.0000 to four decimal places)

In the above table, X_1 and X_2 are, respectively, the scores that could be obtained by recording the results of each look in Areas 1 and 2. The presence of a positive signal on a given look is indicated by "1" and a negative signal by "0."

A somewhat more appropriate display, for our purposes, is given by the summary table below, which shows the probability of each score combination more compactly.

X_1	X_2	0	1	2
0		0.41990	0.32659	0.06350
1		0.09331	0.07258	0.01411
2		0.00518	0.00403	0.00078

From either table we may now compute the three required probabilities

$P_A = P(X_2 > X_1) = 0.40420$ The sum of all the probabilities *above* the diagonal, for the cases in which the inexpensive looks have correctly located the prize.

$P_B = P(X_1 = X_2) = 0.49326$ The sum of all the probabilities *on* the diagonal, for the cases in which the score is tied and we must revert to random application of the expensive look.

$P_C = P(X_2 < X_1) = 0.10252$ The sum of all the probabilities *below* the diagonal, for which the inexpensive look has located the wrong area.

The probabilities above will again add to 1.0000 to four decimal places.

We are now ready to compute the expected cost of the two-stage search procedure, which consists of two looks at each of the two boxes using the inexpensive procedure, followed by application of the expensive detection and acquisition procedure according to the rules originally set forth.

Briefly, this cost will consist of the cost of the inexpensive search, $10,000 for each of four looks, plus the cost of acquiring the prize on the first expensive look, or the cost associated with the random expensive look, or the cost associated with the selection of the wrong area. Thus, in millions, the cost expected from Method II is

METHOD II (for certain location in two stages)

Total Expected Cost (in millions) $= (1)(0.40420) + (1.5)(0.49326)$
$$+ (2)(0.10252) + (4)(0.01) = \$1.3891$$

Comparison of Method II with Method I indicates that the second method reduces costs by

$$1.5000 - 1.3891 = 0.11087 \text{ or about } \$110,870$$

so that here the second procedure is preferable.

Several observations can be made from this simple problem. First, if the reliability of the inexpensive search or detection equipment could be improved for the given cost, then the cost reduction indicated above would be increased substantially. In the same way, it might be worthwhile to pay more per inexpensive look to get a more reliable result at that stage, a trade-off which suggests further study.

Next, with greater cost reductions in the total cost of detection and acquisition, it will pay to look for prizes that are progressively less valuable. Thus, if the costs of detection and acquisition could be cut to $0.5 million, then it would pay to look for prizes above that amount—which would not be sensible under the present circumstances. Further, should we be able to exploit anything found from a false expensive look—as a consolation prize, or prize of lesser value than the one we seek—then the economics of the two-stage search change again. Because consolation prizes are clearly desirable, a systems approach to the search operation would call for some thought about what could be salvaged from a false positive decision. (A broader search objective may be desirable if fortuitous or "serendipitous" findings can be exploited, such as gas and ore, as well as oil.)

As an example, suppose a consolation prize worth $0.5 million would be obtained if the expensive look were made in the wrong area on the first try. (We still assume that there is a much more valuable prize in the remaining area but its exact worth is immaterial in the following computation.) Then, under this new condition, a comparison of Methods I and II would give

METHOD I (certain detection of main prize in one stage with possible consolation prize)

$$(1)(0.50) + (1.5)(0.5) = \$1.25 \text{ million}$$

METHOD II (certain detection of main prize in two stages with possible consolation prize)

$$(1) \ (0.40420 + (1.25) \ (0.49326)$$
$$+ \ (1.5) \ (0.10252 + (4) \ (0.01) = \$1.2146 \text{ million}$$

The net difference between Methods I and II has now dropped to just over $45,000. Thus, in this case, the presence of the consolation prize not only reduces the total cost of both methods, but also makes the random approach relatively more attractive than it was before.

Finally, we can see (although a proof will not be given) that the two-stage-search process becomes more attractive when there are few or no consolation prizes, and when there may be a large number of no-prize areas (more areas than the two used for illustration above). In this case, there would be a large failure total for the expensive looks, which the first-stage search could eliminate or reduce.

Various methods have been proposed and developed for exploiting multistage search procedures in prospecting and similar applications. For further reference, the reader should consult the literature on the subject.[20] Unfortunately for our present purposes, practical search problems of this type often require special study and the use of advanced analytic and computational methods. The example just given, however, illustrates the basic principles involved, and is sufficient as an introduction to this interesting field.

Search For Extreme Values

The use of random search procedures for the location of an extreme value, or set of extreme values, is of immediate interest.

For example, as mentioned previously, the number of sequences that can be made of N distinct items is $N!$. Because $N!$ rapidly increases as N increases, the brute-force search through $N!$ possibilities for a particular sequence of N items that may have the greatest value or lowest cost is an impossibility. Yet, this scheduling or sequencing problem is faced industrially every day. Can a random search procedure help here?

[20] J. H. Engel, "Use of Clustering in Mineralogical and Other Surveys," *Proc. First International Conference on Operations Research,* Operations Research Society of America, Baltimore, Md., 1957. In addition see J. C. Griffiths and L. J. Drew, "Simulation of Exploration Programs for Material Resources by Models," *Quart. of the Colorado School of Mines,* October, 1964; M. Allais, "Method of Appraising Economic Prospects of Mining Exploration over Large Territories—Algerian Sahara Case Study," *Management Science,* 3, 4, July, 1957; United Nations, *Proc. of the Inter-Regional Symposium on Techniques of Petroleum Development,* January 23–February 21, 1962; G. M. Kaufman, *Statistical Decision and Related Techniques in Oil and Gas Exploration,* Prentice-Hall, Englewood Cliffs, N.J., 1963.

Yes, and the results are similar to those shown above. Suppose that N items are to be scheduled, and that it were possible to list all the $N!$ possible schedules, together with a measure of their cost.[21]

Suppose each of these possible schedules can be arranged in rank order by cost, so that the lowest cost schedule will appear first in the list, the next highest cost schedule next, and so on. (Schedules with tied costs are listed adjacently without regard to the particular schedule.) From this rank-order distribution, it is now possible to determine the probability that an optimum, or near optimum, schedule will be found by random sampling, or search. Although, in general, this rank-order distribution will not be known, in many cases it may be approximated to obtain the same results.

To illustrate, suppose that $N!$ possible schedules of N items have been made, evaluated, and arranged in rank order by cost. We may want to find a schedule in the top 10% or top 2% of this list, let us say in the top fraction p. Because the total list is not available, we generate a set of schedules n at random and rank the sample set in order, taking the cheapest sample schedule as the "best" schedule available. This rule gives a geometric reduction in variety to combat the factorial. Thus, the probability that one randomly constructed schedule will be one of the top fraction p, is simply p $(0 \leq p \leq 1)$. The probability that a sample of n will *not* contain one schedule of the top fraction p is $(1 - p)^n$ and therefore the probability that it *will* contain at least one member of the top fraction p is $1 - (1 - p)^n$.

It is interesting to note that the result is only indirectly dependent upon the total size of $N!$ (the population) by the specification of p. To illustrate, suppose that a sample of $n = 100$ is taken from a much larger population ($N!$), so that the sampling may be considered random. Then, if we ask for the probability that at least one of the n items will be in the top 1% ($p = 0.01$), using logarithms we find the answer 0.6335, as follows.

$$(1 - p) = 0.99 = 9.9 \times 10^{-1}$$
$$\log(0.99) = \log(9.9) - 1 = 0.99564 - 1 = -0.00436$$
$$100 \log(0.99) = 100 \times -0.00436 = -0.436$$

To find the antilog of -0.436, we note that

$$-0.436 = 0.564 - 1$$

so that

$$(0.99)^{100} = 10^{0.564} \times 10^{-1} = 0.3665$$

Thus, the probability of not picking one member of the top 1% is 0.3665, and the probability of picking at least one member of the top 1% is $1 - 0.3665 = 0.6335$.

---

[21] The cost of a sequence may be assessed in many ways. However, if we restrict our attention to the cost of pairs in the sequence only (following a Markov chain assumption), the cost of a sequence may be developed from a $N \times N$ matrix of pair costs, applied pair by pair.

In the same way we could find that the probability of picking a member of the top 1% with a sample of $n = 1000$ is 0.99563, and this probability rises slowly with further increases in n.

The reader may complain correctly that the sample of 1000 does very little for the probability of finding a unique optimum in a set of $N!$ equally likely possibilities. For example, if $N = 100$, reference to standard tables gives $\log_{10} 100! = 160$, so that $100! = 10^{160}$. One percent of 10^{160} is still a very large number, 10^{158}, which contains the unique optimum. In fact, the probability of finding the unique optimum with a sample of $n = 100$ is approximately $(100/100!) = 10^{-158}$, a finite, yet infinitesimal probability of success.

How is it then that this sampling method works in practice? It is important to note that if each of the 100! sequences (or items) had a distinct value, and therefore were equally likely, *no search procedure that required examination of each and every case would be beneficial—or physically possible.* However, two factors work in our favor. First, we seldom encounter a problem in which the range of distinctions is so great that we cannot invoke the concept of indifference (see Chapter 7) and be satisfied with a range of possibilities that are sufficiently good as to be called optimum, or successful. This corresponds to the detection area concept in the area-search examples of the previous section. The larger the detection area, or the larger the range of satisfactory answers, the easier the search becomes. Second, the distribution of distinctions is seldom uniform, but is usually clustered, so that some advantage may be taken of the knowledge of this constraint both in specifying a satisfactory answer, and in restricting random sampling to an area containing the optimum.

> *Example:* Suppose that $N!$ sequences could be generated at random and that the values of these sequences could be plotted in a many-step histogram. Suppose also that this histogram could be fitted by a normal curve with $\bar{x} = 1000$ and $\sigma = 100$. Then knowledge of this pattern would tell us that the probability of finding a sequence of cost less than or equal to $\bar{x} - 2.33\sigma = 767$ is about 1%, and we could adjust our sample size to obtain at least one sequence below that value. Moreover, if, because of some structural knowledge of the costs involved, we know how to generate sequences that fall below this cost (767), we could restrict our investigation to that portion of the population, and achieve even better results.

WHEN TESTS CAN BE MADE ON A GROUP OF POSSIBILITIES

We have previously assumed that an optimum to be found must be isolated individually. It may also be true that the condition of one item in the set of possibilities to be examined will provide a group test. When this is possible, the binary splitting method may be employed in a series of yes-no tests which greatly reduce the number of tests required, or which in combination with some individual testing will isolate the required item.

For example, as mentioned previously, the number of yes-no questions required to isolate one item from N is the next integer larger than $\log_2 N$. Thus, if it were possible to use a binary test procedure to locate an item from a set of 100! possibilities, the number of tests required would be $\log_2$ 100! Because $\log_{10}$ 100! $= 160$, and $\log_2 N = 3.322 \log_{10} N$, $160 \times 3.322 = 532$ (rounding off to the nearest integer) tests would be the minimum required to guarantee isolation by the binary procedure if it could be applied. This result again indicates the power of the binary questioning method when it can be employed.

Let us take a case, however, which does not easily permit complete binary testing, but which, nevertheless, permits a group test to be made.

Example: Suppose that blood samples have been taken from N persons, and that each of these samples has been numbered, for later identification. Then, suppose a test (which will have a yes-no, or positive-negative result) is made by pooling a fraction of each blood sample in an overall group test. This may be done, for example, by taking half the blood in each subject's test tube and pooling the blood so obtained. The remaining blood samples will not be pooled, but will be left in the original distinctly identified test tubes. If we are looking for patients who have a certain disease, for which the test has been designed, and if the pooled test will turn out negative if and only if all of the individual samples pooled are negative (one positive sample will cause the pooled test to be positive), we have the following results.

Let $p =$ the probability that a patient has a positive individual test
$n =$ the number of patients pooled

Then, the probability that the pooled test will fail (requiring individual tests of the n patients set aside for future reference) is again $1 - (1 - p)^n$, If there are N individuals to be tested, and if c_1 is the cost of a group test and c_2 is the cost of an individual test, then the expected total cost to test N patients by this procedure is

$$\text{Total Expected Cost (group of N patients)} = c_1 \left(\frac{N}{n}\right) + c_2 n \left(\frac{N}{n}\right) [1 - (1 - p)^n]$$

where the first term on the right-hand side is the cost of group testing, and the second term is the cost of testing n individuals in the expected number of groups that fail the group test. This equation may be minimized for a given value of p by variation of n. It will be seen that, if p is small, the optimum value of n will be large, and vice versa. To illustrate, suppose $p = 0.1$, $c_1 = c_2 = \$10$, and $N = 100$. We now tabulate various choices of $n = 1, 2, 3, 4$, and 5.

n	Group cost	Individual cost	Total cost per 100
1	$1000	–	$1000
2	500	$(10)(2)(50)(0.19) = 190$	690
3	333	$(10)(3)(33)(0.27) = 270$	603
4	250	$(10)(4)(25)(0.34) = 340$	590
5	200	$(10)(5)(20)(0.41) = 410$	610

The lowest cost is $590 per 100, or $5.90 per patient, and represents a reduction in the cost per patient to less than 60% of the individual patient cost.[22] This form of testing is suitable when we can exploit the constraint that all the individuals must be "negative" for the group to be "negative," and when such a group test can be made without examining the individuals.

An oft-repeated logical problem provides another example of group testing in which the number of tests may be reduced to one, by the exploitation of constraints.

Example: A sheik receives eight tribal representatives, each of whom is to pay taxes for his tribe. Payment is made in gold bars, weighing exactly one pound each, and each taxpayer places his payment in a separate pile before the sheik so that each tribe is identified by position. Before the gold bars are gathered together for the treasury, the sheik is informed that one (and only one) of the tribes has cheated by shaving exactly one ounce of gold from each bar tendered in payment. However, before he can reveal the tribe, the informer is murdered by an unknown assailant. With this information available, however, the sheik can easily determine the guilty tribe. For this purpose, he has a scale calibrated in pounds and ounces, and in *one weighing* he is able to isolate the culprit. How is this done?

The solution to this problem exploits both the arrangement of the piles, which is one constraint, and the knowledge of the weights of the good and the defective bars which provide enough additional constraints to produce a unique solution. Assuming that each pile contains eight or more bars, the sheik places on the scale one bar from the first pile, two bars from the second, three bars from the third, and so on for all eight piles. The ounces of shortage indicate the pile containing the shaved bars, thus solving the problem in one test. This result is considerably better than the binary split procedure, because the system of gold piles has been treated as a single eight-state problem instead of a series of

---

[22] This example is cited in W. Feller, *An Introduction to Probability Theory and Its Applications*, Wiley, New York, 1957.

two-state problems, and because the facts of the case permit direct isolation of the one defective state in eight.

To see the effect of the stated constraints, it is worthwhile to consider the procedures the sheik might follow if (1) it were known that only one of the gold bars in one of the piles had been shaved one ounce, or (2) it were known that some of the gold bars in one of the piles had been shaved one ounce each, or (3) it were known that there were one or more bars shaved by one ounce somewhere in the collection of bars. In (1) and (2), a minimum of three weighings using the binary split procedure would be required to isolate the defective pile. In (3) the number of weighings would depend upon the way in which the defective bars were distributed in the piles. (How many weighings would be necessary if there were exactly one defective bar in each of the eight piles—and this fact were not known beforehand?)

Although the examples of this section have been chosen for their dramatic value, group testing often occurs in practice before the investigator sets to work. For example, in a system of N components or blocks, each of which must work for the system to operate, knowledge of system malfunction is essentially the result of a group test that failed. Similarly, when a system is subjected to a response test, that test is a group test, which for the tested input-output relation requires all the blocks in a given chain to be operative. For this reason, a preferred first-response test for a complex system is one that will require the correct operation of all the system blocks, because if this test passes, no further testing may be needed.

When a group test fails, we may then employ a series of block or individual tests as indicated by the failure symptoms or by the logical requirements for isolation, as previously described.

SEARCH WITH PARTIAL INFORMATION

We now present two selected search problems that illustrate how partial information may be exploited to improve the search process.

The Search for a Unimodal Optimum

If we know that an optimum set of conditions for a system exists within a certain range, and that the relationship between a given adjustment and the optimum is "unimodal," i.e., that the adjustment will cause the system to rise steadily to its optimum condition, and that furher adjustment will cause a steady decline from that optimum, we have extremely valuable information to aid in the search process.[23]

---

[23] The normal curve, for example, is unimodal, with the mode at the average. The normal curve falls away steadily on both sides of the average, and has no lower peaks.

For example, suppose a system's output/input ratio (yield) can be varied by a change of a single parameter (say, temperature) x. The relationship between x and the yield $f(x)$ is not known completely, but suppose it is known that optimum adjustment of x lies within the range $0 \leq x \leq L$, and that $f(x)$ can be evaluated within the specified range of x at selected points. Finally, suppose that the yield $f(x)$ is "unimodal," i.e., there is a single optimum x_0 such that x_0 is within or at the boundary of the interval 0 to L, and that $f(x)$ is strictly increasing for $x \leq x_0$ and strictly decreasing for $x > x_0$ (or else strictly increasing for $x < x_0$ and strictly decreasing for $x \geq x_0$).

Under these conditions, the following steps offer an optimum experimental search procedure, which we will first describe graphically, and then improve by more detailed specification.[24]

Suppose that $f(x)$ looks like Figure 10–7. within the interval $0 \leq x \leq L$. The curve shown is "unimodal" as required [which means there is only one hump or peak in the curve for $f(x)$]. Because the value of $f(x)$ must, by this assumption, steadily decrease on either side of the optimum x_0, two initial measurements, x_1 and $x_2 > x_1$, can produce one of the following three outcomes:

$f(x_1) > f(x_2)$: The optimum must lie to the left of x_2, and the region of search can be restricted to the interval 0 to x_2.

$f(x_1) < f(x_2)$: The optimum must lie to the right of x_1 and the search can be restricted to the interval x_1 to L.

$f(x_1) = f(x_2)$: The optimum is in the interval x_1 to x_2. However, to be consistent with what follows, we may restrict further search either to the interval 0 to x_2 or x_1 to L.

The net result of the first two experimental measurements is to reduce the interval 0 to L, to one of the smaller intervals indicated above. Within that reduced interval, there will be one measurement that can be used in the next step. For example, in Figure 10–7, the test shows that the optimum is in the interval 0 to x_2. One added measurement in that interval, say $x_1 \leq x_3 \leq x_2$, will allow the test to be repeated again, and so on thereafter, until the optimum x_0 can be located within a narrow interval, which may be made as small as desired by continued experimental measurements.

The above procedure will work if the location of the experimental measurements is chosen arbitrarily. However, the following rules will provide an optimum selection of these points.

Suppose that it is desired to locate the optimum x_0 within a narrow band. Then we can divide the interval 0 to L into a number of small segments

[24] The search procedure is presented without proof, for which see R. E. Bellman and S. E. Dreyfus, *Applied Dynamic Programming*, Princeton University Press, Princeton, N.J., 1962, Chapter IV, "Optimal Search Techniques."

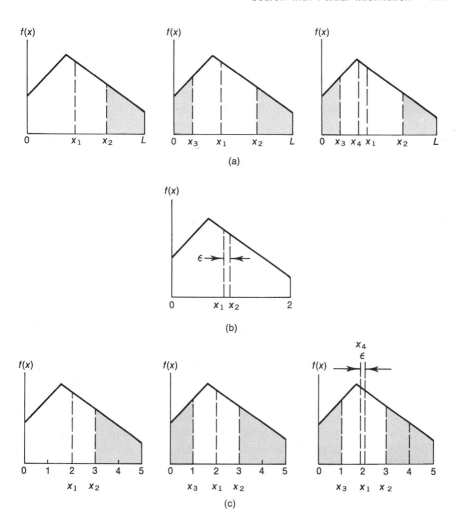

10-7 Procedure for optimal unimodal search in one dimension.

whose width equals that band or interval of isolation. Thus, if we make F divisions, the isolation interval width is L/F, and we can, if we chose, measure the length of L in those units, i.e., five equal intervals of length $L/5$, etc. When this decision has been made, we can consult the following table to determine how many experimental measurements n will be needed, to provide the required isolation.

F:	1	1	2	3	5	8	13	21	34	55	.	.	.
n:	0	1	2	3	4	5	6	7	8	9	.	.	.

In general, the relationship between n and F is

$$F(n) = F(n-1) + F(n-2), \qquad F(0) = F(1) = 0.$$

The latter requirement indicates that one experimental measurement does no more good than none in locating the optimum. (We will continue and explain the table momentarily. However, it may be seen that any value of F in the table is equal to the sum of the previous two values of F.)

Let us consider first the case of isolation into one of two intervals. ($F = 2$, $n = 2$). The problem is first to select the position of the two measurements required, x_1 and x_2. The rule for optimum selection of these two values is[25]

$$x_1 = F_{n-2} \quad \text{and} \quad x_2 = F_{n-1}$$

where for $n = 2$, the appropriate values of F are obtained from the table. In this case, the values for x_1 and x_2 from the table are both 1; i.e., both measurements should be made at the midpoint of the interval. (The method attempts to divide the interval into equal parts in this case.) However, two measurements at the same point will not reveal anything about the location of the optimum in the first or second part! Therefore, suppose the trial value for x_1 is offset by a very small amount ϵ, so that $x_1 = 1 - \epsilon$ and $x_2 = 1$. With this slight modification, the two test measurements will indicate that the optimum is either in the interval (χ to $1 - \epsilon$) or in the interval ($1 - \epsilon$ to 2), where again we have measured x in the number of divisions of the interval 0 to L. Because ϵ can be made arbitrarily small, the problem is resolved by this device. (It is important to understand this case, because if F is greater than 2, the final test always resolves itself into the one described above.)

To improve the precision of the isolation, we may now ask for the interval 0 to L to be divided into $F = 5$ parts. From the table, $n = 4$. For the first two trial values x_1 and x_2 we have

$$x_1 = F_{n-2} = 2 \quad \text{and} \quad x_2 = F_{n-1} = 3,$$

where the interval count is based on divisions equal to $\frac{1}{5}$ of L. Figure 10–7 (c) illustrates the first two selected measurements, from which we may conclude that the optimum (for the case shown) lies to the left of x_2 and is in one of the three segments numbered 1, 2, and 3.

We now have an interval limited to segments 1, 2, and 3, with a measurement at point 2. Now, introducing a new measurement x_3 at interval 1, we may conclude that the optimum lies above x_3, in one of the intervals marked 2 and 3.

---

[25] We offer this rule without proof. The illustrations of Figure 10-7 suggest the optimality of this choice, and the proof may be found in Bellman and Dreyfus, *op. cit.*, p. 154. (The values of $F(n)$ are the so-called Fibonacci numbers that occur in many search problems.)

We now again have a two-part problem, with an existing experimental measurement at the midpoint between intervals 2 and 3. The last measurement x_4 could then be made at that point, but offset by a small amount ϵ, as before. Application of the test as usual will now isolate the optimum in one or the other interval, interval 2 in this case, within the error ϵ.

This procedure can be used for isolation to any degree of precision by increasing F, and always works for one-dimensional optimization. Although the series of values for F, which is a function of n, increases slowly at first, it increases rapidly for larger values of n; e.g., $F(n = 20)$ is greater than 10,000. Thus, the position of a maximum can always be located within 10^{-4} of the original interval length (0 to L) in at most 20 observations x_1 to x_{20}, selected as described above. For large values of n, $F(n)$ is given accurately by $1.45(1.62)^n$ for this procedure,[26] which may be compared with the equilavent binary procedure for isolation when group tests can be made, i.e., $F(n) = 2^n$. Thus, although the method described is not quite as good as the binary split method, it provides geometrical cuts in variety in many cases where the binary split approach is not practical.

The problem of determining optimal search procedures for locating the absolute maximum of a function of N variables is very difficult, and (although we will sketch out one extension) further discussion is beyond the scope of this Chapter.[27]

Hill Climbing Methods

The experimental determination of "optimum" system response usually involves a series of experimental perturbations, or changes, in system conditions in small steps. The steps are generated and examined sequentially. The changes that produce the greatest increase in response guide the investigator to a new set of conditions, and so on, until the optimum is reached. This method is known as "the technique of steepest ascent."

Example: Suppose the output z of a chemical process depends upon two variables: Temperature x and pressure y. The system response $z = f(x, y)$ is a three-dimensional surface, or a two-dimensional contour map, as shown in Figure 10–8a.[28] The contours shown in this hypothetical

---

[26] See Bellman and Dreyfus, *op. cit.*, p. 155. The procedure described above can easily be extended to cover the location of an optimum when x can take on only integer values, as shown by Bellman and Dreyfus on page 156.

[27] Bellman and Dreyfus, *op. cit.*, provide selected references to this point, pp. 178–179. For a survey of experimental procedures, see O. L. Davies (Ed.), *Design and Analysis of Industrial Experiments*, Hafner, New York, 1954, Chapter 11.

[28] Compare Figure 10-8a and 10-8b with Figure 7-8. The contour map also may be used to show three variables, when drawn in three dimensions. A number of interesting experimental surfaces are illustrated in this way in O. L. Davies, *op. cit.*, Chapter 11. For a popular expository article with a bibliography of similar search methods, see J. M. Idelsohn, "Ten Ways to Find the Optimum," *Control Engineering*, June, 1964.

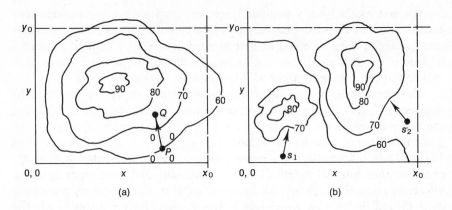

(a)   (b)

10-8 Contour maps of a response surface illustrating the steepest response, or hill climbing, method of search for optimum conditions. (a) has a single optimum. Contours are shown as a percent of the true optimum (which is unknown in general). Search is confined to the "region of interest," selected in advance from previous knowledge. With the single optimum, the method of steepest ascent leads sequentially to the optimum. With the multiple optima of (b), the terminal point depends upon the starting point, and several starting points must be tried to isolate the global optimum.

surface connect points of equal yield on the response surface, and are marked in percentages of the optimum (which is within the 90% contour and not shown). Although the surface is shown for illustration, its shape and the location of the optimum are not known, and experimental observations are expensive, so that extensive systematic measurements in the region of interest (limited to the rectangle bounded by x_0 and y_0) are not feasible. (If observations were inexpensive, we could systematically make a grid of observations or take a large number of random observations in the region of interest and develop Figure 10–8a in this way.)

To start the steepest ascent method, assume that an experiment consisting of four observations about the point P has been conducted. If the error of measurement is small compared to the slope of the response surface, the direction of maximum ascent can be estimated from the experimental points, suggesting an area around point Q for further investigation. The experiment is then repeated about point Q, and so on up the hill. In general, as such a sequence of experiments continues and the investigator comes near the top of the hill, the surface will tend to flatten out, or hump over and call for more careful determination of the path of steepest ascent. (Typically linear estimates of the path are made initially. Upon coming near the optimum—a "near stationary point"—higher-order estimates, such as parabolic path estimates, are used. The computational details of this procedure are given by Davies in the references cited.)

The hill climbing or steepest ascent method works for continuous response surface with a single peak. Should there be several peaks, the terminal point will depend upon the starting point of the search, so that a series of starting points is often used when multiple peaks are suspected, Figure 10–8(b), and the *maximum of the maxima* found by this method is taken as the global optimum.[29]

DYNAMIC PROGRAMING AS A SEARCH APPROACH

To conclude our selected search examples, we turn now to the procedure of dynamic programing,[30] which also seeks an optimum in stages.

There are many systems optimization problems that may be treated either as one search effort involving many combinations or, alternatively, as a series of search problems, each involving a smaller number of combinations. In many cases, the latter choice is beneficial in reducing the computation and evaluation involved in finding the optimizing conditions.

Example: Suppose a lost object is located in one of three areas, labeled 1, 2, and 3. The probability that the item will be found in a given area is given in the table below. Suppose that the cost of making an observation varies from area to area; this cost is also shown below. In addition, suppose that the probability of finding the object (if it is in a given area) is 0.1 per observation; i.e., detection is not certain, but will improve as the number of "glimpses" increases. If a total of $30 is available for search, how should the glimpses, or observations, be allocated to the three regions to maximize the probability of finding the lost object?

	Area $= i$		
	1	2	3
Probability p_i that object is in area i	0.5	0.3	0.2
Cost per glimpse w_i	$10	$ 5	$ 3
Glimpses allocated n_i	n_1	n_2	n_3
Resources allocated $n_i\,w_i$	$n_1 w_1$	$n_2 w_2$	$n_3 w_3$

[29] The philosophy of taking a route to the optimum that follows steps of ever-improving response (increases in the objective function of Chapter 8) is adopted in a number of search methods. For example, it is used in linear programing, Figure 7-4, which, with linear constraints and a linear objective function, leads to the optimum if it exists. Similarly, searches through decision trees may proceed in this way, although several alternative starting points or initial search directions are usually required. For an illustration, see Egon Balas, "An Additive Algorithm for Solving Linear Programs with Zero-One Variables," *Operations Research*, 13, 4, July-August, 1956, pp. 517–545.

[30] See R. E. Bellman and S. E. Dreyfus, *Applied Linear Programing*, Princeton University Press, Princeton, N.J., 1962, especially Chapters I and II.

If we consider area 1, the detection probability is given by the probability that the item is in a given region p_i times the probability that the item will be detected if it is in region i, and n_i glimpses have been made there. The latter probability is given by $(1 - 0.9^{n_i})$, i.e., 1 minus the probability that n_i glimpses will fail to detect the object, if it is present. Thus, the probability of detection in region i with n_i glimpses is

$$P_i(n_i) = (p_i)\ (1 - 0.9^{n_i}).$$

(There are three such equations, with $n = 1, 2, 3$, representing the situation in each region.)

The problem may now be formally stated as

$$\text{Maximize } \sum_i P_i(n_i) \qquad (i = 1, 2, 3)$$

$$\text{Subject to } \sum_i n_i w_i \leqq W \qquad (i = 1, 2, 3)$$

where W is \$30, the total resource available. These two equations simply say that we should obtain the highest detection probability possible for the three areas as a whole, but that we cannot spend more than the total resources available, \$30. Because the lost object must be in one and only one of the three areas, they may be considered independent, and the probabilities add, as shown, presenting a typical resource allocation problem, which arises frequently in systems analysis and design.

Before continuing, it is worthwhile to find the maximum number of glimpses that could be bought in each region if the total resource were spent there. Division of the total available by the cost per glimpse for each region (W/w_i) gives this result as a maximum of three glimpses in Area 1, six glimpses in Area 2, and ten glimpses in Area 3.

One way to proceed with the solution would be to enumerate all feasible combinations of the n_i values, within the \$30 limit, evaluate the total detection probability, and select the combination of n_i that gave the largest detection probability for \$30. Some thought will reveal, however, that even for this simple three-area problem such a tabulation would be extensive, and that for a many-area, large-total-resource problem, the table could get out of hand entirely.

We therefore think of attacking the problem in stages, first considering Area 1, then Area 2, and finally Area 3. To do this we will consider our specific problem as a special case of a more general class of allocation problems, i.e., "imbed" our problem in the larger class, by assuming that the total resource available is not fixed, but may vary from 0 to W. When this is done, the detection probability in a given area will be a function of the resource available (because whatever the resource may be it limits the glimpses that can be made). With this idea in mind, we create a tabulation in which we first consider Area 1 only and compute the probability of detection for various resource levels from 0 to W. (In Table 10.1, only steps of \$10 have been shown for simplicity.)

Table 10.1 Stage 1

W	Possible n_1	$f_1 = P_1 = (0.5)(1 - 0.9^{n_1})$
0	0	0.000
10	1	0.050
20	2	0.095
30	3	0.135

We stop tabulating W at \$30, because this is the total resource available. For future reference, we call the one-stage probability of detection f_1 for each value of W. The value f_1 is the maximum detection probability that can be bought with the W available at each increment in Area 1.

Turning to Stage 2 of our computations, we consider the effects of allocating various levels of the total resource W to the two areas (Area 1 *and* Area 2) in an optimal way. For clarity in this computation, we show in complete detail all figures in Table 10.2, but we note that, in fact, only the lines with an entry in column (6) are of any interest. We allocate a given level of W to the two areas, considering Area 2 first. The number of glimpses allocated to Area 2 is progressively increased. Any left-over resources are allocated to Area 1, and we pick up the *largest* or maximum detection probability available to us from that allocation to Area 1, namely, $f_1(W)$ from Table 10.1. Finally, in column (6) Table 10.2, we show for Area 1 *and* Area 2 the maximum detection probability possible for the specified level of W. This process continues until $W = \$30$, when the tabulation ceases.

In Table 10.2, column (1) shows the level of W allowed as we step to higher values. These steps are now in \$5 increments, because the cost per glimpse is \$5 in Area 2. Then, in column (2) we show all possible values of n_2, from 0 to the maximum possible. In column (3) we show the resources left over $(W - n_2w_2)$. Column (4) shows the detection probability in Area 2 for the value of n_2 specified on the same line. Column (5) shows the detection probability in Area 1, which is the maximum possible for the resource left over $(W - n_2w_2)$. Finally, column (6) shows the sum of columns (4) + (5), which is the maximum for any level of the total resource W. In short, the entries in column (6) represent the maximum detection probability available if the total resource W is allocated to Areas 1 and 2. For future use, we may discard all lines in Stage 2 except those with an entry in column (6), and produce a "Condensed Stage 2" table, which more clearly illustrates this fact (see Table 10.3). The notation f_2 indicates the maximum two-stage

Table 10.2 Stage 2 (Shows Complete Detail of Computation)

(1) W	(2) n_2	(3) $(W - n_2 w_2)$	(4) $P_2 \doteq (0.3)(1 - 0.9^{n_2})$	(5) $f_1(W - n_2 w_2)$	(6) $f_2 = \text{Max}\,[P_2(n_2) + f_1(W - n_2 w_2)]$
0	0	0	0.000	0.000	0.000
5	1	0	0.030	0.000	0.030
10	0	10	0.000	0.050	—
	1	5	0.030	0.000	—
	2	0	0.057	0.000	0.057
15	0	15	0.000	0.050	—
	1	10	0.030	0.050	—
	2	5	0.057	0.000	—
	3	0	0.081	0.000	0.081
20	0	20	0.000	0.095	—
	1	15	0.030	0.050	—
	2	10	0.057	0.050	0.107
	3	5	0.081	0.000	—
	4	0	0.103	0.000	—
25	0	25	0.000	0.095	—
	1	20	0.030	0.095	—
	2	15	0.057	0.050	—
	3	10	0.081	0.050	0.131
	4	5	0.103	0.000	—
	5	0	0.123	0.000	—
30	0	30	0.000	0.135	—
	1	25	0.030	0.095	—
	2	20	0.057	0.095	—
	3	15	0.081	0.050	—
	4	10	0.103	0.050	0.153
	5	5	0.123	0.000	—

Table 10.3 Condensed Stage 2

(Shows Essential Features of Table Above)

W	n_1	n_2	f_2
0	0	0	0.000
5	0	1	0.030
10	0	2	0.057
15	0	3	0.081
20	1	2	0.107
25	1	3	0.131
30	1	4	0.153

detection probability as a function of the level of W. The optimum values of n_2 and n_1 (from Table 10.1) are shown for reference.

Finally, turning to the problem of Area 3, we may consider the Stage 3 tabulation. We proceed just as before. Now, however, we may set $W = \$30$, because this is the last stage. Our objective in the tabulation is to find the optimum allocation of \$30 to Areas 1, 2, and 3 (the original problem). This may be done by first concentrating on Area 3, and progressively increasing n_3 from 0 to the maximum value of 10. Whatever resource is left over at each increment $(W - n_3 w_3)$ is then given maximum use in the two-stage allocation (according to the values of W and f_2 shown in Table 10.3).

Table 10.4 Stage 3 for $W = \$30$ Only

(1)	(2)	(3)	(4)	(5)	(6)
W	n_3	$(W - n_3 w_3)$	$P_3 =$ $(0.2)(1 - 0.9^{n_3})$	$f_2(W - n_3 w_3)$	$f_3 = \max[P_3(n_3)$ $+ f_2(W - n_3 w_3)]$
30	0	30	0.000	0.153	—
	1	27	0.020	0.131	—
	2	24	0.038	0.107	—
	3	21	0.054	0.107	—
	4	18	0.069	0.081	—
	5	15	0.082	0.081	0.163
	6	12	0.094	0.057	—
	7	9	0.104	0.030	—
	8	6	0.114	0.030	—
	9	3	0.123	0.000	—
	10	0	0.131	0.000	—

It is extremely important to note that what we are about to do in Table 10.4 requires reference *only one table back*, namely, to Table 10.3.

For our present purposes the original Table 10.1 is not needed. In Table 10.4, column (1) is $W = \$30$, column (2) shows increments of n_3, column (3) shows $(W - n_3w_3)$, and column (4) shows $P_3(n_3)$. Column (5), which shows $f_2(W - n_3w_3)$, is obtained by setting $W = W - n_3w_3$ in Table 10.3 and reading off the corresponding value of f_2. Column (6) shows the value of $f_3 = max\ [P_3(n_3) + f_2\ (W - n_3w_3)]$ which is the maximum detection probability that can be obtained by allocation of $30 worth of glimpses to the *three* areas.

The solution to the problem posed is that, for $30, a maximum detection probability of 0.163 may be obtained by the allocation of 5 glimpses to Area 3, which is evident from Table 10.4, and 3 glimpses to Area 2, which may be obtained by referring to Table 10.3. (The value of $n_2 = 3$ corresponds to the $15 of resource remaining after $15 has been spent on the 5 glimpses in Area 3.) No glimpses are allocated to Area 1, because no funds remain after the previous optimum expenditures.[31]

Table 10.5   Summary Table for Stage 3[a]

W	n_1	n_2	n_3	f_3
20	0	1	5	0.112
21	0	3	2	0.119
22	0	2	4	0.126
23	1	2	1	0.127
24	0	3	3	0.135
25	0	2	5	0.139
26	1	2	2	0.145
27	0	3	4	0.150
28	0	2	6	0.151
29	1	2	3	0.161
30	0	3	5	0.163

[a] (Note: For $28 an alternate combination will also give $f_3 = 0.151$, namely, $n_1 = 1$, $n_2 = 3$, $n_3 = 1$.)

The procedure described merits discussion. The same method would work if the original problem had provided any number of areas (or if another optimization problem could have been formulated as a series of

[31] Table 10.5, which shows the optimum allocation of glimpses for values of W from $20 to $30 in increments of $1, is provided for reference to show how the allocation of glimpses to the three areas varies with a change in the total resources available. Note that frequently abrupt shifts in allocation are made as the total resource W is reduced. This characteristic of the allocation system may be of particular interest (e.g., in the search for an optimum stock portfolio), because the practicality of abrupt shifts in allocations may be limited by additional consideration (e.g., market effects of large sales of stock).

small searches rather than one grand one). This may be seen by noting how the original optimization problem can be reformulated in the stage-by-stage approach. Note that the column designations of the Stage 3 Table (Table 10.4) are the same as those of the Stage 2 Table, (Table 10.2) with the index i advanced by 1. We could thus state the original problem in the functional equation form[32]

$$f_i(W) = \underset{0 \leq w_i \leq W}{\text{Max}} [P_i(w_i) + f_{i-1}(W - w_i)],$$

where $w_i = n_i w_i$ $(i = 0, 1, 2, 3, \ldots, k)$ and $f_0 = (0)$. This is a multistage search problem. To find f_i we must have already found f_{i-1}, the result of a previous lesser-stage problem. Equation $f_i(W)$ is a so-called recursion equation for this reason. (The recursion starts with $f_0(W) = 0$.)

The procedure illustrated is also efficient for numerical computation on electronic computers (it is useful in obtaining a specific solution to a specific problem without wasting memory space), because only the preceding table need be consulted to form the tabulation for a new stage, as illustrated in our example. The procedure may also be used for approximate solutions to problems involving continuously variable resource allocations, or continuous functions, illustrated here by the discrete probability of object location p_i.

Many additional advantages of this approach and computational techniques of its use are described by Bellman and Dreyfus in the reference cited, which provides substantial bibliographies for added reading.

In conclusion, this example has illustrated Bellman's *Principle of Optimality*, which has been stated as follows.

Principle of Optimality

An optimal policy has the property that, whatever the initial state and initial decision are, the remaining decisions must constitute an optimal policy with regard to the state resulting from the first decision.[33]

In our example, this principle states that for a given level of W in the three-stage problem, whatever decision is made about the level of n_3, an optimal policy must result in a "best" allocation for the remaining resources in Areas 1 and 2. This optimal policy is expressed in the functional equation last presented, and in the final result obtained for our problem. Thus, if $15 is allocated for five observations, or glimpses, in Area 3, then the optimal policy for that initial commitment must be to allocate optimally

---

[32] A functional equation contains another function. In this case f_i depends on f_{i-1}.

[33] See, for example, Bellman and Dreyfus, *op. cit.*, page 15. For additional problems in Dynamic Programing, see M. Sasieni, *et al.*, *Operations Research: Methods and Problems*, Wiley, New York, 1960. An understanding of the technique is enhanced by a survey of the applications cited by Bellman and Dreyfus, which include multistage missile launchings, etc.

the remainder ($15) to Areas 1 and 2, as was done to obtain the optimal over-all solution.

Although we have made our computations from a one-stage to a three-stage problem (or, in general, through k stages), we invoke the Principle of Optimality at each new stage, so that it is invoked for the total k-stage system.

PROBLEMS

10.1   Signal tracing is probably the most frequently used diagnostic technique when probabilistic or logical methods—which could relate symptoms to causes—fail to produce the required results, or when such methods are difficult or impossible to apply owing to insufficient data or other reasons.

A. List applications of the signal-tracing technique that are familiar to you. Imagine other useful applications. You need not restrict attention to a particular type of system; the method is general.

B. An experiment is conducted in which a large group of subjects is split into two randomly selected smaller groups of equal size. A 15-minute lecture on signal-tracing techniques is given to subgroup 1; subgroup 2 is left alone to read *Life* magazine for the same time period. Then both groups are asked to solve a diagnostic problem. In a very complex train of gears and shafts, one or more set-screws are loosened. Each subject is asked to find the loose gears. The solution time is then recorded for each subject. By what ratio would you predict the average solution times to differ between groups 1 and 2?

10.2   An insurance firm has 200,000 annuity holders. Each month the file must be updated because collections, dividends, payments, terminations and additions, and payments on death affect the account balances of these individuals.

Suppose the annuity records are filed in numerical order from 000,001 through 200,000. To assure accurate updating, over-all control balances are computed for each block of 1000 individual accounts by computer, and separately, by hand, for the over-all list. The updating is assumed to be correct if the total balance of a block of 1000 records is within plus or minus $.30 of the computed control total. In addition, the grand total computed from the detail is required to be within plus or minus $1.00 of the hand-computed grand total. (The account variation cited in the check procedure is to allow for modest rounding-off errors introduced by the computation system in figuring the individual account balances.)

A. What do you think of this checking system?

B. How would the numerical order of the proposed filing system be affected by additions to and deletions from the list? Would it make much difference if there were not exactly 1000 individuals in a test block?

C. If the balances do not check as required, the firm wants to find the account, or accounts, in error and make the appropriate corrections. How would you search for the error, or errors, in an efficient manner?

10.3 An insurance company has a master file containing the names of 200,000 policyholders arranged in alphabetical order with last name first. The insurance contracts for these individuals are filed by contract number, and one individual may have a number of policies for different types of insurance.

A system is to be developed to answer rapidly mail and telephone inquiries regarding a given individual's policies. Thus it is necessary to obtain an accurate cross reference between the alphabetical file and the contract serial file.

Unfortunately, several problems arise. First, an individual making an inquiry seldom if ever remembers his policy number, or numbers. Second, several individuals may have the same name and initials; e.g., the New York Manhattan telephone directory has 23 Juan Rodriguez listings with no initial and many more with one or more initials. To make matters worse, inquiries often are made with names at variance with the records (Juan S. Rodriguez may inquire simply as Juan Rodriguez, or vice versa), and indeed the original contracts for the same individual may have been written with a slightly different description (the policy may be for J. S. Rodriguez). Other problems of misspelled names, phonetic misunderstanding, name changes due to marriage, divorce, or legal action add to the ambiguity of positive identification.

Even though it would be possible to identify a given individual (and his contracts) uniquely using subsidiary invariate information such as sex, date of birth, and place of birth, variable information such as present address and historical addresses, and added information such as social security number, the appropriate record or set of likely records must be physically found in the file before such subsidiary information can be checked to obtain a unique verification.

In most information storage systems, the physical location problem required for initial screening can be a lengthy process, because the likely candidates for further check may be widely dispersed in the alphabetical file.

For example, the Manhattan telephone directory has seven J. Rodriguez listings, which are separated from the Juan Rodriguez listings by over 100 other Rodriguez possibilities ranging from Jacinto to Josephine—and extending thereafter through Juana to Justina. Moreover, the records or the inquiry may have the name spelled *Rodriquez*, which is several hundred listings later than the original Juan Rodriguez, or the spelling may have been given as *Rodrigues, Rodragues, Rodreguez* or *Rodrigeuz*, all of which are several hundred listings before Juan Rodriguez. In all, well over 1000 possibilities separate the first from the last reasonable possibility in the single telephone book cited, with many irrelevant listings in between.

A number of solutions to this location problem are in general use: a search for phonetically similar names, a search in a several-level hierarchy of possibilities with increasingly relaxed (or tightened) conditions, dictionaries of alternate spellings or likely possibilities. However, each application presents special problems, and a general optimum search pattern to locate an individual alphabetical name listing under practical conditions has not been found.

A. Suppose the insurance company has its alphabetical file stored in blocks of N names. You may consider the "block" as a physical tray of N index cards. (Some of these index card locations may be empty.) Or, the physical form of storage may be of another "random access" form, such as a magnetic card, or a track of N records on a magnetic disc or drum. Suppose the time or cost of selecting and "withdrawing" the information in a given block is relatively large, but the cost of checking the names and subsidiary information *within* the block after its selection is relatively small. (This is the case in many computer applications.) What are some of the considerations that would determine the size of the block of N names and the first choice of the block for initial inspection? What alternatives would you suggest if a search of the first block selected fails? How would your answers be affected if the alphabetical file contained 20,000,000 names instead of 200,000?

B. How might you proceed in your search if the alphabetical index were stored on some nonrandom access medium, such as magnetic tape, which like a scroll requires strictly sequential search?

C. How would you update the alphabetical master file as new insurance contracts were sold? How would this affect your previous decisions and comments?

D. What applications, other than the insurance search cited, raise similar questions? Under what conditions would an alphabetical search for a name be less severe than in the case of the insurance problem cited?

E. Why is the location problem illustrated here more difficult than the matching and location of names in the Amalgamated Dating Service case of Project D?

F. How would your storage scheme and search process change if the name records were of variable length instead of fixed length, so the number of names in a block would be a variable, too, instead of a constant?

10.4 Four boxes, A, B, C, and D, are arranged in a 2×2 matrix. A lost object is known to be in one of the four boxes.

A. If a search for the lost object is made, what is the probability of finding the object in N looks if the search consists of looking in the boxes at random, i.e., if box A, B, C, or D is first selected at random and inspected on the first look, and if on the second look the selection is again made from the four possibilities at random and so on? (This corresponds to sampling with replacement.)

B. What is the probability of finding the object in 1, 2, 3, and 4 looks if a box, once selected by the above method, is never inspected again if it is empty? (This corresponds to sampling without replacement.)

10.5 Using the same four boxes as in the above problem, suppose the lost object moves between A, B, C, or D at random between each look.

A. What is the probability that the object will be detected in N looks if the search consists of arbitrarily selecting a box and remaining there until the lost object arrives?

B. What is the probability that the object will be detected in N looks if the search proceeds at random (with replacement)?

C. What is the probability that the object will be detected in 1, 2, 3, and 4 looks if the search proceeds without replacement (the same box never looked into again if found empty originally)? Continue to assume the lost object may move to any one of the four boxes between looks with equal probability.

10.6 Using the methods and data of the two-stage search for a valuable prize given on pp. 288–92, find the cost difference between the two-stage search method and the random search and acquisition method described if the reliability of the inexpensive search were increased to $p = 0.5$, where p is the probability of obtaining a true positive signal per look if the prize is present. Assume that the probability of obtaining a false positive signal per look is $\lambda = 0.1$ per look, as in the example given, and that the search cost figures are as before.

10.7 If, in the above problem, the reliability increase to $p = 0.5$ also increased the cost per look of the inexpensive first-stage look from \$10,000 to \$50,000 per look, would that increased cost be justified over the less reliable method (when $p = 0.2$)?

10.8 From the results of the previous two problems, how large must the consolation prize be before the random search and acquisition method is as inexpensive as the two-stage search with $p = 0.2$ and $p = 0.5$?

10.9 Ten prospectors are available to search for ore by one of two methods A_1 and A_2. At least two men must use Method A_1, and at least one man A_2. In each case the search methods are such that the probability of finding ore by either method alone is given by the numbers in the table below. The total effort will be successful if *either* method is successful.

A. What is the optimum allocation of manpower to the two methods to maximize the probability of finding ore with the resources we have? (In the table, $R_1(x_1)$ is the probability of success when x men, $0 \le x \le 10$, are assigned to Method 1, etc.)

TABLE I

$x = \dfrac{\text{No. of}}{\text{men}}$	0	1	2	3	4	5	6	7	8	9	10	*Method*
$R_1(x_1)$	0	.1	.2	.3	.4	.5	.6	.7	.8	.85	.90	A_1
$R_2(x_2)$	0	.2	.4	.5	.55	.58	.59	.60	.61	.62	.63	A_2

B. Could the same problem be solved by another method? If so, suggest what it might be.

10.10   A ship is to be loaded to its maximum capacity, which is 100 weight units. The following commodities, with their weight and value (profit) to us per unit as shown in the following table, are available for loading. We want to maximize the profit of the load, subject to the total weight constraint.

Commodity i	Weight w_i	Value to us v_i
1	49	20
2	50	75
3	51	102

Although the obvious answer (for a feasible solution) is to use one unit of commodity 1 and one unit of commodity 3 (to obtain a weight of 100 units) for a profit of 122 units, the true optimum is 150 units of profit, obtained by loading 2 units of commodity 2.

A. Solve this problem using dynamic programing to achieve the optimum of 150 units of profit. Assume for the purposes of this problem that there are no other constraints but total weight.

B. Would any change in your procedure be required for a larger number of commodities?

C. What changes in your procedure would be required if there were a total cubic footage restriction, assuming the cubic footage of each commodity per unit were given?

D. Why is this a search problem?

E. Can you think of any other problems that would have the same pattern of definition and solution?

[Adapted from R. E. Bellman and S. E. Dreyfus, *Applied Dynamic Programming*, Princeton University Press, Princeton, N.J., 1962, pp. 28–32, where the solution may be found.]

10.11   A system consists of three components in series, such that for the system to work, each of the three components must work. A proposal has been made to increase the reliability of the system by placing additional units of each component type in parallel with the existing components. In the table below, the survival probability of each component type is given from experimental data obtained from an extensive life test to 1000 hours for a large sample of components. This number may be considered the reliability of the component to 1000 hours operation. The cost of each component is also given in the table. Using the method of dynamic programing

A. What is the maximum reliability configuration that can be obtained for the system if the total cost of the system is not to exceed $50.00? What is the system reliability (survival probability) to 1000 hours in this case?

B. What is the minimum cost configuration that will produce a system reliability of 0.90 or greater? What is that minimum system cost?

Component

1	2	3	
0.6	0.8	0.9	Survival probability for individual components
$5	$10	$15	Cost of each component

(Note: for consistency of notation, let n_i be the number of parallel components of type i, $p_i(n_i)$ be the survival probability for the group of parallel n_i components, let the cost of each component be w_i, and the total system cost be W. Also note that there must be at least one of each component type for the system to work.)

PROJECT 6

The Amalgamated Dating Service, Inc. (a fictional firm) seeks to match the characteristics of male and female students who want dates. A databank of one million names and coded characteristics is on hand for this purpose. The system consists of two major files: (1) A serial file and (2) an alphabetical file of names, addresses, and telephone numbers—plus serial numbers for cross reference to the characteristic serial file.

Suppose the serial file has been ordered first into males and females, then into 50 geographic categories. It is assumed that feasible matching is restricted to members of the opposite sex who live in the same area. The remaining detail on each name in the serial file consists of a five-digit serial number (to be used later after matching to extract selected names, addresses, and phone numbers from the address file), and 50 characteristics, each coded as a decimal position. Thus, each characteristic may have up to ten attributes, as indicated by the decimal numbers 0–9. Twenty-five positions show *descriptive* characteristics; twenty-five show *desired* characteristics.

In summary, File (1), the serial master-file, consists of a decimal code of 58 positions: Sex (1), geographical location (2), serial number (5), descriptive characteristics (25), and desired characteristics (25). The serial file is ordered by sex, location, and serial number, with sex the major key.

File (2), the name-address-phone file, is arranged in sex-location-serial sequence, with sex the major key [as in File (1)].

The initial procedure for matching is to take all incoming requests, which have also been coded by the respondent in the fashion above, and order them in sex-location order. The company guarantees at least five names to each requesting individual; therefore, the next step is to make a matching computation, restricted to members of the opposite sex in the same location. Thus, further attention will be restricted to two blocks of individuals: the first block the requesting group, the second block the individuals in the master serial file. The sex of the two blocks will be different, but the location will be the same. Obviously, this restriction greatly reduces the number of possible matches that must be considered.

To be specific in what follows, suppose that a requesting party is male, so that only matches with females in the same area will be considered. Also suppose further that the five required names will be those females who have the highest matching scores (or number of matches) as defined as follows:

First, compute the number of matches between the *last* 25 characteristics of male code (desire) and the *first* 25 characteristics of the females (description). A match will occur if and only if the two decimal digits in columns indexed as above are equal.

Second, in addition to the score computed above, add to that total the number of matches computed by using the *last* 25 positions of each female's code and the *first* 25 positions of the male code.

This grand total will then represent the total number of *mutual* matches, which may be used for ranking females for selection for the male request. (The computation, of course, assumes that the *order* of the 25 descriptive characteristics and the 25 desire characteristics is identical so that the computation just proposed will be meaningful.)

The process of making the matching computation will be carried out for each male request. A similar procedure is to be carried out for each female request after the males have been completed.

A. Devise an appropriate detailed procedure for making the matching computations and draw a block diagram of your method.

B. If some of the characteristics are thought to be more important than others, how could this be taken care of?

C. Because you only want the highest-score five names for each request, can you devise an added procedure to save only the serial numbers of the top five female scores found for each male request, and vice versa?

D. How would the computing and memory facilities available affect your proposed computing and ranking schemes? For example, would you like to have a large amount of high-speed random access memory storage or not? What would be the benefit of getting all the female names and characteristics for a given region in such storage?

E. Suppose as the result of the above procedures you have now obtained a list of the five "best" female matches associated with each male name, with both male and female names in serial number order.

Male *sex/location/serial*		Female *sex/location/serial*			
xxxxxxxx	xxxxxxxx	xxxxxxxx	xxxxxxxx	xxxxxxxx	xxxxxxxx
xxxxxxxx	xxxxxxxx	xxxxxxxx	xxxxxxxx	xxxxxxxx	xxxxxxxx
↓ Ascending order		Ascending order		→	

That is, for each male, handled in serial number order, you have also obtained the five top females, and have their serial numbers in order, too. With this set of data, you are now ready to print letters of introduction for each male. Can you suggest a method of doing this in an efficient manner? What would be the advantage of getting the serial numbers, names, addresses, and telephone numbers of females for a given region in high-speed random access memory?

F. Is there any advantage in having two files instead of one? Can you suggest improvements in the scheme outlined here?

G. In what ways might this whole operation be simplified?

H. How does the Amalgamated Dating operation correspond to the document retrieval operation described in this chapter?

11 | LOGIC AND PROBABILITY
IN SYSTEMS DIAGNOSIS

By all means the fastest diagnostic method is a shrewd guess. If the correct system fault or pattern of faults can be guessed and then verified by carefully selected tests, the time and cost of diagnosis can be greatly reduced.

In a malfunctioning 100-component system, for example, if it were possible to guess the faulty component, pick it out from the rest, and test its effect upon the system as a whole by substitution of a good part (or other isolation and confirmation procedures as discussed in Chapter 10), we would require only one test—the critical verification.

GUESSING WITH LOGICAL PROOF

The skilled diagnostician in any field seems to have this skill of relevant selection of possibilities—the ability to guess the answer to a problem and then to prove that guess is correct. Unfortunately, the process of formal education, which leans heavily upon methodical development of a subject and an orderly deduction of consequences, may inhibit an intuitive flair or willingness to develop shrewd guesses. To guess seems not quite respectable, and the investigator may expect that an orderly progression of steps must be followed in a rigid chain of logic to obtain the answer to his problem.

Seldom, in fact, does diagnosis proceed in this way, particularly for the complex system. Even astute mathematicians, according to Polya,[1] frequently guess the answer to a complex problem and then prove it right: If the equation balances, no matter how the solution was obtained, at least one solution has been found. Indeed, many numerical methods of mathematical analysis operate directly on sequential guessing and verifying of the guess.

Example: Suppose we do not know the square root of the number 10, but we do know that it is somewhere between 3 and 4. We try 3 and find $3^2 = 9$ too low. Then we try 4, and find $4^2 = 16$ too high. We compromise and try 3.2, and find that $3.2^2 = 10.24$ is still a bit high, and that $3.1^2 = 9.61$ is a bit too low. Working back and forth in this way, and checking each time, we can find the square root of 10 to any desirable accuracy. And, the closer our initial guess is to the true answer, the quicker we will reach the correct result by this method.

The same form of guessing is useful in the diagnosis of complex systems. One cannot help but be amused by the advice of a physician of the 1800's who, in his book, *Practical Diagnosis*,[2] advised

If the woman is unmarried and there is no evidence of gastric disorder in her tongue, it is well to remember what Battey, of Georgia, said in regard to this condition: "Always believe a young unmarried woman with abdominal tumor, of high social position and unimpeachable virtue, if she has been watched over by a platonic and abstemious young cousin of the male persuasion while the mother to be out, to be pregnant."

The test is often easy if the hypothesis is right.

The question arises, however, as to how the investigator may come to make shrewd guesses. Does he pull them out of thin air? Is there a guide? Are there any procedures that will improve his ability to make good guesses? In the past, experience has been the teacher.

The analyst of relatively similar systems develops over a period of time a sense of diagnostic relevance that appears uncanny to the novice. Some pediatricians, for example, have examined a quarter of a million newborn infants. A look, a movement, a sound, a suspect coloration, or an abnormality in shape or relative size are diagnostic signals, to such a physician and, as a pattern, suggest hypotheses of health or illness. Diagnosticians in the medical profession, who treat the relatively unchanging human form, can build a wealth of experience of this type.[3] The skilled mechanic,

[1] G. Polya, *Mathematics and Plausible Reasoning*, 2 Vols., Princeton University Press, Princeton, N.J., 1954. See the preface to Vol. 1.

[2] Hobart Amory Hare, *Practical Diagnosis*, Lea Brothers & Co., Philadelphia, 1899, p. 21.

[3] For a diagnostician's popular discussion of the ability to observe see W. Alvarez, *Danger Signals*, Wilcox and Follett, Chicago, 1953.

electronic maintenance man, and management consultant also develop the ability to define and diagnose a familiar system's problems in short order. For example, the partner of a major management consulting firm once reported to the author that his better diagnosticians could get a "quick fix" on most corporate problems in from 4 to 24 working hours, based on previous experience with similar firms and problems. In short, the ability to make rapid appraisals of a "new" situation is a valuable asset, all too rare in practice, that combines a high sensitivity to critical symptoms and a vast experience with problems of a given kind.

There are, however, several reasons why the ability to use logical and probabilistic aids to diagnosis can enhance the skills of the expert diagnostician, and contribute markedly to the diagnostic skills of the less expert investigator.

First, training in logical and probabilistic methods, if approached in the right spirit, enhances the investigator's sensitivity to critical symptoms and probable causes. In a sense, relating symptoms and causes become a habit through practice.

Second, a formal collection of symptom and cause relationships represents a wealth of experience for consideration. For rare difficulties such diagnostic tables may lead to a search for relevant symptoms and causes that had not been considered before.

Third, a formal use of logical and probabilistic methods may permit the detection of changed diagnostic conditions, the projection of possible symptom-fault relationship in newly designed systems, and an increase in the variety of diagnostic possibilities that would not be provided by experience itself.

In this chapter we illustrate a few formal methods of logical search and probabilistic selection that are useful in systems diagnosis and problem solving. We will first introduce some background material, and then apply the suggested techniques.

BOOLEAN ALGEBRA USING DESIGNATION NUMBERS

To further our discussion, we must first descend to the realm of formal logic. Although many excellent works are available on logical analysis, our presentation will avoid much of the usual background, and will stress manipulations most suitable for digital computers. This approach has the advantage that only three logical manipulations need be learned before more complex logical conditions can be analyzed, and the notation used can be greatly simplified by the use of *designation numbers* (which will be explained shortly) rather than by more cumbersome English statements or logical symbols.

In what follows we will first consider conclusions that are either true or false, and then conclusions that are probably true (and therefore to some extent probably false).

This distinction may be compared to the previously discussed difference between a *deterministic* machine and a *probabilistic* machine.

For the deterministic machine, a given set of input conditions (or sequence of input conditions) inexorably leads to fixed and given conclusions (our outcomes), which depend logically upon the input conditions by virtue of the machine's, or logical system's, structure.

For the probabilistic machine, a given set of input conditions may lead to a range of possible output conditions. When the probabilistic relationships are known, it is usually possible to compute a probability of occurrence for each possible outcome, given the input conditions. (The converse may also be possible; i.e, for a given output condition, it may be possible to determine the probability that certain input conditions lead to an observed result.)

The usual computer program, for example, is comparable to a deterministic machine, because a given output, or set of outputs, follows logically from a given input, or set of inputs. The coin-changing vending machine of Chapter 2 is another example.

An example of a probabilistic machine is the market-share model illustrated in Chapter 3, using switching matrices.

It is important to note that both the deterministic machine and the probabilisic machine have structure, but that the two forms of structure are portrayed differently, and lead to different results.

In the remainder of this section we will direct our discussion to the deterministic case.

Statements

Logical manipulations consist of statements and conclusions regarding other statements. Thus, we may make the statement "the system has symptom number 1," an observed fact. Similarly, we may make the statement, "the system has symptom number 2," also an observed fact. Such logical statements may be combined. We could, for example, make the compound statement, "the system has *both* symptom number 1 *and* symptom number 2." From this compound observation we would hope to deduce the truth or falsity of the statement, "the system has cause number 3."

Symbolic Notation

Because the repetition of long statements in English is cumbersome, we adopt a shorthand, calling the first statement "Statement *A*" or simply "*A*" and calling the second statement "Statement *B*" or simply "*B*." Because each of these statements may be either true (the symptom was observed) or false (the symptom was not observed), each statement has a truth value *T* or *F*. Similarly, each possible conclusion has a truth value, *T* or *F*.

Truth Tables, Designation Numbers, and the Logical Basis

A complete listing of all *T* and *F* possibilities for a group of *N* statements may be spelled out in tabular form. The statements are listed as rows and the possible combinations of *T* and *F* are listed as columns. In general, such a table will have *N* rows and 2^N columns, so that the two-statement table will have *two* rows and *four* columns.

Possible truth or falsity

| Statement *A* | *F T F T* |
| Statement *B* | *F F T T* |

If we wish to use a mechanized form of search, a binary notation is convenient: 0 for False and 1 for True, where in mechanical terms the 0 may correspond to "no hole" in a card and the 1 to "a hole." The "hole" or "no hole" dichotomy could, of course, also refer to a magnetized spot (or no spot) on computer tape, or similar binary coding in other memory media. For this reason two-valued logical manipulations are particularly suitable for computer search. Thus, for convenience, it is possible to indicate the possible truth or falsity patterns of two statements as

Possible truth or falsity

| Designation No. 1: Statement *A* | 0 1 0 1 |
| Designation No. 2: Statement *B* | 0 0 1 1 |

In this display, each column again corresponds to a possible combination of truth and falsity of Statement *A* and Statement *B*. Although it would be possible to arrange these columns in any order if all we wanted was a list of possibilities, it is convenient for our later use to develop a standard, or *canonical* form, of display which generates the possibilities in the exact order shown. Note in the last display that the first row consists of alternate 0's and 1's, and the second consists of alternate pairs of 0's and 1's. If there were three statements *A*, *B*, and *C*, we could immediately generate the canonical table of possibilities as

Possible truth or falsity

Designation No. 1: Statement *A*	0 1 0 1 0 1 0 1
Designation No. 2: Statement *B*	0 0 1 1 0 0 1 1
Designation No. 3: Statement *C*	0 0 0 0 1 1 1 1

where now there are 2^3 or 8 columns, and all possible truth and falsity combinations have been enumerated, as may be verified by inspection.

When a table of truth and falsity possibilities has been constructed in the canonical form, it is called a *complete logical basis*. In addition, for convenience we call the series of 0's and 1's in the row for a *particular* statement the *designation number* for that statement. In later examples we will use the designation number of a statement to perform logical manipulations.[4]

The Truth or Falsity of a Compound Statement

Manipulations with two-valued logic are frequently called Boolean Algebra after the mathematician George Boole[5] who first popularized symbolic logic. In most texts, such logical manipulations are illustrated by so-called Venn diagrams, made popular by the mathematician John Venn.[6] In electronic and computer work, switching circuits or other analog elements are often used to illustrate the physical analog of logical statements. In what follows we will illustrate three fundamental logical manipulations by symbolic statements, Venn diagrams, and designation numbers. Thereafter we omit the drawings. *From the three basic operations discussed; i.e., logical addition, logical multiplication, and logical negation, more complicated compound statements can be developed.*

Logical Addition

Many of the fundamental logical manipulations appear to be trivial. However, in breaking up difficult compound statements, the simple operations of logical addition, multiplication, and negation can be used to bring simplicity (T or F) out of apparent chaos. We thus treat the fundamentals first.

The first compound statement of interest is denoted in works of logic as $(A + B)$, which is taken to mean "*either A or B* is true, or both are true." For example, to use a typical logical phrase, we may want to determine whether the following statement is True or False: "The object observed is either a dog or a black object, or a black dog." Thus, if A represents the observation of a dog, and B represents the observation of a black object, the conclusion would be true if either A were true, or B were true, or if both were true.

---

[4] To conform to the notation in R. S. Ledley, *Programming and Utilizing Digital Computers*, McGraw-Hill, New York, 1962, Chapters 8 and 10, the designation number of statement A will be denoted $\#A$, where "$\#$" stands for the phrase "designation number of."

[5] G. Boole, *The Laws of Thought*, London, 1854. Reprint, Dover, New York, 1951.

[6] J. Venn, *The Logic of Chance*, Macmillan, London, 1888.

This statement of logical fact may be reduced to the designation number approach as follows.

Statement *A*: Object observed is a dog   0 1 0 1
Statement *B*: Object observed is black   0 0 1 1
Conclusion: Object either a dog, or black, or a black dog   0 1 1 1

The table may be interpreted to read that the conclusion is true in every instance but one, namely, when neither a dog nor a black object has been observed (column 1 of the basis). The designation number for the conclusion has been obtained by *logical addition,* which should not be confused with binary addition (i.e., the designation number for the conclusion is computed by *adding* according to the rules of logical addition: $1 + 1 = 1, 0 + 1 = 1, 1 + 0 = 1, 0 + 0 = 0.$) Note that the designation number for the conclusion, as shown above, indicates the truth or falsity of the conclusion for every possible combination of 0 and 1, or F and T, for the original statements. Thus, although the final designation number for the conclusion may be lengthy, it gives the logical result for any possible configuration of the logical input, Statements *A* and *B*.

The Venn diagram for this compound statement is given in Figure 11-1a. Boundary A includes the set of all dogs. Boundary *B* includes the set of all black objects. Two circles overlap to represent the set of black dogs. The compound statement $(A + B)$ when true, is meant to include,

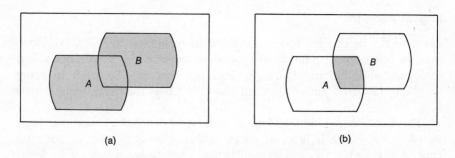

(a)   (b)

11-1 Two basic Venn diagrams. (a) is the Venn diagram of $(A + B)$. All possible members of a set are contained within the square box. Those having characteristic *A* are included within the boundary (*A*); those with characteristic *B*, within (*B*). Those with both characteristics *A* or *B* or both *A* and *B*, i.e., those defined by $(A + B)$, are included within the shaded area (sometimes called the union of *A* and *B*). Conversely, items having neither characteristics *A* or *B*, nor their combination are included in the nonshaded area. (b) is the Venn Diagram of $(A \cdot B)$. The definitions are as in (a), except we now ask for objects having both characteristics *A* and *B* in combination, i.e., for those defined by $(A \cdot B)$. This is the shaded area shown (sometimes called the conjunction, or intersection of *A* and *B*). The nonshaded area within the square represents objects that do not simultaneously have the characteristics *A* and *B*, i.e., those that may be denoted by $(\bar{A} \cdot \bar{B})$.

all objects within the circles *A* and *B*. It should be clear that, if $(A + B)$ is false, (e.g., if the object is a white horse) the object would fall outside the circles in the Venn diagram. This possibility, as indicated above, corresponds to the first column of the complete logical basis composed of the designation numbers for Statements *A* and *B*.

It is helpful to realize that the use of logical addition, or the $+$ sign for the *or* in logic comes from the analogy between the logical operation $(A + B)$ and arithmetic addition. For example,

$$2 \text{ dog objects} + 3 \text{ black objects} = 5 \text{ objects}$$

where "objects" may be either dogs, or black, or black dogs. In effect, this operation corresponds to *grouping* items distinguished by specific characteristics under a more general category.

Logical Multiplication

Another compound statement of immediate interest is denoted by $(A \cdot B)$, which is taken to mean "*Both A and B are true only if A is true and B is also true.*" For example, we would observe a black dog if and only if the object observed were *A*, a dog, and *B*, black. Thus, both *A* and *B* must be true if $(A \cdot B)$ is to be true. This result can be obtained from the complete logical basis by *logical multiplication*, which is also a column-by-column operation (i.e., $1 \times 1 = 1, 0 \times 1 = 0, 1 \times 0 = 0, 0 \times 0 = 0$) as shown below.

Statement *A*: Object observed is a dog	0 1 0 1
Statement *B*: Object observed is black	0 0 1 1
Conclusion: Object is a black dog	0 0 0 1

As with logical addition, the logical product has its analogy with the arithmetic of multiplication. The parallel is most obvious in dimensional analysis in which two less-specific categories are combined to create a more-specific category. Thus, if one man works one day, we may describe the total amount of effort involved (which is a combination of men and time) as one man-day, a logical *and* combination.

Logical Negation

We can denote the falsity of a statement by placing a bar over the statement symbol. Thus, if a dog were not observed, we could denote that fact by $\bar{A}$. The corresponding designation number for the negation of *A* is obtained by switching all 0's to 1's and all 1's to 0's in the original designation number for *A*. A similar manipulation would give $\bar{B}$'s designation number, i.e., the designation number for the statement: "The object observed was not black."

To obtain practice in the use of designation numbers and their manipulation, the reader should consult Figure 11-2, which shows the negation of statements *A* and *B* in various combinations, and the corresponding compound statements produced by logical multiplication and addition. The reader's understanding of these manipulations will be enhanced if he constructs the Venn diagram for each case shown, and also constructs an English statement for each conclusion.

#*A*	0 1 0 1					#*A*	0 1 0 1			
#*B*	0 0 1 1					#*B*	0 0 1 1			
#($A \cdot B$)	0 0 0 1					#($A + B$)	0 1 1 1			

#$\bar{A}$	1 0 1 0					#$\bar{A}$	1 0 1 0			
#*B*	0 0 1 1					#*B*	0 0 1 1			
#($\bar{A} \cdot B$)	0 0 1 0					#($\bar{A} + B$)	1 0 1 1			

#*A*	0 1 0 1					#*A*	0 1 0 1			
#$\bar{B}$	1 1 0 0					#$\bar{B}$	1 1 0 0			
#($A \cdot \bar{B}$)	0 1 0 0					#($A + \bar{B}$)	1 1 0 1			

#$\bar{A}$	1 0 1 0					#$\bar{A}$	1 0 1 0			
#$\bar{B}$	1 1 0 0					#$\bar{B}$	1 1 0 0			
#($\bar{A} \cdot \bar{B}$)	1 0 0 0					#($\bar{A} + \bar{B}$)	1 1 1 0			

(a)	(b)

11-2 The logical negation of statements in logical multiplication and addition. The above tabulations show the designation numbers for two statements *A* and *B*, and the corresponding designation numbers for (a) their conjunction by logical multiplication, and (b) their union by logical addition for all possible combinations of negation for statements *A* and *B*. These results are used in later examples.

More Complex Logical Statements

To see how the designation numbers may be manipulated to resolve the truth or falsity of more complex statements, we ask under what conditions the statement $(\bar{A} + \bar{B}) \cdot (A + B)$ is true? This statement reads, in light of our previous dog example, "The object is *either* not a dog, or not black, or not a black dog *and* is either black, or a dog, or a black dog." In this cumbersome form it is difficult to see what conditions would cause the conclusion to be true. However, we can rapidly reach the correct result by noting that the conclusion is the logical product of two compound statements for which we already have found the designation numbers in Figure 11-2. We may perform the logical multiplication as below.

Designation No. 1: $(\bar{A} + \bar{B})$ 1 1 1 0
Designation No. 2: $(A + B)$ 0 1 1 1
Designation No. 3: $(\bar{A} + \bar{B}) \cdot (A + B)$ 0 1 1 0

The interpretation of this result is that $(\bar{A} + \bar{B}) \cdot (A + B)$ will be true if either of two conditions hold. These specific conditions are those indicated by the statements made in columns 2 and 3 of the original complete logical basis for Statements A and B, which was

Statement A: Object observed is a dog   0   1   0   1
Statement B: Object observed is black   0   0   1   1

Thus, $(\bar{A} + \bar{B}) \cdot (A + B)$ will be true if we have either

(From column 2 of the basis): the object observed was a dog and not black, or

(From column 3 of the basis): the object observed was not a dog and black, and false under the other two conditions.

The relative simplicity of the designation number approach when compared to manipulation of English phrases or symbols, should now be evident.

Logical Identity

Two logical statements are identical if and only if both have the same designation number. This important point often permits proof that two complex logical statements, in fact, mean exactly the same thing.

Example: Using the same definitions of Statement A and Statement B as before, show the identity of the compound statements

$$(\bar{A} + \bar{B}) \cdot (A + B) \quad \text{and} \quad (A \cdot \bar{B}) + (\bar{A} \cdot B).$$

We have already obtained the designation number of the left-hand expression as 0 1 1 0. If we can show that the designation number of the right-hand expression is also 0 1 1 0, we will have proved the identity. In Figure 11-2a we have already found the designation numbers for

$$(A \cdot \bar{B}) = 0\ 1\ 0\ 0$$
$$(\bar{A} \cdot B) = 0\ 0\ 1\ 0$$

which upon logical addition yield 0 1 1 0. The two compound statements are thus logically equivalent ways of saying the same thing, confirming the results of the previous section.

Logical Implication

Although two logical statements may not have identical meaning, the truth of one may *imply* the truth of the other. This situation may arise when the first statement is more specific than the latter. Thus, the fact that one saw a black dog certainly implies that (a) a dog was seen, and (b) that a black object was seen.

Tests for logical implication can also be made using the designation number approach and the following rule: *The truth of statement X implies the truth of statement Y if, and only if, the Designation No. Y has units (1's) in at least those positions where 1's appear in Designation No. X.* Using the suggested example, we have

$(A \cdot B)$: Object was a dog and black   0 0 0 1   (Designation No. X)

    A: Object seen was a dog   0 1 0 1   (Designation No. Y)

Because Designation $\#Y$ has 1's in at least those positions that appear in Designation $\#X$, the first statement's truth implies the truth of the second. We may then say that X implies Y, or $X \rightarrow Y$, where the arrow indicates logical implication.

To summarize what we have covered thus far, we inject a commercial example requiring logical analysis by designation numbers.

Example: The following letter was written on September 1, 1965, by Joseph B. Jones, inventor, 4672 Jones Street, Jonesville, Michigan, and received on September 3, 1965, by Atlas Motors, Friendsville, Mississippi:

> Gentlemen:
> On August 3, 1965, I ordered your Number A463, ⅛ horsepower motors @ $27 ea., delivered. You assured me in confirmation that I would receive the motors in ten days if my credit was good, or in 48 hours if I sent cash. In addition, you indicated that there could be a delay if there were a Teamsters strike at your plant, or if a Civil Rights demonstration interfered with business. Because my operation does not have a Dun & Bradstreet rating, I immediately sent cash, which you acknowledged. I have heard that there were neither recent demonstrations, nor a Teamsters strike in Friendsville. So I am at a loss to explain why I do not have your shipment in hand. Please advise at once.
>
> Very truly yours,
> Joseph B. Jones

Jones got his cash back, due to an unexpected inventory shortage—a possibility not mentioned in the letter. But, from the available facts, how can we use designation numbers to come to the same conclusion as Jones (even though the conclusion is obvious from reading the letter)?

The company made four statements (regarding credit, cash, a strike, and a demonstration). Each of these "questions" could be answered yes or no, so that we can make up a table of statements and possible outcomes, giving four designation numbers, one for each statement. (Yes $= 1$)

Statement		Possible outcomes			
Credit Good	#A	0 1 0 1	0 1 0 1	0 1 0 1	0 1 0 1
Cash Sent	#B	0 0 1 1	0 0 1 1	0 0 1 1	0 0 1 1
Strike Called	#C	0 0 0 0	1 1 1 1	0 0 0 0	1 1 1 1
Demonstration	#D	0 0 0 0	0 0 0 0	1 1 1 1	1 1 1 1

Atlas Motors claimed the motors would be sent if credit were good, *or* if cash were sent, and if *neither* a strike *nor* a demonstration interfered with business. In shorthand form, that would be $(A + B) \cdot (\overline{C} \cdot \overline{D}) = Y$, where Y is shipment of the goods.

Following the rules for designation numbers, we can see if what Jones did implied that shipment would be made. First we find #Y, the shipment designation number.

Adding the designation numbers for (#A + #B) we obtain

$$(\#A + \#B) = 0\ 1\ 1\ 1 \qquad 0\ 1\ 1\ 1 \qquad 0\ 1\ 1\ 1 \qquad 0\ 1\ 1\ 1$$

And for $(\#\overline{C} \cdot \#\overline{D})$ we obtain, remembering that negation reverses the 0's and 1's in the original designation numbers C and D

$$(\#\overline{C} \cdot \#\overline{D}) = 1\ 1\ 1\ 1 \qquad 0\ 0\ 0\ 0 \qquad 0\ 0\ 0\ 0 \qquad 0\ 0\ 0\ 0$$

And finally:

$$(\#A + \#B) \cdot (\#\overline{C} \cdot \#\overline{D})$$
$$= 0\ 1\ 1\ 1 \qquad 0\ 0\ 0\ 0 \qquad 0\ 0\ 0\ 0 \qquad 0\ 0\ 0\ 0 = \#Y$$

expressing the requirements for shipment. We now find the input conditions X.

The facts were that Jones sent cash, because he had no credit, and that no strike or demonstration took place. Thus, $X = (\overline{A} \cdot B) \cdot (\overline{C} \cdot \overline{D})$. Following the procedure above, we may find the designation number for X, #X:

$$(\#\overline{A} \cdot \#B) \cdot (\#\overline{C} \cdot \#\overline{D})$$
$$= 0\ 0\ 1\ 0 \qquad 0\ 0\ 0\ 0 \qquad 0\ 0\ 0\ 0 \qquad 0\ 0\ 0\ 0 = \#X,$$

the designation number representing the conditions of the Jones transaction.

Because there are at least as many 1's in the same position in #Y as there are in #X, $X \rightarrow Y$, and the shipment should have been made. This is an example of deducing the logical consequences of a set of facts and a series of logical statements using the designation number approach. From an input-output viewpoint, X represents the input to the system (the Atlas Motors decision-making and order-handling operation), Y represents the output "shipment."

Boolean Functions and English Statements from Designation Numbers

The analyst may have arrived at a designation number that he wants to put into symbolic form (i.e., into a Boolean Function) or to convert into English. As we have seen, there are usually a number of equivalent compound statements. One problem that arises in equipment design is to find the simplest equivalent statement in terms of physical construction of a logical device. Although we will not pursue that route here, it is convenient to have one way of obtaining an equivalent symbolic or English statement. We will indicate one method here, and leave other methods to the suggested references and problems at the end of this chapter.

Using what is known as the *first canonical form*, we may convert any designation number into an equivalent symbolic statement by noting from Figure 11-2a that the designation numbers for all possible products of two statements A and B are

$$\#(\overline{A} \cdot \overline{B}) = 1\ 0\ 0\ 0$$
$$\#(A \cdot \overline{B}) = 0\ 1\ 0\ 0$$
$$\#(\overline{A} \cdot B) = 0\ 0\ 1\ 0$$
$$\#(A \cdot B) = 0\ 0\ 0\ 1$$

Using this fact and the operations of logical addition, we can express any four-column designation number as *a sum of logical products*.

For example, given the designation number 0 1 1 0 we see by inspection that this designation number could have arisen from the sum of the designation numbers of the two logical products $\#(A \cdot \overline{B}) + \#(\overline{A} \cdot B)$. Thus, one symbolic statement that would result in the designation number 0 1 1 0 is $(A \cdot \overline{B}) + (\overline{A} \cdot B)$. Obviously other equivalent forms exist, but one procedure is satisfactory for our present needs here. By extension, the suggested method of developing an equivalent symbolic form may be applied to designation numbers with a greater number of columns. For example, for an eight-column designation number, which implies three logical statements comprising the rows of the complete logical basis, we would find there are eight possible logical products. By appropriate addition of these products, the eight-column designation number could always be duplicated.

THE CONSTRAINED LOGICAL BASIS

As the reader has imagined by now, when the number of logical statements N increases, the size of the *complete* logical basis increases rapidly, because it will have N rows and 2^N columns. This is clearly an impractical situation. However, things are not nearly as bad as they seem when we remember that many combinations, which are logically possible, are *not* probable, or necessary, or feasible in practice. These constraints eliminate many columns from the complete logical basis, and produce a much smaller *constrained logical basis,* which may be handled as before.

Thus, the logical distinction between a number of statement combinations may be immaterial if the presence of one true statement in the combination is considered to take precedence over the others, as in decision trees and sequential testing. A number of logically possible combinations may technically not be feasible, because they cannot be constructed or because a technological sequence of assembly or operation limits variety. Or, returning to the diagnostic problem, certain possible symptoms and causes may have never been observed in combination, so that the available data are constrained by experience or system knowledge. Indeed, many of the simplification techniques of Chapter 7 and 8 may be employed to reduce a complete logical basis to a constrained logical basis for application in a given case. An example will illustrate the point, and bring us back to our problem of logical diagnosis.

Example: Suppose an order-processing department decides to make shipment of a product on the basis of three statements, *A, B,* and *C.* The complete logical basis for these statements would have three rows and eight columns, as shown below.

	Column No.							
	1	2	3	4	5	6	7	8
Statement *A*: Credit Limit OK	0	1	0	1	0	1	0	1
Statement *B*: Pay Experience Favorable	0	0	1	1	0	0	1	1
Statement *C*: Special Clearance Obtained	0	0	0	0	1	1	1	1
Shipment to be Made	*N*	*Y*	*Y*	*Y*	*Y*	*Y*	*Y*	*Y*
or	0	1	1	1	1	1	1	1
			√		√	√	√	

Suppose, in addition, that a shipment will be made if the credit limit is OK, *or* if the pay experience is favorable, *or* if special clearance has been obtained, *or for any combination of these possibilities.* The resulting action, is shown in the last row in decision-table form. This complete basis and the associated rules for shipment suggest immediate simplification, because if Statement *A* is true, the truth or falsity of Statements *B* and/or *C* is immaterial, and similarly, if *A* is false and *B* is true, then the truth or falsity of *C* is immaterial. The columns so affected are indicated in the table above, and are columns 4, 6, 7, and 8. With these columns deleted and the columns rearranged in the order 2, 3, 5, 1, we have a new constrained basis in which, for example, columns 4, 6, and 8 have been combined with column 2, and column 7 has been combined with column 3.[7] In this new tabulation, the irrelevant table entries are indicated by a dash $(-)$.

Old Column No.

	2	3	5	1
A: Credit OK	1	0	0	0
B: Pay Experience Favorable	$-$	1	0	0
C: Special Clearance Obtained	$-$	$-$	1	0
Shipment to be Made	Y	Y	Y	N
or	1	1	1	0

In this new decision-table format, all the 0's and 1's are relevant to the decision, but the $(-)$'s are not. This new arrangement would seem to pose special problems in view of the manipulations just discussed, because the $(-)$'s are ambiguous, and the standard order of the table columns has not been preserved. However, in fact, no great difficulty arises if we remember the rules for logical implication.

To determine whether or not shipment should be made in a given case, let us renumber the columns in the decision table 1, 2, 3, 4, with the understanding that this definition will refer to the last table shown above. With this modification we may next call the four-place designation number for the shipment conditions $\#Y = 1\ 1\ 1\ 0$, because we have a yes at the foot of the first three columns and a no at the foot of the fourth. We may also indicate the designation number of any incoming order in four columns. For example, if we take the designation number of statement A, as shown in the four-column table, as $\#A = 1\ 0\ 0\ 0$, we see that $A \rightarrow Y$, because $\#Y$ has 1's in at least those positions where 1's appear in $\#A$. Again, suppose the new order exceeds the credit limit, but has favorable pay experience and also has obtained special clearance. As a Boolean function, this state of affairs could be indicated by $(\bar{A} \cdot B \cdot C)$. How can this statement produce a designation number? *If we take the $(-)$'s in the table to be 0's,* we may proceed by logical multiplication and find $\#(\bar{A} \cdot B \cdot C) = 0\ 1\ 1\ 0$, remembering that the four-column designation number results from the constrained basis defined above. Again, because $\#Y$ has 1's in at least those positions where $\#(\bar{A} \cdot B \cdot C)$ has 1's, $(\bar{A} \cdot B \cdot C) \rightarrow (Y)$, and shipment should be made. Finally, we may ask what happens when *none* of the tests can be passed by an incoming order, namely, an order having the condition $(\bar{A} \cdot \bar{B} \cdot \bar{C})$. Again assuming that $(-)$'s are 0's, we find

[7] Note that the $(-)$'s appear to indicate the grouping of several columns in the complete basis. The various conditions which have been grouped are therefore still part of the problem, but will lead to a common action. This form of simplification should be distinguished from column elimination associated with unfeasible or impossible conditions.

$$\#A = 0\ 1\ 1\ 1$$
$$\#B = 1\ 0\ 1\ 1$$
$$\#C = 1\ 1\ 0\ 1$$
$$\#(\overline{A} \cdot \overline{B} \cdot \overline{C}) = \overline{0\ 0\ 0\ 1}$$

and the shipment is *not* made, because $\#Y$ does not now have 1's in at least as many positions as those shown in $\#(\overline{A} \cdot \overline{B} \cdot \overline{C})$.

Using designation numbers in this way reduces a series of tests to a simple matching operation.

ALTERNATE SCREENING METHODS USING MASKING MATRICES

We may also use an alternative procedure, which has computational advantages in some cases. Using the same credit example, suppose we have the original table of statements and shipment conditions, and wish to have an automatic way of eliminating or "masking" the $(-)$'s, indicating "don't care" conditions entered in the decision table as 0's. We may accomplish this by a masking matrix, or a table that has 1's in the relevant test positions and 0's for the $(-)$'s, as shown below.

	Converted decision table	Masking matrix	Test data input
Credit OK	1 0 0 0	1 1 1 1	0
Pay Favorable	0 1 0 0	0 1 1 1	1
Special Clearance	0 0 1 0	0 0 1 1	1

Because in this example shipment is made when *any* of the three conditions, represented by columns 1, 2, or 3 of the decision table, is met, a direct examination of the pertinent test conditions suggests itself. That is, because shipment depends upon logical addition of alternatives we can test input cases against successive *columns* of the decision table, and omit row manipulations. Some reflection will reveal that a column-matching approach may be efficient for two reasons. Because even the constrained basis is likely to have more columns than rows, each test will probably involve fewer characters than the complete designation number of shipment conditions. And, if the column matching stops when the first suitable acceptance condition is met, we can shorten the column testing procedure by arranging the decision table to place the highly probable matches first.

To illustrate the masking procedure, suppose that the test data input shown above in column form has been received; i.e., the order exceeds the credit limit, but has both favorable pay experience and special clearance. This data input does not match *any* of the *columns* in the converted decision table. However, if the input data is masked by logical multiplication of the input data by the masking matrix entries *before* a match is made, the problem is resolved.

Thus, to check the test data input against the first column of the decision table, the masking matrix approach calls for element-by-element logical multiplication of the data input by the *first* column elements of the masking matrix, to produce the computed result shown.

Data input	First column of the masking matrix		Computed result		First column of decision table
0	×	1	=	0	:	1
1	×	0	=	0	:	0
1	×	0	=	0	:	0

This computed result is compared element by element to the first column of the decision table. Because there is *not* a perfect element-to-element match, the test fails, and we proceed to column 2.

Data input	Second column of the masking matrix		Computed result		Second column of decision table
0	×	1	=	0	:	0
1	×	1	=	1	:	1
1	×	0	=	0	:	0

At the second column of the masking matrix, a perfect match is found between the computed result and the second column of the decision table, so that the testing stops, shipment is made, and the testing system is already to receive the next input. Note that in this procedure we are dealing with repeated manipulations with three binary digits, rather than with four as in the previous method. For most decision tables constructed from a constrained logical basis the character difference would be greater. Both methods are entirely equivalent logically, and the choice is a matter of convenience in a given case.[8]

SYMPTOM-CAUSE COMPLEX TABLES

We now return to a diagnostic problem. Suppose that we decide to develop a diagnostic table, Figure 11-3, that will relate all possible combinations of two symptoms and two causes of system failure. Although it may appear different, this table is identical with the complete logical basis discussed previously, because we will consider *all* symptom-cause complexes, repre-

[8] H. W. Kirk, "Use of Decision Tables in Computer Programming," *Communications of the ACM*, **8**, 1, January, 1965, pp. 41–43.

senting *all* combinations of symptoms and causes present or absent. For this reason, the logical statements comprising the *rows* of the logical basis will consist of a list of possible symptoms *plus* a list of possible causes. Although for the two-symptom, two-cause problem, we would have four rows, for n symptoms and m causes there would be $n + m$ rows and 2^{n+m} columns in such a table of *theoretical* possibilities. Figure 11-3 shows such a complete logical basis for the two-symptom, two-cause problem.

It is important to understand clearly that each column represents a symptom-cause complex that *conceivably* could occur. For example, the first column indicates the case when neither $S(1)$ nor $S(2)$ is observed in the absence of both causes $D(1)$ and $D(2)$. Column 12 indicates that both symptoms $S(1)$ and $S(2)$ may be observed when the system has cause $D(2)$ but not $D(1)$. Column 16 indicates that both $S(1)$ and $S(2)$ may be observed when the system has $D(1)$ and $D(2)$ in combination, and so on. The sixteen columns cover all the logical possibilities.

The table shown in Figure 11-3 is of substantial size for such a simple problem. Moreover, if the investigator had such a table before him, it would be worthless. Regardless of the combination of observed symptoms,

	Symptom complexes s^i															
Column number	1	2	3	4	5	6	7	8	9	10	11	12	13	14	15	16
Superscript i	0	1	2	3	0	1	2	3	0	1	2	3	0	1	2	3
$S(1)$	0	1	0	1	0	1	0	1	0	1	0	1	0	1	0	1
$S(2)$	0	0	1	1	0	0	1	1	0	0	1	1	0	0	1	1
$D(1)$	0	0	0	0	1	1	1	1	0	0	0	0	1	1	1	1
$D(2)$	0	0	0	0	0	0	0	0	1	1	1	1	1	1	1	1
Cause-complexes d_j	d_0				d_1				d_2				d_3			
Symptom-cause complex	C_0^0	C_0^1	C_0^2	C_0^3	C_1^0	C_1^1	C_1^2	C_1^3	C_2^0	C_2^1	C_2^2	C_2^3	C_3^0	C_3^1	C_3^2	C_3^3

11-3 The canonical form of the symptom-cause complex table. The combination of the two symptoms, S(1) and S(2), produces a set of four possible symptom complexes, s^i, with $i = 0, 1, 2, 3, \ldots$ shown in the second row of the table. The combination of the two causes D(1) and D(2) also produces four cause complexes d_j with $j = 0, 1, 2, 3$, as shown by the four blocks at the foot of the table. The four symptom complexes and the four cause complexes in combination produce 16 symptom-cause complexes, C_j^i, enumerated in the last row of the above table, by indexing each symptom complex within each cause complex from left to right. It is important to remember in what follows that an upper case S or D refers to a single symptom or cause and that a lower case s or d refers to a "complex," or combination of individual symptoms or causes, present or not.

the investigator could not differentiate, from the table, whether the symptom(s) resulted from Cause (1), or Cause (2), neither, or both.

An important point to be learned from this simple exercise is that knowledge imposes constraints upon possibilities. If all the possibilities were feasible, and if all the possibilities were equally likely, there would be no need to make observations. A flip of the coin would do in making the diagnosis.

But experience, if it is organized at all, is never completely random, by definition. There are some symptom-cause complexes (columns in the Table of Figure 11-3) that just do not occur, and there are some that do occur in certain patterns. The knowledge of these specific constraints as they logically occur thus becomes a large part of diagnostic training, or experience. In short, education and training in diagnostic ability, as in other skills, assumes considerable system constraints. Learning also requires that such constraint will be relatively stable over time, or that possible changes in constraints can be predicted in advance.

To continue with our example, let us assume that only the symptom-cause complexes of columns 6, 7, 8, 11, 12, 15, and 16 (in Figure 11-3) have been observed or are feasible. With this knowledge we may delete all other columns of the complete basis and develop the constrained logical basis shown in Figure 11-4, consisting only of seven feasible or observed columns, representing symptom-cause complexes.

With this table of constrained possibilities in mind, we may now receive a set of observations regarding $S(1)$ and $S(2)$, and seek to make a differential diagnosis regarding $D(1)$ and $D(2)$.

Column number		1	2	3	4	5	6	7
Symptom complex		s^1	s^2	s^3	s^2	s^3	s^2	s^3
(Individual symptoms)	$S(1)$	1	0	1	0	1	0	1
	$S(2)$	0	1	1	1	1	1	1
(Individual causes)	$D(1)$	1	1	1	0	0	1	1
	$D(2)$	0	0	0	1	1	1	1
(Cause complex)		d_1			d_2		d_3	
(Symptom-cause complex)		C_1^1	C_1^2	C_1^3	C_2^2	C_2^3	C_3^2	C_3^3

11-4 The constrained basis of symptom-cause complexes. From experience or system structure, only the symptom-cause complexes represented by columns 6, 7, 8, 11, 12, 15, and 16 of Figure 11-3 have been observed or are possible. This constrained basis, shown above with renumbered columns, represents this diagnostic knowledge. The nomenclature is the same as in Figure 11-3.

For example, suppose the diagnostician receives a report or observes that the system has symptom $S(1)$, but *not* symptom $S(2)$; i.e., the input to the logical search is $S(1) \cdot \overline{S(2)}$. What can be deduced from this observation and the available logical data?

Using the constrained basis of Figure 11-4, and the corresponding designation numbers for $S(1)$ and $S(2)$, we compute the designation number for $S(1) \cdot S(2)$, we compute the designation number for $S(1) \cdot \overline{S(2)}$ to be

$$\begin{array}{r} \#S(1) = 1\ 0\ 1\ 0\ 1\ 0\ 1 \\ \#\overline{S(2)} = 1\ 0\ 0\ 0\ 0\ 0\ 0 \\ \hline \#(S(1) \cdot \overline{S(2)}) = 1\ 0\ 0\ 0\ 0\ 0\ 0 \end{array}$$

This result and the rule for logical implication tell the investigator that the system has cause $D(1)$ and *not* cause $D(2)$, and *not* the combination of causes $D(1)$ and $D(2)$. In other words, (in this case) a unique diagnosis of a single cause can be made from the set of two symptoms.

LOGICAL DIAGNOSIS FROM SYMPTOM-CAUSE TABLES

To illustrate this conclusion, we may approach the data in two ways: By row or by column.

First, the row designation number of $S(1) \cdot \overline{S(2)} = 1\ 0\ 0\ 0\ 0\ 0\ 0$ has a "1" only in the first column, which leads us directly to the first column of the constrained basis and the symptom-cause complex involving $S(1) \cdot \overline{S(2)}$ and $D(1) \cdot \overline{D(2)}$. Thus, we have a unique and immediate diagnosis: $D(1) \cdot \overline{D(2)}$.

Second, we could have scanned the symptom-complex *rows* column-by-column [checking $S(1) \cdot \overline{S(2)}$ for a match] and again found that only column 1 matches the stated conditions. The corresponding cause complex in column 1, $D(1) \cdot \overline{D(2)}$, is the unique diagnosis for the stated symptoms. (As indicated in the previous credit example, the methods are equivalent. A masking matrix is obviously not needed here, because none of the symptom conditions are irrelevant to the diagnosis.)

It is important for what follows to note that if the observation of symptoms had revealed either $S(1)$ or $S(2)$ alone without a statement about the other, or if the observation had revealed the combination $S(1) \cdot S(2)$, a unique diagnosis could *not* have been achieved.

To spell this out, if the observation had revealed $S(1)$ only, without any statement about $S(2)$ being definitely true or false, a scan of the symptom-cause complexes or logical manipulation, as indicated above, would have indicated that the system could have had cause $D(1)$, or $D(2)$, *or both* $D(1)$ *and* $D(2)$ in combination. A similar result would have been obtained if $S(2)$ had been observed without any information about $S(1)$. Finally, the same result would have been obtained from the given constrained basis if $S(1)$ *and* $S(2)$ had definitely been observed in combination; i.e., the observation $S(1) \cdot S(2)$ would not have aided in the differential diagnosis of $D(1)$ versus $D(2)$ or $D(1) \cdot D(2)$.

ACTIONS WHEN DIFFERENTIAL DIAGNOSIS IS NOT UNIQUE

From what has just been said, it should be clear that the observation of a given symptom complex may not lead to a unique diagnosis, and that, in fact, the symptoms observed may or may not narrow the field of choice. This situation, of course, is particularly evident when several cause complexes have a large number of similar symptoms.

Two routes are open to the investigator when the results of a preliminary diagnosis are ambiguous: (1) He may collect more symptoms, i.e., make additional tests and observations which, hopefully, will further narrow the field, or (2) he may resort to a probabilistic choice, and prescribe treatment on that basis. We will discuss each of these approaches in turn.

More Tests From Symptom-Cause Tables

First, note that it would be impractical, because of tabular size, to include in one array all the possible symptom-cause complexes for a system of any great sophistication. Fortunately, such *grand arrays* are not necessary, because clustering effects in symptom-cause-complex data allow large tables to be broken up into smaller ones for specialized use. Rudimentary screening of a few symptoms would usually narrow the field sufficiently to indicate which special, smaller table should be consulted for more detailed search. Moreover, usually only detailed differentiation of causes presents any great diagnostic difficulty.

Second, clearly the collection of some symptoms, or the application of some tests (which is the same thing), is easier than others. For example, an interview of the patient is easier than a physical examination, for both the patient and the physician, and both of these symptom-gathering methods are easier than laboratory tests or exploratory surgery. Similarly, for hardware systems, outside tests are usually easier to perform than inside tests, so that the investigator would usually prefer to take the easier outside alternatives first. Similar remarks could be made about organizational investigations, and systems investigations generally. In short, the investigator will usually prefer to collect symptoms *in a certain order,* determined by cost, ease of application, time, and danger to the system, and to select within this framework the most discriminating tests.

In practice, the investigator uses diagnostic tables not only to lead him to a unique diagnosis, but to do so in an effective manner by indicating symptoms or tests critical to the differential diagnosis for each "stage" of cost, ease, or time criteria.

To illustrate how this can be accomplished, we must resort to a more extensive symptom-cause-complex table, such as the one shown in Figure 11-5. This table consists of 16 symptom-cause complexes (as columns) and an array of 14 symptom possibilities and eight cause possibilities (as rows). For illustration, we will assume a medical example in which the system is a doctor's patient, and the cause of the possible symptoms are diseases. Thus, the table of Figure 11-5 may be thought of as a tabulation of symptom-disease complexes, and the constraints exhibited in the table's configuration representative of medical knowledge about the eight diseases and their associate symptoms.

Using such a table, *in which the diagnostic tests have been ranked* in the order of their difficulty, we may see how the investigation would proceed.

First, the physician examines the patient's history and interviews him. Observation of the first three lines of Figure 11-5 indicates that the collection of $S(1)$ provides no information useful to the diagnosis, because eight diseases show that symptom. The physician thus looks for $S(2)$ and $S(3)$, which will do some good.

Suppose the patient has $S(2)$ and $S(3)$ in combination. This fact throws out symptom-disease complex columns 12-16, and thereby narrows the field initially.

Next the physician proceeds with the physical examination. Of the possible symptoms $S(4)$, $S(5)$, and $S(6)$, only two are necessary, because three will do no better at differentiation than two, as may be seen by scanning rows 4, 5, and 6 of Figure 11-5. Suppose, after physical examination, the patient has $S(4)$ and *not* $S(5)$. Because only columns 3–9 pertain to this combination (by a scan of rows 4 and 5), possible symptom-disease complexes, 1, 2, 10, and 11 may now be eliminated.

The choice of the blood tests $S(7)$ through $S(12)$ is more difficult. As a general rule at this stage, assuming all the tests were equally difficult, the physician would look for the smallest number of tests that would provide a unique diagnosis, if this were possible. (If not, he would look for tests that would most reduce the possibilities.) In this case, there are seven symptom-disease possibilities. If each blood test is reported positive or negative, we may observe (from our binary guessing game of Chapter 5, page 119) that the smallest number of tests that could discriminate between seven alternatives is the nearest integer greater than $\log_2 7$, or 3. (2^3 is eight.) It might take more tests than this, but three tests are the minimum. Thus, the physician would look for a combination of the *three* blood tests that will accomplish this discrimination. The candidates for this selection, again remembering the binary guessing game, would be tests whose rows showed an approximately equal number of 0's and 1's. A scan of the possibilities

Column numbers:	1	2	3	4	5	6	7	8	9	10	11	12	13	14	15	16	
History — S(1)	1	1	1	1	1	1	1	1	1	1	1	1	1	1	1	1	⎫
→ S(2)	1	1	1	1	1	1	1	1	1	1	1	1	1	0	0	0	
→ S(3)	1	1	1	1	1	1	1	1	1	1	1	0	0	1	1	0	
Physical examination — → S(4)	1	1	1	1	1	1	1	1	1	0	0	0	1	1	0	0	
→ S(5)	1	1	0	0	0	0	0	0	0	1	1	1	0	0	0	0	
S(6)	1	1	0	0	0	0	0	0	0	0	0	0	1	1	1	1	
Blood tests — S(7)	1	1	1	1	1	1	0	1	0	1	1	1	1	1	1	0	Symptom complexes
S(8)	1	1	1	1	1	1	1	0	1	1	1	0	0	0	0	1	
→ S(9)	1	1	1	1	1	0	1	0	0	1	0	1	1	0	0	1	
→ S(10)	1	1	1	1	0	1	0	0	0	0	0	0	0	1	0	0	
S(11)	1	1	1	0	0	0	0	0	1	0	0	0	1	0	0	0	
→ S(12)	1	1	1	0	1	1	0	0	1	1	0	0	0	0	0	1	
Bone-marrow tests — S(13)	1	0	1	1	0	0	0	0	0	1	1	1	0	0	0	0	
S(14)	1	1	0	0	1	1	1	0	0	0	0	0	1	1	1	1	⎭
D(1)	0	0	0	0	0	0	0	0	1	0	0	0	0	0	0	0	⎫
D(2)	0	1	0	1	0	0	0	0	0	0	0	0	0	0	1	0	
D(3)	0	0	1	0	0	1	0	0	0	0	0	1	1	0	0	0	
D(4)	0	0	0	1	1	0	0	0	0	0	0	0	0	1	0	0	Disease complexes
D(5)	0	0	0	0	1	0	0	0	0	0	0	0	0	0	0	1	
D(6)	0	0	0	0	0	1	0	0	0	1	1	1	0	0	0	0	
D(7)	1	0	0	0	0	0	1	0	0	0	1	1	0	0	0	0	
D(8)	0	0	0	0	0	0	0	1	0	0	0	0	0	0	1	0	⎭

11-5 A symptom-cause-complex table consisting of 14 symptoms and 8 causes. This constrained logical basis shows tests arranged in the order of progressive difficulty. A medical illustration is used, although the same procedure works for other systems. After each set of diagnostic tests or symptoms collected, the possible diagnoses are reviewed to determine what tests to do next. (From *Programing and Utilizing Digital Computers* by R. S. Ledley. Copyright 1962 by McGraw-Hill Book Company. Used by permission, page 341.)

indicates that $S(9)$, $S(10)$, and $S(12)$ have this desirable distribution, so they are selected. As a check for unique discrimination, we compare the three candidates, as below, in which the column of Figure 11–5 is indicated.

Test	Column
	3 4 5 6 7 8 9 14
$S(9)$	1 1 1 0 1 0 0 0
$S(10)$	1 1 0 1 0 0 0 1
$S(12)$	1 0 1 1 0 0 1 0

Note in the set of numbers above that all columns are unique, and that the columns shown represent an exhaustive list of all the 2^3 possibilities for three statements. The possibility of obtaining the test result shown in column 14 has previously been eliminated by the physical examination, so that the application of the three blood tests in this case will provide a unique differentiation between the symptom disease complexes numbered 3–9.

Continuing, suppose the laboratory report shows that the patient is positive on $S(9)$ and $S(12)$ and negative on $S(10)$; i.e., the patient has symptoms $S(9)$ and $S(12)$, but *not* $S(10)$. This result then points to the symptom-disease complex of column 5, which is a unique diagnosis. Finally, reference to the disease complex of column 5 (at the bottom of Figure 11-5) shows that the patient has *both* $D(4)$ *and* $D(5)$, but none of the other diseases. The bone marrow test is not needed.

This selection sequence shows how the investigator can use diagnostic tables of the sort shown to guide his selection of tests to isolate a complex of diseases. As a further example, it is interesting to note that if (instead of the sequence of events described above) the patient had shown *both* $S(4)$ *and* $S(5)$ upon physical examination, the investigator could immediately narrow his diagnosis to the symptom-disease complexes of columns 1 and 2 in Figure 11-5. However, here the blood tests would have been inadequate because they could not differentiate between the two possibilities. Both bone marrow tests $S(13)$ *and* $S(14)$ would have been required to come to a final and unique diagnosis.

The Use of Probability Tables in Diagnosis

By necessity or by choice, the logical diagnostic sequence described above may not come to a unique conclusion.

For example, because of cost, time, or physical restrictions, further diagnostic tests upon a system may be impossible, uneconomic, or unnecessary.

First, it is often possible to strike an economic balance between the cost of further diagnostic tests and the cost of alternate treatments. A more expensive "gross" treatment may be preferred to a continuation of further tests, say, when a module in a system can be replaced at less cost than a component within that module *plus* the cost of finding the faulty component A similar situation occurs for the physician when a more expensive "broad spectrum" pharmaceutical will treat a block of undifferentiated ailments, within which further diagnosis might isolate the particular offending cause complex, but only at further expense, time, and difficulty. Here the possibility of module or block treatment suggests that diagnosis stop when the required block of cause complexes has been isolated.

Second, either because the complete range of diagnostic tests required for logical isolation is not known, or because time and costs require it, diagnosis may again terminate *when block treatment is not possible*. In this case, some specific treatment may be required even though complete differentiation of possible cause complexes is not possible.

In the latter case, a probabilistic diagnosis is often made in an iterative procedure. A tentative diagnosis is made, based upon choice of the most probable diagnosis. A suitable treatment is used to remove the hypothesized cause complex. If the treatment proves satisfactory, the iteration stops. Should the treatment fail to remove the symptom complex exhibited by the system, that failure is used as an additional test result, the probabilities of alternate diagnostic possibilities are re-evaluated, and the cycle repeats itself until (a) the system difficulty is removed, (b) all possible treatments, or all known alternative diagnostic possibilities have been exhausted, or (c) the system "expires" or shows new diagnostic symptoms. (For example, the stress methods discussed in Chapter 10 are often used in hardware systems to produce symptoms that are more easily diagnosed.)

It is important to understand that the probabilistic evaluations made at each stage of this dynamic diagnosis-treatment iteration will *not in any way* necessarily indicate a trend toward the final diagnosis.

"For example, consider a patient with a disease for which there is a specific test: Until that test is made, the probability of the patient's having the disease might actually grow smaller and smaller with each iteration, but after the test is made, this probability will rise to unity! On the other hand, when it becomes infeasible to make additional tests, the probabilities must play an important role in the choice of treatment." [9]

It is now beneficial once again to detour slightly from our main theme and review the construction of probability tables that may be used in the diagnostic-treatment iteration.

Returning to the logical table of Figure 11-4, suppose that the patient had symptoms $S(1)$ *and* $S(2)$ in combination, so that he may have any of the three symptom-cause complexes C_1^3, C_2^3, or C_3^3. To make the probabilistic diagnosis, suppose that a historical record of case histories indicated a distribution of results shown in Figure 11-6a. This record relates the observed distribution of cases to the constrained logical basis used previously.

For probabilistic computation, it is convenient to rearrange these data into the two-way frequency table shown in Figure 11-6b, which is a standard form for such statistical displays.[10] Each entry in the body of Figure 11-6b corresponds to one of the 16 possible symptom-cause complex columns of the complete logical basis of Figure 11-3. The nonzero entries in the body of Figure 11-6b correspond to the seven symptom-cause complex

[9] Ledley, *op. cit.*, p. 342.

[10] See A. M. Mood and F. A. Graybill, *Introduction to the Theory of Statistics*, McGraw-Hill, New York, 1963, pp. 23–27, or W. J. Dixon and F. J. Massey, Jr., *Introduction to Statistical Analysis*, 2nd ed., McGraw-Hill, New York, 1957, pp. 329–333.

s^i	1	2	3	2	3	2	3	
$S(1)$	1	0	1	0	1	0	1	
$S(2)$	0	1	1	1	1	1	1	
$D(1)$	1	1	1	0	0	1	1	
$D(2)$	0	0	0	1	1	1	1	
Cases observed	600	300	300	300	300	400	200	TOTAL 2400

(a)

		Symptom complex s^i				Row total	
		0	1	2	3		
	0	0	0	0	0	0	
Cause	1	0	600	300	300	1200	
complex	2	0	0	300	300	600	
d_j	3	0	0	400	200	600	
Column Total		0	600	1000	800	2400	GRAND TOTAL

(b)

11-6 Experimental development of diagnostic probability tables. As an example, it is assumed 2400 cases have been observed from the same population. The number of cases observed for each symptom-cause complex is shown. (a) The constrained logical basis showing the number of cases observed for each symptom-cause complex. (b) An alternate display for the data of (a).

columns of the constrained logical basis of Figure 11-4. (It is from this form of historical record that the constrained logical basis may be constructed from the complete logical basis.) The row and column totals for each symptom complex and each cause complex are shown in Figure 11-6b.

To convert the observed frequencies to probabilities, we now divide all entries in Figure 11-6b by the total number of cases observed, 2400. This produces the result shown in Figure 11-7a. The resulting probabilities in the body of Figure 11-7a are the probabilities that given symptom-cause complexes, C_j^i, have been observed. The probabilities obtained from the row and column totals, often called the *marginal* probabilities, represent the probability that a given cause complex has been observed, i.e., $P(d_j)$, and that a given symptom complex has been observed, i.e., $P(s^i)$. For reference the symptom-cause complex probabilities, $P(C_j^i)$, are shown in Figure 11-7b in the form of the constrained logical basis.

Now, using either Figure 11-6b or 11-7a we can compute the *conditional probability* that a particular symptom complex will be observed in the presence of a *given* (or known) cause complex, i.e., $P(s^i|d_j)$ as shown

Symptom complex s^i

		0	1	2	3	$P(d_j)$
	0	0	0	0	0	0
Cause complex d_j	1	0	$\frac{6}{24}$	$\frac{3}{24}$	$\frac{3}{24}$	$\frac{12}{24}$
	2	0	0	$\frac{3}{24}$	$\frac{3}{24}$	$\frac{6}{24}$
	3	0	0	$\frac{4}{24}$	$\frac{2}{24}$	$\frac{6}{24}$
	$P(s^i)$	0	$\frac{6}{24}$	$\frac{10}{24}$	$\frac{8}{24}$	$\frac{24}{24}$

(a)

System-cause complex	C_1^1	C_1^2	C_1^3	C_2^2	C_2^3	C_3^2	C_3^3
$P(C_j^i)$	$\frac{6}{24}$	$\frac{3}{24}$	$\frac{3}{24}$	$\frac{3}{24}$	$\frac{3}{24}$	$\frac{4}{24}$	$\frac{2}{24}$

(b)

11-7 Computation of probabilities from observations. (a) Conversion of observations to probabilities. When all the cells in Fig. 11-6b are divided by the total number of observations (2400), (a) results. The body of this table shows the values of $P(C_j^i)$, the probability that a given symptom-cause complex will appear. $P(s^i)$, the probability of observing a given symptom-complex, and $P(d_j)$, the probability that a given cause complex will be observed, are shown in the outer row and column, respectively. (b) An alternate display of the probabilities in the body of (a) showing values of $P(C_j^i)$ associated with each column of the constrained logical basis. The same result would have been obtained from Fig. 11-6a by dividing the last row of that figure by 2400.

in Figure 11-8a, by dividing each *row* in Figure 11-6b or 11-7a by the *row total*. Similarly, we can compute the conditional probability that a particular cause complex will be observed in the presence of a *given* (or known) symptom complex, i.e., $P(d_j|s^i)$ as shown in Figure 11-8b, by dividing each *column* in Figure 11-6b or 11-7a by the column total.

As an illustration of the use of these tabulations, consider the problem of the patient with $S(1)$ *and* $S(2)$, which corresponds to the set of symptom-cause complexes defined as $C_j^{\,3}$, where the values of j range over those disease complexes associated with symptom complex s^3 in the logical basis. Column 3 of Figure 11-8b gives the values of $P(d_j|s^3)$ and from this tabulation we see that $P(d_1|s^3) = \frac{3}{8}$, $P(d_2|s^3) = \frac{3}{8}$, and $P(d_3|s^3) = \frac{2}{8}$. In this problem it is equally likely that the patient has $D(1) \cdot \overline{D(2)}$ or $\overline{D(1)} \cdot D(2)$, and less likely that he has the combination $D(1) \cdot D(2)$, corresponding to d_3. Although, from the available data, a single choice is not

Symptom complex s^i

	0	1	2	3
0	0	0	0	0
1	0	$\frac{1}{2}$	$\frac{1}{4}$	$\frac{1}{4}$
2	0	0	$\frac{1}{2}$	$\frac{1}{2}$
3	0	0	$\frac{2}{3}$	$\frac{1}{3}$
$P(s^i)$	0	$\frac{3}{12}$	$\frac{5}{12}$	$\frac{4}{12}$

Cause complex d_j

(a)

Symptom-complex s^i

	0	1	2	3	$P(d_j)$
0	0	0	0	0	0
1	0	1	$\frac{3}{10}$	$\frac{3}{8}$	$\frac{1}{2}$
2	0	0	$\frac{3}{10}$	$\frac{3}{8}$	$\frac{1}{4}$
3	0	0	$\frac{4}{10}$	$\frac{2}{8}$	$\frac{1}{4}$

Cause complex d_j

(b)

11-8 Conditional probabilities obtained from Figure 11-6 (b). (a) Values of the conditional probabilities $P(s^i \mid d_j)$. (Note that all rows of the body of this table add to 1.0.) Division of each row by its row total produces the conditional probability $P(s^i \mid d_j)$ in the body of the table. $P(s^i \mid d_j)$ is the probability that symptom complex i will be observed, given the truth of d_j. $P(s^i)$ also results from this computation, as shown. (b) Values of the conditional probabilities $P(d_j \mid s^i)$. (Note that all columns of the body of this table add to 1.0.) Division of each column by its column total produces the conditional probability $P(d_j \mid s^i)$ in the body of the table. $P(d_j \mid s^i)$ is the probability that cause complex j is present, given the observation of symptom complex i. $P(d_j)$ also results from this computation.

indicated by the probability figures, it is clear from the data that the chance of having both $D(1)$ and $D(2)$ is less likely than having a single disease.

It is worthwhile to note that the above conditional probability figures could have been obtained directly from the data of Figure 11-7a as follows:

$$P(d_3 \mid s^3) = \frac{P(C_3^3)}{P(C_1^3) + P(C_2^3) + P(C_3^3)} = \frac{\frac{2}{24}}{\frac{3}{24} + \frac{3}{24} + \frac{2}{24}} = \frac{2}{3 + 3 + 2} = \frac{2}{8}$$

and so on for the other values in column 3 of Figure 11-8(b).

Also, because the fraction $\frac{1}{24}$ is common to both the numerator and denominator of the ratio, it may be eliminated for simplicity. We are only interested in proportions. Thus,

$$P(d_1|s^3) = \frac{3}{3+3+2} = \frac{3}{8}$$

$$P(d_2|s^3) = \frac{3}{3+3+2} = \frac{3}{8}$$

$$P(d_3|s^3) = \frac{2}{3+3+2} = \frac{2}{8}$$

$$\text{Total} = \frac{8}{8} = 1.0$$

(Note that the conditional probability values obtained are *larger* than the symptom-complex probabilities C_1^3, C_2^3, and C_3^3.)

Finally, it will be useful for what follows to introduce another way to compute conditional probabilities, namely, by *Bayes' Formula*[11] which for $P(d_3|s^3)$ is

$$P(d_3|s^3) = \frac{P(d_3)P(s^3|d_3)}{\sum_k P(d_k)P(s^3|d_k)},$$

where the sum in the denominator includes all disease complexes associated with symptom complex s^3. The denominator of Bayes' Formula is a normalizing factor to make the sum of all conditional probabilities involving the d_j's (given s^3) add to 1.0. If it were only necessary to rank the d_j's in order of probability of occurrence, we could let the denominator be any convenient number. To illustrate, we will compute the denominator of Bayes' Formula for $P(d_3|s^3)$ as

$$D = P(d_1)P(s^3|d_1) + P(d_2)P(s^3|d_2) + P(d_3)P(s^3|d_3)$$
$$= (\tfrac{1}{2})(\tfrac{1}{4}) + (\tfrac{1}{4})(\tfrac{1}{2}) + (\tfrac{1}{4})(\tfrac{1}{3}) = (\tfrac{1}{3}).$$

Using this same denominator repeatedly, we find the values in column 3 of Figure 11-8b:

$$P(d_1|s^3) = \frac{P(d_1)P(s^3|d_1)}{(\tfrac{1}{3})} = \frac{(\tfrac{1}{2})(\tfrac{1}{4})}{(\tfrac{1}{3})} = \frac{3}{8}$$

$$P(d_2|s^3) = \frac{P(d_2)P(s^3|d_2)}{(\tfrac{1}{3})} = \frac{(\tfrac{1}{4})(\tfrac{1}{2})}{(\tfrac{1}{3})} = \frac{3}{8}$$

$$P(d_3|s^3) = \frac{P(d_3)P(s^3|d_3)}{(\tfrac{1}{3})} = \frac{(\tfrac{1}{4})(\tfrac{1}{3})}{(\tfrac{1}{3})} = \frac{2}{8}$$

[11] For an interesting example of Bayes' formula in computations evaluating the worth of information, see S. B. Richmond, *Statistical Analysis*, 2nd ed., Ronald Press, New York, 1964, pp. 272–278.

From these values it is clear that the rank order of the values $P(d_j|s^3)$ may be obtained simply from the numerator if there is no need to normalize. In general, all of the values in Figure 11-8(b) could have been obtained in this way, because

$$P(d_j|s^i) = \frac{P(d_j)P(s^i|d_j)}{\sum_k P(d_k)P(s^i|d_k)} .$$

In an exactly analogous way it would be possible to compute the conditional probability of finding a particular symptom complex with a given cause complex by using the Bayes' Formula

$$P(s^i|d_j) = \frac{P(s^i)P(d_j|s^i)}{\sum_k P(s^k)P(d_j|s^k)} .$$

For example, remembering that the denominator of the expression covers only the cause complexes associated with the given symptom complexes, we have *for cause complex 3*:

$$\sum_k P(s^k)P(d_3|s^k) = (\tfrac{5}{12})(\tfrac{4}{10}) + (\tfrac{4}{12})(\tfrac{2}{8}) = \tfrac{1}{4} = D.$$

so that

$$P(s^2|d_3) = \frac{(\tfrac{10}{24})(\tfrac{4}{10})}{(\tfrac{1}{4})} = \frac{2}{3}$$

$$P(s^3|d_3) = \frac{(\tfrac{8}{24})(\tfrac{2}{8})}{(\tfrac{1}{4})} = \frac{1}{3}$$

corresponding to the two values shown in *row 3* of Figure 11-8a.

(The computations just made using Bayes' Formula may be verified by inspection of Figures 11-8a and b. The formula follows directly from the construction of these tables.)

The reader may wonder why the algebraically more complicated Bayes' calculation has been introduced when easier row and column manipulations can be used to obtain Figure 11-8a and b. The answer will become evident when we consider diagnostic applications of the tables.

Suppose we could report diagnostic data in the form of Table 11-8a or b, which is of course true. Which display is more desirable?

At first we would say that Figure 11-8b is better because it gives the answer we want in a particular diagnosis, namely, the probability that the system has a given cause complex, for observation of a given symptom complex. For example, for any observed symptom complex, a column in Figure 11-8b may be selected and the resulting diagnostic probabilities are given directly.

Unfortunately, however, the conditional probability $P(d_j|s^i)$ is subject to the characteristics of the particular population used to compile the statistics. A small epidemic of causes of a particular type can greatly distort the figures for a time. Systems employed or "living" in one environment could not be expected necessarily to produce the same probabilities as those in another. In other words, the data of Figure 11-8b might well be unstable from time to time, and from place to place.

On the other hand, the table of Figure 11-8a, which gives the probability that given symptom complexes will appear *if it is known that the system has cause complex d_j*, is less likely to change with time: The symptom complexes arise from a given cause complex, not vice versa. In medical terminology, the etiology of the symptoms is related to or stems from the disease. It is for this reason that medical texts discuss $P(s^i|d_j)$ rather than $P(d_j|s^i)$.[12] The same argument holds for other trouble-shooting problems. Although we want to find $P(d_j|s^i)$, the constant relationship between symptom complex and cause complex is given by $P(s^i|d_j)$. The required conversion may be obtained from Bayes' Formula.

The numerator of the Bayes' Formula $P(d_j)P(s^i|d_j)$ contains two parts. The first term $P(d_j)$ is the probability that a given cause complex will be observed, and is a characteristic of a given population at a given time. For example, the physician may know that there is flu about at a given time in his community, and thus, he will heavily weight the possibility of flu in a list of possible diagnoses when a patient calls up complaining of lassitude, mild fever, stomach cramps, headache, diarrhea, and nasal congestion (although other cause complexes could lead to the same symptom complex). The second term, $P(s^i|d_j)$, essentially independent of the current patient population, provides the second component of the diagnosis: The structural knowledge of symptoms and causes. The combination of the two provides a probabilistic guide to current diagnosis of the particular case at hand.

Example: Suppose an investigator observes the symptom complex s^3 given by Figure 11-6a; the patient has both symptoms $S(1)$ and $S(2)$. The conditional probabilities of this symptom complex $P(s^3|d_j)$ are given in column 3 of Figure 11-8a. Also suppose that knowledge of the current population cause complexes gives values of $P(d_j)$, also shown in Figure 11-9. [These values for $P(d_j)$ differ from those shown in Figure 11-8b, because we now assume a different population, or a different time.]

Using Bayes' Formula to compute $P(d_j|s^3)$ as before and calling the normalizing denominator D, we get

---

[12] Although medical texts do not now show such probabilities quantitatively, they do verbally, and quantification poses no theoretical problem. Quantification of diagnostic probabilities for hardware systems is relatively common.

d_j	$P(s^3\|d_j)$	$P(d_j)$
d_1	$\frac{1}{4}$	$\frac{1}{4}$
d_2	$\frac{1}{2}$	$\frac{1}{2}$
d_3	$\frac{1}{3}$	$\frac{1}{4}$

11-9 Probabilities required for calculation. The values of $P(s^3 \mid d_j)$ are taken from Figure 11-8a, column 3, and represent the constant relationship between symptoms and given causes. On the other hand, the values of $P(d_j)$ are obtained from current observation of the population and will vary with time and place.

$$P(d_1|s^3) = \frac{(\frac{1}{4})(\frac{1}{4})}{D} = \frac{1}{16D}$$

$$P(d_2|s^3) = \frac{(\frac{1}{2})(\frac{1}{2})}{D} = \frac{1}{4D}$$

$$P(d_3|s^3) = \frac{(\frac{1}{4})(\frac{1}{3})}{D} = \frac{1}{12D}$$

which, by observation, gives a rank order for diagnosis. Or, computing the denominator D as before, we have

$$P(d_1|s^3) = \tfrac{3}{19}$$

$$P(d_2|s^3) = \tfrac{12}{19}$$

$$P(d_3|s^3) = \tfrac{4}{19}$$

which gives the probabilities which must add to 1.0. This result indicates that the cause complex d_2 is considerably more likely than the other possibilities, a conclusion derived from both current knowledge of cause-complex probability and knowledge of the constant relationship between symptom and cause complexes.

A further look at Bayes' Formula is instructive. The numerator, which represents the information we want for ranking cause complexes, consists of the two terms $P(d_j)$ and $P(s^i|d_j)$. The data used to obtain these numbers must be collected, and it is important to note that the population from which the collection is made in the two cases is different.

First, in developing a set of probability values classified as symptom complexes for a *given* cause complex, as shown in Figure 11-8a for $P(s^i|d_j)$, it is desirable to have data on as many cases as possible so that symptom complexes that are rarely associated with a given cause complex will show up in the experimental data, and therefore in the diagnostic table. In short, to develop tables for $P(s^i|d_j)$ we *pool* all our experience. The greater this experience and the wider the diversity of conditions of observation, the more faith we are likely to have in the constrained basis or conditional probability table that results. This is the reason, for example, that vast collections of symptom-cause complexes have been assembled in specialized medical fields, such as rare blood diseases, and have been subjected to mechanized treatment.

Just the opposite view must be taken in the development of the values $P(d_j)$, the probabilities that a given disease complex will be found in a *particular* population at a *particular* time. The usefulness of $P(d_j)$ in Bayes' Formula resides in its specificity to the patient at hand. For this reason, the data collected to develop $P(d_j)$ for a given case should be both reasonably current and restricted to appropriate "patient classification criterion," because vastly different results may be obtained depending upon the data going into the $P(d_j)$ values.

Although in some cases careful judgment is required to select the appropriate "patient classification" for a given purpose (should the patient be classified by his place of residence, his occupation, his age, some facet of his medical history, or some combination of these possibilities?), in many situations the required classification is relatively obvious—to the sensitive observer. Nevertheless, the problem of classification[13] required to obtain appropriate values of $P(d_j)$ raises a question about the values of $P(d_j)$ to be used in a given case, and about the importance of $P(d_j)$ as opposed to $P(s^i|d_j)$ in a given case. For example, in a difficult diagnosis under probabilistic choice, does the skill of the investigator reside in his ability to recall vast tables of conditional probabilities for $P(s^i|d_j)$, or does it reside in his skill at careful patient classification, so that appropriate values of $P(d_j)$ may be used?

To take an extreme example, suppose that in a given subclass of the population patients have a very high relative incidence (and therefore a high probability) of disease complex d_2 of Figure 11-8(a), although in the general population the probability distribution is skewed toward d_1. Then, because the values of $P(s^3|d_j)$ of Figure 11-8(a) do not clearly differentiate between the three possible disease complexes, use of the correct subpopulation and its corresponding values of $P(d_j)$ becomes critical.

Conversely, should the distribution of the disease complexes to be differentiated be uniformly distributed (equally likely) in the general population and its subgroups, to take another extreme case, the differentiation is left to the conditional probability table of $P(s^i|d_j)$. Finally, if both $P(d_j)$ and $P(s^i|d_j)$ are uniformly distributed for the symptoms observed to date, then nothing is left but to look for additional discriminating symptoms, as

---

[13] The careful reader will realize that $P(d_j)$ is itself a conditional probability, i.e., one to be determined only after specification of a given patient classification. Thus, if c_k is one of k possible patient classifications, and a patient belongs to class c_k, then the appropriate formal notation is $P(d_j|c_k)$. For simplicity, hereafter we assume this meaning is clear when we speak of $P(d_j)$.

was done in Figure 11-5, and continue the iteration until some narrowing can be accomplished, or until a gross treatment can be found to cover the undifferentiated diagnostic possibilities.

Thus, both skills, symptom collection and system classification, are important to the investigator, the more important in a given case depending upon the statistical distributions of $P(d_j)$ and $P(s^i|d_j)$ that must be used for differentiation. It is, however, important to note that the distribution of $P(d_j)$ is seldom uniform in a general population of systems, nor identical for its subgroups, nor unchanging with time, so that the stock in trade of the professional diagnostician is a quick ability to classify systems by age, conditions of use, and similar characteristics of current importance. Then an extensive knowledge of constant symptom-cause relationships may be exploited most rapidly.

There is a statistical argument and foundation for the diagnostic "guessing" ability mentioned at the start of this chapter. With a shrewd guess of a few highly likely cause complexes obtained by patient classification, it is possible, either by reference to the constrained logical basis, to tables of $P(s^i|d_j)$ such as Figure 11-8a, or even to verbal listings or personal memory, to select discriminatory tests to confirm the initial hypotheses. Although this procedure may fail in a small percentage of cases, calling for more formal analysis, in the main it will not, and net savings in time and effort will result from repeated use of this strategy.

SUMMARY COMMENTS

In this chapter we have discussed the organization and use of logical and probabilistic tables for diagnosis. We emphasized that the diagnostic procedure is often an iteration in which symptom collection, tentative diagnosis, and treatment follow in a circular pattern which does not necessarily terminate in one cycle.

Although the presentation is highly simplified and reduced to apparently trivial examples, the logical and probabilistic manipulations indicated may easily be extended to more extensive arrays of symptoms and causes, and to more sophisticated forms of manipulation. For example, we can deal with matrices of logical statements, still using the designation number approach.[14] The arguments are essentially unchanged.

Our intent was also to stress the importance of orderly organization of quantitative diagnostic data, which is required for use of the techniques described. In many cases in which such data would be of great value, such as equipment maintenance by field mechanics, maintenance records and quantitative diagnostic data are not available or are so poorly organized as to be useless. Certainly, effective training of maintenance men will require

---

[14] See R. S. Ledley, *op. cit.*, pp. 474–487.

more attention to this deficiency as the systems used by industrial organizations increase in complexity, number, and variety of use. And, the advent of the electronic computer, which greatly facilitates the manipulations suggested, stresses the same point. Although "automatic diagnosis" of systems problems using the storage, retrieval, and testing capacity of the computer is a practical possibility in a large number of cases, this capacity is relatively useless when the organized data required are missing.

Finally, from what we have said it would also be clear that the relevance of the conclusions drawn from a logical or probabilistic diagnosis rests largely upon the accuracy with which symptoms are collected and tests are made. Although to some extent an iterative diagnostic-treatment procedure is self-correcting, because incorrect diagnoses will become evident in the long run, a lengthy sequence of critical tests may be worthless if even one of the symptoms collected is erroneous, or if a single test is positive when it should have been negative. The usual remedies for test malfunction, duplication or the application of redundant tests for check purposes, may alleviate this concern, but this is but another way of saying that inaccurate input data are expensive. There may be some economic or other justification in performing four inexpensive and less reliable redundant tests instead of one expensive sure one. In the end, however, contradictions must be resolved and the input must be correct before a correct conclusion can be drawn.

PROBLEMS

11.1   Consider again the elevator problem of Chapter 2 (Project 2), and suppose the elevator has just come to a stop at the bottom floor and opened its doors. The following statements pertain to the closing of the elevator doors and the ascension of the machine:

> A. Dispatcher starts manually
> B. Weight greater than 1000 pounds
> C. Time greater than t_A (the time set for the lower floor)
> D. Door-open button depressed
> E. At least one call registered
> F. Doors closed
> G. Safety signal on (e.g., hand in door, etc.)

If we follow the rules for the elevator door closing and start the routine specified in Project 2, we can draw a partial flow diagram of the sequence of events as shown below. Similarly, the conditions for door close and elevator start may be written in the logical form

$$[A + B + (C \cdot E)] \cdot (\overline{D} \cdot F \cdot G)$$

By comparison of the logical form and the flow diagram shown, explain the relationship of the logical "OR" statement and the logical "AND" statement to the jumps and sequences of tests in the flow diagram.

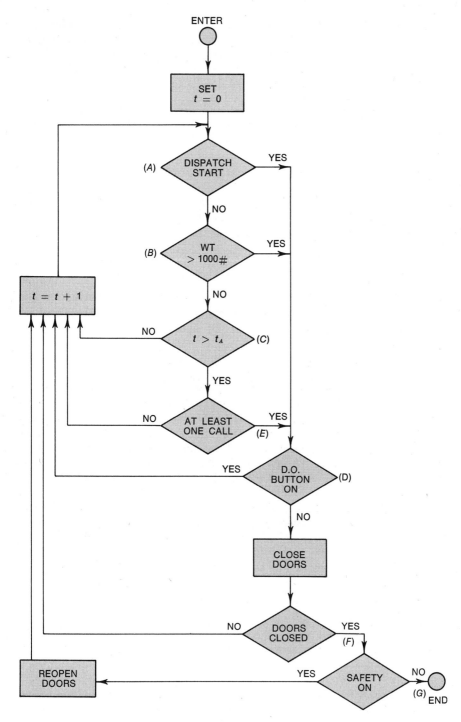

Prob. 11.1

11.2 A corporate spy is attempting to discover what product a firm will manufacture this summer. He knows that it will be either a boat, a lawnmower, or lawn furniture, some combination of these three, or none of them. He also knows that the following materials may (or may not) be used—wood, chrome, fiberglass, and brass—and decides to base his analysis on information gathered about these material inputs. Further he knows the following facts:

1. Wood is definitely used in boats, but not in lawnmowers.
2. Fiberglass will be used in mower frames, and maybe in boats and furniture.
3. Brass is not used in lawn furniture, nor in mowers.
4. Chrome is used on boats, maybe on mowers, but not on furniture.
5. If any of the four materials is purchased, at least one of the products in the above list will be made; however, if none of the materials is purchased, none of the products will be made.

A. Through diligent effort and sneaky observation, the spy finds that the competitor has ordered wood and brass, but not chrome. He cannot however, obtain any specific information about fiberglass at the moment. What specifically can be said about the three products at this stage?

B. For a slight additional expense, the spy suggests that he could find out about the fiberglass order. Would this additional expense pay?

11.3 Richard E. Roxe of the Arizona Safety Council reports this case of an automobile fatality, believed due to an emotional upset. A man whose wife had left him, who had just been fired from his job, who already had serious financial problems, and who had just spent two hours in a bar drove off the road on a curve and was killed. (*Phoenix Gazette*, Arizona Days and Ways Magazine Section, Sunday February 13, 1966, p. 9.) With these facts in mind, to what would you attribute the victim's death?

The verdict of the investigator at the time was suicide. But he was wrong. Further research established these additional facts: The dead man's wife had agreed to return home that afternoon, his boss had fired him after learning he had a new and much better paying job, and he had drunk only two bottles of beer, having promised his wife he would never drink more than one bottle of beer per hour. What would these additional facts lead you to believe, or look for?

The real cause of this accident was a ball-joint front suspension. It had become detached.

A. Comment on this story in light of the probabilistic diagnostic procedures described in this chapter.

B. To what extent does the correct collection of the symptoms of a given case affect the probabilistic or logical diagnosis that may be made regarding it?

11.4 Suppose a test is not certain, but can give a positive result when a cause is not present. This form of problem is prevalent in most tests for specific causes and in many search problems. For example, in X-ray tests for tuberculosis or in industrial tests for faults in parts there is always the chance of obtaining a false positive or a false negative indication from a given procedure. When the incidence of faults is very small, this test "unreliability" can be a serious problem, as indicated in the following example.

Suppose an X-ray procedure is used to detect faults in industrial castings, such as small air pockets, cracks, and fissures. Let T be the fact that a fault is present and $\overline{T}$ be the fact that a fault is not present. Similarly let $(+)$ stand for a positive test indication and $(-)$ stand for a negative test indication. Then the four possible test-fault combinations are given by the table below; here the probability of each specific outcome which becomes a *joint probability* of obtaining *together* a specific test outcome and a specific fault result is shown in symbolic form.

	$-$	$+$	
$\overline{T}$	$P(-\overline{T})$	$P(+\overline{T})$	$P(\overline{T})$
T	$P(-T)$	$P(+T)$	$P(T)$
	$P(-)$	$P(+)$	

Now let $P(+\mid\overline{T})$ = the probability of a $(+)$ X-ray with no fault $= 0.02$
$P(+\mid T)$ = the probability of a $(+)$ X-ray if fault is present $= 0.99$
$P(T)$ = the probability that a casting selected at random will have a fault $= 0.01$.

A. Using the following conditional probability formulas

$$P(+\mid\overline{T}) = \frac{P(+\overline{T})}{P(\overline{T})} \quad \text{and} \quad P(+\mid T) = \frac{P(+T)}{P(T)}$$

find the joint probabilities given in the 2×2 table above.

B. By summing across the rows in the above table, find the probability that a randomly selected casting will or will not have a fault.

C. By summing down the columns in the above table, find the probability that a test when administered to a part selected at random will be $(-)$ or $(+)$.

D. Show that the probability of a positive test result will be associated with the actual presence of a fault, namely $P(T \mid +)$, is given by $0.0099/0.0297 = 99/297 = 1/3$. What is the practical implication of this result? How could this result be improved by a change in the testing procedure?

E. What is the probability of obtaining a positive test result when the part is actually good? (This is the Type I Error of rejecting good parts.)

F. What is the probability of getting a negative test when the part is actually bad? (This is the Type II Error of accepting bad parts.) If the test is critical, why should this number be very small?

G. Is the X-ray procedure for testing castings for faults, as described above, a good screening method?

H. Can you suggest a second testing procedure that could follow the initial test to isolate the truly faulty parts?

11.5 The serial numbers of a set of malfunctioning electronic equipment of the same type, but of two different years of manufacture, 1960 and 1965, have been lost. The equipment is known to have only two distinct modes of failure, F_1 and F_2. Either fault will cause failure of a unit. In the 1960 equipment, F_1 is twice as common as F_2, whereas in the 1965 equipment F_2 is twice as common as F_1. It is further known that of the total set of devices on hand $\frac{3}{4}$ were made in 1960. A single unit is selected and examined for mode F_1 failure. If F_1 is present for this unit, what is the probability that it was made in 1960? Solution requires application of Bayes' Formula. [For further examples of this type, see J. G. Kemeny, J. L. Snell, and G. L. Thompson, *Introduction to Finite Mathematics*, Prentice-Hall, Englewood Cliffs, N.J., 1957, pp. 133–139.]

PROJECT 7

One clause of a standard airline contract (regarding damage) follows.

"(4) Subject to the foregoing: (a) liability of carrier for damages shall be limited to occurrences on its own line, except in case of checked baggage as to which the passenger also has a right of action against the first or the last carrier. A carrier issuing a ticket or checking baggage for carriage over the lines of others does so only as agent. (b) Carrier is not liable for damage to passenger or unchecked baggage unless such damage is caused by the negligence of carrier."

Six logical variables are under consideration, and will be designated by the letters A through F, as follows:

A = damages were in fact caused
B = baggage was involved
C = baggage was checked
D = passengers were involved
E = event occurred on own line of carrier (issuing ticket)
F = there was negligence on the part of the carrier

Using the designation number approach described in the text, create the complete logical basis of 2^6 columns. Then, create the constrained logical basis by crossing off all the columns that are excluded by the terms of the contract.

A. Show that the issuing carrier's liability for damage (i.e., T is true) is

$$T = ABC + ADEF + ABEF = ABC + A(B + D)EF$$

which is to say, that the carrier is liable only if there is damage to checked baggage, or if there is damage to baggage or passenger, which occurred on its own line and is due to negligence of the carrier.

B. Show that the airline's statement of nonliability (in Boolean form) is given by

$$\overline{T} = \overline{A} + AB\overline{CE} + A\overline{B}(\overline{E} + \overline{F}) + A\overline{C}E\overline{F} + A\overline{B}\overline{D}$$

which is to say, the carrier is not liable if there is no damage, or if there is damage to unchecked baggage when not on its own line or without negligence of the carrier, or if there is damage to unchecked baggage which occurred on its own line but without negligence of the carrier, or if there is no damage to passenger and baggage.

C. Is the airline liable for damage of passenger and/or baggage if such damage occurs on its own lines?

D. If there were more than six logical variables, how could you construct the constrained basis without going through the construction of the complete logical basis? For example, how many columns would be eliminated by throwing out all cases for which there was no damage at all?

E. When there are six logical variables or less, the method of "Karnaugh Maps" can be used to simplified logical expressions, check on their consistency, and assure their completeness. (This method has not been described in this book.) Study the reference by B. Beizer and S. W. Leibholz, *Engineering Applications of Boolean Algebra*, cited in full in the bibliography (or any other good reference on Boolean Algebra or switching theory) and apply this technique to analysis of the contract problem above.

12 | SYSTEM SIMULATION

Perhaps no technique of systems analysis has been so grossly misunderstood by the inexperienced investigator as the experimental activity popularly called "system simulation."

REALISTIC SIMULATION

To simulate, according to Webster, is to assume the appearance without the reality. In the same vein, a list of English synonyms for simulate includes feign, deceive, affect, fake, pretend, play, falsify, fabricate, and make believe. However, this is not what we mean when we speak of system simulation.

The systems analyst seeks to construct a model or definition of a system that *is* realistic, and thus one that corresponds to reality in at least a few relevant particulars. We discussed such definition forms in Chapters 1–8. However, if we are to use the system definition for experimental tests we must pay attention to the creation of a model that may be varied and manipulated with ease, particularly if the simulated system is complex. Manipulation of the model, or system definition, gives system simulation its power for the analyst. It is also essential that the system definition used, the manipulations employed, and the conclusions drawn from the manipulalations be realistic, not idealistic. Skeet shooting is not duck hunting, but there is much to be learned from this simulated situation, because there are essential similarities.

Advantages of Simulation

The advantages of "simulating" a system can be easily summarized. The analyst controls many features of the system that he would not usually control in practice, and can therefore relate known manipulations to known results. In addition, he controls the time and cost scales. Many repeated incidents that would take years to experience in reality can be simulated in minutes or seconds. The cost of obtaining such simulated experience is usually much less, and frequently much safer than experimentation with the real object. Thus, training pilots in Link Trainers and even highly sophisticated and expensive jet airliner cockpit mockups that include vibration, noise, and view, is far less expensive and much safer than similar training with real equipment. Similar benefits can also occur with changes in other scales, such as size. With reduced or expanded size, the system can be brought to a human scale, where it can be analyzed more easily.

Simulation also permits the experimental testing of hypothetical conditions that do not exist as yet, so that projections concerning the operation of new equipment, or present equipment under extreme conditions can be made. For example, the System Training Program for radar operators in Europe enables allied military personnel to train against simulated attacking aircraft attempting to penetrate their defense from behind the Iron Curtain. Clearly allied training flights cannot penetrate Free Europe from this direction.[1]

These advantages are so compelling, that a wide variety of simulations, and simulation media have been used.

To illustrate the range of possibilities, we discuss four approaches, which, of course, may be used in various combinations.

Manual Simulation

The ancient "map game" is an example of manual simulation. Played by teams of military officers using a map and movable pieces representing opposing troops, this chess-like exercise has often been used for training in strategy, for testing proposed tactics, or for appraising topological and logistic constraints imposed by the terrain. Following the advice of Machiavelli that the Prince should train himself, as he rode through his kingdom, to

---

[1] "Simulation," Technology Series, Corporate Communication BRT-12, System Development Corporation, Santa Monica, Calif. 1965. The outline of simulation types discussed above follows that suggested in this publication.

imagine the enemy on a hill or in a valley, and consider the advantage or disadvantage his own position gave him, military officers have for centuries engaged in this pastime. The formal trappings—the map to define the characteristics of the combat area, the pieces or markers to define the position and number of troops, and specified rules of capture and movement—bring the game inside, permit changes of scale, and provide the mechanics for keeping score. Such are the elements of a manual simulation.

Similarly much can be learned from manipulating scale models of transportation systems, factory layouts, paperwork systems, and sample product designs. For these purposes, the manual simulation has the advantage of simplicity: It is easily comprehended by the relatively uninitiated, it is inexpensive and relatively easy to create, its setup and preparation time is short, and it does not require exotic equipment.

We may also include in this category small-scale simulations in which mathematical computations are used. For example, it is not uncommon for one or two trials of a complex system to be simulated by hand. By working through all the logical and computational requirements for a few selected tests cases, check points can be provided for more extensive mechanized simulations. If only a few system conditions need be evaluated, the manual approach may be more appropriate than any form of mechanized simulation.

Electrical and Mechanical (Analog) Simulation

During World War II, it became evident that many equipment design and computational problems could be handled by using physical analogs of systems. A physical system, which had the same mathematical properties as the system to be evaluated, but which the investigator could manipulate more easily, was constructed. Thus, electrical analogs of mechanical equipment could often be constructed, and investigated for electrical vibrations more easily than the original mechanical system could be investigated for mechanical vibrations. Other forms of investigations may also be conducted using measurements made on the analog, or simulated system, if the transformations made between the simulated system and the original system are known.

Example: A simple example of a physical system that may be constructed in various forms is the accelerometer, the device used to measure acceleration, the rate of change of speed. Because the devices shown in Figure 12-1a, b, and c, are mathematically equivalent, one can simulate the other, the choice being a matter of convenience.

Figure 12-1a shows an accelerometer consisting of mechanical components: a weight, or mass m, and a spring with constant k. (The larger k, the "stiffer" the spring.) If the frame to which the assembly of mass and spring is attached is accelerated to the right, the mass will be

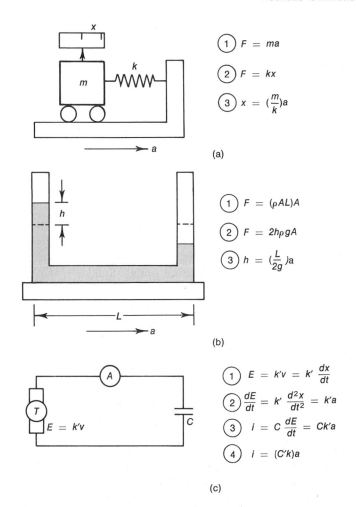

① $F = ma$

② $F = kx$

③ $x = (\frac{m}{k})a$

(a)

① $F = (\rho AL)A$

② $F = 2h\rho gA$

③ $h = (\frac{L}{2g})a$

(b)

① $E = k'v = k'\frac{dx}{dt}$

② $\frac{dE}{dt} = k'\frac{d^2x}{dt^2} = k'a$

③ $i = C\frac{dE}{dt} = Ck'a$

④ $i = (C'k)a$

(c)

12-1 Analogous forms of accelerometers or devices to measure acceleration. (a) A mechanical accelerometer; (b) a hydraulic accelerometer; (c) an electrical accelerometer. The equations describing these devices are explained in the text. (For additional examples, see D. W. Ver Planck and B. R. Teare, *Engineering Analysis,* Wiley, New York, 1958, an introduction to problem formulation in equipment design.)

displaced a distance x to the left, relative to the frame, stretching the spring. The amount of this displacement is determined by the opposing forces set up by the acceleration. A knowledge of physics tells us that the mass will exert a force (tending to stretch the spring) $F = ma$, where the units of F, m, and a are consistent. (For simplicity, we will eliminate the units here, because they provide only a scale factor.) Conversely, the spring resists stretching with a force $F = kx$. Because these two opposing forces must be equal, $ma = kx$, and the displacement is $x = (m/k)a$. In other words, the accelerometer may be made more sensitive by increasing the size of m, or decreasing the stiffness of the spring and therefore its constant k.

In Figure 12-1b a glass tube of cross-sectional area A is filled with a liquid of density ρ. At rest, this liquid will reach the same height in each leg of the "U-shaped" bent tube. However, if the assembly is accelerated to the right, the liquid will rise in the trailing leg and fall in the leading leg. The displacement h of the liquid from its "at rest" position may again be found by analysis of opposing forces. First, the force caused by the acceleration will be that acting upon the liquid in the horizontal member, labeled L in the drawing to indicate its length. This force is again determined by the mass of liquid in this member, namely ρAL, and the acceleration, so that $F = (\rho AL)a$, where ρ is the density of the liquid, A is the cross-sectional area of the tube, and a is the acceleration (all terms are expressed in consistent units). Similarly, the force due to the unequal height of the liquid in the vertical legs is $F = 2h\rho gA$, where g represents the acceleration due to gravity, which tends to pull the liquid to the "at rest" position. The two forces must be equal. When the equations are set equal to each other and solved for h, we find $h = (L/2g)a$, assuming a uniform area A, for the entire tube length. In this result the length L of the lower tube is analogous to the mass m in the first example. In addition, the acceleration due to gravity is analogous to the spring constant k in the first example. To make a more sensitive accelerometer in this case, we could increase L. Because g is a physical constant at a given location, not much can be gained from its change. [The reader may also note that if the cross-sectional areas of the vertical and horizontal legs of the U-tube were unequal, the sensitivity of the device could be increased by having a larger area A_1 in the horizontal member than in the vertical members, A_2. Here, $h = (A_1L/2gA_2)a$.]

Finally, it is also possible to construct an electrical accelerometer, Figure 12-1c. Suppose we had a tachometer T, i.e., a small generator that when turned by a wheel would produce a voltage E proportional to the velocity of rotation,[2] ($E = k'v$). Then, if we use calculus,[3] the rate of change in velocity, or acceleration, would give ($dE/dt = k'(d^2E/dt^2)$) $= k'a$. Also suppose we have a capacitor or condenser C. The current i

---

[2] If the wheel turning the tachometer rests on the ground and rotates as the vehicle containing the accelerometer is advanced, linear velocity and acceleration are related to angular velocity and acceleration by the diameter of the wheel.

[3] Although calculus is not necessary here, we introduce it to conform with the usual presentation. For the reader who is unfamiliar with calculus, the term $dE/dt = k'a$ may be taken by definition to mean that the time rate of change of voltage will be proportional to the acceleration. The remaining expressions follow naturally from this understanding.

that will flow through a capacitor is proportional to the time rate of change of voltage, in particular, $i = C(dE/dt)$. By substitution, we then have $i = (Ck')a$. The ammeter A that measures the current i may thus be calibrated in units of acceleration a. To increase the sensitivity of the electrical accelerometer we may either increase C, or increase the proportionality constant k' in $E = k'v$ by an alternate choice of tachometers. Note also that we have our choice of analogies between the electrical accelerometer and the previous examples. For example, we may choose to relate the capacitor C to the mass m in the mechanical example. In this case, the stiffening of the mechanical spring (larger k) would correspond to smaller proportionality k' in the tachometer. Conversely, we may relate the capacitor to the spring of the mechanical example. Then, the increases of the mass m in the mechanical example would correspond to an increase in the proportionality factor k' in the electrical device. The mathematical relationship is not affected by what we choose to relate for experimentation. So long as the equations describing two systems are identical, the systems are analogous; we may then choose any convenient component analogy within that framework.

By combining analogous components, we can construct many analogous systems. For example, we can use electrical amplifiers as an analog for mechanical gear trains that multiply angular rotation. We can also introduce simple logical elements in the construction of analogous systems: A discrete mechanical device, such as a lever that selects a given motion, is analogous to an electrical switch. The possibilities are endless, and in the past twenty years great ingenuity has been used in the construction of analogous components and systems to ease systems analysis. For many purposes, however, electrical analogies have been preferred because of their ease of construction and manipulation and their low cost.[4]

Analog simulations also allow *simultaneous* measurement of system values in many points in the system, which may be a distinct advantage or requirement in hardware system design. Physical simulations, however, are limited in their precision by the physical precision of their mechanical, electrical, or other components. Usually, precision to two or three significant figures, which may or may not be satisfactory for a given application, results. (Digital computers, as we shall see, avoid this precision limitation.)

---

[4] This is the basis for the analog computer, which is a general purpose simulator consisting of electrical components that may be hooked up in various ways to simulate a particular system. Such equipment can also be used to solve mathematical problems. The first differential analyzer, constructed by Dr. V. Bush during World War II, was an analog device made from mechanical gears, wheels, clutches, and friction discs. These components performed the mechanical equivalent of mathematical differentiation, integration, and similar operations. The modern electrical computer does the same thing, but it uses electrical components.

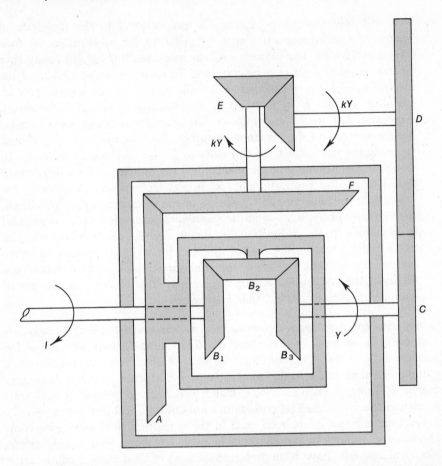

12-2 A mechanical analogy of Lord Keynes' theory of capital movement, following Figure 3-3: The shaded box contains a mechanical differential (similar to that in the rear end of an automobile to permit the rear wheels to turn at different speeds going around curves). The differential acts as a mechanical summing point, or adder. The internal box, containing the gears B is rigidly attached to the gear A and is free to rotate. Shafts I and Y are independent of the box B, and are coupled only through the idler gear B_2. Clockwise rotation of shaft I causes counter-clockwise rotation of shaft Y, which is coupled through the reducing gears C and D to produce a rotation via gears E of gear F which is a fraction of Y's rotation. The arrangement of gear F transmits the rotation kY to gear A, which *adds* this increment to the rotation of shaft Y through movement of the differential box B. The net result of this action is that rotation of shaft I by I revolutions causes a rotation of shaft Y by $Y = I/(1 - k)$ revolutions. For example, if $k = 0.5$, $Y = 2I$. Comparison with Figure 3.3 or analysis of the above figure will reveal that this device represents a true mechanical analogy of the mathematical expression $Y = I/(1 - k)$, the Keynes formula relating income Y with investment I. The fraction k is the fraction of income devoted to consumption. In this mechanical system there is obviously no lag between realization of income, consumption, and production.

Symbolic Simulation

When a system definition can be reduced to a mathematical formula, the system can be simulated by an analog or by a digital computer. However, systems defined by a complex series of logical statements are best handled by a digital machine. The digital computer also permits extensive files of subroutines and, it allows databanks to be introduced into the simulation of systems. Finally, because numbers rather than physical quantities are manipulated, the precision available with simulation on the digital computer is not limited by the physical precision of components used in the computer's construction.

The digital computer can usually perform all the tasks of the analog computer; it also permits greater flexibility in system simulation. Therefore, although it is more expensive than the analog computer (which is used most often in engineering and design work), the digital computer is the first choice for the highly conditional business systems that require a combination of great logical flexibility and precision. Indeed, science and engineering may require precisely these abilities. The wind tunnel, an analog device, is still used, but today it is commonplace to "fly" a new aircraft or missile design on a digital computer, often to save time and money in the construction of physical models and to test behavior that cannot be evaluated in a wind tunnel or similar physical simulator, e.g., satellite re-entry.

By using the digital computer, some earlier forms of manual simulation, such as war gaming, having been greatly expanded in complexity and realism. For example, we can construct war games that include international rather than local complications.

Moreover, we can combine analog and digital simulation advantages by selected use of analog devices and digital capability. Thus, the flight simulator cockpit presents the trainee with a number of analog input and output devices, and analog computer devices can control simulated operating conditions. But digital capability expands the situation to include certain "flight conditions" external to the man-machine interface, such as weather conditions and flight instructions.

The digital computer works with symbols, and the logical requirements of symbolic simulation are substantially greater than those of earlier forms of simulation. Every system relationship and inter-relationship must be precisely spelled out. Special techniques have been developed to simulate physical situations that are foreign to everyday experience. Because the digital computer essentially works sequentially, making one computation or one decision at a time, extensive control routines are required. However, these disadvantages cannot often withstand the overwhelming advantages of flexibility, speed, and precision offered by digital equipment. Therefore, we will devote the latter portion of this chapter to some of the details of this form of system simulation.

Operational Simulation

Operational simulation, so-called to distinguish it from the forms previously discussed, is another variant of simulation.

Factors that are irreducible to quantitative terms or logical statements play an important part in many systems. Only if qualitative factors are deliberately included in such systems is the completeness of the simulation assured. An algorithmic simulation may fail because of the exclusion of highly variable human intervention factors, or other political or social factors. A given simulation problem must be met by applying the appropriate simulation discipline.

We accomplish this by using simulation within operating environments, in which human participants use their judgment and other human abilities to interact with the simulated system. The simulated system, when provided with any necessary "embedding conditions," such as input data, environmental simulation, and sensory stimuli, evaluates the responses of the experimental subjects and feeds back this information. In its most obvious form, this is the classic Link Trainer. However, the same idea may be extended to very large systems. For example, a group of planners may be supplied with industrial input-output data describing a country's economy. The planners may be told that a bomb has been dropped on a given location and they may be given specific damage reports on the industry in that city, together with nation-wide projections of the local disaster by economic structure tables. The planners may then be asked to develop emergency orders for the diversion of shipments from the peace-time pattern so that essential industries can be maintained. The simulated "economy" then evaluates these plans and feeds back the new status to the planners. A series of these cycles not only permits a greater understanding of the inter-relationships in the economy, but also aids in the development and evaluation of emergency plans.

Similarly, large-scale communications systems, such as air traffic control and early warning defense systems, that involve human operators as well as extensive hardware offer another opportunity for operational simulation. Both operator reliability and skill and equipment effectiveness are tested by this means.

Although an electronic computer is not always necessary, the more comprehensive forms of operational simulation would be impossible without the aid of a digital computer. For example, an evaluation of the SAGE system for early warning using simulation, as would be the case with any major command and control system, involves staggering amounts of data and computation. In simulated tests of the SAGE system, 26 computers were used, any one of which could have processed—(in just 24 hours)—all annual income tax returns filed in the United States. Without these powerful central processors, operations simulation could not have been used in SAGE; however, lesser forms of simulation could not have met the critical training and evaluation problems of this system.[5]

Standard Computer Programs and Operations Research Models as Simulators

Thus the present state of the art usually associates large-scale system simulations with an analog computer, or, even more frequently, with a digital computer. The digital computer has another advantage over the analog computer in the exploitation of the stored program and stored data.

Unlike the analog computer, which must be set up for each different simulation project, the digital computer is set up by the construction or selection of a program of instructions, which may then be stored permanently for later use. In this way a large range of available programs for simulating different systems may be collected, just as computer programs are collected for solving repetitive problems. The same argument holds for the data accumulated for a simulation experiment. These data are not lost, and are easily recorded and stored for later use.

For this reason it is often possible to modify or piece together a new simulation "program" from blocks or segments of old computer programs, by using these formerly constructed blocks as subroutines. This is not only beneficial strategy to the analyst, but also useful in creating an accumulated knowledge of simulation technology.

Moreover, the stored program concept calls to our attention the fact that presently available library programs, as they stand, may be used as simulators in many cases. In addition to many "general purpose" simulators that by parameter specification can simulate specific systems (such as inventory control installations, job shops, critical path networks, and the like), standard computer algorithms, or programs, can also be used.

Thus, a standard program for solving linear programing problems is, in effect, a ready-made simulator for testing hypothetical conditions or variants in current practice. Such programs are widely used for this purpose, although often their users do not speak of system simulation when conducting such experiments, but rather use more specific descriptions, such as "parametric programing," to indicate the more specialized application of their work.

SOME CONSTRAINTS ON SIMULATION AND ITS USE

Because of the glamor and the potential of large-scale simulation studies using the digital computer, many investigators have fallen into severe pitfalls by indiscriminate use of this approach.

Simulation is a means to an end, not an end in itself. The purpose of

[5] Example quoted in "Simulation," Systems Development Corporation, *loc. cit.* p. 6.

constructing a simulation experiment is to solve a specific problem, to investigate the characteristics of a specific system, to train operators in a given skill, or to evaluate given alternatives. In some cases, a simulation may be useful in exploratory investigations, or in a few cases the construction of a simulation "to see if it can be done" is an end in itself for educational purposes. But, by and large, to embark upon a large-scale system simulation without clear objectives in mind is to invite disaster.

First, there may be many easier ways to solve a particular problem than by simulation. The solution of an equation may be all that is required for a specific problem. Often a simple manual simulation will suffice.

Second, in absolute terms, digital simulation of a complex system is expensive. Although such a simulation may repay its own cost many times over, it is expensive to design, to develop, and to maintain. Not only must the system be defined in great detail, but vast amounts of specifications and environmental data must be collected and organized. Often extensive computer programs must be written and debugged. Testing and perfecting the simulation programs may use much computer time before the programs are ever used to obtain experimental results. In operational simulation many expensive input/output devices, which frequently require special design and construction, are often needed. Consequently, if the economic usefulness of the results is not kept in mind, and if the technical elegance of the simulation is ineffectively controlled, cost can quickly become prohibitive. Similar remarks can be made about elapsed time. Although the computer may have great speed in carrying out a given simulation, a substantial amount of time usually elapses before such a "production run" can be made. There are often quicker ways to get the job done.

The complexity of many large-scale simulations can also obscure the essential ingredients that validate the simulation, i.e., those that cause it to conform to reality and permit useful predictions to be made. We must determine the critical features to be represented and make clear the rationale for selection of these features. This key to success can be muddled if the investigator attempts to include too much undifferentiated detail in the simulation, and he will always have the urge to do just that in the belief that the computer can handle the detail easily. Although the computer can usually process the detail, often the investigator cannot, with the result that he produces a system simulation he cannot understand. Weird and uncreditable results emerge that the investigator cannot explain because of the innumerable internal interactions he has left to the machine.

Another pitfall is forcing a simulation when it is not justified or possible for the system at hand. For example, many symbolic simulations have been constructed by eliminating all qualitative factors and concentrating only on system factors that can be expressed in quantitative terms for the computer. This is also true in many mathematical studies in operations research and management science, but the urge to eliminate anything that cannot be reduced to a sequence of logical statements is even greater in digital simulation because of the computer's logical demands. If the techniques to represent some object, event, or condition are not available, the simulation should be dropped rather than compromising or simplifying assumptions, because the results obtained will be useless, or worse, misleading. Here another approach, although less "precise," would be more relevant and valid for the problem.

Next, the computing and data-handling ability of the digital computer places a serious burden on the investigator in his specification of the experimental tests and experimental results he will require. The most common pitfall in computer simulation is to "try everything possible" and to "print out everything possible." Because for complex simulations the digital computer can try literally billions of possible input conditions and print out literally mountains of data, careful selection of input conditions and the specific output required is a necessity that greatly tests the investigator's skill. If he does not have a clear understanding of the system he is to simulate, the investigator is not likely to make a very good selection of the input conditions to be tried or to anticipate the summaries and analyses of the output that will be valuable to him. The picture of the analyst surrounded by piles of computer output forms, searching through this maze for something worthwhile, is not only humorous, but also pathetic, frustrating, and expensive. Unfortunately, the picture is not at all uncommon. In scientific and engineering applications, where the analyst usually understands the "physics" of the problem, unrealistic results are more easily screened out. But in business applications, great care is required because of the looser problem structure and the increased amount of detail that often enters the simulation by necessity.

Finally, if the simulation is to take place on a "real-time" basis or faster, as is required in the evaluation of many process control and military applications, the abilities of the computer may be strained if the system simulation is too complex. For example, in air traffic control, to be of any operational use, an evaluation of new input conditions may be required in seconds or fractions of a second. Although the computer may be able to perform rudimentary operations in billionths of a second, the computations required in the evaluation still consume a finite amount of time, and, if too numerous, may exceed the response time required for effectiveness. A similar argument holds for experimental work in which a large number of replications must be carried out for statistical evaluation of given input conditions.

Within these constraints, however, there still remains a wide range of possible applications for digital simulation of complex systems. With this background we will now turn to some of the details of system simulation by computer. For simplicity, however, our approach will be via the route of manual simulation, which may be extended to the computer. The principles required are best illustrated in this way.

Table 12.1 Data for Simulation Example

1. Item routing

Item	Route	If inspection fails, total route becomes
A	1-4-3	1-4-3-2-3
B	1-4-2-3	1-4-2-3-2-3
C	1-2-3	1-2-3-2-3
D	1-4-3	(Scrap, rework not possible)

Note: If material is rejected at inspection it is returned to the Saw and Straighten Operation, except for product *D*, which is scrapped. Assume that the reworked material always passes the second inspection.

2. Machine data

Machine	Setup time (hours)	Running time (hours/unit)
1	1.00	0.01
2	2.00	0.01
3	0.00	0.01
4	1.00	1.00 per batch

Note: Machine 4, the furnace, works on a batch process only. A setup is required before each batch. A batch can be less than but not more than 250 units.

3. Inspection data

The inspection step, Operation 3, rejects 20% of the units passing through it, and units rejected are reworked or scrapped according to the routing data above.

4. Move time

Each move of an order between machines takes 1.00 hours. No job is moved until it is completely finished at a given step. This includes the batch production at machine 4. No partial lots are moved until the entire job is complete.

EXAMPLE OF SIMULATION TECHNIQUE

We can illustrate the details of system simulation by an example. Consider a small job shop, consisting of the machines and flows shown in Figure 12-3. Although this four-machine shop, which may be thought of as a simple metal extrusion plant, is highly simplified, it will illustrate some of the data-handling problems required in more complex simulations. The job shop, in the complex case, is one of the most difficult systems to simulate because of the large number of possible conditions that may be imposed. This fact is

5. Priority of work in case of conflict	Priority determined by last work center, as shown in Figure 12-3 by a, b, c. Runs are not broken to observe priorities, but they are observed at change time.

6. Work load

Item	Units required to finish	Units started
A	500 units	500 units
B	500 units	500 units
C	100 units	100 units
D	100 units	125 units

7. Schedule	The work begins in the order A-B-C-D on Machine 1, and thereafter follows the specified routing.
8. Production lot sizes	The total number of units required is made for each item at one time. Runs are not broken for priorities, or to make work go through the shop faster.
9. Interrelated items or setups	There are none.
10. Internal shop communications	There is no communication between the work centers, so that one work center cannot anticipate the jobs arriving from others. Thus, setup cannot start at a given work center until after a given job arrives at its location.
11. Initial conditions	At time $t = 0$, assume that the shop is empty, that is, that there is no work in process anywhere in this shop.
12. End of simulation	The simulation is to stop when all of the items scheduled, including material reworked, has been completed in the shop. At this point the shop will be empty, and no work will remain for any of the machines.

illustrated by the table of data required for even this simple problem, as shown in Table 12.1. The data of Table 12.1 have been developed for illustration and do not reflect the actual data from an extrusion plant. To simulate a particular system, field data representative of the given system must be collected. Table 12.1 also indicates a number of production conventions that must be specified in detail, and are here developed arbitrarily for test purposes. For example, the priority of work at each machine is to be determined by the last work station that processed a job rather than by

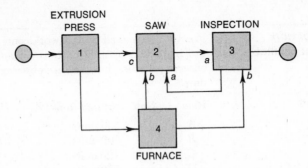

12-3 A block diagram of a simple shop to be simulated. For a specific example, Machine 1 is an extrusion press, Machine 2 is a saw and straightening operation, Machine 3 is an inspection operation, and Machine 4 is a furnace for heat treatment of the extruded metal. This collection of steps is common in the manufacture of extruded shapes, such as aluminum window frames. The data required for simulating this shop are provided in Table 12.1.

some other rule, it is assumed that there are no internal communications between machines in the shop, and a starting schedule and initial conditions are specified.

Some of the complexity of this simple illustration is evident when we ponder the number of alternative schedules, initial conditions, priority rules, work loads and product mixes, machine capabilities, and the like, which could be considered. Each conceivable change from the specified conditions could affect the operation of this shop. Thus, even for this simple system, the choice of the tests to be made and the conditions to be evaluated poses a serious question. This selection problem, of course, is immensely aggravated for more complex systems.

To proceed, we select a particular problem: If at time $t = 0$ the work load is fed to the first machine in the order A-B-C-D (i.e., A first, then B, etc.), at what time may we expect the total list of items to be completed? As we shall see, we could have asked for other results, and, in fact, we could have a voluminous output from this simple simulation. For simplicity, we will concentrate on the single number, representing the time of total work completion.

A Time-Position Chart

Proceeding with the task of answering this question manually, we use a display format called a time-position chart, illustrated in Figure 12-4. In this graphic display, each vertical column represents one of the four machines, the fifth column the state of work completion (finished inventory). Each row in the table represents one hour of elapsed time. Thus, a mark

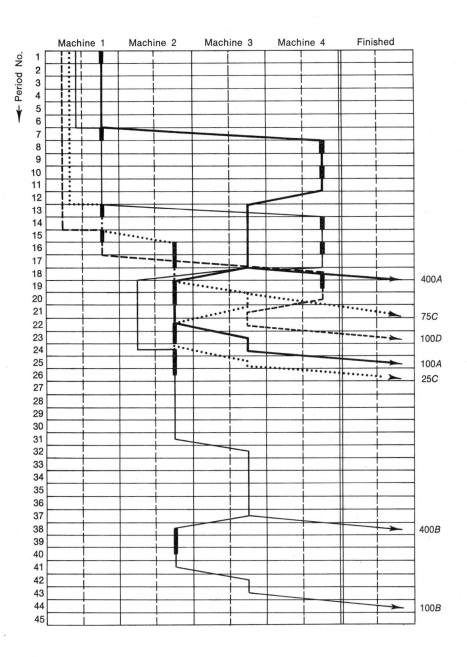

12-4 Manual simulation of job shop problem of Figures 12-3 and Table 12.1. This time-position sheet shows the position of products *A*, *B*, *C*, and *D* at each instant of time and is described in the text.

on this sheet defines the position of a given job at a given time. A horizontal line indicates a movement in position (a job going from one machine to another). A vertical line indicates the passage of time at a given location. For graphic clarity, we will indicate a setup time with a heavy line. By tracing the movement of jobs through the shop on this time-position sheet, we can define the status of the shop at any instant of time. (Such time-position charts are often used in industrial engineering work to analyze material handling operations, product assembly operations, and the like.)

The Problem of a Timing Routine

In developing the time-position sheet from hour to hour, clearly we must keep track of what is going on at each machine, and what is happening to each job. Because the sequence of work is important, this timing may be important in determining the work schedule at a given machine.

There are two basic approaches to the timing problem. The first approach advances the "clock" in discrete steps, say one hour at a time. With each advance in time, we then ask for the status of each machine and each product, thus requiring a complete "status report" at each time increment. This approach corresponds graphically to advancement down the sheet of Figure 12-4 one line at a time.

The step-advance approach has certain advantages. Some systems naturally operate on a discrete time basis. For example, if planning and movement can occur only periodically, we have a system for which points of interest are found only at fixed, equally-spaced time intervals. These, then, would be the points to be simulated. In addition, the discrete-time approach offers some simplicity in statistical summary, because the points to be counted are clearly defined.

Two major drawbacks to this approach, however, greatly reduce its usefulness. First, for systems that are not inherently periodic, there will be some unavoidable roundoff error, because times must be rounded to the nearest fixed increment of the clock. For example, if the fixed simulation increment were one hour and a job took 1.25 hours to complete, we would not be able to express 1.25 hours in the simulation, but must round to one hour. The error thus introduced into the simulation may be serious for a complex system. Although any desired precision is theoretically possible by the time-increment approach (by using smaller and smaller time increments), finer divisions greatly multiply the number of "scans" of the system to determine its status at each increment, and thereby vastly increase the effort required for the simulation. Moreover, as time increment is shortened we would find many increments (and their status evaluation) for which no change in system status has occurred (nothing will have happened). Since these no-change evaluations are of little interest, a great deal of useless effort will have to be expended in the name of precision.

For this reason, another method suggests itself for nonperiodic systems. By precomputing the time of each new change in system status, and by jumping ahead in time to that event (rather than approaching it incrementally) we can have both precision and a great saving in simulation effort and computing time. This advantage usually offsets the greater difficulty of statistical summarization (the jumps must be weighted in statistical summary by the length of the jump) and the more complex timing and control routines necessary for the jump approach.

Because the job shop example is not a periodic system, we will employ the jump approach to fill in Figure 12-4. The distinctions we have just made will be apparent as this work progresses.

Manual Simulation of the Job Shop

Using the data of Table 12.1 and the worksheet of Figure 12-4, we may start the manual simulation. First, at time $t = 0$, Job A starts on Machine 1. The first operation is a one-hour setup. Because no other job is in process, the next event will be completion of setup after one hour. We thus draw a heavy line down column 1, for Product A.

The next event will be the completion of Job A on Machine 1 at the end of hour 6. A line is drawn down column 1 to represent this. At the end of hour 6, when Job A is complete on Machine 1, two new events occur: Job A is moved to Machine 4, and the setup for Job B starts on Machine A. Each takes one hour, so the lines may be drawn for both of these actions.

At the end of hour 7, two new events occur. Setup is finished for Job B on Machine 1 and processing starts, and setup for Job A on Machine 4 starts. The next event is at the end of hour 8, when setup for Job A on Machine 4 is commenced and the maximum of 250 units is batch processed on Machine 4.

At the end of hour 9, the load of 250 units of A is completed on Machine 4, and the machine is set up again for the next batch of 250. Processing is complete on Machine 4 at the end of hour 11.

Working ahead in this way, carefully noting each new event as it is to occur and evaluating the system's status at that time, we may complete the sheet, stopping of course when the last job is complete. Here, that will be when the last 100 units of Job B clear the shop.

To illustrate the care required in deciding the order in which events are to occur and the rules of the simulation we note that at the end of hour 18 both Job B and the rejected portion of Job A (100 units) arrive at Machine 2 for processing. Job C has just been completed at Machine 2 at that time. Because Machine 2 is free for work, a decision must be made: Should Machine 2 now work on Job B or on the rejected portion of Job A? We decide this by the priority rules established for the simulation, namely that at Machine 2, as shown in Figure 12-3, work from Machine 3, the inspection station, shall take precedence over other work. Thus, setup is immediately begun for the rejected portion of Job *A* at Machine 2, *and Job B must wait.* Indeed, Job *B* must continue to wait until 23.25 hours before it can get on Machine 2, because it is again "bumped" by the arrival of the rejected portion of Job *C* from Machine 3.

The answer to the question originally posed for this simulation is that all the work is complete at 43.25 hours, as may be seen from Figure 12-4. It is now instructive to ask what other questions might have been answered from the simulated data now available. Numerous outputs suggest themselves for consideration. We could have asked for the time each portion of each job was complete, as indicated by the arrows entering the "Finished" column. We might have asked for the percentages of idle, setup, and working time on each of the four machines during the simulation. We might have asked for the hours lost due to "interference" or queuing in the shop (5.25 hours available by inspection of the column for Machine 2). We could have asked for moves, the setups, or the operations performed, and so on. These statistics and various figures computed from them could be developed from the simulation results. Clearly, in a more complex simulation, the possible outputs increase rapidly. Our objective in raising these questions is to illustrate the importance of output specification before the simulation is begun, particularly when an electronic computer is assigned the task of creating the status data.

Similarly, even with this simple simulation, we may have asked a series of other questions of the "what would happen if. . ." form. What would have happened here if we had changed the input schedule, the initial conditions, the machine capacities, the setup times, the internal communication rules, the priority rules, the production lot sizes, the input product mix, or the routing requirements? What organization of the shop would be desirable if production cost were more important than production time? If several machines of different capacity were substituted for a given machine? If setups were inter-related? If move time were shortened? Even for this simple example, the possible input conditions and reasons for analysis could put a severe computational burden upon the analyst. For this reason, the computer is helpful for mechanizing the generation of simulated results of the type we have just produced by hand. And, even with the computer, the analyst is not relieved of the burden of asking intelligent questions.

If the reader has carefully followed through this illustration (as he should, attempting to duplicate Figure 12-4 on his own) he will have concluded that hand simulation is not an efficient way to analyze the job shop. Certainly, if there are a number of variations to be tried, there must be a better way to do the job. In addition, the reader will have noted the detailed record-keeping and time computations that must be repeated, he will have found that an error in either can grossly affect the simulated results, and he will have reasoned that a machine can accomplish this more accurately as well as more quickly than a human. The digital computer is used in system simulation, because it is ideal for just these tasks. The analyst may then devote his energies to the formulation of more intelligent questions and improvement of the system definition.

Another remark should be made before continuing. The reader should have learned something about the operation of a job shop by construction of Figure 12-4. In the manual simulation in which the detail is traced step by step, a comprehensible "picture" of the operation studied emerges. We see the idle time, interference, movement time, and other expenditures of effort in their over-all relationship. We see the difference between a mass production assembly line, where job movements are smooth and syncronized, and the job shop, where job movements are erratic, and the machines are alternately idle and then overloaded. The heuristic or suggestive value of such understanding is a major benefit of system simulation, but is usually available only if the simulation is not so complex that the picture or pattern of operation is lost either by summarizing too much or not enough detail. This is yet another reason for careful planning of any simulation exercise. What has been said about the job shop simulation is true in general.

INTRODUCING VARIABILITY IN SYSTEM SIMULATIONS

As if the complexity of the job shop simulation illustration were not enough, we must now introduce a further complication. We have assumed so far that the data used were precisely correct. We have carried out a deterministic simulation. Anyone who follows the rules set forth in the example should arrive at the given answer.

Most systems, however, have probabilistic operations or actions, so that, to be realistic, a simulated system must include these variabilities. For example, in the job shop example, setup times, working times, move times, and inspection reject rates may vary from job to job about the "average" figures given in Table 12.1.

To see how such variability may be introduced into the simulation we again digress and discuss the required techniques.

Sampling from Discrete Distributions

Techniques of experimental estimation by statistical sampling, often called Monte Carlo Methods, are often used when straightforward mathematical methods fail or are cumbersome. The same procedures may be used to generate a time series of data from a known statistical distribution. Both uses find application in simulation problems. First we will illustrate several estimation problems.

Example: Suppose that within a rectangular figure of known area R there is an irregular figure of unknown area A, as shown in Figure 12-5. Suppose our problem is to find the area of the irregular figure A, and we do not know any formal method for doing this. Using a sampling

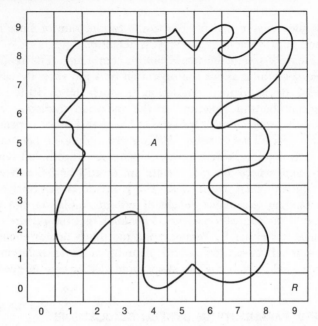

12-5 An estimation problem using the Monte Carlo Method. The rectangular area *R* is known. The problem is to estimate the irregular area *A*. By the Monte Carlo Method as described in the text, a random sample of squares in the grid permits estimation of the ratio *A/R*, and therefore *A*, because *R* is known.

approach, we may proceed as follows. First, divide the vertical and horizontal axes of *R* into equal segments to produce a grid. For convenience, let the grid have ten by ten divisions, producing 100 boxes, each $\frac{1}{100}$ the area of *R*. Number each row $i = 0, 1, 2, 3, \ldots, 9$, and each column $j = 0, 1, 2, 3,, \ldots, 9$. Each small box may then be indexed by the two numbers i, j. We will now randomly select a small box i, j, as shown below, and record a "yes" result if any portion of the irregular figure enters the box selected, and a "no" otherwise. (This decision rule will tend to overestimate the size of *A*, but the error may be minimized by using a larger number of scale divisions. The procedure is not affected by this problem.)

To select the sample boxes a number of procedures could be used. We could place all the numbers 0, 0 through 9, 9 in a hat and draw them out. A more efficient way is to use a random number table, which is a tabulation of digits each of which is equally likely (i.e., each decimal digit has a $\frac{1}{10}$ probability of appearing in the table), and each of which is distributed uniformly throughout the table so that no sequential pattern of occurrence can be found. Table 12.2 shows such a table of random numbers.

Table 12.2   Random Numbers[a]

09 73 25 33	76 53 01 35 86	34 67 35 48 76	80 95 90 90 17	39 29 27 49
54 20 48 05	64 89 47 42 96	24 80 52 40 37	20 63 61 04 02	00 82 29 16
42 26 89 53	19 64 50 93 03	23 20 90 25 60	15 95 33 47 64	35 08 03 36
01 90 25 29	09 37 67 07 15	38 31 13 11 65	88 67 67 43 97	04 43 62 76
80 79 99 70	80 15 73 61 47	64 03 23 66 53	98 95 11 68 77	12 17 17 68
06 57 47 17	34 07 27 68 50	36 69 73 61 70	65 81 33 98 85	11 19 92 91
06 01 08 05	45 57 18 24 06	35 30 34 26 14	86 79 90 74 39	23 40 30 97
26 97 76 02	02 05 16 56 92	68 66 57 48 18	73 05 38 52 47	18 62 38 85
57 33 21 35	05 32 54 70 48	90 55 35 75 48	28 46 82 87 09	82 49 12 56
79 64 57 53	03 52 96 47 78	35 80 83 42 82	60 93 52 03 44	35 27 38 84
52 01 77 67	14 90 56 86 07	22 10 94 05 58	60 97 09 34 33	50 50 07 39
80 50 54 31	39 80 82 77 32	50 72 56 82 48	29 40 52 42 01	52 77 56 78
45 29 96 34	06 28 89 80 83	13 74 67 00 78	18 47 54 06 10	68 71 17 78
68 34 02 00	86 50 75 84 01	36 76 66 79 51	90 36 47 64 93	29 60 91 01
59 46 73 48	87 51 76 49 69	91 82 60 89 28	93 78 56 13 68	23 47 83 41
48 11 76 74	17 46 85 09 50	58 04 77 69 74	73 03 95 71 86	40 21 81 65
12 43 56 35	17 72 70 80 15	45 31 82 23 74	21 11 57 82 53	14 38 55 37
35 09 98 17	77 40 27 72 14	43 23 60 02 10	45 52 16 42 37	96 28 60 26
91 62 68 03	66 25 22 91 48	36 93 68 72 03	76 62 11 39 90	94 40 05 64
89 32 05 05	14 22 56 85 14	46 42 75 67 88	96 29 77 88 22	54 38 21 45
49 91 45 23	68 47 92 76 86	46 16 28 35 54	94 75 08 99 23	37 08 92 00
33 69 45 98	26 94 03 68 58	70 29 73 41 35	53 14 03 33 40	42 05 08 23
10 48 19 49	85 15 74 79 54	32 97 92 65 75	57 60 04 08 81	22 22 20 64
55 07 37 42	11 10 00 20 40	12 86 07 46 97	96 64 48 94 39	28 70 72 58
60 64 93 29	16 50 53 44 84	40 21 95 25 63	43 65 17 70 82	07 20 73 17
19 69 04 46	26 45 74 77 74	51 92 43 37 29	65 39 45 95 93	42 58 26 05
47 44 52 66	95 27 07 99 53	59 36 78 38 48	82 39 61 01 18	33 21 15 94
55 72 85 73	67 89 75 43 87	54 62 24 44 31	91 19 04 25 92	92 92 74 59
48 11 62 13	97 34 40 87 21	16 86 84 87 67	02 07 11 20 59	25 70 14 66
52 37 83 17	73 20 88 98 37	68 93 59 14 16	26 25 22 96 63	05 52 28 25
49 35 24 94	75 24 63 38 24	45 86 25 10 25	61 96 27 93 35	65 33 71 24
54 99 76 54	64 05 18 81 59	96 11 96 38 96	54 69 28 23 91	23 28 72 95
96 31 53 07	26 89 80 93 54	33 35 13 54 62	77 97 45 00 24	90 10 33 93
80 80 83 91	45 42 72 68 42	83 60 94 97 00	13 02 12 48 92	78 56 52 01
05 88 52 36	01 39 09 22 86	77 28 14 40 77	93 91 08 36 47	70 61 74 29
17 90 02 97	87 37 92 52 41	05 56 70 70 07	86 74 31 71 57	85 39 41 18
23 46 14 06	20 11 74 52 04	15 95 66 00 00	18 74 39 24 23	97 11 89 63
56 54 14 30	01 75 87 53 79	40 41 92 15 85	66 67 43 68 06	84 96 28 52
15 51 49 38	19 47 60 72 46	43 66 79 45 43	59 04 79 00 33	20 82 66 85
86 43 19 94	36 16 81 08 51	34 88 88 15 53	01 54 03 54 56	05 01 45 11
08 62 48 26	45 24 02 84 04	44 99 90 88 96	39 09 47 34 07	35 44 13 18
18 51 62 32	41 94 15 09 49	89 43 54 85 81	88 69 54 19 94	37 54 87 30
95 10 04 06	96 38 27 07 74	20 15 12 33 87	25 01 62 52 98	94 62 46 11

[a] From C. W. Churchman, R. L. Ackoff, and E. L. Arnoff, Editors, *Introduction to Operations Research,* Wiley, New York, 1957, p. 176.

The procedure for using this table is to start at any randomly chosen starting point, reading off the sequence of digits that follow any consistent pattern. (Row or column reading is most usual.) For example, in Table 12.2, if we start for simplicity at the upper left-hand corner, the first two-digit random number (columns 1 and 2) is 09. Reading down, the next random numbers are 54, 42, 01, 80, etc. (After arriving at the end of the first two-digit column we could move to the top of the next column and so on.)

Now to continue with the estimation problem, we decide upon a sample size and choose a two-digit random number for each sample box selected. Suppose at first we arbitrarily take a sample of $n = 10$ boxes, using the first ten numbers of the random number table starting with 09. Let the first digit represent the value of i and the second that of j, so that a two-digit number will select a small box from the area R. By inspection of Figure 12-5, record a "yes" or a "no" for each of the ten samples, as below.

Random Number	Result	Random Number	Result
09	No	06	Yes
54	Yes	06	Yes
42	Yes	26	Yes
01	No	57	Yes
80	No	79	Yes

To complete the estimate, compute the fraction p of "yes" answer in the total

$$p = \frac{(\text{number of "yes" answers})}{(\text{sample size } n)}.$$

Because p is an estimate of the fraction of R occupied by A, we have as an estimate for A simply $A = pR$. Here the estimate of A for the sample chosen is $A = 0.7R$. If area R is 100 square centimeters, then our estimate of A from the simulation is 70 square centimeters.

The error in p may be found by recalling that the yes-no results are Bernoulli trials, and that the results will follow the binomial distribution. From this knowledge the formula for the standard deviation of p is $\sigma_p = \sqrt{p(1-p)/n}$, where p is the true value of $p = A/R$. Substituting A/R for p, we have

$$\sigma_p = \sqrt{\frac{A/R(1 - A/R)}{n}}$$

from which it may be seen that the estimate of p (and therefore of A) may be improved by increasing the sample size n, or by making A a large part of R. (R is an arbitrary boundary set up for the sampling procedure.) Conversely, given R and a desired value of σ_p, the sample size required to achieve this result may be obtained from the same formula.[6]

We now consider a different problem using the Monte Carlo approach to estimate a survival probability.

Example: The game of Russian Roulette is played with a six-shooter hand pistol. One of the six chambers is loaded, the chambers are spun, and one participant points the pistol at his head and pulls the trigger. If we assume the spin has randomly placed the loaded cartridge, the probability of survival for one trial is $\frac{5}{6}$, and the probability of death is $\frac{1}{6}$. What is the probability of survival after three trials, if we assume the chamber is rotated at random at each trial? (It is convenient to speak of a probability of survival rather than a probability of death because the participant must survive all three trials to survive this game.)

Applying the Multiplication Law of Probability we find $(\frac{5}{6})^3 =$ 125/216, or a little better than one-half. How could we have obtained this result by sampling?

We now introduce the concept of coding the random numbers drawn from a random-number table. Because the probability of death on one trial is $\frac{1}{6}$ or 0.167, and the probability of survival on one trial is $\frac{5}{6}$, or 0.833, we may code the states Die $= D$ and Live $= L$, rounding to two figures, as

Random numbers	Outcome	Fraction of 100 Random No.
00–16	D	$\frac{1}{6}$
17–99	L	$\frac{5}{6}$

If the random numbers are drawn from the table as before, and if they are interpreted to mean L or D as in the above table, then we have converted the random-number table to a table of L's and D's in which the D's will be $\frac{1}{6}$ of the total number and the L's will be $\frac{5}{6}$.

The Russian Roulette game may now be simulated by developing a table listing a number of experiments as rows, each of which consists of three trials. The table is filled-in using the random numbers in their equivalent interpretation L or D, and noting that the participant will

---

[6] Because the confidence interval for large and small values of p will not be symmetrical for the binomial distribution, a more accurate determination of a sample size for a given confidence interval requires consultation of tables of the binomial distribution. The formula above assumes that the sample size is sufficiently large so that the normal distribution can be used to approximate the binomial.

live only if the simulated experiment terminates in the outcome *L, L, L*. Figure 12-6 shows the result of ten simulated experiments. To obtain the estimate of the survival probability after three trials, we compute the ratio of "yes" results to the total in the last column of Figure 12-6, and obtain ½ for the ten simulated experiments. In the absence of any other information we could use the value of $p = \frac{1}{2}$ as an approximation to the true value and compute the standard deviation of this estimate, as in the previous example. The experimental estimate would come nearer 125/216 as the number of experiments increases.

Next we turn to an extension of the coding procedure just described and ask how we can use random numbers to generate a series of typical outcomes from a given probability distribution.

Example: Suppose the weekly number of failures of a given repair part in the field is given by the probability distribution

$x = $ No. of failures/week	0	1	2	3
$P(x)$	0.4	0.3	0.2	0.1

i.e., in 40 weeks out of 100 there were no failures, in 30 weeks there was one, in 20 weeks there were two, and in 10 weeks there three. Four or more failures in a week have not been experienced. From this distribution, we want to generate a typical history of weekly failures. Again,

Experiment	Random numbers	L or D	Survival?
1	09, 54, 42	D,L,L	No
2	01, 80, 06	D,L,L	No
3	06, 26, 57	D,L,L	No
4	79, 52, 80	L,L,L	Yes
5	45, 68, 59	L,L,L	Yes
6	48, 12, 35	L,D,L	No
7	91, 89, 49	L,L,L	Yes
8	33, 10, 55	L,D,L	No
9	60, 19, 47	L,L,L	Yes
10	55, 48, 52	L,L,L	Yes

$$\text{Estimates Probability of Survival} = \frac{\text{Number of "Yes" Results}}{\text{Total Number of Experiments}} = \frac{5}{10} = \frac{1}{2}$$

12-6 Simulation of a Russian Roulette game. Using random numbers, a series of ten experiments simulating the game has been created. The single experiment consists of three trials at Russian Roulette. The experimental estimate of ½ compares to the theoretical answer 125/216. Greater accuracy may be obtained by replicating the experiments, i.e., creating more of them in total.

this can be done by coding the equiprobable random numbers so that they will correspond to the number of failures (0, 1, 2, or 3) in the proportion indicated by the probability distribution.

To do this conveniently we arrange the probability distribution in cumulative form, showing the probability that the discrete random variable x will be less than or equal to c, the tabulated number of failures

c failures/week	0	1	2	3
$P(x \leqq c)$	0.4	0.7	0.9	1.0

This tabulation provides a guide to the coding below

Random number	Code or value of c
00–39	0
40–69	1
70–89	2
90–99	3

With this coding a sequence of random numbers will produce a sequence of the numbers 0, 1, 2, and 3 with the probability $P(x)$, i.e., 20% will be 2's, etc. To generate the required history's, say for ten weeks, we look up ten random numbers, and convert them by the code table to the appropriate outcome X

Week	1	2	3	4	5	6	7	8	9	10
Random No.	09	54	42	01	80	06	06	26	57	79
X	0	1	1	0	3	0	0	0	1	2

We can continue this process as long as we desire. Note, however, that the generation of this typical history assumes that the probability distribution remains constant during the generation. With very little additional difficulty, however, the investigator could, if he had the need, alter the probability distribution from time to time. The procedure just described is general and can be applied to any discrete probability distribution, and to any continuous distribution approximated by a discrete distribution. We can obtain greater precision by coding a larger number of random digits. Thus, we can code probabilities to four significant figures, by using four-digit random numbers.

It is easy to apply the above procedure to the job-shop simulation example.

Example: Suppose in the job-shop example of Figures 12-3 and 12-4 that the move time was not exactly one hour, but could be approximated by the probability distribution shown below (which has an average of 1.0)

Move Time x (hours)	0.5	1.0	1.5	2.0
$P(x)$	0.4	0.3	0.2	0.1

Then, each time a move occurred in the job-shop simulation we could consult a random-number table, pick the next random number, and find the equivalent move time to use in the simulation. This randomness in move time would produce a distribution of results for the simulation, say for the total completion time. With this probabilistic element in the simulation, we must repeat the simulation procedure a large number of times to obtain an estimate of the average total completion time. The number of repetitions required for a given precision of estimation would depend upon the dispersion of sample results obtained in the simulated total completion times.

The reader should not forget that, in addition to coding discrete variables, as shown above, the same procedures can be used to code and generate attributes at random. Thus, if a light can be red, yellow, green, or out with given probabilities, it would be possible to generate a series of R, Y, G or O outcomes with the required probabilities using the same methods as before.

Sampling From Continuous Distributions

With little difficulty, the above methods can be extended to continuous distributions, as shown in Figure 12-7. First the continuous distribution is converted into a cumulative probability distribution. Graphically, the horizontal distribution represents the range of the random variable to be described, as in Figure 12-7a. The vertical scale has 100 equal divisions if two-digit random numbers are to be coded, 1000 equal divisions for three-digit coding, and so on, and each division is numbered from 00–99, reading up from the origin. This procedure, in effect, approximates the continuous curve with a discrete distribution having 100 steps. To generate the random variable, we again look up a two-digit random number, enter the left-hand scale of the cumulative distribution at that interval, and read across and down, to obtain the corresponding value of the random variable. The required coding is provided by the relation of the equal intervals to the left and the continuous cumulative probability curve. We can handle any continuous distribution in this manner.

Of special importance is the normal probability distribution, which is frequently encountered in simulation work, and which is, of course, continuous. The same procedure holds, except that it is worthwhile to note that by using the standard cumulative normal distribution (which expresses the random variable x in terms of the standardized variable $t = (x - \bar{x})/\sigma$, and

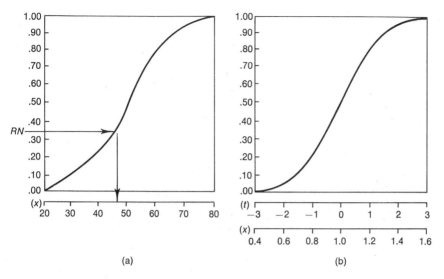

(a)   (b)

12-7 Generation of random variables from the cumulative probability distribution. (a) An arbitrary probability distribution in cumulative form. Values of the variable are shown on the scale below (a). To generate a value of this variable from the given probability distribution, a random number is selected from the random-number table, such as Table 12.2. Moving to the right, this random number selects a point on the cumulative curve. The corresponding value of the variable is found directly below (the random number 35 corresponds to the variable value 46 in this case). The standard cumulative normal probability distribution offers a special case of interest (b). The use of the standard curve, normalized by use of the standard normal deviation $t = (x - \bar{x})/\sigma$, permits the same curve to be used for any normal curve by specification of x and σ. This is illustrated by the second scale below (b), which is for $\bar{x} = 1.0$, $\sigma = 0.2$.

therefore has an average of $\bar{x} = 0$ and $\sigma = 1$), we can generate a series of standardized values that may be used in different applications by the conversion $x = \bar{x} + t\sigma$. For example, the standard scale may be provided, as in Figure 12-7b, and underneath it a series of graphic scales may be provided for graphic transformation of the random normal deviation t into a specific random variable through knowledge of $\bar{x}$ and σ for that case. Figure 12-7b shows a scale that would work for the job-shop simulation if the move time had an average of one hour, a standard deviation of 0.2 hours, and a normal distribution.

The usefulness of the normal distribution in simulation and the frequency of use of the above random generation process suggest that tabulations of random normal numbers be made up, as shown in Table 12.3. This table shows the result of transforming a table of random numbers to random normal deviation (t) by careful mathematical application of the procedure

Table 12.3   Random Normal Numbers[a]

	(1)	(2)	(3)	(4)	(5)	(6)	(7)
				$\mu = 0, \sigma = 1$			
1	0.464	0.137	2.455	−0.323	−0.068	0.296	−0.288
2	0.060	−2.526	−0.531	−1.940	0.543	−1.558	0.187
3	1.486	−0.354	−0.634	0.697	0.926	1.375	0.785
4	1.022	−0.472	1.279	3.521	0.571	−1.851	0.194
5	1.394	−0.555	0.046	0.321	2.945	1.974	−0.258
6	0.906	−0.513	−0.525	0.595	0.881	−0.934	1.579
7	1.179	−1.055	0.007	0.769	0.971	0.712	1.090
8	−1.501	−0.488	−0.162	−0.136	1.033	0.203	0.448
9	−0.690	0.756	−1.618	−0.445	−0.511	−2.051	−0.457
10	1.372	0.225	0.378	0.761	0.181	−0.736	0.960
11	−0.482	1.677	−0.057	−1.229	−0.486	0.856	−0.491
12	−1.376	−0.150	1.356	−0.561	−0.256	0.212	0.219
13	−1.010	0.598	−0.918	1.598	0.065	0.415	−0.169
14	−0.005	−0.899	0.012	−0.725	1.147	−0.121	−0.096
15	1.393	−1.163	−0.911	1.231	−0.199	−0.246	1.239
16	−1.787	−0.261	1.237	1.046	−0.508	−1.630	−0.146
17	−0.105	−0.357	−1.384	0.360	−0.992	−0.116	−1.698
18	−1.339	1.827	−0.959	0.424	0.969	−1.141	−1.041
19	1.041	0.535	0.731	1.377	0.983	−1.330	1.620
20	0.279	−2.056	0.717	−0.873	−1.096	−1.396	1.047
21	−1.805	−2.008	−1.633	0.542	0.250	0.166	0.032
22	−1.186	1.180	1.114	0.882	1.265	−0.202	0.151
23	0.658	−1.141	1.151	−1.210	−0.927	0.425	0.290
24	−0.439	0.358	−1.939	0.891	−0.227	0.602	0.973
25	1.398	−0.230	0.385	−0.649	−0.577	0.237	−0.289
26	0.199	0.208	−1.083	−0.219	−0.291	1.221	1.119
27	0.159	0.272	−0.313	0.084	−2.828	−0.439	−0.792
28	2.273	0.606	0.606	0.747	0.247	1.291	0.063
29	0.041	−0.307	0.121	0.790	−0.584	0.541	0.484
30	−1.132	−2.098	0.921	0.145	0.446	−2.661	1.045
31	0.768	0.079	−1.473	0.034	−2.127	0.665	0.084
32	0.375	−1.658	−0.851	0.234	−0.656	0.340	−0.086
33	−0.513	−0.344	0.210	−0.736	1.041	0.008	0.427
34	0.292	−0.521	1.266	−1.206	−0.899	0.110	−0.528
35	1.026	2.990	−0.574	−0.491	−1.114	1.297	−1.433
36	−1.334	1.278	−0.568	−0.109	−0.515	−0.566	2.923
37	−0.287	−0.144	−0.254	0.574	−0.451	−1.181	−1.190
38	0.161	−0.886	−0.921	−0.509	1.410	−0.518	0.192
39	−1.346	0.193	−1.202	0.394	−1.045	0.843	0.942
40	1.250	−0.199	−0.288	1.810	1.378	0.584	1.216

[a] This table is reproduced in part from a table of the RAND Corporation, and appeared in its present form in C. W. Churchman, R. L. Ackoff, and E. L. Arnoff, *Introduction to Operations Research*, Wiley, New York, 1957, p. 181, from which the following example is also reproduced by permission.

described. (The random numbers used for this were not those of Table 12.2, but a similar set; therefore, do not look for a direct transformation between Tables 12.2 and 12.3.)

Example: Two parts, *A* and *B*, have lifetimes that are normally distributed, with the averages and standard deviations shown below:

Part	Average Lifetime	Standard Deviation
A	100 hours	20 hours
B	90 hours	10 hours

That is, our history about parts *A* and *B* gives us the experimental evidence summarized in these figures. Suppose an assembly were made of one part *A* and one part *B*, so put together that both *A* and *B* must work if the assembly is to work. What is the estimated lifetime of the assembly?

Using Table 12.3 to answer this question, we start (again only for consistency of illustration) in the upper left-hand corner and simulate ten assemblies by obtaining ten random numbers for each part. We convert these standard deviations into appropriate random variables using our knowledge of the average and standard deviation for each part. Because the assembly will fail if either part fails, the lifetime of the assembly will be the *shorter* of the two lifetimes so generated. The results generated are summarized in Figure 12-8. To estimate the average lifetime of the assembly, we average the figures in column (5), Figure 12-8, to get 82.6. (Note that, as we would suspect, this value is less than the average life of either part.) We could also compute the standard deviation of the figures shown in column (5) to estimate the error due to sampling, and to make sample size calculations if greater accuracy were required. In addition to showing the use of random normal numbers, this example also illustrates how logical considerations may be combined with probabilistic simulation, as did the Russian Roulette example of Figure 12-6. In general, complicated decision rules may be employed in a simulation to screen out combinations generated by the random number process.

Some Computer Comments on Random Number Generation

In computer application, table look-up of random numbers and many other functions wastes computer memory space, so that the desired result is often computed.

In random number generation, so-called pseudo-random numbers may be created in various ways. Although it is beyond the scope of this book to consider the merits of alternate approaches, it is interesting to see how the process might be carried out.

	Part A		Part B		Life of assembly
Case No.	(1) Random normal number	(2) Life of part $= 100 + 20(1)$	(3) Random normal number	(4) Life of part $= 90 + 10(2)$	(5) Smallest value appearing in (2) or (4)
1	0.464	109.28	0.137	91.37	91.37
2	0.060	101.20	−2.526	64.74	64.74
3	1.486	129.72	−0.354	86.46	86.46
4	1.022	120.44	−0.472	85.28	85.28
5	1.394	127.88	−0.555	84.45	84.45
6	0.906	118.12	−0.513	84.87	84.87
7	1.179	123.58	−1.055	79.45	79.45
8	−1.501	69.98	−0.488	85.12	69.98
9	−0.690	86.20	0.756	97.56	86.20
10	1.372	127.44	0.225	92.25	92.25
				TOTAL	826.28
				AVERAGE	82.63

12-8 Simulation of assembly lifetime using random normal numbers. Two parts, *A* and *B*, must both work if the assembly of *A* and *B* is to work. The lifetime of the assembly is thus the shortest of the lifetimes of *A* or *B*. In this example ten assemblies are simulated using random normal numbers. The estimate of the average lifetime of the assembly is obtained by averaging column (5) for the ten cases. The error of the estimate may also be computed using the figures of column (5). Average assembly lifetime obtained from this simulation is 82.6 hours. (Data adapted from C. W. Churchman, R. L. Ackoff, and E. L. Arnoff, Eds., *Introduction to Operations Research,* Wiley, New York, 1957, p. 182.)

The midsquare method illustrates a typical approach. With this procedure a starting number b_1 is selected. For illustration, assume a four-digit number. This number is squared, producing a maximum of eight digits. The middle four digits of this eight-digit number are then extracted to produce a second four-digit number. The process is then repeated to generate successive four-digit numbers. These numbers will appear to be "random" to a large variety of tests often used for randomness (average, standard deviation, uniform probability of digits, run tests, and the like), and may be considered random numbers for simulation purposes. Thus, if $b_1 = 1097$, then $b_1{}^2 = 01203409$. Extraction of the middle four digits gives $b_2 = 2304$, and the process is continued. Although procedures of this type will eventually produce a repetition of the series (e.g., if 1097 should ever come up again in the course of number generation), nonrepeating strings of sufficient length for many simulation problems may be generated by careful choice of the starting number. More complex procedures may also be used to generate extensive random strings.[7] Random normal numbers may also be generated in this way by computing the *sum* of *N* random numbers, which by virtue of the Central Limit Theorem in Statistics will be normally distributed. The normally distributed sum is then transformed to the standardized form with $\bar{x} = 0, \sigma = 1$.

Finally, we should note that most computer centers have subroutines available for random number and random normal number generation, so that in a computer implementation of a given simulation these results may be used as blocks, and called as required in the construction of a computer program.

*Computer Simulation Languages

Because of the detailed discussion required and the availability of alternate references, we do not intend here to evaluate or discuss computer languages.[8]

However, to make the reader aware of the major features of these important aids to large-scale system simulation, we will outline current practice. (We will assume in this section that the reader is familiar with introductory computer terms; if not this section may be skipped.)

Today computer programers commonly work with so-called "higher-level" computer languages (FORTRAN, ALGOL, COBOL, AUTOCODER) rather than with more detailed "machine language" (so that the machine may be instructed more simply and with less programer effort for general problems in science and business). The systems analyst, when designing a computer systems simulation, will also use a compiler. Moreover, because a system simulation of any complexity often involves an extensive list of computer statements, many of which may be repetitive, a "compiler" approach with many subroutines is desirable. The reader will recall that computer languages, such as FORTRAN, ALGOL, COBOL, and AUTOCODER, correspond roughly to an encyclopedia. A single statement in the "higher-level" language usually generates, by looking up and compiling the more detailed instructions required in the proper order, a much longer list of detailed statements. For example, the statement "MULTIPLY RATE TIMES HOURS TO GIVE WAGE" may require a series of instructions, first to determine the value of the RATE and the number of HOURS to use in

---

[7] The simple midsquare method is usually replaced with more involved routines to obtain longer cycles of pseudo-random numbers. Such procedures are stored as computer subroutines for use as needed. See T. E. Hull and A. R. Dobell, "Random Number Generators,' *SIAM Review,* 4, 3, July, 1962, pp. 230–54.

[8] In addition to the specific manuals cited, the following general references are of interest: T. H. Naylor, J. L. Balintfy, D. S. Burdick, and K. Chu, *Computer Simulation Techniques,* Wiley, New York, 1966. C. McMillan and R. F. Gonzalez, *Systems Analysis: A Computer Approach to Simulation Models,* Irwin, Inc., Homewood, Ill., 1965. D. N. Chorafas, *Systems and Simulation,* Academic Press, New York, 1965. H. S. Krasnow and R. A. Merikallio, "The Past, Present, and Future of Simulation Languages," *Management Science,* November, 1964.

the computation, and then to perform the repetetive addition, overflow, and other checks necessary for the computer to MULTIPLY, and then store the answer in WAGE. When a compiler routine is used with the higher-level language, the computer itself does this look-up, translation, and compilation, thus saving the programer the job of doing the same.

Special compilers and languages for simulation problems are used, because often the operations needed are not part of the usual general purpose compiler, although, of course with more difficulty, the general purpose compiler could be used.[9] Some of the presently available simulation languages, which we shall discuss presently, exploit the advantages of general purpose compilers, such as FORTRAN, but add to them many additional features, such as timing routines, random number generators, output report generators, matrix manipulation, and notational ability particularly suited to simulation. Often this added ability requires an additional translation, or compilation. For example, the simulation language known as SIMSCRIPT permits instructions to be written in its own language or in its own language intermixed with FORTRAN. These statements are then compiled into a more extensive list of all-FORTRAN statements, and then for a particular computer to be used for computation yet additional compilation and translation is required. For the IBM 7090/94 machine, the FORTRAN statements would be compiled into a more extensive list of symbolic statements and finally into the binary codes the computer can use. Although the program was originally written in SIMSCRIPT, it would be executed in binary machine language. These compilations are relatively complicated, but from the user's point of view they are not burdensome, because they are performed by the machine.

The three simulation languages we will discuss are DYNAMO, GPSS-III, and SIMSCRIPT. The compiler tapes required for these simulation languages are widely available, as are the detailed instructions for their use.

DYNAMO[10] is the name given to a computer language designed for the simulation of systems most easily described by flows with lags and *rates of change of flow*. In mathematical form, such systems might be described by differential equations, or equivalent difference equations that approximate the continuous case. A number of decision rules may also be used. An illustration of such a system is provided by the *over-all* statistics of a manufacturing concern, such as total dollar sales, total dollar inventory, total dollar receivables, and the like. In such gross statistics we are mainly interested in the major relations that exist in cash flow, material flow, and the transla-

[9] For example, for use of FORTRAN in simulation programs, see McMillan and Gonzales, *op. cit.*

[10] Jay Forrester, *Industrial Dynamics*, M.I.T. Press, Cambridge, Mass., 1961. The author describes the suitable types of problems, the method of simulation using DYNAMO, and provides numerous illustrations. A. L. Pugh, DYNAMO *User's Manual.* 2nd ed., M.I.T. Press, Cambridge, Mass., 1963.

tion of one gross measure into another—without the detailed definition of specific internal operations and the computation and display of detailed statistics. For example, as a simple case, if orders received take two weeks to produce and ship, and collection lags another six weeks, and raw material inventory must represent a two-week supply, how will the financial picture of the firm vary if sales have been steady at $10,000 per week for 20 weeks and then begin to increase at a rate of $1000 per week for the next 20 weeks? How will receivables and delays due to raw material shortages increase?

In DYNAMO, a description of the problem is written in a special notation that facilitates this type of problem formulation. In addition, the language has a special report generator that will *plot,* on a standard computer printer, selected variables as a function of time, i.e., time series, for analysis. These abilities allow the investigator to study the "dynamics" of the total system by an analysis of the trends and patterns in the time series so pictured.

DYNAMO can also handle variations in delay and feedback processes, such as computed production decision-rules based on prior system performance. In short, DYNAMO is congenial to the analyst who is familiar with the literature of servomechanisms and the design of automatic control devices, and who thinks naturally in the language and methodology of that field. In many industrial situations, simulation of manufacturing, distribution, marketing, and financial problems may be facilitated by this approach, as Forrester indicates in his widely-quoted book.

GPSS-III (which stands for General Purpose System Simulator, Improved Edition) and SIMSCRIPT are, by contrast, designed for more detailed simulation of specific operations and hardware systems. Both derive motivation and technique from earlier attempts to create a general purpose simulation language that would handle a large number of job-shop type problems in which many changes in flow attributes or routing must be handled, often in combination with extensive analysis of waiting lines or queues. The two languages differ markedly, however, in their approach to system definition.

GPSS-III is an IBM compiler[11] that approaches the definition of the system to be simulated by providing for the analyst's use a number of system "blocks" representing common operations to be simulated. These "components" may be put together in block diagram form (as described in Chapter 2) to form a block diagram of the system to be simulated. From this block diagram, the required computer instructions may be coded relatively easily, using the rules provided for this system. The extensive assortment of block types available with GPSS-III permits the rapid combinatorial construction

---

[11] *IBM Application Program: General Purpose Systems Simulator III* (#B20-0001-0), IBM Data Processing Division, White Plains, New York. Also user's manual #H20-0163.

of a wide variety of system types. This speed of simulation is a definite advantage, as is the fact that the block diagram constructed for this compiler bears close physical resemblance to the block diagram the analyst might use if he created a noncomputer block diagram based on physical observation and described the operations to be performed in ordinary English. In some cases, however, the blocks provided for construction of GPSS-II programs will not accomplish what the analyst wants, or will do so only in a cumbersome way.

The SIMSCRIPT language[12] attempts to provide the most general form of simulation compiler, and uses the listing approach to definition, as previously described in Chapter 4. By defining the entities (temporary or permanent) that make up a system as a hierarchy of categories, together with the attributes and set membership or ownership of each, SIMSCRIPT provides a general method for describing system status at a given time. The extensive timing routine and event-notice listing procedures required with this form of definition form part of the compiler package, so that the analyst is relieved of the burden of their construction and maintenance. This compiler has many special features that make for economy in the use of computer memory, provide extensive tabular report generation and statistical computation with a few instructions, and allow many system parameters to be specified at the time a given simulation run is executed (thus eliminating recompilation of the program each time a variation in experimental conditions is desired). These features, its FORTRAN compatibility and its wide availability, probably make SIMSCRIPT the most popular general purpose simulation language available today.

The beginner, however, may be somewhat overawed by the multitude of special features available with this compiler, and may also have difficulty with the special conditions required to create the specific format used in defining a system with SIMSCRIPT. For example, SIMSCRIPT requires the definition of some entities and events of different types that do not at first appear to be related to the physical characteristics of a given system. Yet, these details are usually required for record-keeping, timing, and statistical summary, and provide much of the power SIMSCRIPT has for simulation of complex systems.

For a further discussion of simulation languages, the reader is referred to the references cited. It is reasonable to assume that proficiency in the use of any simulation language (or any form of computer programing) comes largely with experience in developing and running specific problems on a specific machine—as well as from detailed study of user's manuals. Yet, the

---

[12] H. M. Markowitz, B. Hauser, and H. W. Karr, *SIMSCRIPT, A Simulation Programming Language*, A RAND Corporation Publication, Prentice-Hall, Englewood Cliffs, N.J., 1963. This is a user's manual. Some knowledge of FORTRAN is assumed. See also the specific manuals prepared for a given computer for this compiler.

effort expended by the analyst (say 40 hours) to acquire introductory skills with a given simulation language is greatly rewarded by its possible applications. Even though the analyst does not intend to enter into the details of computer programing, a knowledge of what can be done and the form of definition required will enable him to convey his problem more sensibly to a professional programer. What we have learned about the definition and analysis of systems will be of major benefit to further study and cooperation with computer specialists.

We must always remember that simulation languages and the use of machines to mechanize a system simulation are not substitutes for the analyst's understanding of his system. A computer simulation is no substitute for a bad system definition or a poorly formulated problem. Rather, such fundamental confusion is greatly exaggerated by the mechanics of computer simulation, which should be reserved for detailed experimentation with an already sound and clearly understood system definition.

A Blackboard Simulation Exercise

To illustrate a verification that is desirable before a simulation is mechanized, let us return to the job-shop example of Table 12-1. In working out the completion times for each job using the time-position chart, many of the detailed steps required were worked out by inspection, or by a few computations on a scratch pad. Although some care had to be exercised, particularly with the priority of work assignment at a given machine, no detailed statistical records were required.

Let us repeat that example and perform the same simulation, but let us now set up the procedure to follow more nearly the detailed steps that might be performed by a computer. Our organization of work will approximate a SIMSCRIPT procedure, but will forgo the notational detail employed by that language.

To start we will draw up a shop status board, Figure 12-9a, which shows in complete detail the organization of the job shop. The shop consists of four machines, so we make up a major column for each machine. We may also call the *Move* step an operation (essentially equivalent to Machine 5, if we think of material handling equipment) and make up another column for it. The last major column is called *Finish*, to represent the completion operation (essentially equivalent to a storage operation), and so may be thought of as Machine 6. The six major columns now define the six permanent divisions, or entities, comprising our shop.

Some consideration will reveal that we will need to make three additional distinctions at Machines 1 through 4, namely, whether a Job is waiting in a backlog *Queue*, being *Set up*, or *Running*. For this reason, we provide three subcolumns under each Machine 1 through 4.

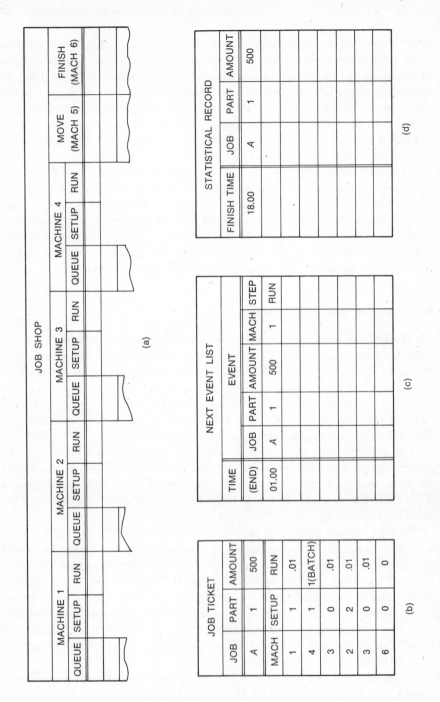

12-9 (a) Table defining system hierarchy for simulation. (b) Job ticket required for routing and timing. (c) Event List required to anticipate next event. (d) Historical record of what has happened (finish times only are shown).

Next, thinking ahead as to how the status of the shop may look at any time, we realize that a backlog or a *Queue* at any machine could consist of several jobs (or none), but that at any time only one order (or none) may be *Set up* or *Run*. Therefore, we provide several rows in each *Queue* column, but only one row under *Set up* and *Run*. For a similar reason, we provide several rows under *Move* and *Finish*.

We may now think of our Shop Status Board as being similar to that used by many shop dispatchers in controlling a shop manually. In such applications, each small square shown in Figure 12-9 is a small pigeonhole or pocket into which a record about a given job may be inserted, the position of the job card telling where it is, and the job-card description providing the detail required to identify a job, tell where it has been, where it is going, and the processing time required at each step. We will use this Status Board as a picture of the shop, which will of course change as time goes on. (Such a board may be physically constructed on paper, out of metal, or drawn on a blackboard). In the computer the pigeonholes would be memory locations.

Because there are four jobs to be completed, we will need four job tickets to start, as shown for Job A in Figure 12-9b. These job tickets correspond to the routing sheets or cards often found physically attached to in-process work in a shop. We will use them to indicate movements in status and to compute operation, move, and completion times. Note that the job ticket consists of two parts: An identification line giving the job name and amount, and a lower section which provides the routing required (progressing sequentially downward on the card) and the setup and running times on each successive machine. In the definition line, a square labeled "Part" has been included. At the start of the simulation, when the job is first assigned, we will refer to the job as Job A, Part 1. Remember, however, that the Inspection Operation will reject a portion of the job for rework. When this is done the job is split into two parts, one of which will go to finish, and one to rework. With this job split we need a double identification for record-keeping, and will therefore refer to the rejected portion of the job as Job A, Part 2. The same rule will hold for the other jobs. (During the simulation there may be more than four job tickets in the shop. The new tickets will be created as may be necessary.)

The second column on the job ticket indicates the number of hours for setup at each machine. The third column gives the production run time per unit of product. Machine 4, the furnace, is a batch operation as shown. Data for the job ticket comes from the specifications previously presented in Table 12.1.

To control the time of movements from one shop category to another, we will need a Next Event List, as shown in Figure 12-11c. Although a sample line is shown, this Next Event List will be clean at the start of the simulation.

Similarly, to compile the statistics required for a display of completion times, we need a Statistical Record on which we will record the required data, which otherwise might be lost during the course of the simulation.

With these forms in hand, the mechanics required for record-keeping and for reporting systems status have been defined. However, the rules for simulating the movement of orders through the shop remain to be clarified, and a detailed statement of what is to be done in the *exact sequence* that is to be followed, must be developed. As we shall see, this is no simple matter.

Examination of the graphic solution already completed reveals that a number of different events can occur. For example, a given job can arrive at a given machine and join a queue. A job in a queue can leave it. Setup can start and be completed. A run can start and be completed. A move can be started, or completed, and so on. Each start or completion of an action, regardless of how minor the apparent action may appear to be, causes a change in system status, by definition. Moreover, the sequence with which these events takes place is dependent upon what is going on elsewhere in the system. What happens when two orders arrive at a machine at the same instant with equal or different priorities?

The problems of defining all the rules of the operation would be less serious if only one specific problem were to be run. For example, knowing the job-shop problem as originally posed, and having the sequence of system status pictured in Figure 12-4, we see that, for the input used, queuing appears only at Machine 2, and not at the other machines. But, in general, queuing could occur at any of the machines so that the rules developed for the simulation must take into account *all possible* contingencies for a range of possible job inputs. This necessity to be exhaustively complete in the specification of the simulated system presents a logical burden upon the analyst and usually requires much trial-and-error development in the design of mechanized simulation. While making these specifications, the analyst must keep his eye on the specific process step under consideration and also on the over-all workings elsewhere in the system.

We may illustrate the detail required and the logical development by looking at the possible events that could occur and listing them. (Often the specification of the events that we want to create in the simulation will be influenced by the record-keeping desired for statistical analysis. In what follows, we suppose that detailed analysis of queue, setup, and run times may be desired in addition to completion times.)

Figure 12-10a shows a diagram of how the sequence of events determining the progress of system status would be controlled by the human analyst (using a paper or blackboard Status Board and the other forms of Figure 12-9) or by the computer using the same system definition. Different events may occur from time to time, as indicated by the blocks labeled with the connectors B through X. The sequence of these events will change, however,

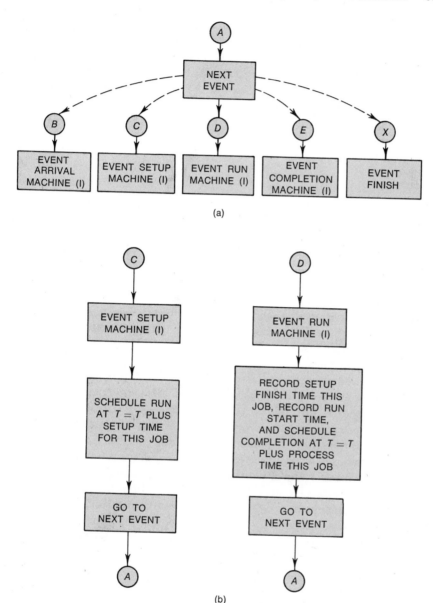

(a)

(b)

12-10   (a) The next event list and its procedure of use as a selection or switching device in generating chains of events. After execution of the procedures associated with a selected event-type, control returns to (A) and the Next Event List. (b) One event causes the scheduling of a subsequent event. In the simplest case, the occurrence of one event will simply cause the scheduling of another on the Next Event List. The steps above are appropriate when Machine (I) is Machine 1 or Machine 2. Alternate action (not shown) would be required when Machine (I) is Machine 3 or Machine 4.

depending upon the external input and the characteristic of the system. Because the simulation must proceed in a strictly sequential way, we must strictly sequence the events that will occur. A chain of events of this type may be generated by the Next Event List. In effect, this list selects or switches our attention and effort to the next sequentially scheduled event and its associated manipulations and computations. As a result one or more future events will be scheduled on the Event Notice List, which always will return control, after completion of the immediate event execution and its associated routine, to the Next Event List and its associated control procedures.

Each event block in Figure 12-10a thus initiates a series of manipulations that are carried out when the event occurs. These manipulations separate blocks, or subroutines, in the simulation which the timing routine using the Event Notice List pieces together, as required—following exactly the procedure a human analyst would perform using the Status Board and associated forms of Figure 12-9. The fact that the simulation can be cut up into modules, each of which may be developed separately, is a definite advantage in planning the simulation. Thus, although there may be a great variety of specific and distinct events, each requiring the execution of a different computation, we can specify each of these computational modules or subroutines one at a time, just as we could specify for the human analyst procedures for each event on different pages of a manual. In this way the possible complexity of a system can be segmented so that it is more easily handled by the analyst (or team of analysts). As we shall see momentarily, the segments of procedure that follow a given event may be trivial or relatively difficult. However, the combinatorial ability of these segments to generate variety permits versatility in simulating a system.

To be specific, as we view the job-shop example, we see that work which arrives at Machines 1 and 2 will be handled in a straightforward manner. There will always be a setup (by reference to the specifications), there are no batching problems, and there is no problem of product rejection, as is the case with the inspection step. This suggests that one procedure be developed for Machines 1 and 2, and that a different procedure be required for Machines 3 and 4, and for other operations such as Move and Finish.

First, consider the setup and run operations for Machines 1 and 2, as indicated in Figure 12-10b. These events, when the scheduled time has arrived, need only schedule new events. The completion of a setup always results in the start of a run, and so a run is scheduled on the Next Event List. The completion of a run can result in a number of different actions, depending upon current system status, but this will be taken care of at the proper time if a completion notice is posted and control returned to the Next Event List as shown.

The procedural steps necessary when an arrival occurs at Machines 1 or 2, or when a job is completed on Machines 1 or 2, are more interesting

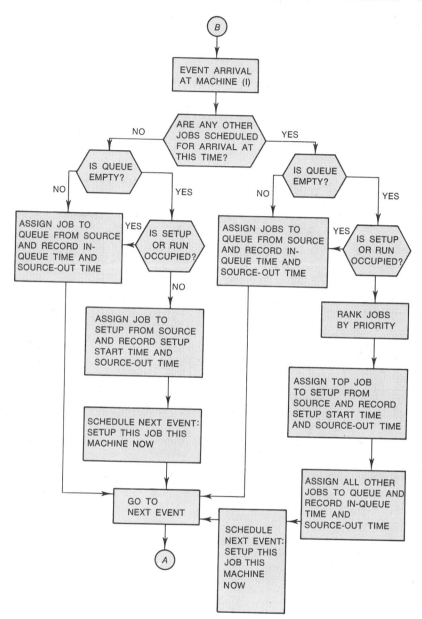

12-11 The specific procedure to be followed after the arrival of a job at Machines 1 or 2 of the job shop example. After completion, control returns to the Next Event List. The action to take for each possible status of the machine and input condition is specified by this block diagram. In the computer literature, this form of detailed procedure specification is often called "systems analysis" to contrast this form of problem formulation with the procedure of "coding" or writing specific instructions for the computer.

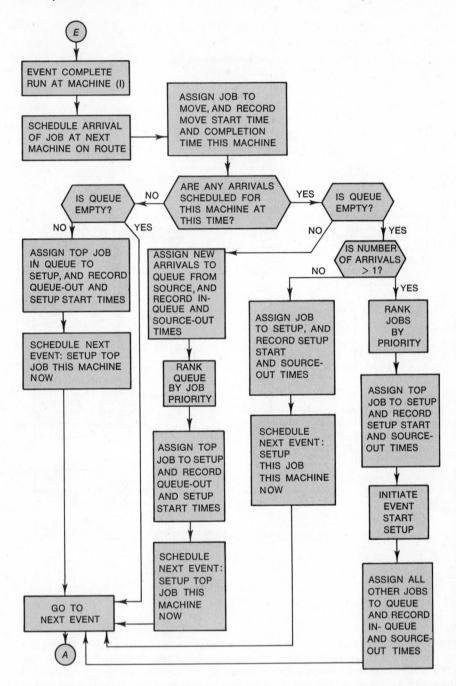

12-12 The specific procedure to be followed after the completion of a job at Machines 1 or 2 of the job shop example. After completion, control again returns to the next event list. Note that job completion will shorten the queue if it is not empty.

and are illustrated in block diagram form in Figures 12-11 and 12-12 respectively. Some careful analysis is required in each of these cases to pick up all the logical possibilities that could occur, and to specify the appropriate action to take for each possibility.

For example, in Figure 12-11, we may think of the various possibilities that can occur. There will be a different situation if

1. More than one arrival comes in at a given instant (or not),
2. The queue is empty (or not), and
3. Setup or Run is occupied (or not).

Because these are yes-no questions, and there are three statements, our knowledge of Chapter 11 indicates that there should be 2^3 distinct possibilities to take care of. However, we may note that the three statements are not logically independent: If the queue is not empty, then setup or run must be occupied because we would naturally move the work along if the machine were idle. That there are only six distinct conditions may be seen from the complete logical basis for the three statements, in which the required 0's for setup and run full are shown.

Condition	Combination		
	1 2 3 4	5 6 7 8	
Other jobs arrived	0 1 0 1	0 1 0 1	
Queue empty	0 0 1 1	0 0 1 1	
Setup or run full	0 0 0 0	1 1 1 1	

Condition Combinations 1 and 2 are thus impossible and may be eliminated, resulting in six distinct combinations. Each of these six possibilities is taken care of by the decision trees of Figure 12-11.

In Figure 12-12 a similar approach may be used. At the time of a job completion, we normally would move up to setup anything in the queue. However, at that exact instant of completion the Next Event List might contain one or more arrivals to occur at the same instant. Should this be true, some of the members of the present queue could be bumped by a higher priority arrival(s); therefore, such possibilities must be taken into account.

Noting as before that if the number of scheduled arrivals in the Next Event List is not greater than zero, the number can certainly not be greater than one, we can construct a logical basis of the possibilities, inserting zeros where required.

Condition	Combination		
	1 2 3 4	5 6 7 8	
Arrivals > 0	0 1 0 1	0 1 0 1	
Queue empty	0 0 1 1	0 0 1 1	
More than one arrival	0 0 0 0	1 1 1 1	

Here Conditions 5 and 7 are impossible and may be eliminated, leaving six distinctions. In addition, Condition 6 (arrivals greater than zero, but queue not empty) provides one more irrelevant condition, because if the queue is not empty one *or* more arrivals will join the queue, and Condition 6 and 2 may be grouped. The five distinctions that remain are taken care of by the decision tree in Figure 12-12.

An examination of all the logical possibilities at each stage of the simulation development is useful to prevent omission of a test combination that should have been included. Such omission is a common error in defining the simulation steps. Although completeness is not so strictly demanded in manual simulation, because the analyst can devise special rules as needed during the course of the simulation, the computer does not have this improvising ability and must be supplied with instructions for every contingency, just as a legal contract hopes to cover all pertinent conditions before they obtain.

Returning now to Figure 12-10, we see that to completely specify the job-shop simulation we will need "Event Routines" for operations on Machines 3 and 4. The presently defined routines will not do, because Machine 3 (inspection) requires a special series of steps to reject 20% of the job, split the job in two parts, and route each separately from there on. Machine 4, which is a batch operation, requires special tests for the number of batches to run for each job, and a different processing time computation. Similarly, the Event Finish requires statistical record keeping and a test for completion of the simulation, and also the initial arrival of Jobs A, B, C, D at Machine 1 must be scheduled. (Construction of these additional flow charts is left as an exercise.)

With the detailed instructions for each type of event routine in hand, say on different pages of a procedural manual, the combination of these routines may be tested manually. For example, we may repeat, in detail, the sequence of events illustrated in Figure 12-4. If the detailed specifications are correct, the results should be the same as before. In this test procedure (which is also left as an exercise) the analyst will find it convenient to record each scheduled event in the Next Event List, and then cross out that event as it is executed. This will provide a complete listing of what has happened in case further analysis is required.

Some remarks are now in order. First, it would be possible to introduce randomness in any of the "Schedule Event" computations by means of the Monte Carlo procedure described in the previous section. In the flow diagrams shown (Figures 12-10b, 12-11, and 12-12) such randomness has not been included in the simulation. Next, to make the Event Routines as general as possible, we note that it would be convenient if we had some indexing ability in "tagging" jobs, selecting order attribute data for test, and selecting machine types. For example, such indexing ability is required in the manual case as the jobs move from one machine to another in the job-shop simulation, because each successive machine requires different setup and processing data (obtained by reference to the next line on the job ticket). Simulation languages, such as SIMSCRIPT, provide this indexing ability (although we have not indicated the notational details in the flow chart illustrations of Figures 12-10 through 12-12). We should also note that many different Event Routines could be developed to accomplish the same ends. For example, it would be possible to handle the different machine types in two Event Routines, like Figures 12-11 and 12-12 for arrival and completion—suitably complicating each by adding additional tests for "Machine Type" and providing the alternate actions required for each. The choice of Event Routine organization is a matter of convenience, and depends largely upon the purposes for which the simulation has been designed.

SELECTING SIMULATION TEST VARIATIONS

Exercising the System

To see if the simulation procedures designed will work for the entire range of possible input cases, it is common to "exercise the system" by developing a series of test inputs that will provide a diagnostic routine for each segment of the simulation program. As described in Chapter 10, if the system can be segmented into a number of independent divisions, each may be tested separately by developing special input cases, or changing the values of initial conditions at each division. In the job-shop example, we would be particularly interested in whether or not the queuing and priority rules worked satisfactorily at each machine, and we could test this by feeding a series of jobs with different priorities directly to a given machine, or to the generalized routine for job arrivals at Machine (I). The other methods of Chapters 10 and 11 may also be used for this purpose. In preparing such test data, and test routines, it is, of course, essential that we know what should happen in response to each test. For example, if a job arrives at Machine A and a queue is present, then that job should join the queue and eventually work its way through setup and run at Machine A. Should this required result fail to occur, we know something is wrong, and the specific failure provides a symptom for diagnosis of the timing sequence or Event Routine construction.

Having satisfied ourselves that the simulated system is logically correct, we may explore the system further.

Validation of the System

If our purpose is to simulate a system in the real world (rather than study the logical operations of the logically defined system set up for manipulation) then it is necessary to confirm that the results of the simulation predict what will happen in reality under the same assumptions. For example, if the simulated system predicts completion times such as those displayed in Figure 12-4, then one validating result would be the observation of similar completion times for the same input sequence and initial conditions in a real job shop. The more such confirming results the analyst can obtain for a variety of cases, the greater confidence he may have in the realism of his simulation model.

The analyst should not be dismayed, however, to find that in systems controlled by human operators, predicted and actual results may differ widely. This is often the case because in the real world shop the rules allocating and sequencing work are often followed inconsistently, or various improvisations and emergency conditions (machine breakdown, faulty material, incorrect machine settings, lost jobs and so on) may occur to disrupt the flow of work. In some cases the realism of the simulation model may be improved *by further complicating it,* i.e., by adding the major contingencies that occur in the real world, but which have been left out of the simulation model for simplicity. Where further complication is intolerable (due to lack of memory capacity, greatly increased running times, and replication requirements for statistical reliability, etc.), something may yet be learned from the simulation model about what would occur under more ideal conditions of shop conformity to plan.

It should also not be surprising that it is easier to validate a simulation model for hardware controlled, or highly logical, systems than it is for human controlled systems. Thus, automated systems, such as telephone networks, computer controlled machines and processes, and electromechanical systems provide logical structures that are amenable to the simulation approach. Hybrid simulation models, which combine both human operators and some computer or hardware processing (previously called Operational Simulation), offer another route to improved validity. In such hybrid simulations we assume that the human operators will respond in practice as they do at simulation time, which may or may not be true.[13]

Heuristic Selection of Test Cases

Because many possible test cases could be used (which would possibly be interesting) in manipulating a simulation model, and because logical

[13] Much criticism has been leveled at some forms of Operational Simulation, because it is not clear that decisions made in the clinical atmosphere of a simulation exercise would be the decisions made by human operators in the more complex real world setting. For example, the most successful "President" in a Management Game would not necessarily be the most successful real world President in the richer context of psychological, financial, and political pressures that set the scene for real Management Decisions. (See W. Cristian, "Don't Bet on Management Games," *Business Automation,* July, 1961.) The use of simulators for training operators is more successful, because much of the operating scene can be created at simulation time. The operation of a radar room, missile control center, or jet cockpit are examples.

screening of conditions may be difficult, experimental conditions are often selected by judgment. In such "heuristic" selection of test cases, the analyst picks out experimental conditions or experimental decision rules that seem interesting, or likely to work, or that have worked in the past, and seeks to evaluate such proposals using the simulation model. For example, in the job-shop example, the analyst may wish to compare the present priority rule (determined by the last machine a job came from) with a rule that is determined by (1) promise date, (2) shortest job in queue, (3) first-in first-out in queue, (a FIFO policy), (4) last-in first-out (a LIFO policy), (5) the length of the queue for the next machine in a job route, or (6) a computed rank, depending upon, say, the value of the job (i.e., dollars tied up in in-process inventory) and the probability of shortage of that item in finished inventory. An evaluation of these possibilities might then proceed for a wide variety of possible product-mix loads arriving at the shop, and the rule that optimized a stated criterion (such as maximum machine utilization, shortest total processing time, minimum dollars in-process, or a computed criterion specified in advance) could be selected. Thus, from the infinitely large number of possible priority rules, a set of reasonable ones is adopted for evaluation.

Parametric Variation of Test Cases

In many simulation problems a question of data sensitivity arises which is often answered by variation of the data inputs and a computation of the resulting effects upon system output. This procedure, often called "sensitivity analysis" or "parametric experimentation," may proceed in a number of ways. For example, the variations proposed may be taken at random, in a systematic way, or they may be taken at the extremes of a range of interest. In the job-shop illustration, we may be interested in the effects of move time upon the sequential status of the shop and the resulting variation in job completion times. Thus, we may introduce a random move time having a given average, standard deviation, and distribution, and generate a series of variable move times using the Monte Carlo method. Or, we may systematically increment and decrement the stated one-hour move time by quarter-hour intervals. Or, we may ask for an evaluation in which the move time was in error by 20%, and concentrate only on those extremes. Should the results (completion times) not be greatly affected by such variations in the parameter move time, then we could conclude that this was not a "critical" parameter in the model, or vice versa. Again the number of parameters that can be so varied in any complex simulation soon becomes astronomical, so that some selection is required when picking combinations of test parameters.

A similar series of experimental variations could be planned for parameters involving machine capacity, processing times, and the like.

Evaluation of Alternate System Designs

Another source of test cases is the availability of alternate proposals for system designs for the performance of a given task, or the processing of a given set of inputs. An obvious approach here is to write alternate simulation programs for each proposed design, and to test these alternate systems under identical input conditions.

A less obvious but more fruitful approach is to design the original simulation model so that alternate design structures can be obtained by the specification of a limited number of control statements, which will, in effect, restructure the simulation model's sequence of operation and thereby simulate the alternate systems, as required. If the class of design alternatives to be evaluated can be anticipated at the outset, much work can be saved by the use of the more general simulation model. For example, if the various operations that might be performed in alternate system designs are anticipated, they may be described in subroutines and pieced together in the proper order by a generalized control routine, with control parameters to be selected at execution time, depending upon the alternate design to be evaluated. The selection of alternate designs remains a problem for the analyst, but their evaluation is greatly simplified by this approach.

SOME COMMENTS IN CONCLUSION

Although we have employed a job-shop example in this chapter to illustrate the timing problems in some highly conditional system simulations, what has been said applies also to the use of system simulators in general. By describing the range of possible simulation mechanics—from manual to highly automated—it was our intent to provide the reader with a feeling for the generality of the approach, and to illustrate that the automated simulation is an extension of the manual simulation which greatly facilitates evaluation and manipulation, but which also places increased burdens of precise definition and logical consistency and completeness upon the analyst. It was also our intent to dwell on the thinking required in the development of a simulation model, rather than to become engrossed in the details of a given simulation language for a computer or the hardware that might be used to implement the logical model. Because most simulation difficulties spring from the definition and specification stage of model development and from inadequate planning for the desired results, our discussion complements the more detailed discussion of simulation languages and mechanics of simulation available in the references cited. For example, after completing this chapter, the reader will have a greater appreciation for the structure of computer simulation languages and will therefore derive greater benefit from simulator user's manuals, which assume the background knowledge we have presented here.

We have also attempted to provide cautionary remarks about the use of system simulation, and to warn that, although it is a powerful and popular technique for systems analysis, simulation is not a universally suitable approach to human training, the development of better decision rules, the selection of human operators or system designs, or the evaluation of all types of proposed systems. The assumptions, requirements, and stability conditions demanded by a simulation may not be present in a system to be simulated; the resources required may not be justified by the case at hand; the analyst may not know what sort of results to print out; there simply may not be time to set up a simulation and experiment. Eugene Burdick expressed these limitations dramatically in his novel, *The 480*, as Curver realizes his formerly effective political simulation is useless under a shift in convention strategy.

> Curver felt physically ill. Three months ago, even a few days ago, it had all been neat and scientific and well thought out. He and Dev had been close to doing the impossible . . . running an unknown for the Republican nomination against a gang of millionaires. And they had done it silently, cheaply, scientifically, and—almost—successfully. Now, because of Kelly, they were going back to the messy, old-fashioned, haranguing days he had read about in books and winced. It was too late to program anything about this new situation through the 7094. They would be flying on intuition and snap judgments from senile old bastards like Lander.[14]

In his bag of tools, the systems analyst has simulation—even mechanized simulation—as a possibility.[15] But there are many other possibilities. And the analyst should not be led to believe that simulation is the only form of systems analysis. The experienced analyst does not make this, sometimes fatal, mistake.

PROBLEMS

12.1 Why would it be desirable to simulate the control and logic system of a new elevator installation or a new elevator control system design, before the units are constructed and installed? What savings could be made by using the simulation technique in this case?

12.2 Again consider the coin-changing vending machine of Chapter 2, Program the logical diagram given in Chapter 2 for an electronic computer, so that

---

[14] Eugent Burdick, *The 480*, McGraw-Hill, New York, 1964, p. 259.
[15] For a bibliography, see M. Shubik, "Bibliography on Simulation, Gaming, Artificial Intelligence and Allied Topics," *J. Am. Statist. Assoc.*, **55**, 104, December, 1960. For current developments consult *Computing Reviews* and *The Communications of the A.C.M.*, both published by the Association for Computing Machinery, New York, and *International Abstracts in Operations Research*, distributed by the Operations Research Society of America, Baltimore, Md.

the operation of the machine may be simulated. Test the logic of the vending machine diagram by making up, or generating, a random sequence of inputs of nickels, dimes, quarters, pennies, and slugs. Show as a printed output from this simulation the coin input and the machine output (product and/or coin) for each transaction completed.

A. Are there any coin input combinations that lead to an incorrect action?

B. In a problem of this type, is there any necessity of introducing a random input for test, or could an exhaustive list of all possible combinations at the input be used instead?

C. After which test (random or exhaustive) would you feel most comfortable, as the designer of this machine? Why?

12.3   To illustrate the usefulness of random normal numbers in simulation problems, work out the following simulation exercise. A hand simulation will be satisfactory.

Three light bulbs are connected in series, so that all must light if any are to light. The average lifetime (in hours) for each bulb differs, and is given with the standard deviation of each below. Assume that the bulb lifetimes are normally distributed with the parameters given.

Bulb	A	B	C
Average lifetime x, hours	100	90	80
Standard deviation σ, hours	30	20	10

As you simulate the three bulb lifetimes, find the life of the simulated assembly (which will be the smallest lifetime of A, B, or C.)

A. Simulate at least 100 assemblies, and tabulate the lifetime simulated for each assembly. Plot a histogram of the assembly lifetimes. Observe how the distribution indicated by the histogram becomes more regular as you progressively add results to the histogram.

B. After completion of the experiment described above, compute the average and stand deviation of assembly lifetimes, using the histogram data or the tabular results. You should get an average of 70. Why is this result smaller than the average lifetime of any of the three bulbs? Why is the standard deviation greater than any of the individual standard deviations?

12.4   President Jones, who heads a small company, is a hard taskmaster. He has three employees. Because of his demands, Jones finds that the probability of survival for one of his workers, if selected from applicants off the street is, in quarters of the year:

1 Quarter	0.4	
2 Quarters	0.3	NO BONUS
3 Quarters	0.2	
4 Quarters or over	0.1	

Because this turnover is expensive, Jones has hit upon the plan of increasing the pay of those who stay with him for one quarter, thereby changing the probability distribution of their survival to the following quarter:

1 Quarter	0.5	
2 Quarters or more	0.5	WITH BONUS

Assuming that both new and old employees who quit are replaced with employees "off the street" how many persons will Jones hire over a three-year period? (*Note:* Set this up as a Monte Carlo Problem, and simulate two years experience, by quarters. Assume the quarters are independent. Compare the results of a complete no-bonus scheme with a bonus scheme.)

PROJECT 8

Simulate a three-level supply system. Suppose there are 125 stores, representing Level 1, each receiving and placing an order for a given spare part (each month) with probability $p = 0.2$, and none with a probability $q = 1 - p = 0.8$. (Thus, total system demand at Level 1 is $125p = 25$, and the standard deviation of the total demand is $Npq = \sqrt{125 \times 0.2 \times 0.8} = 4.5$. (From the above definitions the distribution of this total demand follows the binomial distribution.) The stores always order when demand arises, and they supply to customers at once or they back order, if stock is not immediately available.

In addition, assume that each group of five stores orders from a jobber, so at Level 2 there are 25 jobbers. At the jobber level, suppose the store orders are filled as they come in (if stock is available, or backordered and filled next month, if not). The 25 jobbers order from a single supplier, Level 3, monthly in batches of eleven (an eleven-month supply) when jobber stock falls to two units or less. Assume the supplier has a very large stock on hand, so that jobber orders can always be filled at once.

A. Simulate this supply system by hand or on a computer, and find the distribution of demand at the supplier, Level 3. *Initialize* the jobber stock levels to start at eleven pieces each and store stock levels at one unit each. Simulate at least 150 months, assuming the demand at the stores is, of course, independent.

B. Comment on the size of the supplier's standard deviation of demand. Would you expect it to be more or less than the 4.5 given by theory for the Level 1 demand?

C. How would a change in jobber order size change the distribution of supplier demand? Would a change in initial conditions change the final distribution of supplier demand?

D. Can you distinguish a transient and a steady-state result in this simulation? Should the transient data, if any, be used in accumulating data to describe the supplier demand distribution?

E. In setting up the simulation, make provision for computing the average store and average jobber inventory levels and for recording the number of back-orders at the store and jobber level. What changes in initial conditions and ordering rules would change the average inventory and backorder statistics? How do the ordering rules link the supply levels?

PROJECT 9

Using the method of system definition used in the SIMSCRIPT computer language, as outlined in the last section of Chapter 4, and the job-shop blackboard exercise illustrated in this chapter, simulate the job-shop example on a computer. (As an alternate, use GPSS III, or any other language you prefer.) The data for a deterministic problem are provided in Table 12.1.

A. Compare the results for a deterministic simulation with the results shown in Figure 12-4.

B. Introduce variability into the simulation at one or more points, and compare the results of the probabilistic case with the deterministic case. (A number of replications of the experiment will be required to obtain a distribution of output results.) Why will the output results vary more than you might expect from a casual inspection of this problem?

SYSTEMS TREATMENT

13 | ANALYSIS FOR IMPLEMENTATION

Most systems analysts find that they introduce change in the systems they study. They correct the faults of malfunctioning systems, or seek to improve an existing system. Or, they design new systems and seek to implement them, displacing older systems by new ones. Indeed, the systems analyst, probably has "the future in his bones," to use C. P. Snow's phrase. Otherwise, he would not have taken up his occupation.

Often such changes greatly broaden the scope of the systems analyst's problem and call upon his knowledge not only of technical possibilities but also of institution and culture.

When we consider this broader subject, discussions of the nature of man, a subject central to most of the great systems of human thought, eventually confront us. Based on assumptions or ideas, usually simplified to suit the times, the concepts of the rational man, the sinful man, the man of will and power, the economic man, and the Freudian man have all become the basis for arguments and theories of human behavior that are still with us in many forms.

The latest trend in building a picture of human nature is to consider "behavioral man," who is defined by the sum total of his observed actions, rather than by assumptions about his character. For our present discussion, this latter viewpoint provides a more varied picture of the human scene and a number of detailed observational results that can be used by the systems analyst. Because all operating systems at one or more stages of their definition, development, analysis, and use are affected by human individuals, knowledge of actual behavior patterns in different circumstances becomes an essential ingredient in understanding how systems come about and how they will be accepted and work in practice.

In what follows we present a sketch of a major cultural conflict and a corresponding discussion of behavioral science man that has meaning for the systems analyst who hopes to implement system change.[1]

SOCIAL SCIENCE AND TECHNOLOGICAL CHANGE

Social scientists have long been concerned with the problems of technological change and how they influence the society and the culture in which we live. The reverse problem, of course, is also important because the historical setting, and the tools and ideas presently known, affect the selection of projects considered worthwhile.

In viewing this grand process of technological advancement and social change we generally find a conflict between those who propose change and those who prefer the present state of affairs. In analyzing a given society, for example, it is useful to make a distinction between what Wheelis has called "the instrumental process" and "the institutional process." These are concepts representing two opposing clusters of activities, attitudes, and kinds of criteria for what "good" is. Both processes affect groups within society at a given time, and indeed to a greater or lesser extent they affect the individual at a given time. Thus, our understanding of these processes sheds much light on the ways in which system change may be acceptably introduced, so we shall consider each of them in turn.

The Instrumental Process

The instrumental process, which is concerned with "the facts," stresses replication, verifiability, and usefulness in social life. "The authority of the instrumental process is rational, deriving from its demonstrable usefulness to the life process. The final appeal is to the evidence." [2]

The scientific method approximates the heart of the matter, but the instrumental process is a larger concept that concerns the development of

---

[1] This discussion is abstracted basically from two sources: A. Wheelis, *The Quest for Identity*, Norton, New York, 1958, and Victor Gollancz Ltd., London, especially Chapter III, and B. Berelson and G. A. Steiner, *Human Behavior: An Inventory of Scientific Findings*, Harcourt, Brace & World, New York, 1964. The Wheelis book is a discussion of current psychiatric and cultural problems. Berelson and Steiner report 1045 experimental and observational findings from which general conclusions are drawn in Chapter 17. There, confirming cross references to the literature may be found in abundance.

[2] Wheelis, *op. cit.*, p. 74.

tools and techniques (both physical and mental) used to solve problems. Electric saws *and* the differential calculus are both instruments for this purpose. It includes art, both fine and applied, because materials and methods are required in their completion. The instrumental process is bound to reality, facts are facts, it seems to say. Ignoring them is of no avail. Reality can be altered, particularly if it is clearly observed. Indeed, the better one understands it and the more tools one has to deal with it, the more radically it can be changed.[3]

We may not like the facts, but there they are—for better or for worse. Our job is to proceed with the project at hand. As we proceed with the instrumental process, we learn more and develop more tools, which, in turn, increase the output of the instrumental process and the number of possible combinations of what is already available.

The instrumental process is respected because it is useful, productive, growing, and bountiful in many, though not all, spheres of human life. Yet, from an individual or social viewpoint, for very personal reasons, the instrumental process "is often disparaged as mere problem-solving; for the security it creates, though real, is limited."[4] It may be respected, but not loved.

The Institutional Process

The institutional process, on the other hand, builds certainty, not doubt, for the individual. It seeks stability, sure-footedness, a rock of ages. Change, particularly rapid change, is shunned.

Thus, both the individual and society build strong barriers, both conscious and unconscious, for protection against change. Most frequently, these barriers seek an authority, organization, or tradition—in short an institution—larger than self or even everyday reality. This institutional process is diametrically opposed to what we have previously called the instrumental process.

> Everything mundane is subject to change, and hence certainty is not to be found in the affairs of men. The searcher arrives at his goal [of certainty], therefore, in a realm of being superordinate to man. Solomon put it succinctly: "Trust in the Lord with all thine heart; and lean not unto thine own understanding."[5]

Although religion is one example of the institutional process, the concept is broader than that. The institutional process includes customs, taboos, rites, mores, ceremonial compulsions, magic, kinship, status, coercive power systems, and such modern institutions as private property and the sovereign

[3] Wheelis, *op. cit.*, p. 75.
[4] Wheelis, *op. cit.*, p. 75.
[5] Wheelis, *op. cit.*, p. 74.

state. As such, "The authority of the institutional process is arbitrary; the final appeal is to force."

In particular, the institutional process is bound to human desire and fear. Wishing will make it so, it seems to say. It is unbearable that no one should care; so there must exist a heavenly Father who loves us. Activities of the institutional process do not, objectively, gratify any need or guard against any danger; incantation does not cause rain to fall or game to be plentiful. But such activities may engender a subjective sense of security, and this has always been a factor to be reckoned with—and, indeed, to be exploited. Honor and prestige accrue to the institutional process; for the security it creates, though illusory, is unlimited.[6]

Some Findings about Behavioral Science Man

The matter is put in a slightly different way by Berelson and Steiner, who, after compiling an inventory of scientific findings in the social sciences, summarize that body of knowledge on "behavioral science man." [7]

Perhaps the character of behavioral science man can best be grasped through his orientation to reality. . . . First, he is extremely good at adaptive behavior—at doing or learning to do things that increase his chances for survival or for satisfaction. . . . But there is another way man comes to terms with reality when it is inconsistent with his needs or preferences . . . In his quest for satisfaction, man is not just a seeker of truth, but of deceptions, of himself as well as others. . . . When man can come to grips with his needs by actually changing the environment, he does so. But when he cannot achieve such "realistic" satisfactions, he tends to take the other path: to modify what he sees to be the case, what he thinks he wants, what he thinks others want.

[In the latter case] he adjusts his social perception to fit not only the objective reality but also what suits his wishes and his needs . . . ; he tends to remember what fits his needs and expectations . . . , or what he thinks others will want to hear . . . ; he not only works for what he wants but wants what he has to work for . . . ; his need for psychological protection is so great that he has become expert in "defense mechanisms" . . . he will misinterpret rather than face up to an opposing set of facts or point of view . . . ; he avoids the conflicts of issues and ideals whenever he can by changing the people around him rather than his mind . . . , and when he cannot, private fantasies can lighten the load and carry him through . . . ; he thinks that his own organization ranks higher

[6] Wheelis, *op. cit.*, p. 75.
[7] Berelson and Steiner, *op. cit.*, Chapter 17.

than it actually does . . . ; and that his own group agrees with him more fully than it does . . . ; and if it does not, he finds a way to escape to a less uncongenial world . . . .[8]

The introduction of change, particularly change that seems to the individual beyond his control and which therefore threatens, or reduces perceived security, elicits reactions that are not necessarily logical and that the systems analyst may expect in the course of his work. If the systems analyst proposes change, which is the essence of the instrumental process, he meets the proponents of status quo, for the essence of the institutional process is to stand pat.

Indeed, some institutional processes are so rigid, that the innovator contests them at his peril. In his *Letters from Earth,* Samuel Clemens wrote,

> We do not know how or when it became custom for women to wear long hair, we only know in this country it *is* the custom, and that settles it . . . . Women may shave their heads elsewhere, but here they must refrain or take the uncomfortable consequences . . . . The penalty may be unfair, unrighteous, illogical, and a cruelty; no matter, it will be inflicted, just the same.[9]

And, some habits are so strongly ingrained that they are impervious to change. Many individuals work at night to avoid change. As one elderly worker, who had worked the night shift for forty years expressed it to the author:

> When I went to work there were no cars on the street, only horses. Wagons and horses. Now there are cars, and too many people. Too many. Why do I work at night? Things never change much at night. In the morning there are cars and people. But, things never change much at night. Who needs those cars and people?

It is interesting that the instrumental and institutional processes described above have been compared to the term *ego* and *superego* used in individual psychoanalysis.

In those terms, the ego represents the executive department of the human personality—the instrumental activities that recognize facts, marshall resources, devise plans of action, and get things done.

The superego is the judicial department, which performs a screening function, directs awareness, vetoes unacceptable proposals, and sets values and effectiveness measures used in goal formation. The superego is institutional in character, and derives its "conscience" from the culture, its customs, habits, and mores.

[8] Berelson and Steiner, *op. cit.,* pp. 663–664.
[9] Clemens, S., *Letters from Earth* as quoted in Berelson and Steiner *op. cit.,* p. 642.

Most studies show that the conscience so formed is highly relative to the culture or society in which the individual lives.[10]

For many important issues, constraints upon the superego are set by a small group—those near home as it were. Thus, the constraints are greater where families live together for several generations than where they do not, greater in small towns than in large, greater at home than abroad, greater when there are strong religious beliefs or formal institutional ties than when there are none, greater when only one set of values is perceived than when there are many that seem relative to time or place. We are all familiar with acts and common phrases that illustrate these facts.

Things happen in motels that do not happen in homes, and towels are swiped in distant hotels by persons who would not steal a pin in their hometowns. Some persons, indeed, travel for just this purpose—to lose an unwanted reinforcement of conscience. For them wanderlust is not a lust for wandering but a wandering for lust.[11]

Similarly, methods exist for strengthening the superego or judicial function in the personality (and therefore the institutional function in the culture), and also for reducing its effect. Street lights reduce burglaries, and double-entry bookkeeping reduces embezzlement. Conversely, in surroundings where multiple values are evident and where institutional restrictions are consciously relaxed, the range of acceptable value and goal choices increases, leading to a greater variety of possible actions or considerations and to a greater potential for change. Thus, as institutional restrictions become less (and instrumental efforts are, relatively speaking, more respected), new proposals become more easily accepted by those who must approve and use them and vice versa.[12]

Note also that the capacity of the investigator or the individual to effect system change, or to alter his perception of the facts to suit his needs, is due to his capacity for the creation and manipulation of *symbols*. Language and abstraction form the concepts, ideas, and instructions that permit learn-

[10] For example, see the cases summarized by Berelson and Steiner, *op. cit.*, Chapter 17.

[11] Wheelis, *op. cit.*, p. 101. In 10 months of 1965 the Americana Hotel in New York City is reported to have lost 38,000 demitasse spoons, 20,000 towels, and 475 bibles to its guests. *New York Daily News*, January 24, 1966, p. 23.

[12] The converse effect has interesting psychological implications, although we cannot explore it in detail. For example, when the rate of instrumental change is high in a culture, that area of the individual personality controlled by the superego could be expected to diminish. The individual may thus be involved by a search for certainty in his changing world, yet finds few institutional guides acceptable to him. Wheelis, for example, cites the quest for group consensus and the appeal of mass movements for the individual as evidence of this change in the superego in complex societies. He derives many interesting results from this thesis, one of which is that psychiatry as practiced in many cases treats problems no longer relevant to the present scene. See Wheelis, *op. cit.*, pp. 87–89 and Chapter 7.

ing and the transfer of experience (and the very act of systems definition and analysis).

This capacity, which permits the analyst to generalize, also permits him to change the name of the game to suit his needs.

Although it would appear to be a fact that a rose by any other name would smell as sweet, for individuals who view a scene this invariance of description may not hold. A plain ham-and-cheese sandwich may taste better if it is described as a "wedge of cheddar wedded to a generous portion of prime Virginia ham surrounded by California tomatoes and Florida lettuce and a discrete portion of pure egg mayonnaise." Even though a simple yes or no might suffice, a problem solution may seem more impressive and convincing if couched in mathematical symbols and presented with a slight but correct accent by a man with a Ph.D from Cambridge.

But, because our symbols, our abstractions, and our ability to conjure up favorable or unfavorable impressions with a word or gesture are products of our culture, and because the participant-listener's symbols and abstractions are formed by his culture, a knowledge of how symbols are formed and held is the key to our understanding of culture.[13]

Finally, we should note that institutional problems are magnified as the instrumental process advances with time. Although institutions do change under the impact of technology and instrumental advances, they change slowly and reluctantly, ". . . and make peace, finally, with the conditions which altered them." [14]

But institutional change is *slower* than instrumental change. By the time the institutional process, or the culture, has made peace with instrumental change, ". . . technology has moved on, and the laggard is still trailing." [15] Indeed, the discrepancy between instrumental growth and institutional change becomes worse with time. The combinatorial possibilities of instrumental growth are geometric; more tools, more techniques, more facts, and more concepts lead to a cornucopia of new possibilities. The instrumental process is regenerative, but the institutional process does not partake of this bounty and holds steadfast, unless intimidated, coerced, and pummeled into movement.

The resulting effect is a cultural lag—an ever increasing gulf between what is possible and what is acceptable.[16]

---

[13] A culture is most frequently defined by its community of understanding, and may be measured by the frequency of compatible interactions that occur between its members, as indicated by K. W. Deutsch, *Nationalism and Social Communication*, Technology Press and Wiley, New York, 1953. C. P. Snow expressed the same idea in literary terms: "Without thinking about it, they respond alike. That is what culture means." To speak of a cultural lag is perhaps not so descriptive as to speak of a cultural conflict or gap between the instrumental and institutional community of understanding.

[14] Wheelis, *op. cit.*, p. 82.

[15] Wheelis, *op. cit.*, p. 82.

[16] The culture lag was first discussed in length by W. F. Ogburn, *Social Change*, Dell, New York, 1927.

Introducing Change

Changes that alter no dearly held belief, custom, or mode of habitual operation are often introduced with relative ease in highly technical areas. Tools
may be redesigned, new production methods may be introduced, new
weapons may be brought out; tactics, competitive goals, and impersonal
means may all be changed with relative ease. However, primary group
relations, territorial and religious stability, systems of prestige, customs,
mores, and habits resist activation.

Change is easier to introduce in matters arranged on a scale with
narrow intervals than in those arranged in a sharp dichotomy —i.e., when
the only answer is black or white. Change is easier to introduce when the
elements of change are congenial to the culture, and the society has roughly
equivalent substitutes or existing alternatives. Change is easier to introduce
through existing institutions rather than through new, through individuals
of high prestige and status rather than low, through a third "disinterested"
party rather than directly. Change is easier to introduce if it directly affects
only a small segment of society, rather than the mass, if its side effects are
imperceptible rather than pervasive, and if secrecy instead of full publicity
is the rule. Change is easier to introduce in times of crises and stress than
in more tranquil times.

In short, the introduction of change is eased if the symbols of change
present no apparent alteration or modification of the culture's widely
held symbols. Indeed, change is greatly facilitated if the culture's present
symbols and instructions reinforce the proposed alterations in operation.

To exploit the cultural symbols of the time or to create others that
are only slightly changed but useful, to present a carefully edited story,
to obtain the approval of a high-status group for a project, to associate
the new development with values already held dear—all of these activities
help bridge the cultural gap and make a new proposal acceptable.

Example: Pharmaceutical firms have the problem of introducing and
marketing new drugs as they are developed and tested. Because many
new drugs of a specialized type are introduced each year, the physician
is deluged with circulars, samples, and "detail men" explaining the
virtues of their products, many of which compete for the same type of
treatment. Several drug firms have organized this effort to exploit institutional values held by physicians. Extensive mailing lists are maintained with records on each physician (containing, for example, age,
school attended, organizational affiliations, and the like). When a new
drug is to be introduced, it is often possible to analyze this list and to
compile a relatively shorter list of former professors or maestros who
represent a higher status group. If the maestros react favorably to the

new drug—and their smaller number makes them easier to convince with limited resources—then their approval can have a strong institutional influence in making the technological advance acceptable to the total list.

Example: The elimination of elevator operators (by the substitution of push buttons) to reduce operating costs may well be spoken of as an attempt to improve passenger service, to increase passenger comfort, and to reduce delays in the lobby. The acceptable symbols are stressed, and the less acceptable image of a mercenary landlord throwing old retainers out of work is played down.

Another benefit derives from these seemingly devious devices. Change is easier to introduce in form than in substance: When imposed "from the outside" the forced change may result in overt compliance, but covert resistance. If the proposed change can be made to come "from the inside" (or seem to), the form and the substance of change are more likely to coincide. The change is also more likely to be permanent and not to be a mere verbal acquiescence until the analyst has gone.

Anthropologists also tell us that in the evolution of a culture pattern action comes first and values second. We begin to like what we do. Thus, it is frequently easier to change the values of individuals concerned with a system by alteration of their activities rather than by a direct attack upon their beliefs.

Example: When a system's users are unfamiliar with it they may be afraid of it, and thus hold it in low esteem. However, *after* experiencing success with its use they become more optimistic about their ability to influence their own future, and the values employed by the users in assessment of the system change. Consequently, instead of describing the virtues of a new product or system, a demonstration model is put in the user's hands so that he may convince himself of its value.

Similarly, if behavior can be changed, a change in values usually follows more easily than if the reverse procedure is followed.

Example: These alternate approaches to change are evident in the policies of the Eisenhower and Johnson administrations with regard to racial discrimination. The Eisenhower policy was that social values would change with time, leading to later changes in behavior. The argument for this approach is that when the behavioral change does occur, it will be permanent because it is reinforced by the individual's value structure. The Johnson administration, on the other hand, in urging stronger legislation against discrimination, sought to change behavior from which a change in values would emerge. It is argued that the latter course produces permanent social change more swiftly than the former, although covert resistance may be expected at the outset.

When introducing change in large-scale systems and organizations, policies are much easier to change than procedures. This observation, made by many professional administrators and systems analysts,[17] does not contradict what has just been said, but blends instrumental considerations with it.

First, the detail and variety of specific changes that must be made in procedures to obtain a given result frequently exceed the resources of the controller. And, because procedures usually adapt themselves to the demands of policy, much more can be accomplished in a given time with limited resources by the policy-change approach, leaving resources available for the adjustment of critical procedures when necessary.

But, perhaps more important, a change in policy rather than in detailed procedure, leaves some freedom, although it may be illusory, for the individual to adjust to the proposed change. His values and institutional roadblocks are not directly confronted, and he is more likely to accept "his own" adjustments as good ones.

For similar reasons, making a few large-scale policy changes is often easier and more effective than instituting many small changes. The few major changes can be controlled, and the individual does not develop the frustrations, confusions, and value disturbances that a series of harassing minor alterations will produce.

PROBLEMS OF IMPLEMENTATION

Without going further, it would appear from what has been said that many repetitive difficulties arise when certain kinds of change are proposed and introduced, and that from this experience much has been learned about social and cultural changes. Moreover, numerous techniques and artifices may be used in easing the introduction of instrumental change and in mitigating institutional obstacles. Yet the field is an open one, and much remains to be done.

If this is so, it would appear reasonable to conduct analyses aimed at the implementation of specific systems, or at specific systems improvements —so-called action research—whenever system innovation and improvement are proposed.

For example, the efforts of political scientists and public relations firms to elect a given political candidate, to ease passage of a school bond issue, to reduce racial discrimination, or to promote the fluoridation of drinking water represent research of this type in the social sciences. Market and advertising research also has the same "action" flavor. The same may be

[17] C. J. Hitch, *Decision-Making for Defense*, University of California Press, Berkeley, 1965. (This is a series of four lectures by the former Comptroller of the Defense Establishment.) The reader may also find two other works of interest in the same vein: W. W. Kaufman, *The McNamara Strategy*, Harper, 1964, and E. S. Quade, *Analysis for Military Decisions*, Rand McNally, 1965.

said for the use of psychological tests and research in personnel selection for given occupations. The research is not "disinterested" in its outcome; it is purposeful and goal directed.

Such activities, which we prefer to call analysis for implementation, are often shunned by the scientist (for reasons we shall mention hereafter), although, for a particular purpose and stated objective, analysis for implementation may greatly increase the success of a technical advance, discovery, or improvement.

For example, even relatively simple system changes may raise questions for which the uninitiated analyst is unprepared. The automobile owner hesitates to spend more funds on his car because his children are sick, so he believes the car will run another year—even though the mechanic knows objectively that the vehicle is potentially dangerous. What is the mechanic to do? The patient hesitates to have the clearly indicated operation and believes he will get better. Should the physician retire after stating the bald facts? Persons who have not experienced the disasters of a tornado, flood, or large explosion tend to deny or to disbelieve warnings that danger is near. They search for more information, and often ". . . interpret signs of danger as signs of familiar normal events until it is too late to take effective precautions." [18] Should the weather man report his scientific conclusions and make no interpretation or exhortation to his listeners to take care? A system that takes care of today's conditions is installed, but it does not provide for future contingencies or for "updating" the system as conditions change with time. Later the system efficiently performs functions no longer relevant to prevailing conditions, with possibly disastrous consequences. Should the analyst not concern himself with these problems of implementation and use?

Should the Analyst Concern Himself with the Problems of Cultural Change?

There are many scientists, and thus many systems analysts, who would, on serious grounds, take issue with the proposal that the investigator concern himself with the use made of his work. Rational investigation and logical decision cannot take place, they argue, if one has a vested interest in obtaining a given outcome. This position is strongly held by science as an institution because of the historical struggle to free science, and the instrumental process, from the constraints, the dogma, and the myth-making of institutions.

There is yet another reason for the strength of this position. As older institutional constraints have been removed, others have come into play as the individual searches for the universal certainty which the rational process cannot supply.

---

[18] C. E. Fritz, "Disaster," in R. K. Merton and R. A. Nisbit (Eds.), *Contemporary Social Problems*, 1st ed., Harcourt, Brace & World, 1961, p. 665.

For example, a vote of the majority or a mass movement may threaten the dispassionate scientific pursuit just as much as constraints imposed by a monarch or the clergy. The mathematician does not arrive at a problem solution by conducting a public opinion poll on the street and averaging the answers obtained, even if those polled are other mathematicians! The test is different. It depends upon the demands of a verifiable procedure, not the beliefs of any individuals, regardless of their reputation, their power, their eminence, or their number.[19] If in his choice of variables or the development of alternatives (both of which are subtle selection processes) the scientist consciously begins to favor or exclude one group of possibilities for institutional reasons, or if he must shade his thinking, model building, and verification to meet institutional constraints, he has abandoned the basic tenets of science. Surely, he says, many new discoveries that might otherwise be his will be lost, or worse he will be deluded and falsely evaluate what he observes.

The scientist may also argue that his energies are limited. To worry about implementation will not only debase his pursuit of knowledge but will also embroil him in a conflict of personal values that will consume his limited resources in a wasteful fashion. How can he simultaneously be a myth-maker and an iconoclast?

The dilemma presented by arguments for and against research for implementation is well known, and although exaggerated here for effect it is nevertheless real. The scientist-analyst may choose to avoid the problems of implementation altogether, but someone will implement the results of his work, or not, and the job may be done well, or poorly, depending upon how well the analyst and the implementer understand each other.[20]

Leadership and Organization to Bridge the Cultural Gap

One resolution of this difficulty—which almost always arises in applications of management science and operations research, to name one area of systems

---

[19] For example, one test for an instrumental versus an institutional process is whether a conclusion is validated by the success of a procedure or the agreement of an individual or group in society. Thus, if a surgeon sets a broken arm, that is first aid. If the nurse performs an appendectomy, that is nevertheless surgery. First aid and surgery are instrumental. If a priest administers the sacrament with wine and wafers, it is a holy ceremony; but if a lay person performs the same act, it is a sacrilege. A marriage performed by an unlicensed individual is invalid. The latter procedures are institutional.

[20] An interesting sidelight on this problem is the reluctance of professional people to engage in politics, an attitude encouraged by the Federal Tax Policy. "... Federal tax policy forbids charitable deductions of gifts to organizations engaged in promoting or opposing legislation. Thus, for example, the bulk of foundation money goes to organizations that conduct research, and financial aid for organizations that take public positions, however worthy, is hard to come by. As a result, lobbies representing private interests operate freely and effectively, while those groups that might represent the public interest stay out of politics." C. Abrams, "The City Planner and the Public Interest," *Columbia University Forum,* Fall, 1965.

analysis—is to conduct a project with mixed teams of investigators, some of whom have instrumental skills, and others who have institutional skills. These skills when shared in the work group bridge the interface between the two worlds and permit a smoother transition between problem definition, analysis, and implementation.

Many organizations use similar devices to bridge the gap between instrumental and institutional requirements. For example, often an organization has two leaders instead of one, although one man may be apparently in charge. The role played by one leader is to institute instrumental change. The role played by the other leader is to represent the institutional requirements of the organization and the component individuals. When the instrumental leader causes friction, the institutional leader smooths it over or rephrases the requirements in more acceptable, warmer, more congenial, or more orthodox terms. It matters little who is the obvious leader, so long as the two cooperate (and can stand each other)! Together they will be able to produce more change in the organization than either could accomplish individually. The family unit, to come closer to home, offers a similar example of dual leader effectiveness in creating change in the habits of the young.

A final example from intelligence operations is interesting because it illustrates the power of the same approach, employed to different ends.

Example: Many of the intelligence services of the world employ a method of interrogation in which two interrogators, each employing a distinctly different role characterization, alternately confront the subject. The first man, for example, may affect a stern air, a military costume with riding boots and crop, a crew cut, an air of efficiency and dispatch, and a stern, cruel disposition. As the perfect martinet, he demands the subject talk at once or be shot at dawn, withdraws all physical comfort, inflicts various apparent physical and mental tortures—just as the subject might anticipate. Finally, in exasperation, ordering the firing squad to be assembled, the first interrogator leaves the room. Very likely he has learned nothing, and expected to learn nothing, from the subject. After some time, the second interrogator enters. He is an entirely different type. Dressed in baggy tweeds, probably smoking a pipe, he seems distressed with the subject's plight, orders some food to be brought at once, produces cigarettes, offers apologies for the abruptness of his colleague, and settles down to commiserate with his unfortunate friend. He may offer some personal experiences of his own, some philosophies and observations on life and his friend's present plight. But then, he is unavoidably called from the room, and the subject is again alone. He did not expect this. As the night wears on, the alternate presences continue. First he is threatened, then he is consoled. In the end, although some time may be required, the subject begins to change: He sees the constraints of his former world as less important than before, his values begin to seem irrelevant to his present state, he may even be convinced of the error of his ways and seek to explain himself in his defense. Then he talks, as was intended, most likely to his tweedy friend who in fact was the instrument of the subject's change.[21]

Little more can be said here on this topic, but the administrator of systems analysis projects who seeks to blend instrumental and institutional skills for a given study can benefit from further study of the dual role approach to organization.

ORGANIZATION OF DATA FOR IMPLEMENTATION

To continue, let us suppose the investigator is concerned with the problems of implementation, and that his concern is to anticipate problems that may occur in a specific case, rather than to worry in general.

Many of the examples and points cited in our next few pages follow from underestimates of institutional power to affect routine and emergency operations of instrumental processes.

Why are Implementation Data Scarce?

In most specific cases, the selection of treatments and the anticipation of specific problems and reactions requires high technical competence and experience in a given field. Nevertheless, in a given field, the data of past experience can be organized in an orderly fashion and "what if" questions can be asked for specific analyses of implementation. For example, the collection of symptom-cause relationships described in Chapter 11 might be a typical example for this type of display. (Problem characteristics would then replace symptoms, and probable difficulties would replace causes.)

However, in collecting data for implementation, the purpose of the collection is expanded. The emphasis is not on the apparent difficulties and present symptoms, but on those that *might* appear in the future, or that have been known to occur in the past, given specified side conditions.

In medicine, for example, certain treatments or drugs are known to be "counterindicated" when the patient has a given past history, and these counterindications are reported and publicized in the profession.

In the same way, certain forms of system alteration or modification are known to raise given problems with great regularity. When information systems are installed, or when decision-making processes are analyzed and changed, we encounter the same problems over and over again.

Unfortunately, in the latter case, published warnings and admonitions

---

[21] For an extensive discussion of interrogation and training methods in this form of intelligence operation, see O. Pinto, *Spy-Catcher*, Harper, New York, 1952.

are uncommon. The investigator who analyzes and installs business systems, for example, is seldom forewarned against probable pitfalls, and he seldom has organized, published data to aid his implementation work. We may have diagnostic aids for hardware maintenance, and for trouble-shooting in many fields. However, there has been little emphasis to date on the diagnosis of conceptual or decision-making failures on the part of the analyst when he implements systems change. Where such data are available, the files are kept secret or transmitted from one worker to another as an art—for institutional reasons which should be obvious from our previous discussion in this chapter.

For example, from the 35,000 or so electronic computer installations made in the United States in the past ten years much has been learned and published about electronic difficulties, hardware reliability, component failures, and design defects. Yet little, if anything, has been reported in an organized form about the many specific failures of the systems that have been installed—if those failures were due to faulty decision-making, inadequate system conception, or lack of individual experience and foresight. Little, if anything, has been published about the specific difficulties those systems have encountered as times have changed. Not only is the nature of such data collection and organization difficult, but institutional barriers also prevent publicity. The physician does not testify against his colleagues except within the instrumental framework and the users and manufacturers of computing equipment are not likely to publicize their failures except when the onus can fall upon the hardware details, and frequently not then. The available data are locked in consultants' files, or in the notebooks of internal investigators. The auditor has his check list of devious practices to look for, but he is not likely to publish a statistical account of his, or his clients', difficulties and shortcomings.

The point of these illustrations is that such compilation of problems, even if maintained privately by the investigator, can be a powerful tool in anticipating and preventing a repetition of implementation difficulties. The construction of such a listing is thus one of the major steps in analysis for implementation. It is a valuable step if the result is only a list. It is an even more valuable tool for the analyst, in a given case, if the broad listing can be classified and cross referenced in a hierarchy of problem types, with specific classifications for the anticipated problems of specific system types. In such a tabulation it would be seen that many of the specified problem areas arise when instrumental and institutional processes meet at an interface, when man-and-machine or man-and-man meet.

A Problem Anticipation File

To illustrate one such listing, we now present a selected group of implementation problems that are general enough to provide both a manageable list and a set of categories for further development. For each of these categories, we provide an example.

The reader may add his own examples to this outline. Our aim in the following presentation is to suggest a set of major problems to anticipate in a wide variety of systems implementations, and to leave further development to the reader. The categories chosen are taken from a composite of systems analysis problems in several fields, and are presented in the form of questions to stimulate further discussion and thought.

1. Are the objectives and constraints perceived by the investigator the same as those perceived by the organization?

Frequently, differences in cultural background and the conflict between professional and administrative interests cause the systems analyst to solve the wrong problem. This most subtle of systems mistakes happens so frequently—even when the problem of analysis is stated in writing and agreed to by the analyst and the user—that great care must be taken to reach a common understanding of what is needed.

The trouble is usually not so obvious as maximizing profit instead of minimizing cost, although that type of error is frequent enough. Usually, an objective is stated formally by the system user, but perhaps incorrectly or incompletely. So, the analyst may not at first perceive constraints that the user imposes upon acceptable solutions, or, conversely, he may anticipate constraints that are not in fact considered important. He may often be purposefully deluded.

Example: A major oil company sought a scientific procedure for locating filling stations as new stations were added to the distribution system. Initially, the objective was to locate stations that would return at least a minimum return on investment, as specified by the firm's management. A procedure that included many factors, among them estimated sales of petroleum products at the proposed stations, was developed. Checks of the new procedure indicated that it would locate stations more consistently and reliably than less organized methods. However, the new procedure was rejected by the executives charged with station location. After some time these executives revealed the method was not suitable to them because it included forecasts of station sales, and this limited executive flexibility in acquiring new locations. As it turned out the true objective was to add 200–300 new stations to the system each year. Many proposed station locations could not make the required return on investment, and competition for good locations was severe. Knowing that the computed return on investment was based on internal transfer prices, which also included contributions to profit, the executives often inflated the estimate of station sales to get around what they felt was an unrealistic investment requirement and come up with the required number of new additions (which otherwise would not have been possible). Had the proposed method taken these facts into account, the systems analysis project might have been implemented, rather than rejected. It is not surprising in this instance that proposals for follow-up studies to compare predicted sales and investment return against actual values were also rejected.

The analyst may avoid this pitfall or sidestep it in many cases by investigating in advance alterations in constraints and objectives that may be of possible interest, and by determining how the problem solution is affected by alternate problem statements. He may find that the problem statement contains many noncritical factors, learn which factors are critical, and be prepared for the presentation of alternate proposals should they be required.

Because of his training and knowledge of methodology, the analyst may also tend to frame problem objectives and constraints to make his job easier, unwittingly leading also to the solution of the wrong problem. The work may be professionally competent and workmanlike in every respect, but it may also be irrelevant to the present need. The cliche that the right problem solved approximately is a better result than the wrong problem solved precisely is a fair warning. Most major problems of systems implementation are introduced at the beginning, when the wrong objectives and constraints are assumed in a system definition.[22]

There is another reason for looking carefully into the goals, objectives, and constraints to be used in a systems analysis project or design. The implications of the chosen goals, objectives, and constraints may not be clearly understood at the outset and a solution which seems desirable at first may in fact be fraught with difficulties that once commenced are difficult to overcome.

For example, when automatic or automated systems are given a goal, it is, as the late Norbert Wiener observed, like invoking a form of magic. The goal is interpreted literally, and the full implications of a given instruction or objective must be understood by the analyst if he is to stave off embarrassment and woe.

Folklore, for example, contains stories—ranging from the *Sorcerer's Apprentice* to the *Monkey's Paw*—in which magic, once begun, was difficult or impossible to turn off. The Apprentice learned the words to bring magic to the alleviation of his workday tasks, but forgot how to stop the magic broom and the magic pail of water from overdoing their appointed tasks.

---

[22] "At first it is impossible for the novice to cast aside the minor symptoms, which the patient emphasizes as his major ones, and to perceive clearly that one or two facts that have been belittled in the narration of the story of the illness are in reality the stalk about which everything else in the case must be made to cluster." Herbert Amory Hare, *Practical Diagnosis*, Lea Brothers, Philadelphia, 1899.

(Fortunately, he was saved by the Master's return.) In the *Monkey's Paw* and many similar tales, three wishes were granted. In each case, the first wish was fulfilled, but with unsuspected side effects. And usually in these stories the last two wishes were used to undo the horrors created by the fulfillment of the first.

Thus, at the outset, the analyst should beware lest he have King Midas' touch.

2. Are the effectiveness measures used in the analyses appropriate?

Since goals are formulated from sets of values or effectiveness measures, the measures used may be incorrectly chosen and throw off the analysis.

Example: A classic example, reported by Morse and Kimball[23] from their World War II experience, concerns the installation of antiaircraft guns on merchant vessels. On the one hand, guns installed on these ships were so "ineffective" as to be useless; on the other hand, they made the crews feel safer. Because the guns were expensive and were needed elsewhere, their removal was purposed. Indeed, data on equipment and nonequipped ships showed that only 4% of attacking planes were shot down, a dismal figure that served to indicate the guns were not worth installing or keeping aboard. On second thought, however, it was apparent that the percentage of planes shot down was not the correct effectiveness measure for the guns. Guns were installed on the ship *to protect the ship,* and the proper measure was whether the ship was damaged less with or without a gun. Analyses of the observed data in this light showed the guns definitely increased the ship's chance of survival. Even though the antiaircraft guns did not often shoot down the attacking planes, a gun's use lowered attack accuracy, reduced damage, and often saved the ship. The change of measure changed the decision, and the ships were equipped with guns.

A typical error in selecting effectiveness measures is to scale alternatives by their ability to reach a given objective without regard to the resources consumed, or to seek a resource measure only without regard to effectiveness. The property of "cost-effectiveness," which gives the contribution to effectiveness per unit resource, is often used to remove this problem. Even then, it is essential that the "effectiveness" measure be the one desired.[24]

---

[23] P. M. Morse and G. E. Kimball, *Methods of Operations Research,* Technology Press and Wiley, New York, 1951, pp. 52–3.

[24] These problems were discussed in Chapter 8. See also C. J. Hitch and R. N. McKean, *The Economics of Defense in a Nuclear Age,* Harvard University Press, Cambridge, Mass., 1960, and C. J. Hitch, *Decision-Making for Defense,* University of California Press, Berkeley, 1965. The Operations Research Society of America has a "Cost Effectiveness' Section, which concentrates on problems of measure selection and use.

3. Are the attention and awareness functions of the system correctly oriented?

Newly designed systems or organizations and those that have been in operation for some time can suffer from problems of incorrect awareness or goal rigidity, generally described as "fixation" problems. Goal-directed systems have some form of goal setting and holding function. And, because a system's awareness of alternate possible courses of action, forms of organization, and other goal and value possibilities limits the types of goals and values that will be formulated, goal setting and holding functions of a system can be affected by these factors.

Example: If the reader will tightly hold the thumb of his left hand in his closed left fist, and close his eyes, he will after a time "feel" that his thumb is larger than the other four fingers combined. This "perception" of the size or importance of the thumb, were it constant, could easily alter the individual's work habits, selection of desirable jobs, and even his sensory view of the world about him. The pictures drawn by children, which seem distorted to adults but realistic to children, are another example of how awareness and perception affect the organization of behavior. The senses most acutely tuned to a given scene, and the "mix'" of a system's sensory input types can greatly affect behavior and goal-setting functions. An analysis of the nerve structure of the pig would cause an analyst to believe that the pig considers his snout a very important information source. The pig thus "views the world through his nose." Several authors have discussed this problem of perception and awareness in different contexts.[25]

Difficulties arise if the data required to solve a given problem are not available, are not sought, or are not perceived "realistically," i.e., with respect to the system's survival and growth.

Similarly, the methods used for combining data, generating new goals and values, and updating presently used objectives may cause trouble. On the one hand, the goal setting process may be too rigid. Like the driver who locks his steering wheel and drives over the cliff, many systems can reach disaster if erroneous goal locking is present. On the other hand, lack of goal stability is also a problem. Then, the system acts like a small child who first picks up one toy, then another, in a succession of unrelated activities.

[25] See E. D. Adrian, *The Basis of Sensation: The Action of the Sense Organs,* Norton, New York, 1928, and the same author's *The Physical Background of Perception,* Clarendon Press, Oxford, 1947. Also, D. O. Hebb, *The Organization of Behavior,* Wiley, New York, 1949, and W. Penfield and T. Rasmussen, *The Cerebral Cortex of Man,* Macmillan, New York, 1950. In a completely different vein, the works of Marshall McLuhan are based upon changes in the ratio of sensory inputs from different media, such as the printed page versus television, and their effects upon the individual and society. See *The Gutenberg Galaxy,* University of Toronto Press, Toronto, 1962 and *Understanding Media,* McGraw-Hill, New York, 1964.

Example: During World War II, and even today, postmasters throughout the country are ordered to watch the mail of certain individuals. During the war individuals suspected of Nazi leanings were put on "watch lists." Ten years after the war, some of these lists were still in use because the original orders had not been withdrawn. Obsolete reports, procedures, and objectives may also be found in most large-scale systems.

The shortcomings illustrated in this section can be alleviated by improving the quality of system inputs, and by focusing attention on the procedures the system uses for formulating and updating goals to meet changed conditions.

4. Have operating standards been developed for the system?

If operating standards are not developed when a system is implemented and installed, particularly in lower level operations, errors or deviations cannot be corrected. As a result, even minor deviations create a crisis. Lack of specifications and documented standards for component operations can cause the system to get out of hand, and to deviate unexpectedly and unpredictably from its over-all purpose. In short, planning, control, and design are virtually impossible without the use of standards.

Hardware systems analysts take great pains to provide detailed operating specifications and standards for their equipment. Of equal or greater importance are standards in procedure and information handling systems.

Example: The frequent underestimates of computer programing costs, research and development completion times, and the effort required to introduce new products are examples of cases where even approximate standards could have prevented implementation mistakes. Monitoring these processes against standards for segments of the total job can usually reduce the error between projected and actual cost, completion dates, and promised performance specifications. Should deviations be noted early in the procedure, the projected time, cost, or performance estimates can be revised, or corrective action can be taken early enough to prevent serious problems.[26]

5. Are vital system processes protected against danger or failure?

To lose a leg is not so serious as decapitation. In one instance you can carry on, in the other you cannot. The problem of guarding vital control and flow processes against loss or failure is equally serious for the human being, the organization, the hardware system, or the information system.

---

[26] As one example, see D. Brandon, *Management Standards for Data Processing*, Van Nostrand, Princeton, N.J., 1963. Critical Path Methods and PERT Networks are planning tools often used to introduce project control.

Systems that do not protect these vital processes against damage and the vicissitudes of the environment do not survive, or have difficulty retaining stable continuity of operation.

Example: An extreme example is the protection provided for a military communications center. The new combat operations center of the North American Defense Command (NORAD) is buried deep inside Colorado's 9656 foot Chevenne mountain and protected against any predictable hazards from enemy sabotage to a direct hit by a nuclear bomb. Thirteen computers, each independent, are able to pick up the work of others in case of failure. The installation is shielded against radioactivity and the electromagnetic effects of nuclear explosions. Power, water, food, fuel, and other essential supplies are stored in gigantic reserves. Houses and rooms within the mountain are set on four-foot springs of three-inch steel to protect personnel and equipment from the shock of a blast or an earthquake. The tunnels and chambers that house the central communications and contral center of the military defense effort for the nation are 1400 feet under the mountain top.[27]

Because critical, higher-order systems processes usually involve human operators, the continuity and stability of service of these individuals is often guarded or planned for in systems implementation.

Example: In one large order-processing system 90 sales officers were connected by teletype to a central office, where orders, received as punched paper tape, were rerouted and scheduled to plants through what is called a "torn-tape filter center." The operation of this center, which was current technology in the late 1950's, required operators to read, tear, and redispatch messages on short lengths of paper tape. These operators, at the heart of the information system, were clearly critical to the success of the operation. Employee turnover, divided loyalty, and similar problems that might affect the operation of this vital spot were virtually eliminated by recruiting as operators only divorced women with several children who had never worked for the company or with the equipment before. Trained in these special tasks and held together by their common economic need and background, the girls hired remained on the payroll for many years, and turnover, absences, and job dissatisfaction were astonishingly rare.

6. Has adequate provision been made for updating the system?

Installed systems often have many components or adjustable elements "set" at the time of installation. As time passes, these settings may no longer be appropriate to the system's conditions of operation, so the system fails.

[27] *Time,* June 28, 1966, pp. 52–3.

Example: The November 9, 1965 electrical blackout of the eastern seaboard was traced to a relay located at the Ontario Hydroelectric Commission's distribution plant at Queenston, Ontario, near Niagara Falls. According to the Federal Power Commission's report, the Ontario relay was set to operate a circuit breaker if the power load exceed 375 million watts. It was set at this point in 1963 and was not reviewed. Subsequently, the average power load on the line controlled by the relay increased to 356 million watts, and thus an ordinary upward fluctuation in power tripped the relay and started the whole blackout.[28]

Similar difficulties occur in systems and operating organizations when policies have not been reviewed and are no longer appropriate, when decision making is based on obsolete data, when component operation has deteriorated from design values, when system structure has changed with time but without the analyst's knowledge, or when the goals and values of the system are not kept current with present requirements.

7. Is the system protected against direct falsification or illicit interruption?

Although information errors can occur in many parts of a system, either from mechanical failure or human mistake, there are usually several ways in which to introduce false information into the system purposefully or to intercept confidential information for competitive purposes.

Example: Inventory control systems depend upon correct reports of sales so that orders may be related to demand. However, when reports of sales are made by distributors or agents who have inventory "on consignment" and who collect from customers before remitting to a central source, some direct or indirect alteration of the data may be expected.

For example, commission agents frequently delay reports of sales and use the collected funds as working capital as long as possible. In other situations commission agents were found to be reporting and paying for bulk sales when in fact package goods of the same item were often sold at a higher price. The difference was eventually detected, but the errors were blamed on the computing and inventory system. Similar shading of input data may be expected if there is a strong conflict of objectives and values at an information interface. For this reason, some manufacturers operate their own distribution facilities so that accurate data inputs to data control systems can be assured.

In a similar way, when the competitive objective of organization and system differ strongly, information protection problems arise.[29]

Example: Communications systems, such as telephone lines, computers, teleprinters, and similar devices, all radiate energy as they work.

---

[28] *New York Times,* December 7, 1965, p. 41.
[29] E. E. Sarafin, "Information Protection," *Control Engineering,* May 1965, pp. 105–107.

These signals can often be captured and decoded by an industrial spy, usually with little chance of detection. For example, a teletype machine generates sparks as it prints. Even when located in a shielded room, its signals can be detected from several miles away, and reproduced with suitable equipment if security precautions are not taken. The problem of information protection is increased when information processing facilities are shared, as is the case in real-time computing centers. Planning for the World Trade Center in New York, where computer systems on every ten floors will be shared, includes protection against monitoring systems. Every computer system for defense operations must be protected against monitoring, according to the specification of FED-STD-222 and DCAENS 422-5s, the contents of which are known only to those with clearance. Less exotic forms of data falsification and theft (as well as material spoilage and theft) often present difficulties that are overlooked. For example, material theft, damage, hoarding, and similar activities can cause major data errors in inventory control systems.

8. Are operators actually performing according to the system definition and plan?

Many systems have not performed as predicted because an essential operation was not performed by an operator or group of operators according to the plan assumed by the systems analyst.

Example: Electronic computers are often used to calculate minimum-flight-time and minimum-fuel flight plans for commercial aircraft. These plans take into account weather, wind, load, and similar factors, and are prepared for the pilot just before takeoff. When first introduced, the time and fuel reductions predicted by these schemes failed to materialize. The question arose as to whether the optimizing computations were in error or whether pilot adherence to the computer plan was unsatisfactory. An investigation of the latter problem led to increased pilot cooperation, and the predicted savings were at last obtained.

9. Will the system accept and act upon signs of impending disaster?

Although the desire for survival and perpetuation is often strong in organizations and individuals, and is often designed into procedural and hardware systems, this survival or continuity of operation is often threatened when the system fails to act or delays action in response to clear signs of danger.

There are cases in which the system is not "aware" of impending danger because such input data are not received or sought. But even when such data are in hand, many technical and institutional blocks can prevent correct evaluation and acceptance in time for adequate action. For example, the required pieces of intelligence information may be on the "desks" of several intelligence analysts who do not individually see the emerging pattern of danger and dismiss the isolated pieces of intelligence as unimportant. The organizational leader may have surrounded himself with weak yes-men who fail to tell him the truth. There may be technical delays in transmission, reception, and decoding and possible mistakes along the way. But even when these faults are overcome, the executive, the operator, or the control system often cannot, or will not, accept and act quickly upon the fact that disaster is at hand.

The following is reported in some detail as a modern and classic example of this often neglected implementation problem.

Example: In the major eastern power failure of November 9, 1965, previously mentioned, the first signs of failure were at 5:16:11 P.M. when service was interrupted to only portions of upstate New York and Ontario.

There was a period of some 7 minutes to 12 minutes between the initial disturbance at 5:16 P.M. when the service to the various portions of southern New York and New England finally collapsed. The operators at the various dispatching centers all knew after 5:16 on November 9 that the frequency on their system was going down and that the load had reversed and was placing a large drain on their generating reserves. . . .

The night of the blackout a 62-year-old Con Edison Engineer, Edwin J. Nellis, who has been with the [New York City] utility for 41 years, was on duty at Con Edison's automated Energy Control Center on Manhattan's West Side. At 5:16 P.M., the lights dimmed, and Mr. Nellis called for an instrument check, which showed nothing wrong with Con Edison's generating equipment.

Checking his instruments again, Mr. Nellis noticed a surge of power in from the north, then a surge outward. Con Edison officials report that he immediately called the Niagara Mohawk Company in Syracuse to determine what the trouble was. At the same time he was ordering all 12 Con Edison generating plants to peak power output—to handle any extra demand should the trouble be serious.

Meanwhile, three other stations in the power network, or grid—a station in Flushing, Queens, one in Rockland County and one in Orange County— were reporting troubles of their own to Mr. Nellis.

It was then that the lights dimmed a second time, and instruments showed a tremendous surge of power into New York, then out again. Mr. Nellis was now on the phone to Syracuse, which told him 'of trouble to the north.'

On hearing this, he told Syracuse, "I'm going to cut clear of you," and began pushing the first of eight buttons to cut Con Edison away from the rest of the grid. He also began ordering Con Edison's network stations—42 in all— to shed their loads. He was too late, and in just 2.5 seconds New York City was blacked out—at 5:28 P.M.

. . . In retrospect," the [Federal Power Commission] report said, "it seems likely that a timely shedding of the load in some sections of New York might have avoided a citywide blackout and the breakdown of service elsewhere, as well as facilitating restoration of service. But whether because of lack of clarity in the control room instrumentation or for other reasons, the system operator did not make an immediate clear-cut decision in this emergency."

In reply, Charles E. Eble, president of Con Edison, insisted that the company's operators "followed established procedures and in our opinion made proper and timely decisions in the short space of time available to them."

However, the automatic controls on Con Edison's generators, as T. H. White aptly observed for *Life Magazine*, were quicker "to protect their own," They cut out by themselves when the survival of their generators was threatened by the massive heat of extreme overload.[30]

10. Have potential difficulties at the boundaries of functions, departments, components or modules have adequately "bridged"?

The analyst may in general expect difficulty in system implementation when his system crosses functions or boundaries. Although this statement is true of hardware systems—more interfaces or intercommunications between components generally mean more potential trouble—it is particularly true for procedural and information processing systems that cut across organizational boundaries. Additional care in implementation is always needed to bridge these sources of potential system disruption. Severe measures or implementation decisions may be required if the "boundary problem" is aggravated by a man-machine interface.

Example: To avoid such boundary problems at the outset, many systems analysts take the position that a new procedural or information system should be designed either to be completely manual and so simple that any operator can understand it or, at the other extreme, so automated that no human intervention is required in the intermediate steps from input to output. Many failures with combinations of manual and automated steps are the basis for this conclusion.

11. Has the analyst correctly evaluated his own resources in relation to the task of analysis and implementation?

Gross underevaluation of the time, cost, and personnel requirements for system development and installation is unfortunately the rule for projects specified by performance standards. Similarly, overoptimism is often the rule when a systems project is proposed with fixed resources. Usually too

---

[30] From the Federal Power Commission Report, reprinted in the *New York Times*, December 7, 1965, p. 40, and the report by *Times* reporter Thomas O'Toole describing the sequence of events in New York, p. 41. Copyright 1965 by The New York Times Company. Reprinted by permission. One may well ask what good is an automated information or control system if the operators who have the final word on system action fail to take action or veto the action clearly indicated by the system itself?

much is attempted with too little, with the frequent result that the project flounders, and this leads to general disappointment and losses.

Example: The installation of even a modest data processing facility will take about two years, on the average, although many firms, to their regret, frequently make estimates of a year or less. The many steps required in preparing for a changeover to the computer system invariably bring snags that prolong the effort and raise its cost beyond what was expected.

Similar problems occur when the analysts' range of actions is smaller than is required to handle the system he confronts, and an assessment of this relationship—as discussed in Chapter 6—is in order, particularly when implementation, with its greater variety of difficulties, is confronted.

Finally, systems implementation is subject to many threshold effects that raise questions of resource availability. Often a little implementation does no good, and a basic minimum of resources must be committed to assure any degree of success. If this minimum is not available, attempts at implementation are usually wasted, an economic fact of life of which the analyst should be aware.

12. Is the system chosen for analysis and implementation big enough?

The scope of a system considered may not be large enough to result in any major improvement, or worse, it may lead to unwanted suboptimization. In addition, the costs involved in system analyses and implementation are often relatively fixed after a certain threshold of resources is reached, and may not vary thereafter directly with the size of the system considered. Thus, major improvements or large-scale improvements may be no more costly than lesser efforts, although the payoff can be much greater.

Example: The design of an inventory control system for a small company with 1000 items requires almost as much effort as one for a larger company with 10,000 or 100,000 items, although the absolute dollar improvements in the latter case will usually be much greater. The hardware and paper conversion will be somewhat more costly in the latter case, but development problems, personnel problems, and the political problems of installation are essentially the same. This fact usually places the larger firm in a better position to use systems analysis than the smaller firm.

In the same way, the analyst within an organization should look for systems improvements that will produce the largest payoff first, and should shun forms of implementation that offer only a small return in relation to the cost of analysis and implementation.

For institutional reasons, the reverse strategy is often unwisely chosen. ("Do a series of small projects to prove the worth of research to the organization.") Although this may appear at first to make good political sense, the result is often not as expected. Both the analysts and the organization become discouraged with the lack of demonstrable and dramatic return from the costs incurred after a time. The bold choice carries the risk of dramatic failure as well as dramatic gain; but the piecemeal approach carries the risk that the results of the smaller efforts are not measurable above the noise inherent in a system's reporting and evaluation procedures.

Thus, there is a minimum size for systems analysis projects set, on the one hand, by the threshold cost of analysis and implementation and, on the other hand, by the need for measurable results, which often must be dramatic to be noticed.

PROBLEMS

13.1 Consider the conversion from manual elevators, operated by a staff of faithful and pleasant workers, to an automatic bank of elevators, which would save money in the long run. What are some of the institutional factors that must be faced in a luxury apartment house? In an office building? In a small town? In a large city? By an old owner? By a new owner?

13.2 According to *Women's Wear Daily*, and columnist Samuel Feinberg (December 3, 1965, p. 6), there is a consulting firm in New York City by the name of Einstein Associates specializing in executive search and "counterfeit detection."

In conducting its search for executives, the firm proceeds through two interviews. The first interview, which may take from half an hour to one and one-half hours, is conducted in a relaxed atmosphere at Einstein's headquarters in New York.

"Interviewer and interviewee sit side by side, perhaps smoking, and drinking coffee. This part of the discussion touches on peripheral issues—earliest recollections of home life, schooling, athletic interests, dating, and so on, leading through business experience.

"The stress interview takes place on another day, consumes from two to three hours, and really lives up to its name. The analyst and applicant are seated across a desk from each other. This phase of the interview is designed to keep the man off balance by peppering him with a rapid succession of questions that render him unable to program answers or adhere to fradulent information he may have given during the previous meeting. Rather being job-oriented and dealing with hard-core information, the stress interview draws out comments on both sides of a controversial subject.

"For example, the man might be asked: 'What would you respond if your boss accused you of an act of dishonesty?' The man might be expected to react in one of two ways in his reply: He might act calmly and ask for proof of the charge, thereby indicating he is a secure individual able to rationalize under pressure. Or he might get excited and start a counterattack showing insecurity. If he emerges in the first classification, he might then be asked to play the role of the insecure man and attack the employer. If he stumbles in the changed role, he is probably O.K. If he plays the both parts convincingly, he is suspect. He might be asked to play out five or 10 hypothetical cases. In addition, other questions are raised. Typical: What does he think of his wife? How does he get along with his children? If he fumbles in answers that should come effortlessly, he's practicing delaying maneuvers to give him time to make up palatable, probably fanciful, replies.

"After several hours of stress interviewing, Mr. Einstein contends, it's not possible to continue the fraud; 'the counterfeit executive inevitably unveils himself.'

"Finally, the applicant takes a test battery given by an independent psychological testing laboratory."

As an example of the results of such a procedure, the author of the referenced article cites a case from the consultants' files.

"Three men were being considered by a department store for promotion from buyer to merchandise manager. One man was thought by management to be particularly qualified because of his profit record. During the stress interview with this candidate—he handled contract orders for lamps for institutional use—it was discovered he had been faking back orders for two months so as to paint a false high-profit picture and be in line for promotion."

A. Comment on this form of executive search in view of the stress methods of troubleshooting discussed in Chapter 10 and the conflict between the instrumental and institutional processes discussed in this chapter.

B. From a systems viewpoint, why is the problem of stress and the resolution of institutional and instrumental process important as individuals move up the organizational ladder?

C. To illustrate the effect of institutional background upon instrumental proposals—what do you think of the procedures used by the cited consulting firm? Would you like to be subjected to the stress procedure described? If not, why?

13.3 A review of the work done in the Amalgamated Dating Service, Inc., (Project 6, Chapter 10) indicates that we have concentrated on the technical task of matching codes obtained from a question schedule filled out by males and females. Questions may now be raised about the quality of the original data that went into this system of computations.

A. Would the computing procedure you have devised change if the questions in the schedule were changed, provided the answer code format remained the same?

B. How could the computing method devised aid in an experimental improvement of the question schedule?

C. What type of skills and knoweldge would be required to design and improve the question schedule?

D. Would a team effort be useful in this task?

E. What are the instrumental and institutional factors that affect this application?

14 THREE WAYS TO IMPROVE SYSTEMS

In this chapter we discuss three general routes to system improvement: Modular construction, improvements in information handling, and clarification of the goals and the constraint structure of the system. These methods of system improvement are typical of the design, use, and planning strategies currently used to improve system operation. The reader may wish to add his own strategies to this sample.

MODULAR CONSTRUCTION

Systems design and construction using a number of standardized and well-defined modules provides one way for the analyst to create and maintain systems of great variety with a limited number of distinct component types.

By creating variety by combination, rather than by a proliferation of nonstandard components and subsystems for each new system, the analyst can limit the variety he must control, and at the same time increase the variety of his systems and *their* scope of control. In terms of Chapter 6, which discussed the Law of Requisite Variety, such a ratio of "analyst" to "system" variety is highly favorable, and results naturally in a host of economies and benefits in the production, test, operation, and maintenance of modular systems.

Benefits of Modular Design and Construction

Here are ten reasons why modular design and construction should be considered a route to systems improvement.

1. The reliability of a standardized module produced in volume is greater than that of a custom-built unit. The volume justifies research costs, generates statistics on modes of module failure under different uses, and leads to continuing module refinement and improvement.

2. The module can be produced at a smaller cost than a custom unit. It can be assembled and tested at a smaller cost because the required variety of equipment is smaller, because automated assembly and test equipment can be designed and used, and because assembly and test procedures can be standardized.

3. The module package, particularly its interconnecting links, can be perfected for reliability and ease of attachment to other module packages. The physical connecting devices for components, or the documentation and ease of interconnecting information blocks can be improved.

4. The designer working with proved components can generate and evaluate alternate designs quickly and less expensively than otherwise. Often blueprints and similar custom design details can be eliminated by references to modules by code name or number in highly simplified specifications or worksheets.

5. Stocks of modules can be simplified by reducing the number of special modules held. Because the design and production modules can be made the same, system prototypes can be made from stock at small expense.

6. Management functions, such as purchasing, production planning, price estimation, cost accounting, and most industrial engineering activities, are greatly simplified by the use of modules. Module costs and module production and operation times are known and may be assembled with ease to get total cost and time estimates of small variance for the design, construction, and use of proposed systems.

7. Knowledge of module specifications and methods of operation may be transmitted with ease to operators and users of systems in many different locations. This means that many people who are familiar with the given modules can be made familiar with a variety of systems with little difficulty. Training, documentation, and similar systems implementation tasks are thus eased.

8. Standard variations in basic modules may also be made in a standardized way, providing an additional source of variety. For example, standard clothing designs can be "sized graded" automati-

cally from the basic pattern, providing a variety of garments from the single original design.[1]

9. Modular construction eases maintenance problems by allowing easy probe insertion between standard modules, and by allowing easy module replacement, fault diagnosis, and treatment. Failure epidemics can be prevented by compartmentalizing failure sources in their modules. Routine test procedures, simplified test equipment, and interchange of operators and repairmen become possible with modular construction.[2]

10. The fact that information or material modules can be handled as blocks rather than as a multitude of pieces can greatly speed material and information handling procedures, and thus cut their cost. Containerized cargo shipments are popular for this reason.[3] Because information modules can be stored and called for by code, messages about these modules can be shortened, and message transmission and translation efficiency can be increased by exploiting the modular concept.

Modular benefits of the type described above are apparent today in the design, construction, use, and maintenance of modern systems, and we can expect the trend to increase because of its success.[4]

Some Trade-Offs When Using Modular Construction

Several considerations are important when using the modular concept to obtain systems improvement.

The number of distinct modules to stock or to use, the "size" of such modules, the manner of modules interconnection, and the potential variety of modular construction are related questions in planning for modular systems.

The answer to such questions must come from the specific application, but we can make a few general comments.

---

[1] "For the Apparel Industry: Automatic Patterns," *Women's Wear Daily,* December 12, 1965, p. 15.

[2] For an interesting example developed for the Navy by the Bureau of Standards, see G. Shapiro *et. al.,* "Project FIST: Fault Isolation by Semiautomatic Techniques," *IEEE Spectrum,* August, 1964 (Part I), and September, 1964 (Part II).

[3] "Airlines Adopt Cargo Standards," *New York Times, December* 14, 1965, p. 77.

[4] The trend to modules in system design is apparent in both capitalist and socialist societies. Two sources are cited for comparison. M. K. Starr, "Modular Production—A New Concept," *Harvard Business Review,* November-December, 1965, treats the subject from the consumer market viewpoint in a competetive economy. At another extreme, modular construction is also urged in the planned economy by K. Klimenko and M. Rakovsky, in "The Technological and Economic Problems of Automation in the U.S.S.R.," which originally appeared as a part of "Social Consequences of Automation," *International Social Science Bulletin* (UNESCO), X, 1, 1958 and is reprinted in H. B. Jacobson and J. S. Roueck, *Automation and Society,* Philosophical Library, New York, 1959, pp. 416–432.

The greater the variety of modules, the greater the variety of combinations that can be made with a given number selected from the list of available modules. The reader will recall that the number of distinct messages than can be made with exactly r letters taken from an alphabet of N characters is N^r. The situation is often similar with physical modules. Additional variety in the character set, or list of module types, greatly increases the variety of available combinations. But this increase in system variety comes at the price of module proliferation. Thus, a balance must be struck between the amount of system variety required and the number of module distinctions necessary. The trick, of course, is to find the minimum number of module distinctions that will provide the maximum number of *useful* system distinctions, because many system combinations, which theoretically could be produced from a given set of module types, will not be feasible or desirable. The techniques of Chapters 11 and 12 are frequently useful in this evaluation.

If, in addition to distinct module types, the modules can be interconnected in various ways, the system variety that can result from a selection of r modules from a list of N distinct module types is much greater than N^r. The bricklayer can construct a variety of structures with his single module, the brick. Clearly, different module types that can be connected in various ways—like a tinkertoy—can generate many more. The possibility of multiple interconnection greatly complicates the job of estimating the variety of systems that *could* be constructed from a given assortment of types, but it greatly extends the module's potential for generating variety.[5] Thus, such forms of module design are widely used, and alternate interconnection modes in effect increase the number of module types available to the user.

The "size" of a module presents another possible trade-off. The larger the module, the fewer the modules in the system, so that large modules mean less potential system variety. Conversely, the larger module is often easier to handle, faster to combine, easier to find if faulty, and reduces the number of troublesome interconnection points. The advantage of increasing the relative size of system modules must therefore be weighed against the potential system variety which is forgone when using the big block.

Modules may also be sized for physical convenience, to balance the cost of replacement and repair against the alternative of replacement and discard, to optimize diagnostic sequences, or on other grounds. The choice, in such cases, is dictated by the application.

Our main point in this discussion, however, is that the resolution of module size, variety, and interconnection method is a basic system decision

[5] Many firms disclaim responsibility for use of their modules when the variety of possible combinations precludes detailed evaluation of all possibilities. For example, the Digital Equipment Corporation of Maynard, Massachusetts, manufacturers of "Digital Flip-Chip Modules" used in computer construction states clearly in its catalogue that the company ". . . makes no representation that the interconnection of its modular circuits in the manner described . . . will not infringe on existing or future patent rights."

when modular systems are planned. The initial selection commits the designer's scope and method of operation by setting the specifications for his resources.

For example, the standard module for exterior house construction is 48 inches. The 4′ × 8′ plywood panel is a familiar result. To save material, contractors usually build houses to that module. On the other hand, interior finish work, fixtures, and furniture, such as cabinets, rugs, counters, and couches, are often constructed on a 36 inch module. The 9′ × 12′ rug is an example. Unfortunately, these different module sizes often conflict. The kitchen is a foot or so too big, or too small, for its cabinets. Rugs and furniture often fit awkwardly in rooms designed to save exterior cost. The resolution of this problem is to consider the compromise that would reduce the *total cost* of both exterior and interior labor and supplies in the production of the furnished home. When this is done, the architect often finds it is better to waste some exterior material and save on interior material and labor, which is relatively more expensive.

Thus, the commitment to a module list and module specifications must be made with reference to the total system, or set of systems, that will be constructed and used as a completed package. But, this burden is small in comparison to the benefits that can be obtained from the use of carefully selected modules.

IMPROVED INFORMATION HANDLING

Improvements in information handling ability provide a second general approach to system improvement, because current operating decisions and long-range planning are affected by such capability, or the lack of it. Moreover, information handling improvements are usually less costly than physical improvements that would have equal effect.

Even a cursory look at recent trends in information handling technology would reveal drastic revisions in scope, speed, cost, media, and versatility, and a more detailed consideration reveals some startling changes in the concept and potential of the information handling process.

To improve a system through improvement of its information handling system, we may first consider these trends and exploit them.

The New Logistics of Information Handling

The historic logistics of information handling are archaic in today's technology. Consider the library. To find a book you must physically go to the library, fill out a form, wander through the stacks, or wait in line. Frequently the book is out, lost, stolen, or misfiled. If your book is found, it may be mutilated, defaced, or worn. Even in the best of circumstances you must physically withdraw the book, and then return it. To scan many references, you must repeat this frustrating and often fruitless process. The comparison and recombination of information is literally a physical chore.

By contrast, consider the electronic databank or master file that is provided with remote input/output devices. A request for information may be made to such a system from a remote location. No physical transportation is required. The response time is measured in seconds. If the system has what you want, you may have your own copy at your own location at once, reproduced from a master copy, which is in mint condition. The master copy never leaves the file; therefore, it is never lost, stolen, or worn. You need not return your copy, and you can destroy it after use. Indeed, the display may be electronic, e.g., on a television tube, so that destruction is easy. If your original request was faulty and you do not get what you want, you can easily repeat the request. You can make many requests and compare results, without geographical movement of a single document or yourself. The process involves reproduced patterns of intelligence, not physical movement of material.

This change in the logistics of information storage and retrieval profoundly affects the type of questions that will be asked, the types of comparisons that will be made, and the degree of control that can be applied to systems design and use.

File Scope and Flexibility

It is not surprising that the scope of electronic master files has drastically increased in the past few years. In 1900, massive files of income tax forms finger prints, auto registrations, insurance policies, mailing lists, or inventory records did not exist. Today, each of these applications calls for files of millions or tens of millions of records. The demand for volume storage and retrieval coupled with the ever decreasing cost, as well as the flexibility and potential for information transmission of electronic memory media has made possible monster electronic data files in almost every government and industry office.

Although we have always had libraries and file cabinets, the change in scope has another dimension. If data stored in fast access form are organized according to the modular principles of the previous section, data elements can be recombined and restructured at will. With this modular format and electronic storage media, file scope becomes an asset, rather than a burden, because the fast generation and analysis of a variety of data combinations becomes a feasible and productive act.

The following example, taken from a current application, illustrates what can be done with relatively simple equipment if the data are properly organized.

Example: Alexandria, Virginia, a city of 120,000 persons, recently placed records pertaining to taxes, street lighting, road repair, crime, city parks, welfare cases, housing code violations, health hazards, fires, mortalities, census figures, and other data in a consolidated file, or databank keyed to street address and to land parcel.

The city's two master files consist of three reels of magnetic tape—the equivalent of over 250,000 punched cards. The first file is by street section, and contains 120 items of information about the 3518 blocks and intersections in the city; the second, or Land Parcel File, contains 91 types of information about 20,000 parcels of land. As many as 15 different requests for information can be processed against these files at the same time.

Thus, although the main purpose of the master files is for tax billing, major planning and urban renewal studies, and street maintenance (which paid for the development and maintenance of the files), statistical analyses that may be needed for other purposes, such as a correlation of crime statistics with lighting, may be obtained at very little cost.

The detail of the Alexandria master files will indicate the kind of integration of information that is at the heart of a successful databank.

Information contained in the Street Section File includes: eight items of classification, such as census tract and planning district; 48 public works and traffic items, such as number of street lanes, signalization, mass transit, parking meters, sidewalks, curbs and gutters, width, condition, and type of pavement, and construction data, 12 items of information are about the types and locations of street lights, fire alarm boxes, and fire hydrants; and 53 items deal with activities of the Police, Fire, Health, and Welfare Departments and contain such information as the number and kinds of crimes and arrests, welfare cases, and nursing visits.

The Parcel File includes information on the location, size, value, ownership, use, zoning, and sales price of every parcel, plus a variety of other items, such as number of school children, delinquent taxes, and refuse collection zones. For each parcel with information on one or more buildings there is a subrecord with 21 items of information about each building, including size, use, date and type of construction, and condition. An additional subrecord for each establishment (business) in each building gives information about location, type, and size of the establishment.[6]

The organization of these files and the ability of the computer to extract and summarize information in any needed combination leads to the versatility illustrated by one week's requests for information by Alexandria city officials.

[6] John K. Parker, "Operating a City Databank," *Public Automation,* June, 1965. (The article appears on pp. 1–4 of the monthly feature insert entitled *OUTPUT.* For this application, Alexandria uses a service bureau equipped with an IBM 1401, four tape drives, and a 12,000 character core memory, thus illustrating that modest computer installations can handle a job, even on a part-time, batched basis.)

The City Manager wanted to evaluate the city's street lighting program by determining what relationship existed between the types of street lights on each of the city's 3518 blocks and intersections, and the number and types of crimes and accidents. The Traffic Director asked for a survey of the 1200 intersections in the city showing those where five or more accidents had occurred in the past three months, giving the type of signalization, classification of street, type of pavement, and width of intersection. The Director of Public Works wanted a report of the condition of all sidewalks in the city. The Police Chief requested a summary of all crimes and arrests for each neighborhood. The Urban Renewal Administrator wanted a survey made of two proposed urban renewal areas to analyze the density and location of welfare cases, minimum housing code violations, health hazards, fires, mortalities, crimes, and arrests. The Parks Superintendent called for an alphabetical list of the 2318 blocks in the city, listing the length of block, width of right of way, and type of sidewalk — he planned to use the list to schedule and to record the work of his tree trimming crews.[7]

In most cities the time and cost required for such planning reports would be prohibitive. But with Alexandria's databank the requests were filled by Friday of the same week. The cost involved three hours of staff time and $67.50 for computer rental at the service bureau.

Review of this example will give the reader an insight into the planning and control improvements that can be made in management information systems at relatively little cost when careful attention is given to the exploitation of data scope, modular data organization, and flexible storage media.

It is also important that analytical methods in statistics, engineering, logic, mathematics, operations research, and management science will be given greater power by such stored data—which are the inputs for these methods and procedures.

Skill Files

Another generally unappreciated change in information handling capability comes from the exploitation of skill files.

Although libraries are full of "how to" books and references, the individual must refer to, learn, and apply what is there by himself. Often the process is imperfectly, or erratically carried out. It is also time-consuming and costly.

But, computers and devices like numerically controlled machine tools can execute procedures in great detail and precision from prerecorded and stored routines *without* human intervention. The revolution in procedural capability of modern systems is not difficult to understand when the impact of this fact is fully appreciated.

[7] John K. Parker, *op. cit.*

The difference in old and new capability may be illustrated by the student of statistics who is asked to compute the standard deviation of a large set of data. Using the old approach, he would refer to a book, learn the method of computation, manipulate the data, and come up with an answer—a process that must be repeated for each new problem. Using the stored skill approach, the student would call for the stored machine instructions for computing the standard deviation, enter the required data (or retrieve them from his prestored master file), and request execution. The machine would perform the computation *under its own direction,* do so within a predictable time and at a predictable cost, and with a precision and speed that is unlikely under manual direction.

Moreover, the skill once committed to procedure and stored need not be "learned" again by the operator or user. Such skills can grow in scope as new jobs are worked out and stored. The stored skills can be transmitted easily from one machine location to another, then executed instantly. Thus, a number of workers in remote locations can share their store of skills, a fact that greatly multiplies the productive output of each. In addition, the individual learning process does not hamper the application of this bank of skills. The operator may devote his attention to development, maintenance, and selection. He is freed from the burden of detailed procedure, but retains its benefits. His machine will do the job.

In short, combinations of systems to exploit the improved logistics of information handling, the databank, and the skill bank provide an intelligence capability package of awesome power and potential for growth. The analyst who exploits these resources in his system definition and design can reap corresponding rewards in systems improvement.

Creative Information Processing

Total systems that exploit the new information logistics, data scope, and skill files have yet another important application for the analyst. They permit him to "converse" with machines, and as a result to enhance his creative abilities.[8]

The analyst has available, often on a time-shared, real-time basis, ever growing data and skill resources from which to draw, select, and recombine. Thus, he is able to interact with the information system by asking for new combinations, projections, and results. He can see the simultaneous comparisons of many alternatives, essentially at once, and he can modify these results at will.

Under these circumstances, the analyst can use his creative ability to the fullest extent in asking for interesting and unusual combinations. He

[8] For an expository article on such conversational mode systems, see R. L. Aronson, "Time-Sharing to the Fore: Scientific and Business Users Close the Computer Loop," *Control Engineering,* September, 1965, pp. 133–136.

can use his human ability to recognize unusual or novel results. He will be aided in implementing such innovations by the system's ability to perform in short lead times, the delays of training and learning are eliminated or drastically reduced when machines direct other machines. Machines that are so directed accept novelty with ease.[9] They are not captives of institutional constraints.

Finally, the quality of plans the analyst can produce will also improve under these new circumstances. As the analyst sees more alternatives and asks for new combinations, there is a high probability that one or more of them will be better than those culled from a smaller set in the past.

Indeed, the entire method of training, thought, and activity of the systems analyst will be affected in the future by these new capabilities, as will his systems designs, diagnoses and treatments.

GOAL AND CONSTRAINT REFINEMENT

As a consequence of improvements in modular construction and data handling, the analyst has available a third general route to systems improvement—the refinement of the goal and constraint structure of his system.

With stored data and skills available, the analyst can more easily investigate the effects of alternate system goals and alternate system constraints that set the strategy of long-range plans. And because such investigation will be increasingly easier from a processing viewpoint, the analyst will investigate.

The Trend in Long-Range Planning

The trend toward greater emphasis on strategic planning is already apparent. For example, in 1961 in a survey conducted by the Stanford Research Institute, 60% of the nation's 500 largest corporations reported some form of long-range planning, and 20% of a sample of 3600 smaller firms were also engaged in such efforts.[10] These results were higher than those previously observed, and the upward trend continues.

As the cost of electronic files and real-time communication decrease, and as the scope of databanks and the range of skill files increase, casual attention to long-range planning will become obsolete. There will be closer integration of long-range strategic planning and tactical operations.

[9] For example, the creation of new die sets for the production of new model automobiles currently follows a sequence of analyst-computer design, machine refinement of procedural details, and production on numerically controlled machine tools. Production changeover times are correspondingly reduced, and model change is easier.

[10] J. K. Allen, "The Rising Acceptance of Corporate Strategy," *J. of the Stanford Research Institute,* January, 1965.

As one example, the integration of operating and capital budgets will become commonplace, although in many organizations this tie-in is often not current practice. It will be possible to relate long-range capital expenditures to long-range personnel requirements. Long-range forecasts of product line profitability, diversification, and divestment will be related to facilities planning and technological trends. The sensitivity of system performance to present and projected constraints—imposed by capital, resource, and skill availability—will be evaluated and exploited by an ever increasing number of systems managers. Growth will be adaptive and more controlled than in the past.

Again, it may be argued that systems designers and systems managers have always engaged in long-range planning, contemplation of their goals and constraints, and integration of strategy and tactics. One need only read Vegetius on *Military Institutions* or Clausewitz *On War* to be convinced of this previous concern.

Yet again, the character of the problem has been changed by the technological changes cited. Numerous precepts were the usual content of texts on strategy of the past, but often only chance or historical quirk caused the maxim or proposal to be useful.[11]

With the new logistics of information handling, and the modular construction of resource arrays, data files, and skill files—plus their increasing scope—the current and long-range usefulness of management policies can be checked in detail.

The New Realism in Policy Formulation and Revision

This checking ability forces the system goal and the management precept to agree with empirical reality and permits early correction if wrong. Moreover, the ability to prepare and store contingency plans for rapid use—to construct if need be a wide variety of alternate actions rapidly from the physical and informational resources previously on hand—gives an operating system and its users a new corrective power, the ability to recover quickly when a current strategy is defective. The same abilities provide the system with the power to refine its operation under more stable conditions and to generate new goals and plans realistically. There is no doubt a new

---

[11] Flavius Vegetius (4th Century) was a Roman military writer who produced a work entitled *The Military Institutions of the Romans.* Vegetius was not a practical soldier and did not realize that the military reform and revival of the ancient organization of the legion, as he proposed, was impossible because of the evolution of warfare in his time. However, when the evolution of the crossbow and gunpowder deprived the cavalry of its shock-power, the tactics of Vegetius became ideal for armies, and his work became a military bible for European soldiers for hundreds of years. Karl von Clausewitz (1780–1831) a Prussian writer and military teacher also provided many strategic precepts, but today many of his admonitions are quaint, if not obsolete.

potential for realistic and swift goal adaptation and long-range planning is at hand.

Thus, the third route to systems improvement requires the analyst to use the currently available technological trends to improve system adaptability and planning.

A SUMMARY STATEMENT

In the past thirteen chapters of this book and in our present discussion of system improvements, we have taken a sample of current systems thought and presented it in a sequence moving from systems definition, to systems analysis, to systems implementation and treatment. Although other examples and other techniques could have been used, the outline of our presentation provides the reader with a framework for his own future study of the systems field. The future expansion of "systems thinking" argues for a continuation of the efforts the reader has already made.

If you have come this far you now have a basic vocabulary, a set of concepts, and a selected set of techniques from which to proceed. The daily newspapers, the popular press, and the scientific literature will continue to provide an ever increasing supply of specific examples, cases, and techniques, which may be selected to be congenial to your own interest and specific needs. A clipping file and notebook may be suggested again as an aid in the reader's updating.

In addition to this background information, we intended to give the reader some lasting fascination for at least one example of systems application, methodology, or concept. In this chapter we hoped to reinforce that interest by citing three powerful trends in current technology and systems thinking as they relate to systems improvement and to the analyst's future work. If this attempt was successful, the author is well pleased.

If the reader's interest has been caught, it remains only to remind him that he is now embarked on a stimulating but sometimes hazardous journey into the future—best expressed by an old Chinese proverb:

"Riding a tiger, it is difficult to dismount."

PROBLEMS

14.1   In modern computer systems designed for versatility of use, a basic module of data representation is often chosen within which a variety of data configurations can be made. Data storage capacity is then rated by the basic module, often called a "byte" or a "slab."

For example, consider a "byte" which consists of a block of 12 binary bits. This block of 12 bits can be used to represent (1) two 6-bit binary coded alphabetic characters, (2) three 4-bit numeric decimals, (3) four 3-bit octal * characters, or (4) 12 pure binary characters.

A. Why is the choice of byte size (12 binary bits) an important basic decision in the information handling system?

B. A computer memory is known to have a capacity of 1000 bytes, as defined above. How many alphabetic characters could this memory contain? How many decimal characters? How many octal characters? How many binary characters?

C. Why would it be important for a computer to know that incoming information is all numeric, or all alphabetic? Why would it be desirable to use different modes of coding for these two forms of information? How would module use change under these two different input conditions? What dispensation must be made of the module or byte configuration if the computer does not know whether incoming information is numeric or alphabetic?

14.2 An interesting device to improve the performance of a system is the inclusion of a "look-ahead" feature in its design. For example, experienced copy typists read several words ahead of their actual typed words. Experienced radiotelegraph operators lag their transcription behind what they hear. Modern real-time computers also make use of a similar feature and "look ahead" at work to be done, so that data and subroutines needed for shortly following jobs will be on hand when needed.

A. Consider this feature and the balance between the amount of lag (required for look ahead) and the variety of response that can be gained, by using this delay to make corrections and reallocations of resources versus the possible danger or loss that could occur from delay.

B. In what way could the look-ahead feature be used without danger, or with mitigated danger, in information handling systems?

C. Comment on the following quotation from S. W. Ransom and S. L. Clark, *The Anatomy of the Nervous System,* Philadelphia: Saunders, 1959 (Tenth Edition), pp. 381–382. How does this description of the human nervous system relate to the operation of real-time computing systems? In what ways could advance instruction or advice aid in the response preparation described below?

"The more elaborate the development of the nervous system, the greater its capacity to react with discrimination to stimuli. To put it in other terms: The more intercalary neurons in the nervous system the more

---

* An octal character is a number based on the base eight. Thus, decimal seven is seven in octal, but decimal eight is 10 in octal ($1 \times 8 + 0 \times 1$). Octal numbers are sometimes used in computer computations, because one octal character can be represented by three binary bits without loss of code positions, a fact not true of decimal representation. Thus, the decimal number 13, which is 15 in octal ($1 \times 8 + 5 \times 1$), could be represented in binary by 001 101, requiring only six binary bits. But if we use the 4-bit binary coded decimal code, the decimal number 13 would appear in binary as 0001 0011, for a total of eight binary bits.

possible internuncial paths are there between the incoming sensory stimulus and the outgoing motor ones and the less sterotyped the response may be. Man with his most highly developed nervous system has the greatest opportunity for variation in response to stimuli. With more internuncial neurons between the receptor and effector, there is a delay in response to a stimulus, and so it is possible to state that the cerebral cortex must affect action in at least three ways: by delaying the response to stimulus, allowing for a choice in the response, and aiding in integrating the action involved. The time of conduction being relatively brief, the advantages in choice and integration of the response more than compensate for the implied danger of the delay."

14.3 Why does the ability to forecast results in detail coupled with the ability to compare the actual results with the forecasts lead to more realistic planning?

PROJECT 10

According to *Business Week*, May 14, 1966, pages 164–166, ("Information becomes a hot item"), businessmen see in the growth of databank services a "fantastic market." The magazine explains: "Oldline information suppliers are being joined by a diversity of new sources, including computer makers, economists, consultants in engineering and programming, market research outfits, Western Union and other communications companies. And there's a flurry of mergers, acquisitions and joint operations as the computer specialists try to tie in with existing databanks and information services."

For example, the article cited reports a number of databank services as of the article's date:

1. International Telephone & Telegraph Corp. has a databank for economic forecasting and one on world trade statistics for the United Nations.

2. Bunker-Ramo Corp. has a financial data service with on-line stock prices.

3. McGraw-Hill is selling new computer-produced construction market data through its F. W. Dodge Co. division the old-line construction data supplier.

4. IBM has formed a new Information Marketing Group to sell data obtained by combining Dun & Bradstreet's file of corporate information on 390,000 U. S. businesses (95% of all manufacturing) and the Commerce Department's "input-output" data on interindustry transactions. These combined files will be used by the computer to provide customers with market potential estimates, lists of customers, estimates of market share and the like.

5. Some 2000 economic series will be stored by a private service in a computer at Carnegie Institute of Technology in Pittsburgh, on tap by Teletype for economic analysis and forecasting.

6. Compustat, a service of Standard & Poor's, subsidiary of McGraw-Hill, provides complete computer tape records on 1000 companies' stock prices, sales, earnings, dividends, capital investments—a total of 60 items.

7. Legal Research Service, Inc., and Western Union Telegraph Co. in a joint venture provide legal precedents direct by Telex printer to law offices, based on a ten-digit inquiry code and a master file of over 1-million coded cases.

Many other databanks—from medicine to government—in combination with real-time communications and data processing facilities are currently in the process of revolutioning the information-handling and data-analysis capability in many industries and administrative departments.

A. Make a study of the databank and information-handling capability of an industry of interest to you and report on the effects the current trends in technology will have upon your specific area of interest.

B. What effects will these facts have on your own chosen field of interest—in terms of your own employment and promotion possibilities?

APPENDIX A

MATRIX OPERATIONS

A *matrix* is a tabular array of data, organized in a standard form, which may be handled as a package in mathematical calculations. A matrix's size is called its *order*, and is denoted by its rows m and its columns n. Thus, a matrix with three rows and four columns is a 3×4 matrix, or a matrix of order 3×4.

In standard notation a matrix's rows are numbered $i = 1, 2, 3, \ldots, m$, and its columns $j = 1, 2, 3, \ldots, n$, so that a given cell in the matrix, found at the intersection of row i and column j, is denoted by the *subscript* (ij). Thus, a number in row 2, column 3 is designated x_{23}. Figure A-1 shows the standard nomenclature.

The matrix operations of *addition* and *subtraction*, which are defined only for matrices of the same order, follow the usual rules of algebra. The sum of two matrices of the same order is a matrix of identical order which has as its entries the sum of the corresponding cells of the first two matrices. Thus, if c_{ij} is a cell in the matrix sum, and the corresponding cells in the matrices added are a_{ij} and b_{ij}, respectively, then matrix addition can be defined as performing the operation.

$$c_{ij} = a_{ij} + b_{ji}$$

for all $m \times n$ combinations of i and j. As in usual algebra, for the result to make sense, the row and column definitions of the matrices added must be identical.

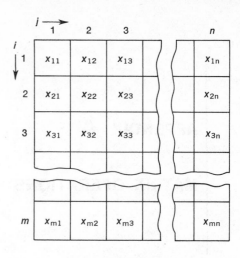

MATRIX [A]

A-1 Standard Matrix Notation. The meaning of table entries is provided by *position.* The *transpose* of matrix A, denoted by A^1, is obtained by swapping rows and columns in the table, i.e., by an interchange of data position and by an interchange of subscripts so that the entry for x_{13} is moved to position x_{31} (and so on, for all the cells.)

Example: At two warehouses, we stock *small, medium,* and *large* sweaters in *red, blue,* and *white.* The stock on hand at the first warehouse is denoted by a table, designated below as matrix [A], that at the second warehouse as matrix [B], and the sum of the two, the total inventory in the system, as matrix [C]. For shorthand notation, the operation of matrix addition is often abbreviated $[A] + [B] = [C]$, *or* $\mathbf{A} + \mathbf{B} = \mathbf{C}$, the bracketed or boldface capital letter denoting the whole matrix, rather than one of its cells.[1]

	S	M	L
R	2	3	5
B	1	6	2
W	7	6	3

WAREHOUSE 1

$+$

	S	M	L
R	4	5	2
B	6	2	7
W	5	8	3

WAREHOUSE 2

$=$

	S	M	L
R	6	8	7
B	7	8	9
W	12	14	6

TOTAL SYSTEM

Matrix subtraction is defined by the operation of subtracting each cell of [B] from the corresponding cell of [A] to obtain the cells of [C].

---

[1] Some authors use the alternate form $[a_{ij}] + [b_{ij}] = [c_{ij}]$, or simply $A + B = C$, when the meaning is clear. The complete array is often shown in brackets or parentheses for simplicity, rather than in boxes as shown here.

Matrix subtraction is thus equivalent to algebraic addition with the sign of the subtrahend changed. Thus, if $[A]$ is stock on hand and we sell $[B]$, then we have $[C]$ left, as below.

	S	M	L
R	2	3	5
B	1	6	2
W	7	6	3

$-$

	S	M	L
R	2	1	2
B	0	2	2
W	5	2	1

$=$

	S	M	L
R	0	2	3
B	1	4	0
W	2	4	2

Note that in matrix addition and subtraction, the units, i.e., the row and column designations, remain fixed throughout the operation. No transformation of units takes place. The rules for addition and subtraction are the same for any order matrix; we repeat the required operation for each corresponding cell (ij) until all $m \times n$ combinations have been completed.

Matrix multiplication requires special treatment. For simplicity, it can be thought of as a form of accumulate-multiply operation. To introduce this topic, we will first consider matrices that have only one row or one column.

A matrix with a single row is called a *row vector*; a matrix with a single column is called a *column vector*.[2] Suppose we consider a row vector with three column positions, $i = 1, 2, 3$, and a column vector with three row positions, $j = 1, 2, 3$. Then, we may define vector multiplication as the accumulative multiplication operation

$$a_1 b_1 + a_2 b_2 + a_3 b_3 = c$$

in which the final answer is a single number. Note that in this operation the units of vector $[a]$ and vector $[b]$ *are* transformed, and that for a correct answer, the column units (or dimensions) of the row vector must be the same as the row units of the column vector.

Example: In the warehouse we have *small, medium,* and *large* sweaters priced according to size. Suppose we have a row vector giving the total number of units in inventory by size, and a column vector giving the unit price by size. The vector multiplication operation gives the total value of inventory in the warehouse—in dollars, *not* pieces. In general, the resulting units will be those of the row vector *row* and the column vector *column*. For this example the size of the garment is lost.

---

[2] A row or column vector is usually denoted in lower case by one of the equivalent forms: $[a]$, **a**, or simply a, when the meaning is clear. For ease in typesetting, parentheses are often used to replace the boxes shown above.

$$
\begin{array}{c}
\text{Number} \\
\text{of Units} \\
\text{in stock}
\end{array}
\quad
\begin{array}{ccc}
S & M & L \\
\hline
\boxed{10 \mid 15 \mid 10}
\end{array}
\quad \times \quad
\begin{array}{c}
\$ \text{ Ea. Unit} \\
\begin{array}{c|c}
S & 2 \\
M & 3 \\
L & 4
\end{array}
\end{array}
\quad = \quad
\boxed{105}
\quad
\begin{array}{c}
\text{Number of} \\
\$ \text{ in stock}
\end{array}
$$

Input vector [a]   Transform   Output
                       vector [b]   vector [c]

To be certain we understand how the row and column units combine, we can write out the calculation in detail:

$$(10 \text{ small})(\$2/\text{small}) + (2 \text{ medium})(\$3/\text{medium}) +$$
$$(4 \text{ large})(\$4/\text{large}) = \$105$$

Note that the row vector *column* dimensions and the column vector *row* dimensions always cancel out in the multiplication of the individual terms, leaving a uniform dimension for each term. Only when this is true can we sensibly perform the addition operation.

To reinforce the idea of a transformation, it is helpful to think of a block diagram, as shown in Figure A-2. Here three inputs (in pieces) come into a box, which converts them to a single output (in dollars). The inputs come from the row vector; the required transform comes from the column vector; and the transformation comes from the multiplication of the row by the column vector.

Having mastered this idea, we may now apply it to an entire matrix, although some care is required. Two matrices [A] and [B] may be multiplied

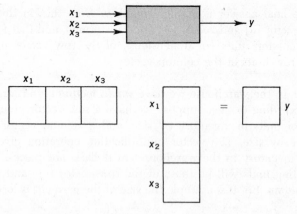

A-2 Vector multiplication as a transformation operation. The multiplication of the row vector with three inputs by the column representing the black-box transform produces the transformation to one output variable.

only if the number of columns of [A] is equal to the number of rows of [B]. The resulting product [C] will be a matrix with the same number of rows as [A] and the same number of columns as [B]. A helpful formula to remember is

$$[A] \times [B] = [C]$$
$$m \times p \quad q \times n \quad m \times n$$

Thus, if [A] is an $m \times p$ matrix and [B] is a $q \times n$ matrix, then [C] is an $m \times n$ matrix. The operations we perform are identical to vector multiplication, except we consider each possible row and column vector multiplication.

Example: Consider the inventory given by matrix [A] of the previous addition example, by size and color. Suppose we make a different dollar evaluation for each size sweater, but make no distinction by color. What is the total value of merchandise in the warehouse if we wish to retain the color classification? The result is shown below, the multiplication of each inventory matrix row times the price column vector.

	S	M	L			$			$
R	2	3	5		S	2	R	33	
B	1	6	2	×	M	3	= B	28	
W	7	6	3		L	4	W	44	

Thus, to obtain $33, we perform the arithmetical computation: $(2 \times 2) + (3 \times 3) + (5 \times 4) = 33$; to obtain $28: $(1 \times 2) + (6 \times 3) + (2 \times 4) = 28$; and to obtain $44: $(7 \times 2) + (6 \times 3) + (3 \times 4) = 44$.

In general, when we multiply two matrices of appropriate order according to this procedure, each possible row-by-column combination gives a number, which we enter in the answer matrix cell corresponding to the intersection of the chosen row and column. Thus, multiplication of row (1) of the first matrix by column (1) of the second matrix would produce a result for cell $(1, 1)$ of the answer, the process being repeated until all cells of the answer matrix are filled.

Example: The easiest way to understand the operation is to see a few correct numerical examples:

$$\begin{array}{|c|c|} \hline 1 & 2 \\ \hline 3 & 4 \\ \hline \end{array} \times \begin{array}{|c|c|} \hline 2 & 4 \\ \hline 6 & 8 \\ \hline \end{array} = \begin{array}{|c|c|} \hline 14 & 20 \\ \hline 30 & 44 \\ \hline \end{array} \qquad \text{(a)}$$

$$\begin{array}{|c|c|c|} \hline 1 & 2 & 5 \\ \hline 3 & 4 & 6 \\ \hline \end{array} \times \begin{array}{|c|c|} \hline 2 & 4 \\ \hline 6 & 8 \\ \hline 1 & 2 \\ \hline \end{array} = \begin{array}{|c|c|} \hline 19 & 30 \\ \hline 36 & 56 \\ \hline \end{array} \qquad \text{(b)}$$

$$\begin{array}{|c|c|c|}\hline 2 & 3 & 4 \\\hline\end{array} \times \begin{array}{|c|c|c|c|}\hline 1 & 2 & 0 & 3 \\\hline 1 & 1 & 2 & 0 \\\hline 0 & 2 & 3 & 1 \\\hline\end{array} = \begin{array}{|c|c|c|c|}\hline 5 & 15 & 18 & 10 \\\hline\end{array}$$ (c)

It would be impossible to matrix-multiply in the following two cases, because the row and column requirement is not met.

$$\begin{array}{|c|c|}\hline 1 & 2 \\\hline 3 & 4 \\\hline\end{array} \times \begin{array}{|c|c|}\hline 2 & 4 \\\hline 6 & 8 \\\hline 1 & 2 \\\hline\end{array}$$ (d)

$$\begin{array}{|c|c|c|}\hline 1 & 2 & 5 \\\hline 3 & 4 & 6 \\\hline\end{array} \times \begin{array}{|c|c|}\hline 2 & 4 \\\hline 6 & 8 \\\hline\end{array}$$ (c)

It is also good practice to watch the units in matrix multiplication. For example in case (c) above, consider a problem in which we order "assortments" of small, medium, and large as given by vector $[a]$, each of which contains the distribution of colors red, blue, white, and yellow (by size) as shown in matrix $[B]$. The number of garments of each color we will get is given by $[a] \times [B] = [c]$, and the computation is both numerically and dimensionally correct, as shown below.

	Size					Color			
						R	B	W	Y
	S	M	L		S	1	2	0	3
Number ordered	2	3	4	$\times$ M	1	1	2	0
				L	0	2	3	1

	Color			
	R	B	W	Y
= Number ordered	5	15	18	10

However, consider another application—one in which the numerical computations may be performed, but the result is wrong because the units are not correctly matched. Suppose we again have the inventory given by $[A]$ in the addition example. Also suppose the value of the stock varies by both size *and* color. We want to find the inventory value by size and color, retaining the detailed classification as we go from pieces to dollars.

At first glance, we might be tempted to use direct matrix multiplication of the piece inventory [A] by the value distribution [B], because the row and column requirement is met and we could come up with some numbers. But there is no way to match the units of size and color to get a sensible answer by *matrix* multiplication as it is defined.

	S	M	L
R	2	3	5
B	1	6	2
W	7	6	3

Units on hand

	S	M	L
R	2	3	4
B	3	4	5
W	4	5	6

Value each by
size and color

The haberdasher would have no difficulty in coming up with the result

	S	M	L
R	4	9	20
B	3	24	10
W	28	30	18

Value of inventory
by size and color

and he would obtain this answer by multiplying corresponding cells of [A] and [B] to get the cells of [C], i.e., he would find $c_{ij} = a_{ij}b_{ij}$ (whether he knew he was performing this fancy operation or not). But, *this result and operation are not matrix multiplication*, by definition.

The reader may have concluded by now that matrix multiplication is useful when a transformation of units[3] is needed, which is not the case in the last example. Matrix multiplication, like vector multiplication, is a transformation operation, a point we shall return to in a moment.

Before continuing, the reader should note that the sequence in which matrices are multiplied is critical, because, in general, $AB \neq BA$. First, consider two matrices of the same order, which may be multiplied using the rules above. By direct application of these rules, we see, for example, that

$$\begin{array}{|c|c|}\hline 1 & 2 \\\hline 3 & 4 \\\hline\end{array} \times \begin{array}{|c|c|}\hline 0 & 1 \\\hline 6 & 8 \\\hline\end{array} \neq \begin{array}{|c|c|}\hline 0 & 1 \\\hline 6 & 8 \\\hline\end{array} \times \begin{array}{|c|c|}\hline 1 & 2 \\\hline 3 & 4 \\\hline\end{array}$$

[3] A matrix, such as a *transition matrix*, may indeed have the same row and column designations, say states (see Chapter 2). But although the state *names* are not changed by matrix multiplication, the states occupied, or the state probabilities are.

Moreover, if two matrices are not of the same order, matrix multiplication may not be defined when the sequence of multiplication is reversed; a 2×3 matrix may be multiplied by a 3×4 matrix, but a 3×4 matrix cannot be multiplied by a 2×3 matrix. Finally, a check of the definitions of the rows and columns of the two matrices to be multiplied will usually indicate that a reverse of the multiplication sequence, even if possible, will not make dimensional sense, nor be numerically equal to the original sequence of operations. The critical nature of the sequence of matrix multiplication will be mentioned again as we discuss matrix *inversion*, a topic we introduce via the following discussion of simultaneous linear equations.

A major application of matrix methods is in the solution of *simultaneous linear equations*. For example, suppose we have two simultaneous linear equations with two unknowns

$$8x_1 + 4x_2 = 400$$
$$5x_1 + 10x_2 = 400$$

which have the general format

$$a_{11}x_1 + a_{12}x_2 = C_1$$
$$a_{21}x_1 + a_{22}x_2 = C_2$$

Before discussing a matrix solution for these equations we will benefit from doing a little algebra in which we study a standard arithmetic method that will progressively eliminate variables from *any* set of simultaneous linear equations, i.e., a *canonical* procedure for getting the job done. We use the numerical example above for clarity and indicate the solution steps required.

Step 1: Divide the first equation by 8, the coefficient a_{11}, to give

$$x_1 + \tfrac{1}{2}x_2 = 50$$
$$5x_1 + 10x_2 = 400$$

Step 2: Subtract 5, the coefficient a_{21} *times* Equation (1) from Equation (2), leaving

$$x_1 + \tfrac{1}{2}x_2 = 50$$
$$0 + 7.5x_2 = 150$$

Step 3: Now, continuing the cycle, divide Equation (2) by 7.5, the coefficient a_{22}, leaving

$$x_1 + \tfrac{1}{2}x_2 = 50$$
$$0 + x_2 = 20$$

Step 4: Subtract 0.5, the coefficient a_{12}, *times* Equation (2) from Equation (1), leaving

$$x_1 + \ 0 = 40$$
$$0 + x_2 = 20$$

Thus, the solution is $x_1 = 40$, $x_2 = 20$.

Note that we have progressively eliminated variables from left to right using repetitive *division, multiplication,* and *subtraction.* The method may be extended to n equations in n unknowns, although the amount of work goes up rapidly with the size of the array.

However, in general, using the above process we always obtain (1) a unique solution, as above, (2) no solution because the equations are *inconsistent,* e.g., $x_1 + x_2 = 1$, and $x_1 + x_2 = 2$, or (3) an infinite number of possible solutions because the equations are *not independent,* e.g., $x_1 + x_2 = 1$, and $2x_1 + 2x_2 = 2$. The canonical procedure will fortunately point up the latter two special cases by showing a contradiction, to indicate inconsistency (e.g., $0 = 2$), or by dropping two variables (or more) in a subtraction, to indicate there are two or more dependent equations somewhere in the set.

Clearly we could write the two equations just solved in matrix and vector form[4]

$$\begin{bmatrix} 8 & 4 \\ 5 & 10 \end{bmatrix} \begin{bmatrix} x_1 \\ x_2 \end{bmatrix} = \begin{bmatrix} 400 \\ 400 \end{bmatrix}$$

where the first matrix, say $[A]$, is the *matrix of coefficients* of the two equations in which the position in the matrix corresponds to the position of the coefficients in the equation array; and where the column vectors, $[x]$ and $[c]$, represent the unknowns and the constants to the right of the equality, respectively.

Thus, the set of two equations in two unknowns may be written in matrix and vector notation simply as[5]

$$Ax = c$$

a general notation that will do for *any* system of n linear equations in n unknowns.

---

[4] For simplicity, hereafter we use brackets (instead of boxes) to indicate a matrix or a vector. Two adjacent brackets indicate multiplication.
[5] Also for simplicity, we will understand that a variable without a subscript is a matrix or a vector.

If the reader does not see this equivalence, he should carry out the matrix multiplication required, noting that *two matrices (or vectors) are equal if and only if each of their corresponding cells is equal.*

$$\begin{bmatrix} 8 & 4 \\ 5 & 10 \end{bmatrix}\begin{bmatrix} x_1 \\ x_2 \end{bmatrix} = \begin{bmatrix} 8x_1 + 4x_2 \\ 5x_1 + 10x_2 \end{bmatrix} = \begin{bmatrix} 400 \\ 400 \end{bmatrix}$$

We may now introduce the following concepts, which follow naturally from ordinary algebra.

The equality of a matrix equation is not altered if:

(1) The elements in a row of a matrix equation are multiplied (or divided) by a constant (since this amounts to the multiplication or division of both sides of the equation by the same number), or if

(2) The elements in a row of the matrix equation are added or subtracted from another row (since this amounts to the addition or subtraction of equal amounts from both sides of the equality).

Using these ideas and what we have just learned about the canonical procedure for variable elimination, let us solve the same equations by the much neater *detached coefficient tableau method.*

We first place the matrix *A* and the constant column *c* in a *tableau*, as below. (The vertical line represents an "equals" sign with the coefficients on the left and the constant column on the right.)

$$\left(\begin{array}{cc|c} 8 & 4 & 400 \\ 5 & 10 & 400 \end{array} \right)$$

We now apply the canonical rules of row division, multiplication, and subtraction as before—but we now apply these rules to each tableau row as if it were an equation—to get

$$\left(\begin{array}{cc|c} 1 & 0.5 & 50 \\ 0 & 7.5 & 150 \end{array} \right) \qquad \text{after Steps 1 and 2, and}$$

$$\left(\begin{array}{cc|c} 1 & 0 & 40 \\ 0 & 1 & 20 \end{array} \right) \qquad \begin{array}{l} \text{after steps 3 and 4 of the} \\ \text{canonical procedure.} \end{array}$$

The answer, $x_1 = 40$, $x_2 = 20$, may, of course, be read off by reference to the *position* of the values remaining in the last *tableau*. For example, we have a "1" in the x_1 column and a 40 in the constant column, which may be read as $1x_1 = 40$, or simply $x_1 = 40$. The final solution should always show a left-hand side containing 1's down the diagonal of the coefficient matrix, with 0's elsewhere. (It *is* possible that some of the entries in the constant column will be negative or zero, but if we can develop the diagonal by application of the canonical procedure, we are assured of a unique solution to the problem.)

The beauty of the *tableau* procedure is that we could easily have solved for two (or more) sets of conditions, i.e., constants, while we were doing the rest of the work. For example, suppose we started out with

$$\begin{pmatrix} 8 & 4 & | & 400 & 600 \\ 5 & 10 & | & 400 & 300 \end{pmatrix}$$

where we have two columns of constants on the right, representing two cases, and our equality considerations apply to the 400,400 column as Case 1 and to the 600,300 column as Case 2, although *our procedure of solution does not change* from the one-case computation.

Following the standard rules again, but applying them across the *entire* row, including both cases, let us see what happens:

$$\begin{pmatrix} 8 & 4 & | & 400 & 600 \\ 5 & 10 & | & 400 & 300 \end{pmatrix} \quad \text{start}$$

$$\begin{pmatrix} 1 & 5 & | & 50 & 75 \\ 0 & 7.5 & | & 150 & -75 \end{pmatrix} \quad \text{after steps 1 and 2.}$$

$$\begin{pmatrix} 1 & 0 & | & 40 & 80 \\ 0 & 1 & | & 20 & -10 \end{pmatrix} \quad \text{after steps 3 and 4.}$$

The answer for Case 1 is, as before, $x_1 = 40$, $x_2 = 20$, found in the first column of constants. The answer for Case 2, $x_1 = 80$, $x_2 = -10$, appears in the second column of constants. Note that the detailed computations on the *left-hand* side of the *tableau* are in no way affected by the introduction of the additional case. Note also that this procedure may be extended to any number of cases by adding more columns to the *right-hand* side of the tableau.

For reasons that will shortly be clear, let us solve another example using the same two equations, but under two different constant conditions, namely,

$$\begin{pmatrix} 8 & 4 & | & 1 & 0 \\ 5 & 10 & | & 0 & 1 \end{pmatrix} \quad \text{start}$$

$$\begin{pmatrix} 1 & 0.5 & | & 0.125 & 0 \\ 0 & 7.5 & | & -0.625 & 1 \end{pmatrix} \quad \text{after steps 1 and 2.}$$

$$\begin{pmatrix} 1 & 0 & | & 0.167 & -0.067 \\ 0 & 1 & | & -0.083 & 0.133 \end{pmatrix} \quad \text{after steps 3 and 4.}$$

In the final table we have rounded-off to three figures, but, to that accuracy, the solutions may be read as before from the final tableau by remembering that the "1" in row 1 represents x_1 and the "1" in row 2 represents 2.

Again, for reasons of later need, we should note the interesting outcome when we multiply the original *matrix of coefficients* A by the matrix formed from the two solution columns in the final tableau, considering these columns now to form a 2 × 2 matrix B. If matrix A is multiplied by matrix B, we get another 2 × 2 matrix I, which has 1's along its main diagonal and 0's elsewhere:[6]

$$\begin{bmatrix} 8 & 4 \\ 5 & 10 \end{bmatrix} \times \begin{bmatrix} 0.167 & -0.067 \\ -0.083 & 0.133 \end{bmatrix} = \begin{bmatrix} 1 & 0 \\ 0 & 1 \end{bmatrix}$$

We have already seen that a system of n equations in n unknowns may be written in matrix notation as $Ax = c$. If it were possible to *divide* matrices, we might have an easy solution for the "unknowns" of our problem by dividing to obtain $x = c/A$, remembering, of course, that we were dealing with blocks of data, not just single numbers. (If we could divide, the resulting column vector x would give all n solutions to a set of n simultaneous linear equations in n unknowns.)

But, unfortunately, matrix division is not defined, because, in general, matrix multiplication is not *commutative*,[7] that is, $AB \neq BA$. (The reader should convince himself of this by trying a few simple examples.)

Because we cannot tell whether $x = c/A$ arose from $Ax = c$ or from $xA = c$, which, in general, would be different, the equivalent of matrix division, defined to avoid this pitfall, is called *matrix inversion*.

To introduce this topic, we must first define a special square matrix, called the *identity I*, which we have seen before, namely, for the 2 × 2 case,

$$I = \begin{bmatrix} 1 & 0 \\ 0 & 1 \end{bmatrix}$$

The identity I acts like a "1" in ordinary arithmetic and *is* commutative

$$AI = IA = A$$

Now, we may think of the inverse of a matrix as roughly the same as a reciprocal.[8] For example, suppose we can find a matrix B, which when multiplied by matrix A gives the identity I. Then B is *by definition* the inverse of A and is denoted by $B = A^{-1}$

---

[6] The result shown, is of course, subject to rounding-off errors. In this case the exact identity requires final rounding-off to one decimal place. The interested reader may wish to check the matrix multiplication shown. He will discover the effects of minor rounding-off decisions, and understand that this can be a major problem in many computations of this type.

[7] Although it is always associative, i.e., $ABC = A(BC) = (AB)C$.

[8] A reciprocal is, of course, defined as follows: If a is a number, then $1/a$ is its reciprocal, and multiplication by a number's reciprocal is equivalent to division by that number. This principle is often used in slide-rule computations to save work.

If we can find matrix B, then it must have the following properties:

$$AB = AA^{-1} = BA = A^{-1}A = I$$

which shows that a matrix and its inverse are not only commutative, but their product is the identity I.

If we can find the inverse of the matrix A, then the solution of a set of simultaneous linear equations can be obtained directly, because

$$Ax = c$$
$$A^{-1}Ax = A^{-1}c$$
$$Ix = A^{-1}c$$
$$x = A^{-1}c$$

Moreover, we can solve the equations by a simple matrix multiplication. For example, returning to the two equations already solved by the *detached coefficients tableau method,* we find that we have already found A^{-1} for the coefficients matrix A, namely,

$$A = \begin{bmatrix} 8 & 4 \\ 5 & 10 \end{bmatrix} \qquad A^{-1} = \begin{bmatrix} 0.167 & -0.067 \\ -0.083 & 0.133 \end{bmatrix}$$

and, according to our argument, the solution for Case 1, the constants 400, 400, may be obtained directly as

$$x = \begin{bmatrix} 0.167 & -0.067 \\ -0.083 & 0.133 \end{bmatrix} \begin{bmatrix} 400 \\ 400 \end{bmatrix} = \begin{bmatrix} 40 \\ 20 \end{bmatrix}$$

which checks out upon multiplication of A^{-1} by the constant column vector.

To refresh our memory, let us formalize how we obtained the inverse of matrix A. To obtain *the inverse of a square matrix*[9] A, create the *tableau* $(A|I)$, where I is an identity matrix of the same order as A. Using the *canonical procedure,* convert the original tableau into the tableau $(I|B)$, i.e., into the final solution, if it exists. If the final solution tableau can be found—and it can be, if A does indeed have an inverse—then B is the unique inverse of A, or A^{-1}.

Why is it worthwhile to go to the trouble to find the inverse of matrix A? In addition to the ease of notation and other theoretical benefits derived from use of the inverse, the repeated solution of large systems of linear equations can be obtained most efficiently by this approach.

Returning to our last example, we observe that because the number of columns of the inverse is always equal to the number of rows of the constant column x, we can treat a number of cases as a number of constant columns, form a matrix of them, and solve any number of cases in *one* matrix multiplication. For example, taking the two cases we solved for

[9] For simplicity we restrict our attention to square matrices.

and indicating by dots the many others we might want to investigate, we have

$$x = \begin{bmatrix} 0.167 & -0.067 \\ -0.083 & 0.133 \end{bmatrix} \begin{bmatrix} 400 & 600 & \ldots \\ 400 & 300 & \ldots \end{bmatrix} = \begin{bmatrix} 40 & 80 & \ldots \\ 20 & -10 & \ldots \end{bmatrix}$$

The solutions for x_1 and x_2 appear in the first and second rows of the result; each column represents a different set of constant conditions. Clearly, the combination of electronic computers with procedures such as this greatly extends our ability to solve large-scale systems of simultaneous linear equations.[10] (In fact most matrix applications of this type are now standard library programs at electronic computing centers; no programing is required to obtain the use of the machine capability.)

This survey of matrix topics is sufficient to follow the examples in this book. The reader's attention to Reference 1 and 2 will be of great benefit for further study. Other references are cited for supplementary reading.

However, as a final point, we should return to the concept of the matrix as a transform, and matrix multiplication (and inversion) as transformations resulting from the application of a transform.

The reader may remember that a *function*, such as $y = 3x$, gives us a point in xy space for every specified value of x, since to every x there corresponds a y. A *transformation* on the other hand maps a whole set of points—a function or set of functions—from one set of dimensions (or coordinates) into another. Thus, for linear systems of the type we have been discussing, the coefficients in the matrices shown are transform coefficients and may be thought of in those terms; the act of applying them is a transformation.

A simple example will suffice. Suppose we have two sets of equations, represented by the two matrices of Fig. A-3. In this case we have adopted the usual "from-to" convention that inputs shall go from a row to a column, which may be seen by a comparison of the equations with the corresponding matrices. The corresponding block diagram is also shown for reference in Fig. A-3.

The multiplication of A by B maps all points of the output variables y_1 and y_2 into z_1 and z_3, and the resulting matrix C can be used to write equations for z_1 and z_2 in terms of the original input variables x_1 and x_2, as shown. The single "black box" C now contains the detail of both A and B.

---

[10] The question may arise whether the tableau procedure or the inverse matrix approach is more efficient in a given solution of n equations and n unknowns. A suggested rule of thumb (which can vary widely depending upon the computer programs available) is to use the inverse method if the number of variables exceeds *three,* and if the number of cases to be solved exceeds *two.* (Reference 3, pp. 52-53.) If only one specific solution of a set of specific equations is needed, then the inverse procedure takes more time and work.

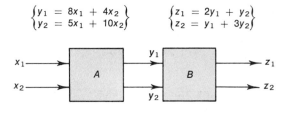

$$\begin{cases} y_1 = 8x_1 + 4x_2 \\ y_2 = 5x_1 + 10x_2 \end{cases} \qquad \begin{cases} z_1 = 2y_1 + y_2 \\ z_2 = y_1 + 3y_2 \end{cases}$$

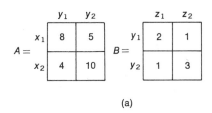

(a)

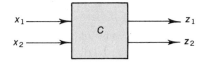

(b)

A-3 Matrix Multiplication as a transformation. Two matrices A and B correspond to the transforms provided by the boxes A and B of the flow diagram. The multiplication of A by B, given in (a), transforms the inputs of A into the outputs of B, producing the equivalent box C, given in (b). Linear equations, corresponding to the matrices are also shown. Matrix inversion may be thought of as the reverse of this process.

Without other information, we cannot recover A and B once the grouping has been done. (See Chapter 7.)

Suppose, however, we posed the inverse question: "How do we get back to where we came from?" For example, having found that $AB = C$, we might want to get B back again. To do so we have to perform the inverse of what we have just done—"un-multiply" the matrices (or map back from the xz space in which we are now to the original yz space of matrix

B.) Clearly the solution to the problem, from our previous arguments, is to perform the operations

$$A^{-1} AB = A^{-1}C$$
$$B = A^{-1}C$$

assuming, of course, we know the original matrix A or its inverse A.$^{-1}$

Using the methods previously discussed for finding the inverse of a given matrix, we find that

$$A = \begin{bmatrix} 8 & 5 \\ 4 & 10 \end{bmatrix} \qquad A^{-1} = \begin{bmatrix} \frac{1}{6} & -\frac{1}{12} \\ -\frac{1}{15} & \frac{2}{15} \end{bmatrix}$$

where we have kept the fractions to prevent rounding-off. Multiplying the inverse by *C*, we have

$$B = A^{-1}C = \begin{bmatrix} \frac{1}{6} & -\frac{1}{12} \\ -\frac{1}{15} & \frac{2}{15} \end{bmatrix} \begin{bmatrix} 21 & 23 \\ 18 & 34 \end{bmatrix} = \begin{bmatrix} 2 & 1 \\ 1 & 3 \end{bmatrix}$$

which is what we wanted to get. Some of the mystery of matrix multiplication and inversion can now be removed: Matrix multiplication is a transformation of dimensions in one direction; matrix inversion reverses the transformation process.

We have discussed here only matrix operations for linear matrices—those with constants in their cells. However, matrix operations are not so limited: A matrix cell may contain a real or complex variable, or it may contain real or complex functions. The basic operations remain the same. The interpretation and application of matrices using nonlinear and complex entries is, however, left to the suggested references.

REFERENCES

1. J. G. Kemeny, *et al.*, *Finite Mathematics with Business Applications*, Prentice-Hall, Englewood Cliffs, N.J., 1962, Chapter V. (This excellent text provides both explanation and example. Full illustration of the tableau method for solution of simultaneous linear equations by matrix row operations.)
2. R. Dorfman, P. A. Samuelson, and R. M. Solow, *Linear Programming and Economic Analysis*, McGraw-Hill, New York, 1958, Appendix A. (This is a distinguished work directed primarily at economists. However, the Appendix, "The Algebra of Matrices," is highly recommended after Kemeny because of the lucid description of the geometrical equivalent of matrix operations.)
3. An-min Chung, *Linear Programming*, C. E. Merrill, Columbus, Ohio, 1963, Chapter II. (Chapter II is also a matrix review in a somewhat more usual vein. It offers a clear explanation of matrix inversion using classical methods, with particular application to the linear transformations used in linear programing as a specific technique.)

APPENDIX B

MATHEMATICAL TRANSFORMATIONS

A model or system description may be easier to analyze if we transform the original model into a mathematically equivalent, yet less cumbersome form. We then analyze the transformed model and retransform the results into the desired model solution. Figure B-1 illustrates the sequence of steps in this process.

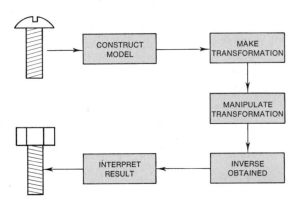

B-1 The procedure of using a mathematical transformation to ease analysis. Reading from left to right and top to bottom, the first step is to make an abstraction from the real world. This model may then be transformed to another, more convenient form, then manipulated as desired. Thereafter the procedure is reversed. The results of the manipulation, stated in "transform terms," are converted back to the original model format. Finally, the model results are interpreted in the real world context. Any form of transformation that is one-to-one is suitable. Several possibilities are discussed in the text.

TWO SIMPLE MATHEMATICAL TRANSFORMATIONS

A wide range of mathematical transformations can be used in this way. One such transformation, familiar to the student of algebra and trigonometry, is the conversion of xy coordinates into polar or circular coordinates, with the origin at $x = 0$, $y = 0$, as illustrated in Figure B-2.

Thus, the unique point $x = 3$, $y = 4$ is also uniquely specified by giving the values

$$r = \sqrt{x^2 + y^2}, \qquad \theta = \tan^{-1} y/x,$$

so that the point x, y may also be given by r and the angle θ, or simply $r \angle \theta$, here $5 \angle 53°$, and θ is measured from the right-hand x axis.

Conversely, given the circular notation $r \angle \theta$, we can go back to the xy coordinates by using the fact that

$$x = r \cos \theta, \qquad y = r \sin \theta,$$

which permits us to transform the xy coordinates of a point to circular coordinates and then back to xy coordinates.

Note also that the above transformation (and its inverse procedure) will in fact transform or map all points in the xy coordinate system into the polar or circular coordinate system on a one-to-one basis (and that the inverse procedure will in the same way map uniquely all points in the circular coordinate system back into the xy coordinate system.)

This is the distinction between a mathematical function and a mathematical transformation: The function, say $y = f(x)$, gives us specific values of the dependent variable y for given values of the independent variable x;

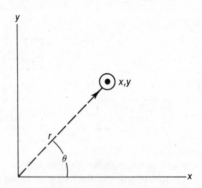

B-2 Cartesian to polar coordinates. A common mathematical transformation is that transforming the Cartesian xy coordinates of a point to polar coordinates, which define its position by the radius vector r from the origin O to the point together with the angle θ measured from OX to OP. The transformation is unique and may be reversed at will, as indicated in the text.

the mathematical transformation, on the other hand, transforms all functions in one set of coordinates into unique functions in another set of coordinates. In short, functions assign numerical values to numerical values; transformations, sometimes called operators, assign functions to functions.

Example: An interesting transformation that converts lines to points (and vice versa) forms the basis for a recent patent (Patent No. 3,069,654, P.V.C. Hough, "Method and Means for Recognizing Complex Patterns," Dec. 18, 1962). Suppose we have a straight line in the xy plane, which intersects the x and y axes at points u and v, respectively. One possible line/point transformation is to define a new set of axes, say s and t, and to let a point in st space be given by the line in xy space by using the *intercepts* u and v to compute

$$s = u; \qquad t = \frac{u}{v},$$

as shown in Figure B-3(a). In this way, every possible line in the xy space will be mapped into a unique point in the st space. Similarly, every point in st space can be converted into a line in xy space by noting that

$$u = s; \qquad v = \frac{s}{t},$$

where, again, u and v are the intercepts of the line at the x and y axes, respectively. The alternate displays may point up patterns in experimental data, because if a number of points in st space should fall into a straight-line pattern, they will be transformed into a series of concurrent lines (crossing at about the same point in xy space). Conversely, approximately concurrent lines in xy space will map into approximately colinear points in st space.[1] In various applications, conversion from one form of display to the other may aid the analyst in "seeking" an otherwise hazy pattern. For example, the Hough patent considers the detection of particle tracks in bubble chamber photographs (an experiment performed in physics). Photographs of bubbles gave points in st space. The objective was to find if there were any "tracks" or trajectories present that would indicate the presence of particles shooting through the bubbles. By converting the points to lines and looking for coincident lines in xy space, lines crossing near the

---

[1] In particular, if a series of points in st space should fall in a line given by $s = b + mt$, then the intercepts of the corresponding lines in xy space are $[t, t/(b + mt)]$, and each of these lines will pass through the common point in xy space given by $(-b/m, 1/m)$.

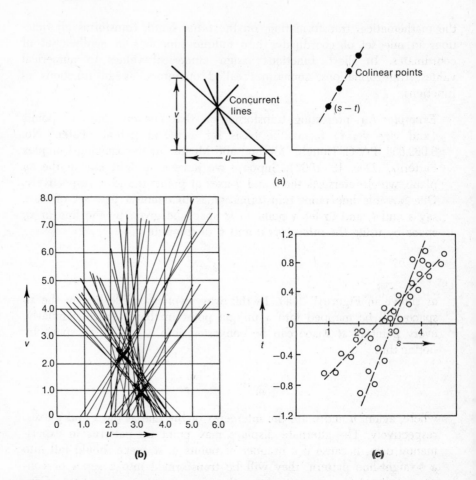

B-3 (a) The line-point transformation. (b) Radar bearings as lines. (c) Radar bearings as points. As discussed in the text, the intercepts of a line produce two numerical values that can be used to locate a unique point in "point space," as shown in (a). An application discussed in the text is illustrated by (b) and (c). (Source: Airborne Instruments Laboratory, Division of Cutler-Hammer.)

same point indicated such possible tracks in the bubble picture. In another application, suggested by Airborne Instruments Laboratory. (IEEE *Spectrum*, August, 1965, p. 5), the reverse procedure was used to resolve somewhat conflicting bearings taken by radio location equipment. Figure B-3b shows the bearings, plotted as lines in *xy* space, with the intercepts for each line being *u* and *v*, respectively, as before. The picture looks confusing. However, when the lines are transformed into points in *st* space, the points appear roughly colinear, and a line may be fitted to them, as shown in Figure B-3c. Reversing the procedure, if we map the line in *st* space back into the *xy* space, it will appear as a point, denoted in Figure B-3b by a large "X". It is interesting to note that we would probably not have selected the position of the "X" mark as shown, had we attempted to do so by inspection of Figure B-3a alone.

The usefulness and application of mathematical transformations, such as the one illustrated in the example, is limited only by the ingenuity of the analyst, and so it is frequently useful to imagine other equivalent ways in which a system description may be displayed.

MORE COMPLEX MATHEMATICAL TRANSFORMATIONS

Two well-known transforms, the *Laplace transform* and the *z transform,* are widely used in the analysis of systems that can be described by *linear differential equations* and *difference equations,* respectively. Applying the Laplace transform to a differential equation, or a *z* transform to a difference equation, converts these more complicated expressions into an algebraic form that can be handled more easily. The Laplace transform and the *z* transform, as we shall see, allow the analyst to compute the output response of a linear system to inputs that are, respectively, continuous and periodic. These transforms greatly simplify the analyses of linear systems that exhibit lag and feedback. Without the use of the Laplace or the *z* transform in these cases, it is usually very difficult to obtain an equation expressing the output from the system in "closed" form, i.e., without recourse to numerical evaluation of specific input values.

Although, fortunately, we may describe how to use the Laplace and *z* transforms compactly, a description of why these transforms work and the basis of their development is unfortunately beyond the scope of this appendix. A complete understanding of the theory of these transforms, moreover, requires the reader to be familiar with the subject known as "functions of a complex variable," which is usually somewhat beyond the mathematical level currently available to most nonmathematicians. The references at the end of this appendix are for those who wish to obtain more background on what is to follow here, which will be limited to an "appreciation" of the subject. However, we will assume hereafter that the reader has had at least a first course in calculus, because this will be necessary for the discussion.

The z Transform

To illustrate the *z* transform, we will first show how to obtain the *z* transform of a function, then how to find the transfer function of a system in *z* transform terms, and finally how to obtain the output of a system using the previous two z transforms.

Suppose the input to a system varies with time,[2] but occurs periodically, at equally spaced intervals, say minutes, hours, weeks, or months. To indicate discreteness, we will call the input $f(n)$ and denote the successive values of the input function by $a_0, a_1, a_2, a_3, \ldots, a_n$, so that, in general, $f(n) = a_n$.

We will understand that n does not take on negative values, or equivalently, that $f(n)$ is identically zero for negative n.

Example: Two examples will illustrate the notation. Suppose first that the successive values of $f(n)$ are equal to 1 for $n = 0, 1, 2, 3, \ldots$, but equal, of course, to zero for values of n less than 0. Figure B-4a shows this "step" input. Next, consider the case in which the input increases linearly, so that $f(n) = n$, as shown in Figure B-4b. In the first case $a_0 = a_1 = a_2 = a_3 = \ldots = 1$, and in the latter case $a_0 = 0$, $a_1 = 1$, $a_2 = 2$, $a_3 = 3, \ldots$, and so on. In general, the successive a's can take on any arbitrary value, positive or negative, it being understood that $f(0) = a_0$, $f(1) = a_1$, $f(2) = a_2$, $f(3) = a_3$, and so on to indicate the value of the input at a given time. In most cases of interest, we will devise a formula for providing the a's, as in the above case when $f(n) = 1$ and $f(n) = n$.

Now consider what would happen if we multiplied each term or value of the input $f(n)$ by z^n and added corresponding terms to obtain

$$F(z) = a_0 + a_1 z + a_2 z^2 + a_3 z^3 + a_4 z^4 + \cdots = \sum_0^\infty f(n) z^n$$

When this is done, the relationship between $f(n)$, the original function, and $F(z)$, the transformed function, will be unique—we can go from $f(n)$ to $F(z)$ and vice versa, just as we did in the xy coordinate to polar coordinate transformation and line/point transformation (although the method is not

[2] Both the z transform and the Laplace transform usually deal with time-varying functions, and transform the time coordinate into a "frequency" coordinate by a theorem due to the mathematician Fourier. Roughly stated, this theorem says that over a specified time interval any time-varying function may be duplicated or "synthesized" by a large number of sinusoidal waves (sines and cosines) of varying amplitude and frequency, which are superimposed to equal the original function. This transformation provides a standard mode of analysis (dealing with sinusoids always). This underlying principle is purposefully disguised in our presentation to avoid the introduction of complex numbers. However, a reasonably nontechnical explanation of background theory may be found in Reference 7, with a more rigorous and detailed treatment in Reference 5. The numbers z and s in the z transform and the Laplace transform, respectively, are complex numbers used to generate the sine wave frequencies required for synthesis.

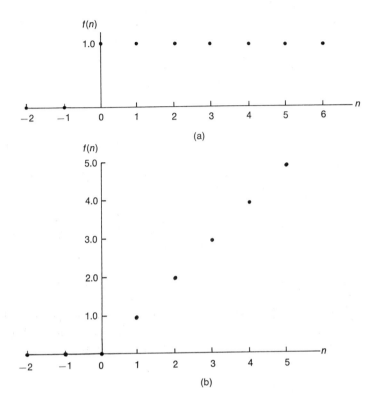

(a)

(b)

B-4 Figures illustrating the notation for discrete functions. (a) A discrete step function. (b) A discrete ramp function. The function $f(n)$ takes on values only at equally spaced intervals of time or in the sequence numbered $n = 0, 1, 2, 3, \ldots$ The function $f(n)$ is 0 for all negative values of n.

yet obvious). Values of $F(z)$ will be limited provided that $f(n)$ does not increase faster than geometrically.[3]

[3] Some engineering and mathematical texts (such as Kaplan, Reference 5) define the z transform as

$$F(z) = \sum_{0}^{\infty} f(n)z^{-n}$$

where the script z is most frequently used to indicate the negative exponentiation. Although the transform tables developed for the alternate definitions will be different, the same results are achieved by the consistent application of either. Whether or not the series defining $F(z)$ [or $F(z)$] converges is a question to be raised in either case. In most cases of interest $F(z)$ will converge if $|z| < 1$, and $F(z)$ will converge if $|z| > 1$. The reader should obviously take care to determine which of the definitions above is used in a given reference source before computations are made.

Example: Applying this treatment to the "step" input given in the previous example, we have

$$F(z) = 1 \cdot 1 + 1 \cdot z + 1 \cdot z^2 + 1 \cdot z^3 + \cdots$$

Remembering that the sum of a geometric series is $1/(1 - z)$ when z is less than unity, or by cross-multiplication, we obtain

$$F(z) = 1 + z + z^2 + z^3 + \cdots = \frac{1}{1 - z}$$

We have just found $F(z) = 1/(1 - z)$, the z transform of $f(n)$, when $f(n) = 1$, a "step" function.

Continuing in the same way, we find the z transform for $f(n) = n$, a "ramp" function, namely,

$$F(z) = 0 \cdot 1 + 1 \cdot z + 2 \cdot z^2 + 3 \cdot z^3 + \cdots = \sum_{0}^{\infty} nz^n$$

$$= z(1 + 2z + 3z^2 + \cdots)$$

$$= z \frac{d}{dz}(1 + z + z^2 + z^3 + \cdots) = z \frac{d}{dz}\left(\frac{1}{1 - z}\right),$$

where we recognize that the series $(1 + 2z + 3z^2 + \cdots)$ is the first derivative of $(1 + z + z^2 + z^3 + \cdots)$, the sum of which is $1/(1 - z)$. Taking the derivative of $1/(1 - z)$, we end up with

$$F(z) = \frac{z}{(1 - z)^2},$$

which is the z transform of a ramp, $f(n) = n$.

If we continue in this way for a number of cases, we can construct a table of functions $f(n)$ and their corresponding z transforms, $F(z)$, such as Table B.1.

It is particularly important to note from the transform pair table, Table B.1, that shifting the origin of the time axis one unit to the left, and in effect "delaying" the input one unit, is equivalent to replacing $f(n)$ by $f(n - 1)$. Moreover, if $f(n)$ is replaced by $f(n-1)$ and $F(z)$ is the z transform of $f(n)$, then the z transform of $f(n - 1)$ is $zF(z)$. Thus, *we can indicate a delay of one period by multiplying the z transform of the function by z.* Similarly, we can indicate a delay of two periods by multiplying by z^2; in general, we can indicate a delay of r periods by multiplying the z transform by z^r. (The procedure reverses itself for an advance, or a shift of the time origin to the right. To advance the input by one time period, we divide the z transform by z, and to advance r time periods, we divide by z^r.)[4]

[4] If $f(n) \neq 0$ when $n = 0$, i.e., if $f(0) \neq 0$, then the value of $f(0)$ must be subtracted from $F(z)$ before the division operation, as shown in transform pair (5) of Table B.1.

Table B.1ª   z Transforms

Pair	Function	Transform
T_1	$f(n)$	$F(z) = \sum\limits_{0}^{\infty} f(n)z^n$
T_2	$af_1(n) + bf_2(n)$	$aF_1(z) + bF_2(z)$
T_3	$f(n-1)$	$zF(z)$
T_4	$f(n+1)$	$\dfrac{1}{z}[F(z) - f(0)]$
T_5	$\begin{array}{ll} 1 & (n=0) \\ 0 & \text{otherwise} \end{array}\Big\}\begin{array}{l}\text{unit}\\\text{impulse}\end{array}$	1
T_6	$1 \quad (n \geq 0) \quad \text{unit step}$	$\dfrac{1}{(1-z)}$
T_7	$n \quad (n \geq 0) \quad \text{unit ramp}$	$\dfrac{z}{(1-z)^2}$
T_8	a^n	$\dfrac{1}{(1-az)}$
T_9	na^n	$\dfrac{az}{(1-az)^2}$
T_{10}	$a^n f(n)$	$F(az)$
T_{11}	$(-1)^n$	$\dfrac{1}{(1+z)}$

ª *Assumptions:* $f(n) = 0$ for all $n < 0$. $f(n)$ can take on values only at equally spaced intervals numbered $n = 0,1,2,3, \ldots$. In the above table a and b are constants.

Example: We know from the above example that the z transform of $f(n) = 1$ for $n > 0$, and $f(n) = 0$, otherwise, is $F(z) = 1/(1-z)$. We argue from the table of transform pairs that the z transform for $f(n) = 1$, $n > 1$, and $f(n) = 0$, otherwise (which is equivalent to the original function with n replaced by $n-1$), should be $zF(z)$, where $F(z)$ is the z transform already found. This may be shown by direct application of the definition. For the new function,

$$\text{For } f(n): F(z) = 1 \cdot 1 + 1 \cdot z + 1 \cdot z^2 + 1 \cdot z^3 + \cdots = \frac{1}{1-z}$$

$$\text{For } f(n-1): F(z) = 0 \cdot 1 + 1 \cdot z + 1 \cdot z^2 + 1 \cdot z^3 + \cdots$$

$$= z(1 + z + z^2 + z^3 + \cdots) = \frac{z}{1-z}$$

That division by z will produce the original transformation, or "advance" the input back to the original position, is obvious from the result.

We have shown how to find the z transform of simple discrete functions, how to advance and delay these functions in time by the simple process of dividing or multiplying the z transform by z for each period of advance or delay, respectively, and we have developed a table of transform pairs.

Clearly, one of the major virtues of the z transform is that a shift in the time scale—an advance or a delay of an input function—may be accomplished with great ease when the function has been converted to its z transform. Moreover, it should be clear that a large table of transform pairs would eliminate much of the tedium of transform pair development, because, once the transform pair has been written down, there is no need to repeat this work. Finally, because of the uniqueness of the transform pairs, the reader should realize that if someone provided him with a z transform that appeared in his table of transform pairs, he could immediately write down the function $f(n)$ associated with it, because that function would also appear in his table. By this means we go from the z transform to its inverse, $f(n)$.

With this information available, we now consider a system and develop its transfer function in z-transform terms. To do this we will consider a specific case in which the output of the system, $y(n)$, is given by

$$y(n) = ax(n) + (1 - a)y(n - 1)$$

where $x(n)$ is a current input variable, $y(n - 1)$ is the output of the system at the last previous instant of time, and a is a constant $(0 < a < 1)$. This equation is familiar from page 47. Our purpose is to find the ratio of the output $y(n)$ to the input $x(n)$, but to do this in terms of expressions containing z, namely, to find the transfer function $Y(z)/X(z)$.

To proceed, we first assume that we can find $X(z)$, the z transform of the input, since we know how to do this. We will also assume that we will be able to find the z transform of the system output $Y(z)$. Remembering that if $Y(z)$ is the z transform of $y(n)$, then $zY(z)$ is the z transform of $y(n - 1)$, we may now write the equation in z-transform terms as

$$Y(z) = aX(z) + (1 - a)zY(z)$$

Collecting terms and solving for the ratio $Y(z)/X(z)$, we get the required transfer function of the system as

$$\frac{Y(z)}{X(z)} = \frac{a}{1 - (1 - a)z}.$$

And, in particular, if we set $a = 0.5$, we will have found the z-transform transfer function for the system described by the difference equation on page 48. Note that the ability to indicate a one-period delay in time by multiplying by z allowed us to collect all the terms in $X(z)$ and $Y(z)$ and to obtain the transfer function *even though there was a lag*. In the original expression, we could not have collected terms in this way, because $y(n)$ and $y(n - 1)$ would not have been the same.

We now come to the final phase of the analysis. Suppose we want to find the output from the system described by the transfer function $Y(z)/X(z)$. How can we do this?

Given a specific input function $x(n)$ and therefore $X(z)$, which may be found from it, we may obtain $Y(z)$ as[5]

$$Y(z) = X(z) \cdot \frac{Y(z)}{X(z)}$$

Example: Suppose the input to the system *is* $x(n) = 1$, for $n > 0$, and $x(n) = 0$, otherwise, which is the "step" function previously discussed. Then the output of the system—in z-transform terms— is given by

$$Y(z) = \frac{1}{1 - z}\left[\frac{a}{1 - (1 - a)z}\right]$$

Similarly, suppose the input to the system is $x(n) = n$, for $n > 0$, and $x(n) = 0$, otherwise, which is the "ramp" function previously discussed. Then the output of the system is given by

$$Y(z) = \frac{z}{(1 - z)^2}\left[\frac{a}{1 - (1 - a)z}\right]$$

[All the examples given here assume system linearity, so that the transfer function $Y(z)/X(z)$ is independent of the input to the system, and may be tested for any desired input function $X(z)$ without modification.] The function $Y(z)$ gives the total picture of the system output, given the specified system input, but does so in terms of the "operator" z. What remains is to convert from $Y(z)$ to $y(n)$, which requires that we find the inverse transform of $Y(z)$.

The reader may now realize that the complete output specification of the system is available through his knowledge of $Y(z)$, yet he may also realize that the inverse transformation $y(n)$ is not immediately obvious, because in neither above case does the z transform obtained (and therefore its inverse) appear in Table B.1. This is the usual situation.

However, if it were possible to break up the more complicated z transform representing the system output into a sum of simpler terms which *did* appear in the table, we could get the final result, the inverse of the z transform output, by inspecting the table.

The technique usually used for this purpose is called the "method of partial fractions," and is described at length in References 4 and 7. However, a short example will suffice here.

---

[5] The multiplication shown is not always correct, but will be so for the usual case in which the transformation is made at the discrete intervals of time $n = 0, 1, 2, 3, \ldots$ and not at others. For more complex cases, see Reference 4.

By the method of partial fractions we seek to find a *sum* of "simpler" fractions which is identically equal to the single, more complex, fraction that is to be broken up. Two rules cover most cases. If the denominator of the fraction to be broken up can be factored without obtaining repeated terms, then that fraction may be expanded into a sum of fractions each of which has as its denominator one of the nonrepeated factors. A somewhat different treatment is required when the factors are repeated. The two methods are illustrated in the following example.

Example: In the z transform

$$Y(z) = \frac{1}{1-z}\left[\frac{a}{1-(1-a)z}\right]$$

the denominator is already factored into two nonidentical terms, namely, $1-z$ and $1-(1-a)z$, which may be used to form the denominators of two partial-fraction terms in an expansion with two unknown numerators. Thus,

$$Y(z) = \frac{1}{1-z}\left[\frac{a}{1-(1-a)z}\right] \equiv \frac{A}{1-z} + \frac{B}{1-(1-a)z}$$

is a suitable expansion, where the numerators A and B are found by enforcing the identity. The rapid way to solve for A and B is as follows: To solve for A, multiply both sides by the denominator of A, $(1-z)$, and set $z = 1$. This immediately yields[6]

$$A = \frac{a}{1-(1-a)} = 1.$$

Now repeating the same treatment, multiply both sides by $1-(1-a)z$ and set $z = 1/(1-a)$, which yields

$$B = -(1-a).$$

We may now write

$$Y(z) = \frac{1}{1-z} - \frac{1-a}{1-(1-a)z},$$

and we are fortunate: Both terms on the right can be found in Table B.1 (remembering that multiplication by a constant does not affect the

---

[6] The short-cut method of solving for the numerators A and B rests upon the fact that the equality must hold (the two sides must be *identically* equal) for *any* value of the variable z, which for the purposes of the algebraic manipulation may be varied at will. This is a useful algebraic device, when we use the method of partial fractions, because it is usually possible to eliminate by the proper selection of z all numerators except the one under evaluation.

result of the inversion). By inspection, then, we find from Table B.1 that the inverse of $Y(z)$ for the step-input case gives

$$y(n) = 1 - (1 - a)(1 - a)^n = 1 - (1 - a)^{n+1}$$

The interpretation of this result is that the first term is the "steady-state" result—the system levels off to the value of the step input—and the second term is the "transient" term that dies out with time. This result, the complete specification of the system output, given the system input, works for all values of $(0 \leq a < 1)$ and for all possible step functions, because if $x(n) = A \cdot 1$, where A is a constant scaling factor, then $y(n)$ is given simply by $Ay(n)$, a constant times the result already obtained.

Turning to the case of the ramp input to the system, we find that we have *repeated* factors in the denominator of the fraction to be broken up, namely, the factor $(1 - z)^2 = (1 - z)(1 - z)$. In cases of this sort, an expansion of the form below is used:

$$Y(z) = \frac{z}{(1-z)^2}\left[\frac{a}{1-(1-a)z}\right] = \frac{Az}{(1-z)^2} + \frac{B}{(1-z)} + \frac{C}{1-(1-a)z}$$

That is, the repeated factor is repeated in the expansion in ever-decreasing powers and with decreasing powers of z in the numerator. This form of expansion usually produces transforms that can be found in Table B.1. Again, we solve for unknowns, A, B, and C, as before. To solve for A, multiply both sides by $(1 - z)^2$ and set $z = 1$, which gives $A = a/[1 - (1 - a)] = 1$. To solve for C, multiply both sides by $1 - (1 - a)z$ and set $z = 1/(1 - a)$, which gives (after clearing fractions) $C = (1 - a)/a$. Finally, if we set $z = 0$ on both sides of the partial fraction expansion, we get $B = -C$ or $B = -(1 - a)/a$, so that

$$Y(z) = \frac{z}{(1-z)^2} - \frac{1-a}{a}\left(\frac{1}{1-z}\right) + \frac{1-a}{a}\left[\frac{1}{1-(1-a)z}\right]$$

is the completed expansion in partial fractions.

Each of the terms in the expansion may now be found in Table B.1, with the corresponding inverse terms

$$y(n) = n - \frac{1-a}{a} + \frac{1-a}{a}(1-a)^n.$$

The interpretation of this solution is that the system follows the ramp input (term 1), but never quite catches up by the amount shown (in term 2), and also shows a transient at the start, which dies out with time (term 3). All of this is available from the closed formula representing the output of the system in response to a ramp input.

The examples shown do not exhaust the manipulations that may be necessary to find the inverse of a z transform. Indeed, the art of using these transforms lies in the analyst's ability to break up a cumbersome fraction into simpler forms that can be recognized in the transform-pair table. Only experience and a knowledge of the alternate methods for accomplishing the required result can improve the speed and success of this type of analysis. The references cited must be recommended for this purpose.

Yet, although we have not made an exhaustive excursion into the possible applications of the z transform, the reader should now have a feeling for the manipulations involved in its application, and he should realize the importance of being able to handle lags and advances in a discrete time function with algebraic ease. Note that the z transform finds wide application in the analysis of sampled-data systems (reference 4) and in the analysis of discrete Markov Processes (reference 6).

In conclusion, the trouble entailed in developing a solution using the z-transform approach is usually worthwhile if a closed expression is desired for a wide range of possible system parameters. To develop the output for a specific system input and specific system parameters, direct numerical evaluation of the difference equation describing the system may be less work. In any case, it is usually worthwhile to check the z-transform results by comparison with the first few terms of a specific solution computed from the original difference equation.

The Laplace Transform

The Laplace transform is the counterpart of the z transform when the input to a system, and the system transfer function, are continuous, rather than discrete in character.[7]

The procedure of transformation and inversion by the Laplace transform is essentially the same as that described for the z transform.

To define the Laplace transform, consider the function $y = f(t)$, where y takes on values continuously as the time t advances.

Example: As before, to make the notation clear, consider the step input, but let $f(t) = 1$ for $t > 0$, and $f(t) = 0$, otherwise. This function is shown in Figure B-5a. The value of the input holds continuously over time, and presents itself to the system continuously, rather than at discrete periods of time. Similarly, consider the input function $f(t) = t$, for $t \geq 0$, and $f(t) = 0$, otherwise, shown in Figure B-5b. This is the equivalent of the ramp input in continuous form. The distinction is that t may take on all values greater than zero, not just integral values.

---

[7] In reality, the z transform is a special case of the Laplace transform, although, for the purpose of exposition, it is convenient to reverse the order of presentation.

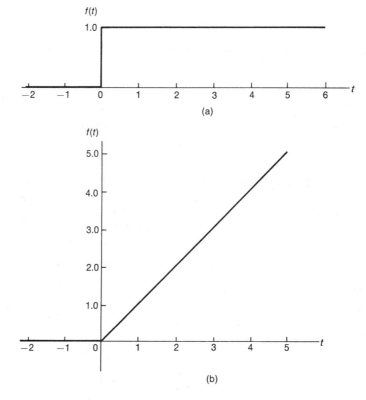

B-5 Figures illustrating the notation for continuous functions. (a) A continuous step function. (b) A continuous ramp function. The function *f(t)* takes on values at all values of the independent variable *t*. The function *f(t)* is 0 for all negative values of *t*.

Now consider what would happen if we carried out the following integration, which converts $f(t)$ into a new function $F(s)$ defining the unique Laplace transform:

$$F(s) = \int_0^\infty f(t)e^{-st}\,dt$$

Example: Using the two former examples of the step and the ramp inputs, but treating them as continuous inputs rather than discrete inputs, we may find the Laplace transform of each. Thus, for the step input, $f(t) = 1$, for $t \geq 0$, and $f(t) = 0$, otherwise, we have

$$F(s) = \int_0^\infty e^{-st}\,dt = \frac{e^{-st}}{-s}\Big|_0^\infty = \frac{1}{s};$$

and, for the ramp input, $f(t) = t$, for $t \geq 0$, and $f(t) = 0$, otherwise, we have

$$F(s) = \int_0^\infty te^{-st}\, dt,$$

which, upon integration by parts,[8] gives

$$F(s) = \frac{te^{-st}}{-s}\bigg|_0^\infty + \frac{1}{s}\int_0^\infty e^{-st}\, dt = 0 + \frac{1}{s^2}e^{-st}\bigg|_0^\infty = \frac{1}{s^2}.$$

Continuing this way, as before, we may construct a table of Laplace transform pairs, such as Table B.2.

Table B.2 Laplace Transforms[a]

Pair	Function	Transform
T_1	$f(t)$	$F(s) = \int_0^\infty f(t)e^{-st}\, dt$
T_2	$af(t) + bg(t)$	$aF_1(s) + aF_2(s)$
T_3	$\dfrac{df(t)}{dt}$	$sF(s) - f(0)$
T_4	$\dfrac{d^2f(t)}{dt^2}$	$s^2F(s) - sf(0) - \dfrac{df(0)}{dt}$
T_5	$\int_0^t f(t)\, dt$	$\dfrac{1}{s}F(s)$
T_6	$\begin{cases} f(t - a) & t > a \\ 0 & t < a \end{cases}$	$e^{-as}F(s)$
T_7	1 (unit step)	$\dfrac{1}{s}$
T_8	t (unit ramp)	$\dfrac{1}{s^2}$
T_9	e^{-at}	$\dfrac{1}{(s + a)}$
T_{10}	$\sin at$	$\dfrac{a}{(s^2 + a^2)}$
T_{11}	$\cos at$	$\dfrac{s}{(s^2 + a^2)}$
T_{12}	$e^{-bt}\sin at$	$\dfrac{a}{(s + b)^2 + a^2}$
T_{13}	$e^{-bt}\cos at$	$\dfrac{s + b}{(s + b)^2 + a^2}$

[a] *Assumptions:* $f(t) = 0$ for $t < 0$. In the above table a and b are constants.

[8] Integration by parts is a standard manipulation in calculus:

$$\int u\, dv = uv - \int v\, du.$$

Note from the table, that differentiating a function of t multiplies the Laplace transform equivalent by s. That is, if $F(s)$ is the Laplace transform of $f(t)$, then $sF(s)$ is the Laplace transform of $df(t)/dt$.[9] Conversely, if $F(s)$ is the Laplace transform of $f(t)$, then $(1/s)F(s)$ is the Laplace transform of the integral of $f(t)$, $\int_0^t f(t)\, dt$.

Example: Using the step function, $f(t) = 1$, $t \geq 0$, as an example, let us find the Laplace transform of $\int_0^t f(t)\, dt$. In this case $\int_0^t f(t)\, dt = \int_0^t dt = t$. The Laplace transform of $f(t) = t$, from Table B.2, is $F(s) = 1/s^2$. But, also from Table B.2, the Laplace transform of $f(t) = 1/s$. Thus, if $F(s) = 1/s$ is the Laplace transform of $f(t) = 1$, then $(1/s)(F(s) = 1/s^2$ is the Laplace transform of $\int_0^t f(t)\, dt = t$. The reverse procedure also holds. If $f(t) = t$, then $df(t)/dt = 1$, and the corresponding Laplace transforms, from the table, are $1/s^2$ and $1/s$, respectively. Thus, differentiation corresponds to multiplication by s.

With this information available, we may now proceed as before to develop the transfer function in Laplace transform terms for a system that can be described by a differential equation.

Example: Suppose we have a control system which operates continuously according to the following equation, where a and b are constants and $y(t)$ and $x(t)$ are the output and input, respectively:

$$y(t) = ax(t) - b\left(\frac{dy(t)}{dt}\right).$$

Assuming that we can find the Laplace transform of $x(t)$, from Table B.2 or by the definition, and, therefore, obtain $X(s)$, and that we will be able to find the output $Y(s)$ as a result of the analysis, we may convert the differential equation into the equivalent Laplace transform relationship

$$Y(s) = aX(s) - bsY(s),$$

if we remember that differentiation of a time function is equivalent to multiplication of its Laplace transformation by s. Collecting terms in $Y(s)$ and $X(s)$ and solving for $Y(s)/X(s)$, we obtain

$$\frac{Y(s)}{X(s)} = \frac{a}{1 + bs},$$

which is the transfer function of the system, expressed in Laplace transform terms.

---

[9] When $f(t) \neq 0$ for $t = 0$, i.e., when $f(0) \neq 0$, then the value of $f(0)$ must be subtracted from $F(s)$, as shown in transform pair (T_3), Table B.2. The same holds for higher order derivatives at $t = 0$, as shown in (T_4).

This transfer function (in s) may now be subjected to various input functions expressed in Laplace transform terms.

Example: If $a = 1$ and $b = 4$ in the above expression, show that the output from the system will be $y(t) = t - 4 + 4e^{-t/4}$ when the input is $x(t) = t$. To show this, we find $Y(s)$ by multiplying $X(s)$ by the transfer function $Y(s)/X(s)$. The correct value of $X(s)$ for a ramp input is, from Table B.2, $1/s^2$. The value of $Y(s)$ is, therefore,

$$Y(s) = \frac{1}{s^2} \cdot \frac{a}{1 + bs}$$

Using the method of partial fractions, as described for the z transform, we break this fraction up into the three fractions

$$Y(s) = \frac{1}{s^2} \cdot \frac{a}{1 + bs} = \frac{A}{s^2} + \frac{B}{s} + \frac{C}{1 + bs}$$

and solve for the unknown numerators as before to obtain

$$A = 1, \qquad B = -4, \qquad C = +16,$$

so that

$$Y(s) = \frac{1}{s^2} - 4\left(\frac{1}{s}\right) + 4\left(\frac{4}{1 + 4s}\right).$$

Each of the terms to the right may now be found in Table B.2, so that the inverse of each term is also available, giving the required result

$$y(t) = t - 4 + 4e^{-t/4}$$

The output follows the input in the long run (term 1), but there is a constant lag of 4 units (term 2) and a dying transient (term 3).

Example: It is interesting to compare the above result with that which we would have obtained if the system had been described by the difference equation

$$y(n) = cx(n) - d[y(n) - y(n - 1)]$$

in which the first difference $y(n) - y(n - 1)$ is used to represent the differential. (This could occur in practice, for example, if a sampled data system were used instead of a continuous system.) Solving for the transfer function, we obtain

$$y(z)[(1 + d) - dz] = cx(n)$$

$$\frac{y(z)}{x(z)} = \frac{c}{(1 + d) - dz}$$

$$= \frac{c/(1 + d)}{1 - dz/(1 + d)}$$

If $c = 1$ and $d = 4$, we have $c/(1 + d) = 0.2$, $d/(1 + d) = 0.8$, and

$$Y(z)/X(z) = \frac{0.2}{1 - 0.8z}.$$

For a ramp input, as before,

$$Y(z) = \frac{z}{(1 - z)^2} \frac{0.2}{1 - 0.8z} = \frac{Az}{(1 - z)^2} + \frac{B}{1 - z} + \frac{C}{1 - 0.8z}.$$

Using the method of partial fractions, we find $A = 1$, $B = 4$, and $C = 4$, so that

$$y(n) = n - 4 + 4(0.8)^n.$$

This result compares directly to the result obtained for the differential equation, and gives very nearly the same numerical result, because $(0.8)^n$ and $e^{-t/4}$ approximate each other closely.

t or n	$e^{-t/4}$	$(0.8)^n$
0	1.000	1.000
1	0.779	0.8000
2	0.607	0.640
3	0.472	0.512
4	0.368	0.410
5	0.287	0.328

The discrete approximation to the continuous case could be improved by decreasing the interval of measurement for $f(n)$, assuming the transformation of the system could also take place at those more frequent points. A discussion of this extension, however, must be left to the references.

SOME COMMENTS ON STABILITY CRITERIA

Suppose that a system receives a "shock" or an impulse. Then, if that system is stable, we would assume it would settle down to its initial position, and not assume a new condition. This stable system is comparable to the weighted doll often used by children, which, when tilted, reverts to its former position, although it may wobble back and forth before coming to rest. Mathematically, a similar criterion may be established. For example, if a discrete time system receives an impulse, we may require that the sum of the output pulses emerging from it be bounded, or have some limit. In other words, the original impulse will eventually die out, and will not continue, or increase in amplitude as time passes.

To illustrate, consider the discrete system described by the linear difference equation

$$y(n) = ax(n) + by(n-1)$$

The transfer function for this system is (in z-transform terms)

$$\frac{Y(z)}{X(z)} = \frac{a}{(1-bz)}.$$

When subjected to a unit impulse, for which, from Table B.1, the z transform is $X(z) = 1$, we find that the output is $Y(z) = a/(1-bz)$, so that the output is $y(n) = a(b)^n$. [Examination of Table B.1 will indicate that the response of a discrete system to a unit impulse is its transfer function. Remember that the unit impulse in this case is defined as $f(0) = 1$, for $n = 0$, and $x(n) = 0$, for $n > 0$.] Now the output $y(n) = a(b)^n$ will be bounded (and eventually return to zero) if $|b| < 1$. If $|b| > 1$, the series of terms $y(n)$ increases without limit, so that the sum of these terms will also increase without limit, and the system is not stable. If $b = 1$, there will always be a output terms, and an infinite sum of such terms will reach infinity, so that the system is not stable in this case. However, should b become negative, the output terms $y(n) = a(-b)^n$ will provide an alternating series of terms (positive and negative) which will be bounded if b is greater (algebraically) than -1, and which will increase without limit if b is smaller than or equal to minus 1. (In short, the output series will converge if $b^2 < 1$, or $|b| < 1$, the well-known condition for the sum of a geometric series to exist.)

Checks of this type are of major interest. The references cited treat this subject at length, and further discussion must be left to them. However, it is of particular interest to note that the initial value and the terminal value of a system's output to a given input may be found by inspection of the z-transform or Laplace-transform format as follows:

Function type	Final value	Initial value
$f(n)$	$\underset{n\to\infty}{\text{limit}}\ f(n)$	$\underset{n\to 0}{\text{limit}}\ f(n)$
$F(z)$	$\underset{z\to 1}{\text{limit}}\ (I-z)F(z)$	$\underset{z\to 0}{\text{limit}}\ F(z)$
$f(t)$	$\underset{t\to\infty}{\text{limit}}\ f(t)$	$\underset{t\to 0}{\text{limit}}\ f(t)$
$F(s)$	$\underset{s\to 0}{\text{limit}}\ sF(s)$	$\underset{s\to\infty}{\text{limit}}\ sF(s)$

Thus, for example, if

$$Y(z) = \left(\frac{1}{1-z}\right)\left(\frac{a}{1-(1-a)z}\right),$$

the example given on page 484, and if we only wanted the terminal value of $y(n)$, the output of the system, as n approaches infinity, we could use the result of the second line in the above table, multiply $Y(z)$ by $1 - z$ and set $z = 1$. The number obtained by this procedure 1, as indicated for the complete result for $y(n)$ in this case, is the final value of $y(n)$, as shown on page 485.

REFERENCES

1. R. G. Brown, *Forecasting for Inventory Control*, McGraw Hill, New York, 1960. Provides a brief introduction of z transforms applied to inventory control problems.
2. R. G. Brown, *Smoothing, Forecasting, and Prediction of Discrete Time Series*, Prentice Hall, Englewood Cliffs, N.J., 1963. A sequel to the above reference. Provides further description of z-transform analysis to discrete time series.
3. F. B. Hildebrand, *Advanced Calculus for Engineers*, Prentice-Hall, Englewood Cliffs, N.J., 1949 (and later Editions). Provides an introduction to Laplace transforms, with engineering applications.
4. J. R. Ragazzini and G. F. Franklin, *Sampled Data Control Systems*, McGraw Hill, New York, 1958. Written for control engineers, this text illustrates application of both z transforms and Laplace transforms, separately and in combination.
5. W. Kaplan, *Operational Methods for Linear Systems*, Addison Wesley, Reading, Mass., 1962. This comprehensive treatment covers Fourier, Laplace, and z transformations and provides a rigorous foundation and derivation for each. Written for mathematicians and advanced engineers, it is hardly a first book for the uninitiated, although it is the standard for formal treatment of the subject.
6. R. A. Howard, *Dynamic Programming and Markov Processes*, M.I.T. Press and Wiley, New York, 1960. Howard gives applications of z transforms in the analysis of Markov Processes.
7. A. Tustin, *Mechanism of Economic Systems*, Harvard University Press, Cambridge, Mass., 1953. This is an introduction to linear control theory for economists, and provides an excellent introduction to the subject of mathematical transformations in the early chapters.
8. B. C. Kou, *Automatic Control Systems*, Prentice-Hall, Englewood Cliffs, N.J., 1962. A standard treatment of control systems using the transform approach.
9. M. F. Gardner and J. C. Barnes, *Transients in Linear Systems*, Wiley, New York, 1942. An introduction to the subject with mechanical and electrical examples.

APPENDIX C

SOME PRINCIPLES OF CODING FOR COMMERCIAL USE

Our purpose here is to illustrate a few forms of coding used in industrial and commercial practice. We will not consider codes used for secrecy of transmission, as in Reference 6, nor codes from an information-theory viewpoint, as in Appendix D, nor as a statistical problem, as in References 3, 4, and 5.

CODE SELECTION

In most commercial coding applications it is desirable to have a *unique* representation for an item, event, action, idea, or concept which may be described in many ways. For example, a product code or employee identification number is designed to identify one and only one product or employee.

However, the selection of the particular code that will be used, even though unique, offers a classic example in economic trade-offs. On the one hand, some capacity or investment in facilities is required to transmit, process, and manipulate codes. On the other hand, the capacity required in each of these phases of processing is affected by the choice of code format. In general, the shorter the code, the smaller the cost of transmission, storage, data entry, sorting, and human handling. The longer code, however, requires less translation and "look-up" capacity and processing, and often provides greater versatility in data extraction, statistical analysis, and category combination.

As a result, in selecting a given code format, in terms of the number of characters employed, the code structure, and the character set used, the over-all system of code use must be considered.

Example: Consider two airline reservation systems. In the first, originally used by United Airlines and designed by Teleregister Corp., a 20-character code was used. This system identified flight segment, date, and seat available for sale. In this nationwide system, with central processing at Denver, Colorado, and data entry through agent sets at airports and reservation offices, a 2-second response time from data entry to reply was obtained. However, restricting the code to 20 characters for fast transmission and processing did not allow storage of customer detail, which was often desirable.

In a second system, designed by IBM and known as the SABRE system, a 250-character code was used. This system, originally installed by American Airlines, included customer detail, as well as the usual reservation information. Although the SABRE system provided much greater flexibility of statistical analysis, control of reservations in detail, and many side advantages, it was *millions* of dollars more costly than the simpler Teleregister design. To obtain equivalent response time, processing and communication facilities had to be much faster, memory capacity much more extensive, and switching and queuing problems in the communication network were much more severe. Moreover, the agent's sets became much more complex and expensive.

The choice of one system over the other was thus an economic problem. The long-range economic value of the more extensive abilities provided by the longer code structure and the more expensive processing facilities of the SABRE system involved computations of the extra or marginal revenue that could be generated through tighter control and greater utilization of the seat-mile capacity of jet fleets. To obtain a cost-effectiveness evaluation of alternatives, the total system of information processing and flight capacity utilization had to be considered.

In this sense, the problem of code selection is not only a technical problem but one of system economics, and coding "efficiency" from an economic viewpoint is seldom the same as the statistical efficiency of coding, as defined in Appendix D. Statistical efficiency of coding implies efficiency in transmission without regard to use. The economic efficiency of a code is largely dependent upon the uses to which the code will be put in a larger system context.

In practice, the selection of a code structure usually involves an evaluation of a number of alternatives originally proposed for a specified number of end uses. The net advantage of each alternative is then computed to make the choice. In this major evaluation, which commits the system design and sets the course of future system operation, many of the techniques described in Chapters 9 through 14 are useful, and simulation of alternative designs is common.

Remembering always that this first stage in the selection of a code format is the most critical, we now turn to a discussion of several code types used in commercial systems. References 1, 2, 7, 10, and 13 suggest a number of alternatives.

To compensate for changes in code use with time, and to provide some flexibility in category combination, some structure is usually preferred in commercial codes at the expense of code length. This fact may be illustrated by a comparison of block and serial codes.

BLOCK AND SERIAL CODES

Two extreme forms of code types are the block code, in which character, position, and choice have meaning, and the serial code, in which characters are applied arbitrarily in sequence.

A serial code represents a one-for-one code to item listing in strict code sequence, which produces a short code that is easily applied, but that has no meaning (other than perhaps a correlation with the time of item coding). If there are N items in a list, and a character set of r items is used for the serial code, the minimum number of code positions required is given by $\log_r N$, rounded up to the next integer. Thus three decimal digits (000–999) are required to list 1000 serial items, and three decimal digits (000–499) are also required to list 500 items serially.

Block code length will depend upon the dimensions required and will usually contain more positions than the serial code for the same length item list. However, since both the position of a character and its value in a block code can be given meaning, the extra length is usually offset by ease of manipulation, interpretation, analysis, sorting, and similar operations.

At the extremes of the strict serial code and the unique block code two problems, which may be taken care of by modifications of both extremes, arise. The serial code may be difficult to maintain if items are to be deleted and added to the list over time. The block code always faces the possibility that new items cannot be uniquely described by the categories already chosen and frozen in the code structure. To various degrees this form of problem is resolved by blocking the serial code or serializing the block code, as illustrated in the following example.

Example: The alphabetical list of employees in the list below contains the data from a personnel file. To develop a serial code, we apply sequential numbering (or similar sequence of symbols) to the list. Thus, ADAMS is employee 1, BROWN is employee 2, etc. New names are added to the bottom of the list and obsolete names deleted from the list as conditions change. Often deleted names, and their serial position, can be reassigned after a time if no confusion results.

ADAMS, J. W., Law, L.A., Married, Owns Home, Has Group Insurance

BROWN, John, Foreman, L.A., Single, Rents, No Group Insurance

CLARK, Miles, Accountant, Chi., Divorced, Rents, Has Group Insurance

GRANT, R. Engineer, N.Y., Single, Rents, Has Group Insurance

HENRY, R. Foreman, L.A., Married, Owns Home, No Group Insurance

JONES, A., Engineer, L.A., Married, Owns Home, Has Group Insurance

For a complete block code, we develop the categories of interest, and code the level or attribute of each category, or dimension, so that a unique item code will result. For example, suppose for a five-digit block code we have adopted the conventions shown below for the personnel file.

CODE POSITION	1	2	3	4	5
Code Number	Employee Type	Plant Location	Marital Status	Home Owner	Group Insurance
1	Engineer	N.Y.	Married	Yes	Yes
2	Accountant	Chi.	Single	No	No
3	Foreman	L.A.	Divorced	——	——
4	Lawyer	——	Separated	——	——
5	Secretary	——	Widowed	——	——

Now ADAMS instead of being employee 1 could be called employee 43111, and from the code structure, we know that ADAMS is a *lawyer,* living in *Los Angeles,* who is a *married homeowner* on our *group insurance* contract. In other words, knowing the code format, the code is "self-interpreting."

In addition, using the block code principle, we can now find in the file, say, all married persons on the group insurance contract by considering *only* those names with a "1" in column 3 and a "1" in column 5, providing an easy 2-digit extraction of information for this type of question. The expense in this example lies in using five decimal digits rather than one, as in the serial code. The saving is in the ease of statistical extraction, the ability to call for any combination of categories directly using simplified sorting procedures. The danger with this procedure is that a new individual may not be uniquely described by the blocks now chosen, but may duplicate an existing item.

Two standard variants between the serial and block code extremes frequently are used to obtain the advantage of compactness and some ease of extraction and interpretation.

First, we may *block the serial code* if the item list is not likely to change in length or contents. We do this by sequencing the items listed in some meaningful order *before* coding. Thus, suppose the employee names are first alphabetically sorted *within* given plant locations, in the sequence New York, Chicago, Los Angeles. Then, when reading or extracting the serial code, we know that all employees with a serial number greater than "3" work in Los Angeles.

Unfortunately, this code format becomes obsolete if a change in the item list occurs. This complication can be alleviated by reserving "empty" spaces in the original assignment of serial codes, but, because it is difficult to predict where items will be added or deleted in the future, such "tight" coding is an undesirable alternative for lists that are apt to change.

The second alternative is to *serialize the block code,* the procedure used in the Dewey Decimal System employed in libraries. In this approach we block the major categories of interest and carry a trailing serial number to provide unique identification. In our example, we could use a code structure

Position	Category
1	Plant location
2	Marital status
3	Serial

e.g., ADAMS could be called #311, indicating he lives in Los Angeles, is married, and has the arbitrary serial number "1" for that category combination.

The serialized block code may be considered the most popular of the well-known formats because updating and file maintenance are easy. To add or delete an item we adjust the trailing serial number. The major categories and breakdowns remain unchanged. As conditions change, our original code format does not become obsolete and require a complete renumbering or recoding of the files with which we work.

In each case the coder's ingenuity can be increased by a careful analysis of the needed categories, the symbols used for coding, and the methods of file operation and data-handling to be used.

For example, a coder looking at our example might suggest combining the categories "plant location" and "marital status" into one decimal position when he sees a total of nine characters (less than the ten decimals available) would do the job:

1	New York	Married
2	New York	Single
3	New York	Divorced, etc.
4	Chicago	Married
5	Chicago	Single
6	Chicago	Divorced, etc.
7	Los Angeles	Married
8	Los Angeles	Single
9	Los Angeles	Divorced, etc.

Here we have serialized *within* a block to achieve a shorter code with only a small sacrifice in analytical ease.

Finally, we should note that symbols other than decimals can obviously be used. Alphabetic characters would give 26 subclassifications for a given code position, so that alphabetic and alpha-numeric codes may be desirable if they can be handled by the data-processing facilities to be used. In general, the maximum number of distinct codes obtainable with a combination of character types will be the product of the characters available at each code position. (With block coding and its variations, the *usable* combinations will usually be less than the maximum figure.)

It is interesting to note that block code length can be as short as a serial code if each and every available combination in the block code is used. For example, we may have the following items for which only two characters are available per position (binary code), i.e., 0 and 1. We have the following items on our list.

	SERIAL	BLOCK
A married female	00	00
A married male	01	01
A single female	10	10
A single male	11	11

As shown in the table, the serial code can be made equivalent to the block code and vice versa.

HIERARCHIES IN CODE STRUCTURE

So that items may be identified, handled, and processed at various levels of generality, it is desirable to structure block codes in the genus-species form described in Chapter 4. This form of hierarchy need not necessarily be positional, since the position of the characters in a code can always be re-ordered. However, it is frequently convenient to organize a code from left to right, so that the left-most character is the most general class, and positions to the right represent inferior subclasses. The postal ZIP Code and the bank code used to sort checks are examples. The five-digit ZIP code gives from left to right the postal division of the country, the distribution center within the postal division, and the local post office within the distribution center classification. Similarly, the bank code gives the Federal Reserve district, Bank identification, Branch, and Customer Account Number in that descending hierarchy of importance reading from left to right at the bottom of the check.

A similar approach is used in other familiar applications. Thus, magazine mailing lists, which run into millions of names are usually coded for efficiency in sorting and list maintenance. A typical code starts with the ZIP Code, which is used for making up mailing bundles, statistical analysis by location, and the like, and follows with a number of alphanumeric characters in descending order of importance. The coding and list maintenance procedures used by TIME Inc., may be found in Reference 14. In setting up such a system, statistical analyses of the categories most likely to be selective are usually made. For example, in recording names for later sorting or searching, the second letter of the last name usually has very little selective value, and is therefore frequently deleted in developing an identifying block code. References 1, 2, and 13 discuss the problem of hierarchies in some detail.

DANGERS IN CODING AND ERROR DETECTION AND CORRECTION

When a code is applied, read, or manipulated, an error may be introduced. Often such errors can be serious. For example, suppose in a payroll application the salesman's commission is coded: *A*, 50%; *B*, 25%; *C*, 10%; *D*, 5%. Should an appropriate *D* code be incorrectly entered as an *A*, a substantially incorrect paycheck would be written (if the salesman has sold anything that pay period!). Various methods for detecting such errors are therefore used in most commercial codes, as well as in communication and computing codes. A computed check digit is a typical device for this purpose. For other devices, see Reference 5.

DEVELOPMENT OF CODES FROM MESSAGE OR ITEM CONTEXT

In general information retrieval applications, in which the items to be identified or retrieved may be described in a large number of ways, or under categories not uniformly present for all items, a more serious problem of code development and application exists. See References 1, 2, 12, and 13 for a discussion of this problem. In such cases, it is common to use key words, phrases, concepts, or subjects derived from the text of a document or from a standard list of possibilities to build an indexing code for each item. The same procedure is used for item requests. In this more general situation uniqueness of description is not assured, nor can it be assured that the request for items specified by a given set of descriptors will be found in the file. The references cited give various approaches to this as yet unsolved problem. Reference 13 illustrates the fact that such problems are not only those of librarians, but also of commercial users of large data-banks of intelligence information.

THE USE OF CODES IN INTEGRATED DATA-PROCESSING SYSTEMS

The basic principle of integrated data-processing systems is that once information is entered into a system, maximum use should be made of it without further data entry. This means that input data and files must be structured to exploit the common features of both.

For example, the most common form of commercial integrated data processing starts with an order for a product as an initiating document. This original input then initiates a chain of events—credit checks, inventory checks, production orders, purchase orders, cost accounting, production planning, invoicing, accounts receivable, shipping, and other operations—terminating the order's execution. Since many of these activities involve files, computations, and decisions that can be keyed to the item and the customer description, a code is often developed to organize files and computations in these basic categories.

The form of this organization is best illustrated by an example.

Example: Old John Distillers, Ltd., is a major corporation which acts as a holding company for numerous smaller corporations engaged in the distillation, blending, bottling, and distribution of spirits. Old John controls 45 corporations, sells six basic spirit types (Gin, Bourbon, Scotch, Canadian, etc.), sells under 60 different brand names, bottles 26 sizes (from small one-drink bottles to gallons in various increments), engages in both domestic and export business, offers many special packages (Christmas, Father's Day, etc., as well as wooden crate, cardboard carton, and similar variations), and distributes in up to 1000 subclassifications of geographical area.

To uniquely describe a product-customer combination, the code shown in Figure C-1a has been proposed. The product block code shown in the first line is the key to the system of later data processing.

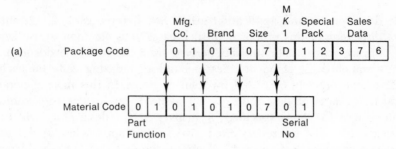

(a) Package Code

	Mfg. Co.		Brand		Size		M K 1		Special Pack		Sales Data	
	0	1	0	1	0	7	D	1	2	3	7	6

Material Code

0	1	0	1	0	1	0	7	0	1

Part Function   Serial No

(b)

Part List	Package 0101-07D12
Bottle	01-0101-0701
Cap	02-0199-0701
Front Label	03-0101-0701
Back Label	04-0199-0701
Shoulder Label	05-0199-9902
Foot Label	06-0101-9901
Carton	07-0101-0701

Package Specifications

Pack List	Part No. 04-0199-0701
0101-07D12	
0102-07D01	
0103-07D12	
0107-07D12	

Part Cross Reference (For all parts showing a 9 anywhere in the part code)

C-1 A code for integrated data processing in a given application. (a) Product and material codes, which are structured for integrated data processing. (b) A typical cross reference available from the structured codes. The example, discussed in the text, is a package and material code application for a distillery. The package code uniquely identifies each product sold, and provides for statistical analysis by financial account, spirit type, brand, size, market, area sold, etc. The material code, related to this basic structure permits comparison of package designs, analysis for common materials, etc. The basic code structure can also be used in other forms of record keeping and computation in cost accounting, production planning, and marketing.

This 12-position code is defined as follows:

Position	Meaning
1,2	Corporation identifier (45 categories)
3,4	Brand identifier (60 brands)
	Position 3, spirit type (6 types)
	Position 4, serial number
5,6	Bottle size (26 sizes)
7	Domestic and export code (up to 26 letters)
8,9	Special package identifier (up to 100 as needed)
10,11,12	Customer code
	Position 10, major area within domestic and export class
	Position 11, subclass within major area
	Position 12, customer serial within area subclass

Using these definitions, a particular order from a given customer would have the same code identifiers in positions 7, 10, 11, and 12. An order from a customer might then read as follows:

Customer D376	Number of cases	Product type
(common to all	120	010107D12
items ordered	60	022106D06
at right)	72	117208D31

This order could be entered into the system by means of a standardized form, or sent by teletype from the customer to the factory for processing, thus avoiding a second typing operation.

Once the coded information is received, the customer and product codes provide keys to files that are needed for later operation:

Code key	Files
Customer Code	Credit
(keyed to	Accounts Receivable
D376)	Statistical Analysis
	Name and Address
	Shipping instructions
Product Code	Inventory Status
(keyed to	Production Specifications
product codes	Statistical Analysis
ordered)	Cost accounting
	Production Planning
	Materials Needed per unit

Cross references between the two sets of files are possible using the combined customer-product code.

Moreover, if product materials, work centers, and employees are further identified by a code, further cross-references can be built up. One example is illustrated by the second line of Figure C-1a and Figure C-1b. In this example, the materials used in the bottling operation have been coded by function, corporation, brand, size, and serial number. These materials can be associated with a given product by reference to the corresponding blocks of the code, as shown in Figure C-1a, and a cross reference showing product-materials or material-packages can be prepared. In the material code, a "9" is used to indicate common usage on several product types. The material code allows financial analysis by material type, corporation, brand, and size, and the specifications, shown in coded form, permit the computation of materials required for a given production run.

As an illustration of a side use of such files, it will be seen that a listing of material types in numerical order (from left to right) will place together all materials of the same types. From such a display, for example, an analyst may see how many different bottle types are used and where common bottle types are employed for several brands and sizes. The availability of such organized data aids in package design, the greater use of common materials, and in the evaluation of the cost of design changes, to mention a few applications.

The reader may now imagine other ways in which such integrated files may be used in this operation, and may wish to try his hand at improvement of the code structure proposed.

For example, if binary-coded-decimal data processing equipment were used, providing theoretically up to 64 characters per position, a much shorter code structure could be devised by a combination of serial and block approaches. Would this be desirable? How important is the ease of human interpretation in the construction of the code structure? Should the product and customer codes have check characters built in? Should a check computation be included in the coded order? What are some proposals for such checks? Could variable length codes be used to any advantage in this application? Which of the files should be on a random-access basis and which should be stored on less expensive media, such as tape? If the computer used to process these data has a given addressing format for memory location, would that have any bearing on the product and customer codes chosen? If there are 100,000 distinct material types, what would be the problems of converting from the present form of description to a new material code of the type shown, as opposed to another alternative? What are the economic advantages of using a customer, product, and material code of the type shown?

DOCUMENTATION

When information is initially entered into a system, or when it is later requested, it is important that the coding and decoding (or indexing and request) formats be clearly understood and applied. For this reason, many precautions must be taken to assure uniformity of code application.

In most man-machine organizations the first prerequisite to this end is the creation of standardized methods of applying and using codes and a standardized nomenclature both of which are reduced to writing.

Such documentation of a code structure and code use is unfortunately often left as a detail to be completed after the coding or indexing work has started or ended. Or, since precise and complete documentation may appear costly in relation to the initial coding effort, short-cuts may be taken. In particular, a procedure for updating the coding effort as new conditions arise may be left to chance, so that over time, as personnel come and go, the consistency, completeness, and relevance of the codes used in current application suffer greatly.

Since a major commitment in system design is made at coding time— one that affects system cost and usefulness for generations of later decisions —the expense required to obtain complete documentation, documentation updating, and long range documentation planning is easily justified.

In short, although the task is expensive, often plodding and tedious, and frequently a psychological burden for the systems analyst with expansive plans for the future, the importance of adequate documentation of a coding system and its use cannot be overstressed. Although the aphorism "A job worth doing is worth doing well" is worn out by now, it applies with certainty to the job of code development and maintenance.

REFERENCES

1. C. P. Bourne, *Methods of Information Handling*, Wiley, New York, 1963.
2. Allen Kent, *Textbook on Mechanized Information Retrieval*, Interscience, New York, 1963.
3. E. N. Gilbert, "A Comparison of Signalling Alphabets," *Bell System Tech. J.*, 31, 1952, 504–522.
4. D. A. Huffman, "A Method for Construction of Minimum Redundancy Codes," *Proc. I.R.E.*, 40, 1952, 1098–1101.
5. R. W. Hamming, "Error Detecting and Error Correcting Codes," *Bell System Tech. J.*, 29, 1950, 147–160.
6. H. F. Gaines, *Cryptanalysis*, Dover, New York, 1956.
7. "In Coding Its Structure that Counts," *Control Engineering*, October, 1962, p. 100.
8. Henry Metcalfe, *The Cost of Manufacturers and the Administration of Workshops, Public and Private*, Wiley, New York, 1885.
9. Oberlin Smith, "The Nomenclature of Machine Details," *American Machinist*, September 19, 1881. (This article on standardization of nomenclature is reprinted completely in Metcalfe's historic work, listed above.)
10. R. H. Gregory and R. L. Van Horne, *Automatic Data Processing*, 2nd ed., Wadsworth, Belmont, Calif., 1965. (The reader of this appendix will benefit from the discussion of COBOL computer programing contained in this work. The file organization requirements of COBOL illustrate the coding principles described here.)
11. R. S. Ledley, *Programming and Utilizing Digital Computers*, McGraw-Hill, New York, 1962. (Again, this work with its emphasis on number systems and Boolean Algebra offers many insights into the coding problem.)
12. G. Salton, "Progress in Automatic Information Retrieval," *IEEE Spectrum*, August, 1965.
13. W. F. Williams, *Principles of Automated Information Retrieval*, Business Press, Elmhurst, Ill., 1965.
14. Armour Research Foundation, *Computer Applications 1960*, Macmillan, New York, 1961.

APPENDIX D

INFORMATION MEASURES

A *source* of information is characterized by the variety of its output. If a source can emit N distinct characters, then the variety that can be generated is N. It is convenient to measure variety in logarithmic form, to the base 2. When variety is so measured, the number resulting represents the number of yes-no, or binary questions, that would be necessary to determine which one of the N characters had been emitted, if the N characters were emitted at random. Thus, variety in binary digits, or bits $= \log_2 N$. Remembering that $\log_2 N = 3.322 \log_{10} N$, since $\log_b N = (\log_a N)/(\log_a b)$, we may compute the number of bits, using logarithms to the base 10, as usually tabulated.

For example, the variety of the sexes is 1 bit, since $\log_2 2 = 1$. The variety of 52 playing cards is 5.7 bits, since $\log_2 52 = 3.322 \log_{10} 52 = 3.22 \times 1.760 = 5.7$. The logarithmic measure has advantage in converting multiplicative combinations into simple additions. Thus, if a male or a female can select one of 52 cards, the number of distinctions that can be made of the form "male: Ace of spades" is $2 \times 52 = 104$, or more simply, the variety can be measured as $1 + 5.7 = 6.7$ bits.

If the source S with a character set N emits a string of characters it is possible to determine the frequency of each character's appearance in the string. If these frequencies are stable with time (stationary) when collected by a given sampling process, we may compute the probability of each character's appearance from these data and call that set of N probabilities $p_i (i = 1, 2, 3, \ldots, N)$. From the character probabilities it is now possible to compute a measure of the actual information transmitted by the source in terms of variety and compare this measure to the potential variety, $\log_2 N$. This probabilistic measure is called the *entropy* of the source.

For example, a source emits four characters, A, B, C, and D. Its character variety is $\log_2 4 = 2$. The entropy of the source H is defined as

$$- p_1 \log p_1 - p_2 \log p_2 - p_3 \log p_3 - p_4 \log p_4$$

(for the four-character source). The negative signs are used in the definition to obtain a positive result, since the values of p_i will be a number less than unity.

The entropy measure takes on its maximum value when all characters are emitted *with equal probability*, i.e., when $p_i = 1/N$. Thus, for the four character case, this maximum is

$$H_{\max} = (4)(-\tfrac{1}{4})(\log_2 \tfrac{1}{4}) = \log_2 4 - \log_2 1 = 2 \text{ bits}, \quad \text{or} \quad \log_2 N.$$

If the characters are emitted with another probability distribution, the entropy of the source will be less. For example if $p(A) = 0.4$, $p(B) = 0.3$, $p(C) = 0.2$, and $p(D) = 0.1$, the entropy of the source is

$$H = - 0.4 \log_2 0.4 - 0.3 \log_2 0.3 - 0.2 \log_2 0.2 - 0.1 \log_2 0.1$$

or

$$H = 3.322 \, (- 0.4 \log_{10} 0.4 - 0.3 \log_{10} 0.3 - 0.2 \log_{10} 0.2 - 0.1 \log_{10} 0.1)$$

which upon evaluation, using a table of common logarithms, is 1.846 bits. Note that $\log_{10} 0.4 = \log_{10} \tfrac{4}{10} = \log_{10} 4 - \log_{10} 10$. We thus look up $\log_{10} 4$ in the common logarithm table and get 0.6021. Since $\log_{10} 10 = 1.0000$, $\log_{10} 0.4 = 0.6021 - 1.0000 = -0.3979$. Substitution of these values in the above expression for H gives the required result, which is positive because of the negative signs in the definition. Thus,

$$H = 3.322 \, (0.4 \times 0.3979 + 0.3 \times 0.5229 + 0.2 \times 0.6990 + 0.1 \times 1.0000) = 1.846$$

The fact that a source emits with a probability distribution that is not equally likely for all characters is another way of saying that there is some constraint in the language used.

The efficiency of the language in transmitting information, as measured by the entropy of the source, is

$$\text{Efficiency} = H/H_{\max} = H/\log_2 N.$$

For the four-character source just discussed, the efficiency of messages generated by characters emitted at random according to the specified probability distribution is $1.846/2.000 = 0.923$. The language *redundancy* is the complement of efficiency

$$\text{Redundancy} = 1 - \text{Efficiency}$$

Thus, the language generated by the four-character source above has a redundancy of $1 - 0.923$ or 0.077.

A word about the interpretation of entropy as used here: The entropy of the source is a statistical average of what may be called the character entropy, h_i. Thus, in the above problem, the character A may be said to have a character entropy of $-(3.322) \log_{10} 0.4 = (3.322)(0.3979) = 1.33$ bits. Similar evaluations may be made for B, C, and D. However, the source emits these characters with given probabilities, so the entropy of the source is the weighted sum, or average value

$$H = -\sum_1^N p_i h_i = -\sum_1^N p_i \log_2 p_i$$

The source is thus said to emit an average of H bits per symbol. Notice that character entropy increases with the rareness of the character in the emission, as indicated by p_i. The entropy of the source, which refers to the set of symbols generated, provides a measure of the disorder of the emission or the unpredictability of the characters emitted, and is thus maximum, as we have seen, when the emitted symbols are equally likely. Another way of interpreting this result is to say that the source transmits the greatest information per character when the characters themselves are equally likely to occur. This result has great importance in increasing the efficiency of an information source, because by appropriate coding procedures, the emission from a source may be made to approach this ideal "maximum information" condition.

So far we have discussed a source that emits "monograms" or single uncorrelated characters. We could also have considered a source that emits diagrams, or pairs of correlated characters. For example, due to the structure of a language, the sequence of letters in a word is not random, but constrained; in English a "q" is always followed by a "u" and a "t" is likely to be followed by an "h." Markov processes, in which the probability of transition from one state to another is the conditional probability $p(j|i)$, are another example of two-character correlation.

In a way exactly analogous to the monogram calculation, it is possible to compute diagram, entropies—and indeed to compute entropies for longer strings of correlated characters, common in many human languages. The reader is directed to the references for these computations. However, we note that the addition of statistical correlation between parts of a message always tends to *reduce* the information value per character, and therefore the entropy of the source. (To illustrate, newspaper English, taken on a monogram basis provides about 4.14 bits per character. The interpretation of this number is that instead of a 26 character alphabet, another character set containing 18 symbols, giving $\log_2 18 = 4.14$, would do the same job if these 18 characters were used with equal probability. However, when diagram correlation in the English language is taken into account, the computed information value per character drops to 3.56 bits, equivalent to a new set of only 12 equally probable symbols. Although the computations rapidly get out of hand for very long strings, Shannon has concluded (Reference 3) that "The long-range statistical effects (up to 100 characters) reduce the entropy [of common English] to something of the order of one bit per letter, with a corresponding redundancy of roughly 75 per cent."

Thus, in conclusion, for a source to be most efficient—for it to transmit the largest amount of information per character—the sequence of characters must be uncorrelated and the symbols themselves must be equally probable in the string. Coding procedures to achieve these conditions are often used to improve the efficiency of an information source, as defined here. Such procedures also have an important bearing on the secrecy of transmission, because messages coded for maximum efficiency do not provide code breaking guides that can be gained from a knowledge of language structure.

REFERENCES

1. R. V. L. Hartley, "Transmission of Information," *Bell System Tech. J.*, 7, 1928, pp. 535–563. (Hartley originally suggested the information measure $h_i = -\log p_i$.)
2. C. E. Shannon, *The Mathematical Theory of Communication*, University of Illinois Press, Urbana, Ill., 1949.
3. C. E. Shannon, "Prediction and Entropy of Printed English," *Bell. System Tech. J.*, 30, 1951, pp. 50–64.
4. A. D. Hall, *A Methodology for Systems Engineering*, Van Nostrand, Princeton, N.J., 1962, pp. 384–396.

APPENDIX E

SUGGESTIONS FOR A STUDY
OF YOUR HOMETOWN[1]

(EDITOR'S NOTE): Because of the importance in applied anthropology of early field training, preferably in the second year of concentration, it is obviously necessary for this kind of training to take place in and around the University. Consequently, we believe that our readers who are concerned with teaching programs will be interested in this memorandum which Dr. Lamb gave to his students at M.I.T. Needless to say, the memorandum is primarily concerned with urban studies and should be considered not as a complete description of field technique, but rather as points of emphasis with which the student might not otherwise be familiar).

This memorandum is written as if you were visiting Hometown for the first time and as if your company or organization had instructed you to arrive as quickly as possible at a comprehensive knowledge of Hometown so that you might effectively represent it there. Towards the end of the memorandum I shall have something to say about the advantages you, with your long experience in the community, would have over a newcomer in your *own* Hometown.

To do this job of community-analysis there are certain tools you will obviously need. A map of Hometown is your first tool, for a brief glance at it will provide the trained eye with more facts than could be secured from any other source. (This of course depends upon the map; most street maps are featureless without an accompanying street directory).

[1] By Robert K. Lamb (deceased). Reprinted from *Human Organization*, Summer, 1952, by permission of the Society for Applied Anthropology.

Once upon a time, about 1890 or before, American street directories were even more useful than they are today, but they are still an indispensable part of any such investigation as this. There are three principal divisions of the average directory: (1) the alphabetical name section for individuals and business firms, organizations, etc.; (2) the street directory listing each house or building, and usually each separate family or business occupant of such buildings; (3) the classified advertising section. Most, if not all such directors also contain an introductory section in narrative style, containing facts about the town statistically arranged from the census and other sources; there is usually also a section devoted to the city government, giving the principal office holders, and often a great deal of detail about the personnel of the various city services.

For the fastest orientation it is ideal if you can find a series of older maps of the city (usually accessible at the public library) so that you can trace the characteristics of the city's growth.

Before you have gone much further with your investigation it will be advisable to learn more about the earlier inhabitants. For this purpose you will need another tool: one or more volumes of local history, usually to be found in the form of county-wide accounts of the history and biographies of the area, with sections devoted to the towns and cities in each county.

Other tools will be suggested later, but we shall start with those mentioned and see whether after a week in town we could arrive at any understanding of its social structure.

Let us start first with the county history. Here we shall assign fictitious names to typical characters. Soonor or later in the county history we will come across the name of Jedediah Early who was connected with the Early Trust Company; perhaps we shall also be able to establish that William A. Newcomer married one of the Early girls. If we can also connect the Early and Newcomer families with the foundation of the Hometown Manufacturing Company we have a good running start on a reconstruction of the way people have earned their living in Hometown for many years. This is, of course, a roundabout way of approaching the matter. There are probably in the county history many names of families who have moved away, and others whose names have died out, at least in the direct line, although middle and even first names may survive.

The quickest way to find out where the major economic decisions are made in Hometown is to go to the public library and ask to see a copy of Rand McNally's *Bankers' Register* (if the library does not have it, go to one of the local banks). There you will find the names of all the Hometown banks as of the year of publication; however, because of the mortality of banks after 1929 there are great advantages in looking up two volumes: the current one and one prior to 1929. Take this list of banks and look up another publication, Moody's *Banks.* Here you will find the names of the directors of your Hometown banks, together with the history of the mergers which have taken place and which have contributed to the present condition of these banks. In this book there will also be found a current bank statement of assets and liabilities, and probably the dividend record.

Another set of tools becomes necessary: a card file. Some people prefer 3″ x 5″ cards because they are handy to carry; others use 5″ x 8″ because they provide more space for notations. Use one card for each bank and record the names of the directors on the ruled side and the history of the bank on the reverse, unruled side. Then make a separate card for each bank director, with his name (last name first) in the upper left-hand corner. Put his address if it is available on the top right, and his directorships (with his principal connection on top) in the middle. On the reverse side of the card record his personal history, date of birth and parentage at the top, marriage, children, education, etc. These cards should be alphabetically filed in the boxes in which the cards were bought, thus dispensing with the added expense of buying special files.

Card files become your most important source of information, and you will find that it is necessary to cross-reference them constantly. They constitute the basic difference between our approach and that of the census-taker: We are primarily interested in individuals and their patterns of relationship, while he is interested in the overall statistical aggregates.

With the list of bank directors in hand, turn now to another tool volume: Poor's *Register of Directors*. Here are listed all the most important corporate directors in the United States. These men do not always record their directorships, but the listing is as complete as the editors are able to make it on the basis of their investigations. From Poor's *Register* you can find the *other* corporate directorates held by Hometown bank directors. This will lead you at once to the names of all important Hometown businesses, for banks tend to accumulate to themselves the leading financial and business talent in town. This method of analysis will be successful provided Hometown's bank is not part of a chain of banks which merely maintains a manager in your town. But unless your town is very small it did once have a bank, and not so very long ago, so that a study of earlier editions of the volumes cited above will reveal the names of Hometown's bank directors.

Such volumes as these may not be available in many cities and towns but if there is a university in the neighborhood its library may carry them; they should also be found in large city public libraries. In many cities there are often business libraries attached to the Chamber of Commerce, or elsewhere, and usually your Hometown banks subscribe to some or all of these publications. If, among its successful sons who have moved away, your town numbers a broker in some big city or a metropolitan banker, a letter to him may bring your library a copy of one or more of these volumes which although perhaps a few years out of date will still be useful for your general purposes. The names of the directors of your banks for the current year can be ascertained by asking the local bank for a copy of its annual statement, which is usually published in a small folder on the back cover of which is a list of the directors. Business connections which are not corporate, such as partnerships or firms, will usually be found in your street directory.

Turn now to the Hometown Manufacturing Company in your directory where the names of its officers and chief supervisory employees will probably appear. This will enable you to plot on the map the residences of superintendents or foremen, and operating management. You will find that while only the top men live on High Street or in "Hills and Dales," the others often tend to live as close to these neighborhoods as they can afford, the older men nearer High Street, the younger nearer "Hills and Dales."

A number of directories also designate the place of employment of those who work in the Hometown Manufacturing Company by some such mark as "Hometown Mfg.," for example. This will enable you to plot on the map the residences of those employed at the factory. When the craft or special skill of the worker is also indicated, as it is in most directories, you can find out where the several grades of workers live. (It should be understood that the word "grades," as used here, has a purely technical usage, such as "machinist" or "foremen," and is a means of distinguishing the probable wage received, since this tends to determine what rent workers can pay, and other economic facts we are trying to establish).

Once you have begun to accumulate cards for individual residents in different parts of the city, and have marked their cards according to their occupations, you are on the way to the preparation of a residential map of the city. It will be advisable to devise a system of symbols to designate the different income grades and occupational groups, and attach them to individual residents on the map in order to show the approximate location of their homes on the streets of the city.

Incidentally, if you are enterprising, one map bought from the local bookseller who handles the Hometown street directories will enable you to trace any number of copies on transparent paper. Once you have plotted on your maps the location of your bank directors, corporation directors, superintendents, foremen, and workers in the factory, you are ready to branch out into a neighborhood-by-neighborhood investigation of Hometown; this will include its churches, neighborhood and nationality clubs, formal and informal social groups, political and business groups, etc.

Such an investigation will lead you back in the direction of your census materials, which are also to be found in the public library. But the model for the investigation is not to be found in the census, but in the publications of social workers. For information about census tracts it will be necessary to approach someone connected with a public or private charity, or a governmental office dealing with welfare or relief. In many cities (and their number is increasing), students have made area studies of the different neighborhoods, showing the number of cases of one sort or another falling in a given area; types of sickness, law violations, social maladjustments such as juvenile deliquency, have been indicated area by area on city-wide maps. This is one of the most fruitful parts of any study you may make of Hometown. However, these findings must be considered very carefully and you should avoid arriving at a hasty conclusion on the basis of any one type of case as it appears on the map.

From this wealth of material, a comprehensive pattern of neighborhood distribution of these various groups will emerge. By turning to the street section of your Hometown directory you may be able to discover whether or not the resident is a home-owner and sometimes whether he has a telephone. This information will help to confirm your guesses about income status. By working back and forth between the street section and the alphabetical section of your volume, you will be able to verify your sampling on a street by street basis. In this way you will soon know a great deal about the distribution of Hometown population—group by group—and income—class by class. If your company were interested, for example, in a door-to-door selling campaign, this information would be of considerable help.

For some purposes it may be necessary for your company to know the national origins of different groups in the community. In past times many of these groups tended to live in their own separate neighborhoods and to develop separate national institutions, such as churches, parochial schools, clubs and organizations of one kind and another. Increasingly these distinctions arising from national origin are breaking down in this country. The younger generation is tending to move out to newer suburban developments where they mingle with people of other national origins. This is part of the "melting pot" of which the Americans are so properly proud. A study of your Hometown as prepared by the method described above will reveal, however, that the "melting" process is far from complete in many communities.

Any study of local politics will reveal that politicians are highly aware of group differences of all kinds, including those just described, and that they are a factor in the political, social and economic life of the community. By turning to the first section of your Hometown directory where information about City Hall and other city services is listed, a card file can be made on the political structure of Hometown. A study of this file will show that it reflects some of the divisions within the community, as already indicated in the foregoing.

The life of most communities is still dominated to a large extent by the oldest inhabitants and their descendants. Usually they exercise the chief influence on the boards of local banks, and insofar as businesses are locally owned they tend to retain a controlling interest. But today this is by no means a universal pattern since the influence of out-of-town corporations has become more and more important in all but the leading cities of the country. As a first approximation we can say that the social system of a community (with its various organizations, such as the Community Chest, Red Cross, etc.) leans heavily upon the families of those long established in the community; the economic leadership is drawn from the ranks of newer individuals and groups; and the political leadership is even more frequently in the hands of the representatives of newer groups.

To understand the social system of the community insofar as it can be distinguished from the political and economic systems, it is usually necessary to begin with the churches as the oldest, local, social institutions. These are in turn distributed throughout the community, and a map showing their location will be very instructive and assist in pointing up some of your other findings. Since most churches are not only religious but neighborhood social organizations, incorporating many nonreligious activities, a study of the leadership of these subgroups within the church will also contribute to your understanding of the community.

Any young businessman coming to the city for the first time and expecting to establish residence there will want to know about the other social and charitable organizations, their functions and their representation of various groups. Some of these can be called "total community" organizations, for instance the Community Chest, or, within the business community, the Chamber of Commerce. Others are representative of special groups in the community. One of the most significant keys to the social grading system is to be found in the structure of the more exclusive clubs. There is usually a club to which only the older inhabitants are admitted, and their method of choosing even among this older group displays their attitude as to the necessary qualifications for membership in the inner circle of their group. If you can secure a list of their membership and compare it with other parts of the social structure, such as leadership in total community organizations, churches, charities, and clubs, you will have a useful key to the relationship between the older and newer groups in town.

In this type of study it is easy to lose sight of the fact that getting a living is the backbone of community life and that the jobs held by men and women are bound to be the ruling factors in their lives. The increase of absentee ownership of factories and stores, and even of newspapers and banks in towns and cities of the United States, makes it more and more difficult to understand the patterns of organization of individual communities. To find out what is happening to these plants and businesses you need new tool volumes. For industries, consult Moody's (or Poor's) *Industrials.* One or the other of these will give you a picture of the extent to which your local factory is still locally controlled, or to what extent control has passed to out-of-town groups. While these sources are adequate for our present purposes, if a really extensive study of these matters were being made, it would be necessary to consult the records of the Securities and Exchange Commission in Washington. If the language used is unfamiliar, some acquaintance who has experience with reading such source material should be called upon for help. Here you may find that the local company (though still locally owned) has perhaps undergone a series of mergers prior to arriving at its present size; if you are interested in the historical aspects of the community it will be worthwhile studying the companies that merged to form the existing one. The story of your local industries is paralleled by what has happened to your local, privately-owned electric light, gas, water, and street transportation system or systems. A similar tool volume is available for investigation of these companies in Moody's (or Poor's) *Public Utilities.* All of these facts should be recorded on file cards and properly catalogued.

In a short space of time you will now have gathered a very comprehensive picture of the life of Hometown. (The size of the community will of course determine the length of time this job will take, although much will depend upon your previous experience in making such studies). I venture to say that you will know many things about the community which might have escaped your notice even if you had lived there all your life. Nevertheless there are many things you cannot find out by these mechanical methods. The most important facts which tend to elude this approach are of a personal order. It is essential to live long years in a community in order to be aware of some of the most important of these facts. As an outside observer, or even one who has had a short residence in the community, you cannot hope to find a completely adequate substitute for this experience. However, as the representative of your company, you are expected to find a short-cut which will be the best possible substitute for such long residence.

The best substitute for your own long residence is to gain access to certain of the oldest inhabitants. Experience will show that there are certain people in the community, not always members of the socially elect group but frequently drawn from among them, whose type of mind reproduces the patterns we have just described, without resort to our complicated methods. Frequently these individuals have recently retired from the most influential positions in the community and are still active in the local historical society. If you are properly introduced and they respect you as a scientific inventigator and believe you have the best interests of the community at heart, they will often be of invaluable assistance to you in providing that type of information which can generally come only from a lifetime knowledge of their town or city. You will do well to try to find at least one such person (and if possible several) who is willing to assist you and who will talk to you freely. By working with more than one of these individuals you will be able to triangulate your results and so avoid some of the inevitable effects of bias. Even the most objective of these persons is bound to see the life of his community from a slightly different vantage point than would any other such observer. You must learn to make allowances for these differences of point of view.

If you, the reader, are yourself a lifelong resident of Hometown, you will be able to supply the same sort of information as this oldest inhabitant, and you will want to correct your bias by the methods I have described. Nevertheless a lifelong resident will have a great advantage over our supposed representative of an out-of-town company. You will know, for example, who married whom, and what the grandparents and even the great-grandparents of many of your fellow residents contributed to the life of the community. Without having to make maps of the historical growth of the community, you will know at what point in time which suburbs developed, and just when different local businesses came under out-of-town control.

Without referring to the files of the local newspapers (which by the way are indispensable to our visitor-observer) or having to talk to the local newspaper editors, you will know just which events in the life of Hometown are of the greatest importance in the estimation of its citizens. You will know when crises arose in the life of the community and how they were solved. You will know what effect the depression and mass unemployment had on the town or city and what happened when labor tried to organize the local plants and businesses. Above all, you will know the personalities and dispositions of the human beings who make up Hometown, and you will realize what an important part such personal traits can play in the average community. In short, these mechanical methods I have recommended are bound to produce a de-humanized picture. It is essential for the observer to try to restore the characteristics of a living community, with its hopes and fears, its shared pleasures and its sorrows.

One of the most elusive things you must try to understand is "community spirit," and in this connection you must attempt to discover what individuals or groups in the community hold the symbols of community leadership at any given time.

Outside of the churches there are two places to look for the symbols of community integration. One of these focal points is the cemetery and the other is the patriotic organization. No community, modern or ancient, can be understood without reference to these two sets of facts. It has been said that "the most important people in Hometown are dead." Even to American society, with its gaze fixed upon expansionism and the future, ancestors are of great symbolic importance. If ancestors in general are important, those who participated in our military history are of great significance. Certain patriotic organizations in each community tend to be regarded by the rest of the community as safeguarding the symbols of patriotism. It is necessary to study the structure of these patriotic organizations as an important factor in the advancement of Hometown life, to be present on the day of their most symbolic activity, Memorial Day, and watch the course taken by the parade—from High Street down through the business section of the town and out to the oldest cemetery. This will usually contribute many useful facts about the nature of community spirit.

All this is bound to sound like an overwhelming job; for the largest cities, of course, it is much too great an undertaking for any single individual to carry out in a reasonable period of time, even as a first approximation. Nevertheless, if you will re-read these proposals with care you will find ways and means for short-cutting and sampling, depending upon the size of your community; after operating with this outline for only a few weeks, the characteristics of your community will take on new significance even if you have lived there all your life.

BIBLIOGRAPHY

The following listing contains, in addition to the references cited in the text, a number of added entries that may be of interest to readers of this book.

These entries give material that may be used for student project assignments and have been drawn from current topics in diagnosis and improvement of complex systems (police work, municipal problems, medical diagnosis, real-time information systems, financial analysis, input-output economics, small and large group studies in the social sciences, etc.).

Many of the standard works in fields related to systems analysis have also been included, although no attempt has been made to provide an exhaustive list. The reader may add to the references shown those of particular interest to him. This is a starting file.

The listing order is by senior author. Because the list is limited, subject groups may be generated by visual scan.

Several sources of current developments in systems analysis should be consulted to keep up to date. A few specific examples are

1. *Business Week* (McGraw-Hill, 330 W. 42nd St., N.Y., N.Y.) contains two or three articles weekly of interest to business readers.

2. *Computing Reviews* (Association of Computing Machinery, 221 E. 43rd St., N.Y., N.Y.) provides bimonthly abstracts of over 100 domestic and foreign periodicals reporting applications and technical developments. *Communications of the A.C.M.* (same source) contains longer monthly reports and expository articles on new developments, with late news as a back-of-the-book feature. A permuted title and subject index, which covers in two volumes all citations from 1960–1963 and 1964–1965, is available for *Computing Reviews*. In addition, special bibliographies are printed by the A.C.M. Consult the Association at the address above.

3. *Control Engineering* (Ruben H. Donnelly Publishing Co., 466 Lexington Ave., N.Y., N.Y.) contains information about new developments and products. Although the magazine is slanted to process control applications, the news section is of general interest.

4. *International Abstracts in Operations Research* (Operations Research Society of America, Mt. Royal and Guilford Aves., Baltimore, Md.) provides bimonthly abstracts of journals devoted to operations research.

Abrams, C. "The City Planner and the Public Interest," *Columbia University Forum,* Fall, 1965.

Adrian, E. D. *The Basis of Sensation: The Action of the Sense Organs.* New York: Norton, 1928.

———. *The Physical Background of Perception.* Oxford: Clarendon Press, 1947.

Allais, M. "Method of Appraising Economic Prospects of Mining Exploration over Large Territories—Algerian Sahara Case Study," *Management Science,* 3, 4, July, 1957.

Allee, W. C. *The Social Life of Animals.* New York: Beacon, 1951 (paper).

Allen, J. K. "The Rising Acceptance of Corporate Strategy," *J. Stanford Res. Inst.,* January, 1965.

Alsop, S. "His Business is War," *Saturday Evening Post,* May 21, 1966, p. 29.

Alvarez, W. *Danger Signals.* Chicago, Ill.: Wilcox and Follett, 1953.

Adaptation to the Environment (Handbook of Physiology, Volume 4). American Physiological Society. Baltimore: William & Wilkins, 1964.

Anton, H. R., and P. A. Firmin. *Contemporary Issues in Cost Accounting.* Boston: Houghton-Mifflin, 1966.

Arbib, M. *Brains, Machines, and Mathematics.* New York: McGraw-Hill, 1964.

Armour Research Foundation. *Computer Applications 1960.* New York: Macmillan, 1961.

Aronson, R. L. "Time-Sharing to the Fore: Scientific and Business Users Close the Computer Loop," *Control Engineering,* September, 1965, pp. 133–136.

Ashby, W. R. *Introduction to Cybernetics.* New York: Wiley, 1963 (paper) (originally, London: Chapman-Hall, 1961).

Balas, E. "An Additive Algorithm for Solving Linear Programs with Zero-One Variables," *Operations Res.* 13, 4, July-August, 1956, pp. 517–45.

Bateson, G. "Social Planning and the Concept of Deutero-Learning," in T. E. Newcomb, and E. L. Hartley (Eds.), *Readings in Social Psychology.* New York: Holt, 1947.

Beckenbach, E. F. (Ed.). *Applied Combinatorial Mathematics.* New York: Wiley, 1964.

Bedford, N. M., and V. Balarduni. "A Communication Theory Approach to Accounting," *The Accounting Review,* 37, 4, 1962.

Bedford, N. M., C. H. Griffin, and I. H. Williams. "The Emerging Role of Mathematical Methodology in Accounting," *N.A.A. Bulletin,* June, 1962, p. 33.

Beer, S. "Simulation of Industrial Operations," *J. Royal Stat. Soc.,* Series A, General, 122, 4, 1950, pp. 484–510.

Beizer, B., and S. W. Leibholz. *Engineering Applications of Boolean Algebra* (Electrical Manufacturing Magazine reprint series). New York: Gage Publishing Co., no date given, about 1961.

Bell, Alexander Graham Association for the Deaf, Inc. *Pediatrics and Disorders in Communication.* Reprint Number 835, Washington, D.C., 1965.

Bellman, R. E. *Adaptive Control Processes: A Guided Tour.* Princeton, N.J.: Princeton University Press, 1961.

Bellman, R. E. and S. E. Dreyfus. *Applied Dynamic Programming.* Princeton, N.J.: Princeton University Press, 1962.

Benedict, R. *Patterns of Culture.* New York: New Am. Library, 1947 (paper).

Berelson, B., and G. A. Steiner. *Human Behavior: An Inventory of Scientific Findings.* New York: Harcourt, Brace & World, 1964.

Bernstein, J. *The Analytical Engine: Computers, Past, Present, and Future.* New York: Random House, 1964, also, Vintage Books, 1966 (paper).

Bharucha-Reid, A. T. *Elements of the Theory of Markov Processes and Their Applications.* New York: McGraw-Hill, 1960.

"Bibliography of Computer Applications in Medicine and the Biological Sciences," *Comm. ACM,* April, 1963.

Black, S. "A Reporter at Large: Burglary," *The New Yorker* (Part I) December 7, 1963, pp. 63–128, (Part II) December 14, 1963, pp. 89–152.

Block, H. D. "The Perception: A Model for Brain Functioning 1," *Rev. Modern Phys.,* **34,** 1, January, 1962.

——. "Learning in Some Simple Non-Biological Systems," *Am. Scientist,* **53,** 1, March, 1965, pp. 59–79.

Bonini, C. P. *Simulation of Information and Decision Systems in the Firm.* Englewood Cliffs, N.J.: Prentice-Hall, 1963.

Boole, G. *The Laws of Thought.* London, 1854. Reprint, New York: Dover, 1951.

Borko, H. *Computer Applications in the Behavioral Sciences.* Englewood Cliffs, N.J.: Prentice-Hall, 1962.

Bott, E. "Concept of Class as a Reference Group," *Human Relations,* **7,** 3, 1954, p. 259.

Bourne, C. P. *Methods of Information Handling.* New York: Wiley, 1963.

Bowden, B. V. *Faster Than Thought: A Symposium on Digital Computing Machines.* London: Pitman, 1953.

Boyle, E. "What the Computer Means to the Accounting Profession," *J. Accountancy,* January, 1966, pp. 56.

Brandon, D. *Management Standards for Data Processing.* Princeton, N.J.: Van Nostrand, 1963.

Bridgman, P. W. *The Logic of Modern Physics.* New York: Macmillan, 1946.

Bright, J. R. *Automation and Management.* Cambridge, Mass.: Graduate School of Business, Harvard University, 1958.

Brown, G. S., and D. P. Campbell. *Principles of Servomechanisms.* New York: Wiley, 1948.

Brown, R. G. *Forecasting for Inventory Control.* New York: McGraw-Hill, 1960.

——. *Smoothing, Forecasting and Prediction of Discrete Time Series.* Englewood Cliffs, N.J.: Prentice-Hall, 1963.

Bunge, M. *The Myth of Simplicity.* Englewood Cliffs, N.J.: Prentice-Hall, 1963.

Burdick, E. *The 480.* New York: McGraw-Hill, 1964 (also in paper).

Burington, R. S. *Handbook of Mathematical Tables and Formulas,* 4th ed. New York: McGraw-Hill, 1964.

Camrus, M. "Information Storage Density," *IEEE Spectrum,* July, 1965, pp. 98–105.

Cannon, W. B. *Wisdom of the Body.* New York: Norton, 1932.

——. *The Way of an Investigator.* New York: Norton, 1945.

Chappel, E. D., and C. S. Coon. *Principles of Anthropology.* New York: Holt, 1942.

Chappel, E. D., and E. Lindemann. "Clinical Implications of Measurements of Interaction Rates in Psychiatric Interviews," *Applied Anthropology,* January-March, 1942, pp. 1–10.

Chappel, E. D., and L. R. Sayles. *The Measures of Management—Designing Organizations for Human Effectiveness.* New York: Macmillan, 1961.

Cherry, C. *On Human Communication.* New York: Technology Press and Wiley, 1957.

Chorafas, D. N. *Systems and Simulation.* New York: Academic Press, 1965.

Chung, A. *Linear Programming.* Columbus, Ohio: Merrill, 1963.

Churchman, C. W., R. L. Ackoff, and E. L. Arnoff (Eds.). *Introduction to Operations Research.* New York: Wiley, 1957.

Churchman, C. W. "Problems of Value Measurement for a Theory of Induction and Decision," *Third Berkeley Symposium on Mathematical Statistics and Probability,* December, 1954 and June-July, 1955.

Clemens, S. "Letters from Earth," in B. Berelson and G. A. Steiner, *Human Behavior, An Inventory of Scientific Findings.* New York: Harcourt, Brace & World, 1964.

Cohen, M. R., and R. Nagel. *An Introduction to Logic and Scientific Method.* New York: Harcourt, Brace & World, 1934.

Cristian, W. "Don't Bet on Management Games," *Business Automation,* July, 1961.

Davies, O. L. (Ed). *Design and Analysis of Industrial Experiments,* rev. ed. New York: Hafner, 1956.

Dept. of U. S. Air Force, *Guide for Auditing Automatic Data Processing Systems.* Washington, D. C.: Government Printing Office, 1961.

DeSola Pool, I., and R. Abelson. "The Simulmatics Project," *Public Opinion Quarterly,* Summer, 1961.

Deutsch, K. W. "Mechanism, Organism and Society," *Philosophy of Science,* **18**, 3, July, 1951, pp. 230–52.

——. "Mechanism, Teleology, and Mind," *Philosophical and Phenomenoligical Res.* **12**, 2, December, 1951, pp. 185–222.

——. "On Communication Models in the Social Sciences," *Public Opinion Quarterly,* **16**, Fall, 1952, pp. 358–80.

——. *Nationalism and Social Communication.* Cambridge, Mass.: M.I.T. Press and New York: Wiley, 1953.

———. *Political Community at the International Level.* Doubleday Short Studies in Political Science SSPS-1. Garden City, N.Y.: Doubleday, 1954.

———. "Innovation, Entrepreneurship, and the Learning Process" in A. H. Cole, (Ed.) *Change and the Entrepreneur; Postulates and Patterns for Entrepreneurial History.* Cambridge, Mass.: Harvard University Press, 1949.

Dixon, W. J., and F. J. Massey, Jr. *Introduction to Statistical Analysis,* 2nd ed. New York: McGraw-Hill, 1957.

Dorfman, R. P., P. A. Samuelson, and R. M. Solow. *Linear Programming and Economic Analysis.* New York: McGraw-Hill, 1958.

Downs, M. P., and G. M. Sterritt. "Identification Audiometry for Neonates: A Preliminary Report," *J. Auditory Res.,* 4, 1964, pp. 69–80.

Duncan, A. J. *Quality Control and Industrial Statistics.* Homewood, Ill.: Irwin, 1959.

Eigenstadt, S. N. "Studies in Reference Group Behavior," *Human Relations,* 7, 2, 1954, pp. 191–216.

Eiteman, D. K. "A Computer Program for Financial Statement Analysis," *Financial Analysts' J.,* November-December, 1964.

Ellis, D. O., and F. J. Ludwig. *Systems Philosophy: An Introduction.* Englewood Cliffs, N.J.: Prentice-Hall, 1962.

Engel, J. H. "Use of Clustering in Mineralogical and Other Surveys," *Proc. First International Conference on Operations Research.* Operations Research Society of America, Baltimore, Md., 1957.

Etzioni, A. *Complex Organizations: A Sociological Reader.* New York: Holt, 1961.

Fair, W. "The Corporate C.I.A.," *Management Science,* July, 1966, pp. B489–B503.

Feigenbaum, E. A., and J. Feldman (Eds). *Computers and Thought.* New York: McGraw-Hill, 1963.

Feller, W. *An Introduction to Probability Theory and Its Applications,* Vol. I. New York: Wiley, 1957.

Festinger, L. "The Analysis of Sociograms Using Matrix Algebra," *Human Relations,* 2, 1949, pp. 153–158.

Festmyer, L., J. Torvey, and B. Willetman. "Self-Evaluation as a Function of Attraction to the Group," *Human Relations,* 7, 2, 1954, pp. 161–74.

Flagle, C. D. et al. (Eds.). *Operations Research and Systems Engineering.* Baltimore, Md.: John Hopkins Press, 1960.

Forrester, J. *Industrial Dynamics.* Cambridge, Mass.: M.I.T. Press, 1961.

"For the Apparel Industry: Automatic Patterns," *Women's Wear Daily,* December 12, 1965, p. 15.

Forsyth, E., and L. Latz. "A Matrix Approach to the Analysis of Sociometric Data," *Sociometry,* 9, 1949, pp. 340–47.

Friedd, I., and D. Vickers. "Portfolio Selection and Investment Performance," *J. Finance,* Summer, 1965, pp. 391–415.

Fritz, C. E. "Disaster," in R. K. Merton and R. A. Nisbit (Eds.), *Contemporary Social Problems.* New York: Harcourt, Brace & World, 1961.

Gaines, H. F. *Cryptanalysis*. New York: Dover, 1956.

Gardner, J. W. "How to Prevent Organizational Dry Rot," *Harper's Magazine*, October, 1965, p. 20.

Gardner, M. F., and J. L. Barnes. *Transients in Linear Systems*. Vol. I. New York: Wiley, 1942.

Gatto, O. T. "AUTOSATE: An Automated Data Systems Analysis Technique," (Memo RM-3118-PR), The RAND Corporation, Santa Monica, Calif., 1962, 50 pp.

———. "AUTOSATE," *Comm. ACM*, **7**, 7, July, 1964.

Gilbert, E. N. "A Comparison of Signalling Alphabets," *Bell System Tech. J.*, **31**, 1952, pp. 504–22.

Glasstone, S. *Sourcebook on Atomic Energy*. Princeton, N.J.: Van Nostrand, 1950.

Goode, H. H., and R. E. Machol. *Systems Engineering*. New York: McGraw-Hill, 1957.

Gordon, M. *Sick Cities*. New York: Macmillan, 1963.

Gordon, D. L., and R. Dangerfield. *The Hidden Weapon: The Story of Economic Warfare*. New York: Harper, 1947.

Grabbe, E. M. *Automation in Business and Industry*. New York: Wiley, 1957.

Grant, E. L. *Statistical Quality Control*. New York: McGraw-Hill, 1952.

Greenberger, M. (Ed.). *Management and the Computer of the Future*. New York: Technology Press and Wiley, 1962.

Gregory, R. H., and R. L. Van Horn. *Automatic Data Processing*, 2nd ed. Belmont, Calif.: Wadsworth, 1965.

———. *Business Data Processing and Programming*. Belmont, Calif.: Wadsworth, 1963.

Griffiths, J. C., and L. J. Drew. "Simulation of Exploration Programs for Material Resources by Models," *Quart. Colo. School Mines*, October, 1964.

Grinker, R. R. (Ed.). *Toward a Unified Theory of Human Behavior*. New York: Basic Books, 1956.

Guetzkow, H., and J. Gyr. "An Analysis of Conflicting Decision Making Groups," *Human Relations*, **7**, 3, 1954, pp. 367–81.

Hall, A. D. *A Methodology for Systems Engineering*. Princeton, N.J.: Van Nostrand, 1962, pp. 384–96.

Hamming, R. N. "Error Detecting and Error Correcting Codes," *Bell System Tech. J.*, **29**, 1950, pp. 147–60.

Harary, F., and I. Ross. "Identification of the Liaison Persons of an Organization Among the Structure Matrix," *Management Science*, April-July, 1955, pp. 251–58.

Hare, H. A., M.D. *Practical Diagnosis*. Philadelphia: Lea Brothers, 1899.

Hare, V. C. Jr. "Systems Analysis," in R. T. Eddison and D. B. Hertz, *Progress in Operations Research*. Vol. II. New York: Wiley, 1964.

Hartley, R. V. L. "Transmission of Information," *Bell System Tech. J.*, **7**, 1928, pp. 535–63.

Head, R. V. *Real-Time Business Systems*. New York: Holt, 1964.

Hearle, E. F., and R. J. Mason. *Data Processing System for State and Local Govern-ment.* Englewood Cliffs, N.J.: Prentice-Hall, 1962.

Hebb, D. O. *The Organization of Behavior.* New York: Wiley, 1949.

Heinicke, C., and R. F. Bales. "Developmental Trends in the Structure of Small Groups," *Sociometry,* **16**, 1, February, 1953, pp. 7–15.

Herbst, P. G. "Analysis of Social Flow Systems," *Human Relations,* **7**, 3, 1954, p. 327.

Hertz, D. B. "Risk Analysis in Capital Investment," *Harvard Business Review,* July-August, 1962.

——. "The Computer and the Communications Case," *McKinsey Quarterly,* **2**, 3, 1966.

Hildebrand, F. B. *Advanced Calculus for Applications.* Englewood Cliffs, N.J.: Prentice-Hall, 1962.

Hitch, C. J. "An Appreciation of Systems Analysis," *Operations Research,* November, 1955, pp. 466–81.

——. *Decision-Making for Defense.* Berkeley: University of California Press, 1965.

Hitch, C. J., and R. N. McKean, "Suboptimization in Operations Problems," *Operations Research,* 1953, pp. 87–99.

——. *The Economics of Defense in the Nuclear Age.* Cambridge, Mass.: Harvard University Press, 1960.

Hoar, F. M. (Ed.). "The Information Revolution," *New York Times,* May 23, 1965, Section 11, pp. 34.

Hoel, P. G. *Introduction to Mathematical Statistics,* 3rd ed. New York: Wiley, 1962.

Hoernes, G. E., and M. Heilweil. *Interduction to Boolean Algebra and Logical Design: A Program for Self-Instruction.* New York: McGraw-Hill, 1964.

Howard, R. A. *Dynamic Programming and Markov Processes.* New York: Technology Press and Wiley, 1960.

——. "Dynamic Programming," *Management Science,* **12**, 5, January, 1966, p. 317.

Huffman, D. A. "A Method for Construction of Minimum Rendundancy Codes," *Proc. IRE,* **40**, 1952, pp. 1098–1102.

Huggins, W. H. "Signal Flow Graphs and Random Signals," *Proc. IRE* **45**, 1957, pp. 74–86.

Hull, T. E., and A. R. Dobell. "Random Number Generators," *SIAM Review,* **4**, 3, July, 1962, pp. 230–54.

IBM *Application Program: General Purpose Systems Simulator III* (#B20-0001-0). White Plains, N.Y.: IBM Data Processing Division; also user's manual #H20-0163.

IBM *General Information Manual: Introduction to IBM Data Processing System Form* F22-6517-2. White Plains, N.Y.: IBM Data Processing Division.

Idelson, J. M. "Ten Ways to Find the Optimum," *Control Engineering,* June, 1964.

Ijjri, Yuji. *Management Goals and Accounting for Control.* Chicago, Ill.: Rand McNally, 1965.

"Information Becomes a Hot Item," *Business Week,* May 14, 1966, p. 164.

Jacobs, J. *Death and Life of Great American Cities.* New York: Random House, 1961.

Jahoda, M., M. Deutsch, and S. W. Cook (Eds.). *Research Methods in Social Relations. Part Two: Selected Techniques.* New York: Dryden, 1951.

Janda, K. F. *Data Processing: Applications to Political Research.* Evanston, Ill.: Northwestern University Press, 1965.

Jerger, J. J. *Systems Preliminary Design.* Princeton, N. J.: Van Nostrand, 1960.

Joplin, H. B. "The Accountant's Role in Management Information Systems," *J. Accountancy, A.I.C.P.A.,* New York, March, 1966, p. 43.

Kahn, R. "The House of Adolph Ochs," *Saturday Evening Post,* Oct. 19, 1965, p. 32.

Kalish, D., and R. Montague. *Logic; Techniques of Formal Reasoning.* New York: Harcourt, Brace & World, 1964.

Kaplan, W. *Operational Methods for Linear Systems.* Reading, Mass.: Addison-Wesley, 1962.

Katona, G. *Organizing and Memorizing: Studies in the Psychology of Learning and Teaching.* New York: Columbia University Press, 1940.

Kaufman, G. M. *Statistical Decision and Related Techniques in Oil and Gas Exploration.* Englewood Cliffs, N.J.: Prentice-Hall, 1963.

Kaufman, W. K. *The McNamara Strategy.* New York: Harper, 1964.

"Keeping Ahead on Real Time," *Business Week,* March 27, 1966, p. 167.

Kenemy, F. G., et al. *Finite Mathematics With Business Applications.* Englewood Cliffs, N.J.: Prentice-Hall, 1962.

Kemeny, J. G., J. L. Snell, and G. L. Thompson. *Introduction to Finite Mathematics.* Englewood Cliffs, N.J.: Prentice-Hall, 1957, pp. 133–39.

Kent, A. *Textbook on Mechanized Information Retrieval.* New York: Interscience, 1963.

Kent, S., *Strategic Intelligence for American World Policy.* Princeton, N.J.: Princeton University Press, 1949.

Kirk, H. W. "Use of Decision Tables in Computer Programming," *Comm. ACM,* 8, 1, January, 1965, pp. 41–43.

Klimenko, K., and M. Rakovsky. In "The Technological and Economic Problems of Automation in the U.S.S.R." (originally, "Social Consequences of Automation," *International Social Science Bulletin (UNESCO),* 10, 1 1958) reprinted in H. B. Jacobson and J. S. Roueck, *Automation and Society.* New York: Philosophical Library, 1959, pp. 416–32.

Koopman, B. O. "The Optimum Distribution of Effort," *Operations Research,* 1, 2, 1953, pp. 52–63; "The Theory of Search: Part I, Kinematic Bases," 4, 3, 1956, pp. 324–46; "The Theory of Search: Part II, Target Detection," 4, 5, 1956, pp. 503–31; "The Theory of Search: Part III, The Optimum Distribution of Searching Effort," 5, 5, 1957, pp. 613–26.

Korvalinks, J. W., and H. G. Trentin. "Management Information Systems," *Management Science,* September-October, 1965, p. 27.

Kou, B. C. *Automatic Control Systems.* Englewood Cliffs: Prentice-Hall, 1962.

Krasnow, H. S., and R. A. Merikallio. "The Past, Present, and Future of Simulation Languages," *Management Science,* November, 1964.

Laning, C. B. "Forces and Trends in State and Local Government EDP," *Public Administration Rev.* **25**, 2, June 1965, pp. 151–55.

Lazarsfeld, P. F. *Mathematical Thinking in the Social Sciences*. Glencoe, Ill.: Free Press, 1954.

Ledley, R. S. *Programming and Utilizing Digital Computers*. New York: Mc-Graw-Hill, 1962.

Ledley, R. S., and L. B. Lusted. "Reasoning Foundation of Medical Diagnoses," *Science*, **5**, 130, 1959, pp. 9–21.

Lennard, H., and A. Bernstein. *The Anatomy of Physchotherapy*. New York: Columbia University Press, 1960.

Leontief, W. W. *The Structure of the American Economy 1919-1939: Empirical Appl. of Equilibrium Analysis*. 2nd ed. New York: Oxford University Press, 1951.

Leontieff, V. *The Structure of the American Economy*. New York: Oxford University Press, 1951.

Lerner, A. P. *The Economics of Control*. New York: Macmillan, 1944.

Lerner, E. M. (Ed.). *Readings in Financial Analysis and Investment Management*. Homewood, Ill.: Irwin, 1963.

Lerner, E., and W. Carleton. *A Theory of Financial Analysis*. New York: Harcourt, Brace & World, 1966.

Levitt, T. *Innovation in Marketing: New Perspectives for Profit and Growth*. New York: McGraw-Hill, 1962.

Lewinsohn, R. *Science, Prophecy, and Prediction*. Greenwich, Conn.: Fawcett, 1962 (paper).

Li, C. C. *Introduction to Experimental Statistics*. New York: McGraw-Hill, 1964.

Lincoln, F. "Billy Prince's Somewhat Silver Spoon," *Fortune*, January, 1956, p. 126.

Lindemann, E. "Individual Hostility and Group Integration," *Human Organization*, Winter, 1949, pp. 5–10.

Lipsky, R. C., and K. Lancaster. "The General Theory of Second Best," *Rev. Economic Studies*, 1956-57, pp. 11–32.

Lorens, C. S. *Flowgraphs: For the Modeling and Analysis of Linear Systems*. New York: McGraw-Hill, 1964.

Lowry, I. *A Model of Metropolis*. Memorandum RM 4035-Re. Santa Monica, Calif.: The RAND Corp., 1965.

Lubar, R. "Armour Sees Fat Years Ahead," *Fortune*, October, 1959, p. 117.

Lynch, W. A. "Linear Control Systems—A Signal Flow Graph Viewpoint," in E. Mishkin and L. J. Braun, *Adaptive Control Systems*. New York: McGraw-Hill, 1961.

Lynd, R. S. *Knowledge for What?* Princeton, N.J.: Princeton University Press, 1939.

McCracken, D. D., H. Weiss, and T. H. Lu. *Programming Business Computers*. New York: Wiley, 1959.

Machol, R. E. *System Engineering Handbook*. New York: McGraw-Hill, 1965.

McKean, R. N. *Efficiency in Government Through Systems Analysis*. New York: Wiley, 1958.

McLuhan, M. *The Gutenberg Galaxy*. Toronto: University of Toronto Press, 1962.
——. *Understanding Media*. New York: McGraw-Hill, 1964.

McMillan, C., and R. F. Gonzalez. *Systems Analysis: A Computer Approach to Decision Models*. Homewood, Ill.: Irwin, 1965.

McNamara, R. S. "McNamara Defines His Job," *New York Times Magazine*, April 26, 1964.

McRae, T. W. *The Impact of Computers on Accounting*. New York: Wiley, 1964.

Mann, Floyd, Likert, and Rensis. "The Need for Research on the Communication of Research Results," *Human Organization*, Winter, 1952, pp. 15–19.

Mao, J. C. T., and C. E. Sarndal. "A Decision Theory Approach to Portfolio Selection," *Management Science*, April, 1966.

March, J. G., and H. A. Simon. *Organizations*. New York: Wiley, 1958.

Marcosson, I. F. *Adventures in Interviewing*. London: John Lane (The Bodley Head), 1920.

Markowitz, H. M. *Portfolio Selection: Efficient Diversification of Investments*. New York: Wiley, 1959.

Markowitz, H. M., B. Hauser, and H. W. Karr. *SIMSCRIPT: A Simulation Programming Language*. Englewood Cliffs, N.J.: Prentice-Hall, 1963.

Martin, J. *Programming Real-Time Computing Systems*. Englewood Cliffs, N.J.: Prentice-Hall, 1965.

Mason, S. J. "Feedback Theory: Some Properties of Signal Flow Graphs," *Proc. IRE*, 41, September, 1953, pp. 1144–56, and 44, July, 1956, pp. 920–26.

Massachusetts Institute of Technology. *Notes on Operations Research*. Cambridge, Mass.: Technology Press, 1959.

Masse, P. *Optimal Investment Decisions: Rules for Actions and Criteria for Choice*. Englewood Cliffs, N.J.: Prentice-Hall, 1962.

Mendelson, E. *Introduction to Mathematical Logic*. Princeton, N.J.: Van Nostrand, 1964.

Menzel, H., and E. Katz. "Social Innovation in the Medical Profession: the Epidemiology of a New Drug," *Public Opinion Quarterly*, 19, 1956, pp. 337–52.

Mercer, J. "Gemini Malfunction, Was It the Computer?" *Control Engineering*, July, 1965, p. 24.

Metcalfe, H. *The Cost of Manufacturers and the Administration of Work Shops Public and Private*. New York: Wiley, 1885.

Miller, D. W., and M. K. Starr. *Executive Decisions and Operations Research*. Englewood Cliffs, N.J.: Prentice-Hall, 1960.

Miller, G. A. *Language and Communication*. New York: McGraw-Hill, 1951.

Milsum, J. H. *Biological Control Systems Analysis*. New York: McGraw-Hill, 1966.

Minsky, "Steps Toward Artificial Intelligence," *Proc. IRE*, 49, 1, January, 1961.

Mishkin, E., and L. Braun, Jr. *Adaptive Control Systems*. New York: McGraw-Hill, 1961.

Montagu, E. *The Man Who Never Was*. New York: Lippincott, 1954, also Bantam Books, 1965.

Mood, A. M., and F. A. Graybill. *Introduction to the Theory of Statistics*, 2nd ed. New York: McGraw-Hill, 1963.

Morgenstern, O. *On the Accuracy of Economic Observations*, rev. ed. Princeton, N.J.: Princeton University Press, 1964.

Morrison, P., and Morrison, E. (Eds.). *Charles Babbage and His Calculating Engines.* New York: Dover, 1961.

Morse, P. M., and G. E. Kimball. *Methods of Operations Research.* Cambridge, Mass.: M.I.T., 1951.

Mosteller, F. *Fifty Challenging Problems in Probability with Solutions.* Reading, Mass.: Addison-Wesley, 1965.

National Bureau of Standards, *Current Research and Developments in Scientific Documentation.* No. 7, National Science Foundation, November, 1960.

Naylor, T. H., J. L. Balintfy, D. S. Bordick, and K. Chu. *Computer Simulation Techniques.* New York: Wiley, 1966.

Nemhauser, G. L. *Introduction to Dynamic Programming.* New York: Wiley, 1966.

Neuschel, R. F. *Management by System.* New York: McGraw-Hill, 1960.

Newman, J. R. *The World of Mathematics.* New York: Simon & Schuster, 1956, Vol. 4.

Nizer, L. *My Life in Court.* Garden City, N.Y.: Doubleday, 1961.

Nortan, J. H. "The Role of Subjective Probability in Evaluating New Product Ventures," *Chemical Engineering Progress Symposium,* 59, 1963.

Ogburn, W. F. *Social Change.* New York: Dell, 1927 (paper).

O'Hara, C. E. *Fundamentals of Criminal Investigation.* Springfield, Ill.: Thomas, 1961.

Oppenheimer, J. R. *Science and the Common Understanding.* New York: Simon & Schuster, 1954.

Orcutt, C. H. "Simulation of Economic Systems," *Am. Economic Review,* **50,** December, 1960, pp. 893–907.

Paine, N. R. "Case Study in Mathematical Programming of Portfolio Selection," *Applied Statistics,* **15,** 1, 1966, 24–36.

"Parameters of Science," in *American Documentation Institute, Proceedings of the Annual Meeting, 1964.* New York: Spartan Books, 1964.

Parzen, E. *Modern Probability Theory and Its Applications.* New York: Wiley, 1960.

Pavlov, I. P. *Experimental Psychology and Other Essays.* New York: New York Philosophical Library, 1957.

Pediatrics and Disorders in Communication. Reprint No. 835, The Alexander Graham Bell Association for the Deaf, Inc., Washington, D.C., 1965.

Penfield, W., and T. Rasmussen. *The Cerebral Cortex of Man.* New York: Macmillan, 1950.

Perry, J. W., and A. Kent. *Tools for Machine Literature Searching.* New York: Interscience (Wiley), 1958.

Peterson, W. A., and N. P. Gist. "Rumor and Public Opinion," *Am. J. Sociology,* September, 1951, **57,** 2, pp. 159–68.

Pfeiffer, J. *The Human Brain.* New York: Harper, 1955.

Pinto, O. *Spy-Catcher.* New York: Harper, 1952.

Polya, G. *Mathematics and Plausible Reasoning.* Princeton, N.J.: Princeton University Press, 1954, 2 vols.

Polya, G. *How to Solve It,* 2nd ed. Garden City, N.Y.: Doubleday, 1957 (paper).

Prager, W., and W. Freiberger (Eds.). *Applications of Digital Computers.* Boston: Blaisdell, 1963.

Pugh, A. L. *DYNAMO User's Manual,* 2nd ed. Cambridge, Mass.: M.I.T. Press, 1963.

Quade, E. S. *Analysis for Military Decisions.* New York: Rand McNally, 1965.

Quine, W. Mathematical Logic, rev. ed. Cambridge, Mass.: Harvard University Press, 1951.

Ragattini, J. R., and G. F. Franklin. *Sampled Data Control Systems.* New York: McGraw-Hill, 1958.

Rajchman, J. A. "Computer Memories: A Survey of the State of the Art," *Proc. IRE,* **44,** 104, January, 1961.

Randall, J. H., Jr. *The Making of the Modern Mind.* rev. ed. Boston: Houghton-Mifflin, 1940.

Ransom, S. W. *The Anatomy of the Nervous System.* 10th ed. rev. by S. L. Clark. Philadelphia: Saunders, 1959.

Rehder, R. R. "Communication and Opinion in a Medical Community: The Significance of the Detail Man," *J. Acad. Management,* **8,** 4, December, 1965.

Reik, T. *Listening With the Third Ear.* Garden City, N.Y.: Farrar, Strauss, 1948.

Richardson, F. L. W., Jr. "Usefulness of Internal Mapping in Field Techniques," *Human Organization,* Summer, 1950, pp. 31–32.

Richmond, S. B. *Statistical Analysis,* 2nd ed. New York: Ronald Press, 1964.

Riesz, R. R., and H. D. Irvin. "Simulation in Engineering," *Bell Lab. Record,* **36,** 1958, pp. 238–41.

Ritow, I. *A Servomechanism Primer.* Garden City, N.Y.: Doubleday, 1963, also Dolphin (paper).

———. *Advanced Servomechanism Design.* Garden City, N.Y.: Doubleday, 1963, also Dolphin (paper).

Rome, B. and S. Rome. "Programming the Bureaucratic Computer," *IEEE Spectrum,* December, 1964, pp. 72–92.

Rosenblueth, A., N. Wiener, and N. Bigelow. "Behavior, Purpose, and Teleology," *Phil. Sci.,* **10,** 1943, pp. 18–24.

———. "The Role of Models in Science," *Phil. Sci.,* **12,** 1945, pp. 316–22.

———. "Purposeful and Non-Purposeful Behavior," *Phil. Sci.* **17,** 1950, pp. 318–26.

Ruesch, J., and G. Bateson. *Communication.* New York: Norton, 1951.

Salton, G. "Progress in Automatic Information Retrieval," *IEEE Spectrum,* August, 1965, pp. 90–103.

Samuelson, P. A. *Foundations of Economic Analysis.* Cambridge, Mass.: Harvard University Press, 1947.

Sarafin, E. E. "Information Protection," *Control Engineering,* May, 1965, pp. 105–7.

Sasieni, M. W., *et al. Operations Research: Methods and Problems.* New York: Wiley, 1959.

Sass, M. A., and W. D. Wilkinson. *Computer Augmentation of Human Reasoning.* Washington, D.C.: Spartan, 1965.

Schuster, D. H. *Logical Electronic Troubleshooting.* New York: McGraw-Hill, 1963.

Seifert, W. W., and C. W. Steeg (Eds.). *Control Systems Engineering.* New York: McGraw-Hill, 1960.

Serrell, R. M., M. Astrahen, G. W. Patterson, and I. B. Pyne. "The Evaluation of Computing Machines and Systems," *Proc. IRE,* May, 1962.

Shannon, C. E. "Memory Requirements in a Telephone Exchange," *Bell System Tech. J.,* **29**, 3, July, 1950, pp. 343–49.

——. "Prediction and Entropy of Printed English," *Bell System Tech. J.,* **30**, 1951, pp. 50–64.

Shannon, C. E., and W. Weaver. *The Mathematical Theory of Communication.* Urbana, Ill.: University of Illinois Press, 1949.

Shapiro, G., *et al.* "Project FIST: Fault Isolation by Semiatomic Techniques," *IEEE Spectrum,* August, 1964 (Part I), and September, 1964 (Part II).

Sharpe, W. F. "A Simplified Model for Portfolio Analyses," *Management Science,* June, 1963, pp. 227–83.

——. "Mutual Fund Performance," *J. Business,* January, 1966, pp. 119–38.

Shewhart, W. A. (W. E. Deming, Ed.). *Statistical Method from the Viewpoint of Quality Control.* Washington, D.C.: The Graduate School, Department of Agriculture, 1939.

Shubik, M. "Bibliography on Simulation, Gaming, Artificial Intelligence and Allied Topics," *J. Am. Statist. Assoc.,* **55**, 104, December, 1960.

Simmons, R. F. "Answering English Questions by Computer—A Survey," *Comm. ACM,* 8, 1, January, 1965, pp. 53–69.

Simon, H. A. "How Computers Can Learn from Experience," in W. F. Freiberger and W. Prager, (Eds.), *Applications of Digital Computers.* Boston: Ginn, 1963.

——. "Administrative Decision Making," *Public Administration Review,* **25**, 1, March, 1965, pp. 31–37.

——. *The Shape of Automation for Men and Management.* New York: Harper, 1965.

Simulation. Technology Series, Corporate Communication BRT-12. Santa Monica, Calif.: System Development Corporation, 1965.

Sloan, A. P. *My Years with General Motors.* Garden City, N.Y.: Doubleday, 1964.

Smith, O. "The Nomenclature of Machine Details," *Am. Machinist,* September 19, 1881.

Snow, C. P. *The Two Cultures: And a Second Look.* Cambridge, Mass.: Cambridge University Press, 1964.

Soroka, W. W. "Experimental Aides in Engineering Design Analysis" *Mech. Engineering,* 1957, p. 831.

Spiegel, M. R. *Theory and Problems of Statistics.* New York: Schaum, 1961.

Star, J. "Chicago Shows a Way to Police Reform," *Look,* October 19, 1965, pp. 43–49.

Starr, M. K. "Management Science and Marketing Science," *Management Science,* **10**, 3, April, 1964.

Starr, M. K. "Modular Production—A New Concept," *Harvard Business Review,* November-December, 1965.

——. *Production Management, Systems, and Synthesis.* Englewood Cliffs, N. J.: Prentice-Hall, 1964.

Starr, M. K., and D. W. Miller. *Inventory Control: Theory and Practice.* Englewood Cliffs, N. J.: Prentice-Hall, 1963.

Stauffer, S. A., et al. *Measurement and Prediction* (Volume IV in *Studies in Social Psychology in World War II*). Princeton, N.J.: Princeton University Press, 1950.

Stonborough, T. H. W. "The Continuous Consumer Panel," *Appl. Anthropology,* January-March, 1942, pp. 37–42.

Sullivan, H. S. *Conceptions of Modern Psychiatry.* New York: Norton, 1953.

——. *Interpersonal Theory of Psychiatry.* New York: Norton, 1953.

Sutherland, I. E. "Sketchpad: A Man-Machine Graphical Communication System," *Proc. Am. Federation of Info. Processing Societies, May, 1963.* Baltimore, Md.: Spartan Books, 1963, pp. 329–46.

Taylor, M. D. *The Uncertain Trumpet.* New York: Harper, 1960.

Thompson, D. W. *On Growth and Form,* Vols. I and II, 2nd ed. New York: Cambridge University Press, 1959 (reprint).

Truxal, J. G. *Automatic Feedback Control System Synthesis.* New York: McGraw-Hill, 1955.

Tully, A. *CIA: The Inside Story.* New York: Morrow, 1962.

Turing, A. "Can A Machine Think?" in Volume 4, *The World of Mathematics.* J. Newman (Ed.). New York: Simon & Schuster, 1956.

Tustin, A. *Mechanism of Economic Systems.* Cambridge, Mass.: Harvard University Press, 1953.

Unger, S. H., "GIT—A Heuristic Program for Testing Pairs of Directed Line Graphs for Isomorphism," *Comm. ACM,* 7, 1, January, 1964.

United Nations, *Proc. Inter-Regional Symposium of Techniques of Petroleum Development,* January 23–February 21, 1962.

U.S. Air Force, Dept. of, *Guide for Auditing Automatic Data Processing Systems,* Washington, D.C.: Government Printing Office, 1961.

Van Ness, R. G. *Principles of Punched Card Data Processing.* Elmhurst, Ill.: Business Press, 1962.

Vegetius, Flavius Renatus, (Edited by T. R. Phillips). *Military Institutions Of the Romans.* Harrisburg, Pa.: Stockpole, 1952.

Venn, J. *The Logic of Chance.* London: Macmillan, 1888.

VerPlanck, D. W., and B. R. Teare. *Engineering Analysis.* New York: Wiley, 1954.

Von Neumann, J. "The General and Logical Theory of Automation," in Volume 4, *The World of Mathematics.* J. Newmann (Ed.). New York: Simon & Schuster, 1956.

Walter, W. G. "A Machine That Learns," *Sci. American*, August, 1951, pp. 60–63.
——. *The Living Brain*. New York: Norton, 1953.
Warren, E. K. *Long Range Planning: The Executive Viewpoint*. Englewood Cliffs, N.J.: Prentice-Hall, 1966.
Weiss, R. S., and E. Jacobson. "A Method for the Analysis of the Structure of Complex Organizations," *Am. Soc. Rev.*, **20**, 1955, pp. 661–68, in A. Etzioni (Ed.). *Complex Organizations: A Sociological Reader*. New York: Holt, 1961.
Weldon, F. L. "In-Company Operations Research," *ORSA Bulletin* (abstract), May, 1962, **10**, p. 13.
Weyl, H. *Symmetry*. Princeton, N.J.: Princeton University Press, 1952.
Wheelis, A. *The Quest for Identity*. New York: Norton, 1958.
White, T. H. "Revolution in the Pentagon," *Look*, April 23, 1963, pp. 31–44.
Whyte, W. H., Jr. "The Web of Word of Mouth," *Fortune*, November, 1954, p. 140.
Wiener, N. "Speech, Language and Learning," *J. Acoust. Soc. Am.*, **22**, 1950, pp. 696–97.
——. *Cybernetics and Society*. 2nd rev. ed. Garden City, N.Y.: Doubleday, 1954.
——. *The Human Use of Human Beings: Cybernetics and Society*. 2nd rev. ed. Garden City, N.Y.: Doubleday, 1954.
——. *Cybernetics, or Control and Communication in the Animal and the Machine*. 2nd ed. Cambridge, Mass.: M.I.T., 1961.
Wilde, D. J. *Optimum-Seeking Methods*. Englewood Cliffs, N.J.: Prentice-Hall, 1963.
Wilkes, M. V. *Automatic Digital Computers*. New York: Wiley, 1956.
Williams, W. F. *Principles of Automated Information Retrieval*. Elmhurst, Ill.: Business Press, 1965.
Wilson, O. W. *Police Administration*, 2nd ed. New York: McGraw-Hill, 1963.
Winter, B. B. "Optimal Diagnostic Procedures," *Inst. of Radio Engineers* (now *IEEE*), *Transactions on Reliability and Quality Control*, Vol. RQC-9, 1960, pp. 13–19.
Woman's Day, "Wonderful World of Maps," October, 1964, pp. 6–9.
Wood, M. K. "PRAM, An Economic Programming Model," *Management Science*, May, 1965.
Woodbury, M. "Problems in Electron Forecasting," Armour Research Foundation, Computer Applications Symposium, October, 1956. *See: Computer Applications*. New York: Macmillan, 1956.
Woodbury, M., M. Gertler, P. White, and H. Rusk. "The Candidate for Coronary Heart Disease," *J. Am. Med. A.*, May, 1959, pp. 149–52.
Woodbury, M. A., and M. Lipkin. "Coding of Medical Histories for Computer Analysis," *Commu. of the ACM*, October, 1962.
——. "Recent Developments in the Science of Diagnosis," in W. Freiberger and W. Prager, *Applications of Digital Computers*. Boston: Ginn, 1963.

Yovits, M. C., G. T. Jacobi, and G. D. Goldstein. *Self Organizing Systems*. New York: Interdisciplinary Conference of Self-Organizing Systems, Pergamon, 1959.

Zipf, G. K. *Human Behavior and the Principle of Least Effort*. Cambridge, Mass.: Addison-Wesley, 1949.

INDEX

ABC systems, of inventory control, 168, 169
Accelerometers, analogous forms of, 360, 361, 362 and *n.*, 363
Addition, logical, 323–25
matrix, 457, 459
Addition rule, for black box combination, 35
for flow graph reduction, 66
Aircraft carriers, and capability problems, 226
ALGOL, 389
Algorithm, efficiency of, 156
Alphanumeric data, 117, 118
Analog computer, 363 *n.*, 365, 367
Analytic storage, data of, 122
Anthropology, applied, 510
Arcs and nodes, in graph theory, 16
Ashby, W. R., 136 and *n.*
Ashby's Law of Requisite Variety, 135–36, 138–43, 148, 442
consequences of, 143–45
derivation of, and outcome table, 144
and information theory, 149–50
for rate of variety in coded form, 147
reasons for use by systems analyst, 144–45

and system size, 149
Assembly operation, 162
Attribute, permanent, of entity in SIM-SCRIPT approach, 98, 99
of relationships of flow diagram, 20
temporary, of entity in SIMSCRIPT approach, 98, 99
AUTOCODER, 389
Automatic Systems Analysis (AUTO-SATE), 98
AUTOSATE (Automatic Systems Analysis), 98

Bank code, 500
Basic English, 167
Bayes' Formula, 346–50
Behavior, human, theories of, 413
Behavioral science man, 416–19
Behaviorism, 30
Bellman's Principle of Optimality, 309–10
Binary numbers, 116–18
Binary splits, in trouble-shooting, 264–67
Bits, 117, 119
per unit time, channel capacity measured in, 150
Black box, 29, 86, 238
defined, 29–30, 31